The Ecology, Land Use
and Conservation of the
CAIRNGORMS

Frontispiece   The northern slopes of the Cairngorms seen across the Insh Marshes, Strathspey.
                                                                  Photo: Jonathan Stacey.

Preceding page   The Lairig Ghru, a deep, glacially-excavated valley which bisects the Cairngorms massif in a north – south direction. Photo: Roy Dennis.

The Ecology, Land Use
and Conservation of the
CAIRNGORMS

Edited by
Charles Gimingham

PACKARD PUBLISHING LIMITED
CHICHESTER

THE ECOLOGY, LAND USE AND CONSERVATION OF THE CAIRNGORMS

First published in 2002 by Packard Publishing Limited,
Forum House, Stirling Road, Chichester, West Sussex, PO19 7DN, UK.

A CIP record of this book is obtainable from the British Library.

ISBNs: 1 85341 102 7 (cased)
1 85341 117 5 (limp)

Cover painting by Eric Auld.
Edited by Michael Packard. Index by June Morrison BSc MIBiol RI.

Typeset by Dorwyn Limited, Rowland's Castle, Hampshire.
Printed and bound by Downland Reprographics Limited, West Stoke,
    Chichester, West Sussex.

Contents

Authors' addresses   vii

Acknowledgements   viii

1 Introduction C.H. GIMINGHAM   1
The Conservation Value of the Cairngorms   2
Conflicts of Interest   2
Designations   3
The Need for Integrated Management   4
The Aims of the Book   4
The 'Cairngorms Area' – Zonation   4
Some Preceding Studies   6

Part 1 The Ecological Basis   7

2 The Physical Geography I.M. BROWN and
C.M. CLAPPERTON   8
Climate   8
Geology   10
Pre-glacial Geomorphology   12
Glacial Geomorphology   14
Periglacial Geomorphology and
Contemporary Geomorphic Processes   17
Soils   18
Overview   20

3 Vegetation C.H. GIMINGHAM   23
Studies of the Plant Ecology of the
Cairngorms   23
Vegetational History   24
Studies on Vegetation within the Potential
Forest Zone   25
Altitudinal Zonation   30
Pattern and Process at High Altitudes   32
The Larger Fungi of the Mountains   38
Disturbance and Restoration   39
New Plant Ecological Research in the
Cairngorms   39

4 Birds and Mammals ROY DENNIS   43
Birds   43
Moors   46
Diurnal Raptors   46
Native Woodlands   48
Lochs, Rivers and Marshes   49
Farmland and Settlements   51
Rare Bird Colonists   52
Mammals   52

5 Insects of the Cairngorms M.R. YOUNG and
K.R. WATT   54
Insects of the High Tops   55
Insects of Woodlands   56
Insects of Lowland Heathlands   57

The Defoliation of Upland Heathlands by
Moth Larvae   58
Rare Insects in the Cairngorms   58
Threats to Insects in the Cairngorms   64
Conclusions   65

6 Ecology of Aquatic and Sub-aquatic Habitats
M.B. DAVIDSON, R.P. OWEN and
D.W. MACKAY   67
Aquatic Habitats of the Cairngorms   67
Physical Interactions   67
Chemical Characteristics   68
Zonation   70
Aquatic and Wetland Flora   71
Plant Communities in Standing Waters   73
Wetlands   73
The Fauna   74
Water Quality and Pollution   75
Abstraction and Catchment Transfers   77
Flood Alleviation   78
Fish Farming   79
Forestry   79
Tourism and Recreation   79
Climate Change   80
Habitat Degradation and Deforestation   80
Protection Measures for Conservation   81
Knowledge and Awareness   82

Part 2 Key Issues   85

7 Land Use in the Cairngorms
D.M. SHUCKSMITH   86
The Evolution of Land Use   86
Land Use and Land Management Today   89
Settlements and the Local Economy Today   93
Conclusions   95

8 Agriculture K.J. THOMSON   97
Historical Background   97
Physical Features   100
Farming Support   100
Farming and Forestry   102
Farming and the Environment   102
Farming and the Leisure Sector   104
The Future for Farming in the Cairngorms
Area   104

**9 The Native Woodlands – History, Decline
and Present Status**
N.A. MACKENZIE   107
Post-glacial Origins   107
Early Forest Clearance   109
The Commercial Exploitation of the Forest   109
The Decline of the Forest   111
The Last Forty Years   111

Current Status and Management 116
Conclusions 117

10 Man and Woodlands J. ATTERSON and
I. ROSS 120
  The Destruction and Exploitation of the
    Natural Forest 120
  Forest Regeneration 121
  Large-scale Exploitation and Regeneration 122
  Forest Research 125
  Discussion 126
  The Future 127

**11 Red Deer and Their Management in the
Cairngorms** B.W. STAINES and
R. BALHARRY 130
  Background 130
  Red Deer Habitats 131
  Red Deer Biology 131
  The Cairngorms Deer Population 132
  The Issues 134
  Concerns 135
  Conclusions 137

12 Grouse and Moorland Management
P.J. HUDSON 139
  Methods and Description of Sporting Estates
    in the Cairngorms 139
  Historical Changes in Red Grouse Numbers 140
  Historical Review of Grouse Research 140
  Spatial Variations in Numbers of Red Grouse
    Shot between Estates 142
  Temporal Changes and Population Biology of
    Red Grouse 143
  Inimical Factors Influencing Chick Production
    and Their Management 143
  Variation in Numbers of Other Game Birds 145
  Conclusions 146

13 Fish Populations R. GARDINER and
D.W. MACKAY 148
  The Various Species 150
  Fisheries 154
  Importance in the Food Web 155
  Threats to the Populations 155

14 Open Air Recreation in the Cairngorms
J.W. MACKAY 160
  Origins 160

Recreational Value 161
Changing Patterns of Recreation 162
The Expansion of Skiing 163
Active Pursuits in the Hills 164
Recreation on Land Adjacent to the Massif 164
The Visitors 165
The Impact of Recreation 165
Management and Planning for Recreation 166
Prospect 167

15 Conservation of Nature and Landscape
E.M. MATTHEW 169
  Landforms and Features 169
  Pattern of Life in the Core Mountain Area 170
  The Wider Area 171
  History of Conservation 172
  Where We Are Today 178
  The Future 182

Part 3 The Future of the Cairngorms 184

**16 Towards an Integrated Management
Strategy** C.H. GIMINGHAM 185
  What Is Going Wrong? 185
  Stages in the Evolution of a Management
    Strategy 189

17 The Cairngorms in the Future
C.H. GIMINGHAM 200
  Implications of Ecological Analysis 200
  Partial Solutions 202
  Towards a Comprehensive Administrative
    Mechanism 206
  1997 Onwards – A National Park for the
    Cairngorms 208

List of Figures 210

List of Tables 211

List of Plates 212

Authors' Biographies 214

Index 216

Addresses of the Authors

J. ATTERSON
40 Muirfield Road, Inverness, IV2 4AU.

R. BALHARRY
Loch na Leoba, Old Glen Road, Newtonmore, PH20 1EB.

I.M. BROWN
UK Climate Impacts Programme, Union House, 12-16 St. Michael's Street, Oxford, OX1 2DU.

C.M. CLAPPERTON
Roscobie House, Corsee Road, Banchory, Kincardineshire, AB31 5RT.

M.B. DAVIDSON
Scottish Environment Protection Agency, Greyhope House, Greyhope Road, Torry, Aberdeen, AB11 9AD.

ROY DENNIS
Inchdryne, Nethybridge, Inverness-shire, PH25 3EF.

R. GARDINER
Freshwater Laboratory, Fisheries Research Services, Faskally, Pitlochry, Perthshire, PH16 5LB.

C.H. GIMINGHAM
Department of Plant and Soil Science, University of Aberdeen, Cruickshank Building, St. Machar Drive, Aberdeen, AB24 3UU.

P.J. HUDSON
Department of Biological and Molecular Sciences, University of Stirling, Stirling, FK9 4LA.

D.W. MACKAY
Succoth Farm, Glass, By Huntly, Aberdeenshire, AB54 4YL.

J.W. MACKAY
Scottish Natural Heritage (National Strategy), West Lodge, Airlie, Kirriemuir, Angus, DD8 5NP.

N.A. MACKENZIE
Norbu, Lochgarthside, Gorthleck, Inverness-shire, IV2 6YP.

E.M. MATTHEW
Bridge Cottage, Montgarrie, Alford, Aberdeenshire, AB33 8AP.

R.P. OWEN
Scottish Environment Protection Agency, Greyhope House, Greyhope Road, Torry, Aberdeen, AB11 9AD.

I. ROSS
The Ross Partnership, Bearfold, Ordie, Dinnet, Aboyne, Aberdeenshire, AB34 5LS.

D.M. SHUCKSMITH
Department of Land Economy, University of Aberdeen, St. Mary's, Old Aberdeen, AB24 3UF.

B.W. STAINES
Department of Zoology, University of Aberdeen, Tillydrone Avenue, Aberdeen, AB24 2TZ.

K.J. THOMSON
Department of Agriculture and Forestry, University of Aberdeen, MacRobert Building, 581 King Street, Aberdeen, AB24 5UA.

K.R. WATT
Department of Zoology, University of Aberdeen, Tillydrone Avenue, Aberdeen, AB24 2TZ.

M.R. YOUNG
Department of Zoology, University of Aberdeen, Culterty Field Station, Newburgh, Ellon, Aberdeenshire, AB41 0AA.

Acknowledgements

THE CONTRIBUTORS to this volume express their gratitude to all their friends and colleagues, too many to mention individually, who have given generous help with comments and information. Special thanks, however, go to the following whose help in commenting on parts of the text and/or providing valuable information led to substantial improvements:

> Chapter 3: Gordon Miller; Roy Watling; Jennifer McConnel and Clare Woolridge;
> Chapters 3 and 9: Brian Huntley and Judy Allen;
> Chapter 5: David Barbour, Keith Bland, Geoff Hancock, David Horsfield and Iain MacGowan;
> Chapter 13: Peter Shackley; David Hay and Brian Morrison; Les Watson; Bob Laughton, Adrian Hudson and Brian Shields; Peter Maitland; Ron Greer; Jimmy Oswald and John Macdonald;
> Chapter 15: Murray Ferguson;
> Chapters 16 and 17: Malcolm Payne.

The Institute of Hydrology and Scottish Natural Heritage are thanked for permission to use information from a report prepared by the Institute of Hydrology for the Nature Conservancy Council for Scotland, *Flood Alleviation in Upper Speyside: Modelling and Environmental Study* (1991). Grateful acknowledgement is made to the Cartographic Services in the Department of Geography and Environment, University of Aberdeen, for preparing the maps used in Chapters 1, 7, 16 and 17. The details of these were derived from maps drawn for the Report of the Cairngorms Working Party by the Scottish Office Design Print and Publications Section. The map for Fig. 16.1 was derived from the Countryside Commission for Scotland's publication, *Vehicular Tracks in Upland Scotland* (Perth, 1978), by permission of Scottish Natural Heritage.

The following are thanked for permission to reproduce illustrations: The British Library (Plate 67, Roy's Survey Maps C.9.b.27 (8/1); The Royal Museum of Scotland (Plate 66); the Librarian of the Cairngorm Club, Aberdeen (Plates 91, 92, 93, 94)); the Librarian of Special Collections, University of Aberdeen (Plates 19, 20, from the A.S. Watt Cairngorms Expedition Archive); the Institute of Terrestrial Ecology (Plate 46, computer cartography at the ITE Banchory Research Station by Philip Bacon and Frank Diers); the Forestry Commission (Fig. 3.1); the Editor of *Botanical Journal of Scotland* (formerly *Transactions of the Edinburgh Botanical Society*) (Fig. 3.2); The Joint Nature Conservation Committee and J.S. Rodwell (Figs. 3.3, 3.9, 3.10); the Editor of *Journal of Ecology* (Figs. 3.4, 3.6, 3.7, 3.8, 3.12, 3.13); the Editor of *The Lichenologist* and Academic Press (Fig. 3.11); the Editor of *Biological Conservation* (Fig. 3.15); S. Warren (Fig. 3.5); P. Pryor (Fig. 3.15).

We are especially grateful to the Carnegie Trust for the Universities of Scotland, The Cairngorms Partnership and Scottish Natural Heritage for their generous help towards meeting the cost of the colour plates, which make such a valuable contribution to this volume. Those who took the photos are named beside each Plate and they are warmly thanked for making them available.

The Editor wishes to thank all the authors for their collaboration in bringing this volume to fruition, and Michael Packard for his hard work in the copy editing, production and publication of the volume. It should be added that the views expressed by the authors are their own and not necessarily those of the organizations for which they work or have worked.

CHAPTER 1
Introduction

C. H. GIMINGHAM

FOR many reasons, the Cairngorms merit description as the jewel in the crown of Scotland's natural heritage. The extensive high plateaux (Plate 1), dissected by steep-sided valleys, rank amongst the finest areas of near-natural and semi-natural ecosystems in Britain. This mountain core, with its streams (Plate 2) and lochs, descends towards surrounding straths where remnants of native woodland are set in a cultural landscape of great beauty. The lower ground has a long history of various land uses which have supported a number of thriving settlements, while the area as a whole has become a magnet for visitors seeking either the inspiration to be derived from its 'wilderness' quality or the stimulus of participation in a range of open-air pursuits.

This is without question a magnificent area, made up of many aspects each pre-eminent in its own category. The outstanding mountain scenery, whether viewed as a distant backdrop from the neighbouring lowland or from within as a dramatic foreground of rocky corries and boulder fields, leaves no doubt that this is a very special place with a unique appeal to residents and visitors alike. For many this appeal is strongly linked to remoteness, a concept expressing the opportunity offered to penetrate far from roads and human artefacts, and to the apparent 'naturalness' of much of the landscape. These very characteristics also account for much of the significance of the area in terms of its wildlife – its flora and fauna. The extensive montane habitats support tundra-like or arctic-alpine plant and animal communities over a larger continuous area than anywhere else in Britain, and provide important refuges for a considerable number of rarities. Furthermore, at lower altitudes, the foothills and straths contain some of the finest remnants of native 'Caledonian' pine forest and of native deciduous woodlands, as well as important examples of heathland, both dry and wet, and many other types of vegetation with their associated fauna. Forests, woodlands, scrub, moorland and wetlands present a distinctive and attractive mosaic of habitats.

These assets are of value not only in so far as they form a part of Scotland's 'natural heritage', but also in international terms. Nowhere else in the world is there such a massive block of high ground, set in a strongly oceanic climate at a latitude of about 57°N and formed largely of granite, though with more varied geology around the periphery. The landscape of deeply dissected plateaux with rocky tors, boulder fields, cliffs, steep corries and high altitude lochs, has been determined by the interaction between geology and glaciation. The glaciers are long gone but evidence of their action is everywhere apparent (Plate 3). In high summer the mountains are free from snow, apart from one more or less permanent patch, while even in winter snow cover is variable, being subject to intermittent thaw or, in exposed places, periodic removal by high winds. Environmental conditions at the high altitudes are therefore harsh and exacting, and bring about a strong resemblance to Arctic terrain (Plates 4, 5).

THE CONSERVATION VALUE OF THE CAIRNGORMS

Topographical and geomorphological features of pre-glacial, glacial and post-glacial origin are exceptionally well represented in the Cairngorms, and are better seen here than in many mountain systems of other countries because of the disappearance of snow in summer. From the perspective of geomorphology alone the Cairngorms are of international importance, particularly because of the way in which continuing changes at the present time can be related to a long, unbroken record of landscape evolution. For similar reasons, the vegetation and fauna incorporate many components of international significance. The plant communities, for the most part composed of species tolerant of low levels of available nutrients, include elements typical of oceanic climatic conditions which are lacking in more continental mountain systems. Relatively localized outcrops of the more basic rocks, mainly in peripheral locations around the mountain core, are of special value because of the diversity of species of arctic-alpine distribution which they support. In addition to the drier, stony ground there are also wide expanses of montane blanket bogs of distinctive composition.

The fauna, notably the birds and insects, is also of outstanding interest. Again, some of the characteristic species are restricted to oceanic conditions, while the arctic-alpine environment and vegetation provide habitats for birds such as dotterel and ptarmigan whose breeding densities here are higher than in any other parts of their ranges. Other rare arctic species visit the region, occasionally staying to breed.

Part of the importance of the high plateaux lies in the fact that they are still in a near-natural condition, little altered by human impact. Thus, in addition to the intrinsic conservation value of these mountain ecosystems, they offer an extensive 'natural laboratory' in which the interplay between a stressful physical environment and the organisms that live in it can be investigated. Because of this, they may provide a vital means of detecting some of the effects of global climatic change or atmospheric pollution.

The ecological importance of the Cairngorms, however, is by no means confined to the mountain core. The gradients in habitat conditions between the high levels and the valley floors are reflected in gradual transitions of vegetation and associated animal life. Admittedly much of the native forest at the lower altitudes has been removed or altered by man but there are still sizeable remnants of semi-natural pine-birch forest which contain characteristic plant and animal species, while in a few places the natural tree limit and upward transition from scrubby woodland (*krummholz*) through fringing juniper to montane heath can be observed and compared with their counterparts in Scandinavia. In the river valleys there are marsh and aquatic ecosystems which are also of international importance.

The Nature Conservation Review (Ratcliffe, 1977) lists 10 criteria for site assessment and selection: size (extent), diversity (both of species and communities), naturalness, rarity (of species, communities and habitats), fragility, typicalness, recorded history, position in an ecological/geographical unit, potential value (potential for enhancement through appropriate management) and 'intrinsic appeal'. There can be few areas in Britain apart from the Cairngorms which rank so highly in respect of all these criteria. The various aspects of this 'conservation value' are considered in more detail in later chapters, but here it is worth making special mention of the 'position of the Cairngorms in an ecological/geographical unit'. Ratcliffe argues that where a single geographical area embraces many of the characteristic formations, communities and species of a district it has special advantages for nature conservation. It comes as no surprise that he includes the Cairngorms among his few examples of such areas. Indeed the fact that these mountains and their surroundings incorporate not only many unique features but also a wide representation of the ecosystems typical of the region provides an extremely powerful argument for the effective conservation of the whole.

Kai Curry-Lindahl, a noted Swedish biologist, was therefore fully justified when he described the Cairngorms as 'Britain's foremost conservation area' in his preface to *The Future of the Cairngorms* (Curry-Lindahl, Watson & Watson, 1982). His comment stresses the exceptional importance of the area and also implies a responsibility for maintaining and ensuring the continuance of its special features. This task, however, is by no means a straightforward one because it has to be integrated with a variety of legitimate human demands on the area, while resisting those which must be judged undesirable. The needs of those who live and work in the region and have inherited on the lower ground a landscape used for agriculture, forestry and other aspects of estate management, have to be considered as well as the interests of others who come from outside for informal recreation such as hill walking, climbing, the study of natural history and archaeology, or as tourists to enjoy the scenery, or for the more organized activities of skiing, deer stalking and grouse shooting.

CONFLICTS OF INTEREST

In an area of such local, national and international importance it is not unexpected that conflicts of interest have arisen, some of which have flared up into major controversies. Chief among these are the conflicting demands of different kinds of land use. For example, the importance attached to deer stalking by privately owned estates has been difficult to reconcile with the needs of nature conservation or the survival and restoration of native woodlands, while the proliferation of vehicle tracks in the hills is heavily criticized for its adverse effects on the landscape. In the past, extensive commercial afforestation using non-native conifers, whether by private estates or the Forestry Commission, has been attacked on account of its influence on scenery and wildlife. To a lesser extent, badly controlled burning on the moors of the foothills, together with some aspects of predator control, has aroused criticism from naturalists and others. Those concerned with promoting access for tourism and certain kinds of popular recreation have been in conflict both with nature conservationists and with walkers and mountaineers who wish to preserve the 'wilderness' quality of the mountains. All these 'key issues' are considered more fully later in the book.

The most public, and at times acrimonious, disputes have been between the promoters and users of downhill skiing facilities and campaigners for the protection of landscape, wildlife and other aspects of the environment. The skiing centres at Coire Cas on the northern slopes of the mountains and at Glenshee in the south-east, together with access roads and ski lifts operating in summer as well as winter, have brought jobs and a degree of prosperity to parts of the area. Easy access to the plateau is appreciated not only by skiers but also by those who may not otherwise be able to enjoy the experience of being on a high mountain. Against these advantages must be set disturbance to wildlife, scarring of the landscape, loss of wilderness quality, and footpath erosion at high altitudes under the pressure of thousands of pairs of feet each year. While these facilities are now well established and fairly generally accepted, there have been strongly-fought public inquiries over proposals for their extension.

In all these cases much has been made of the conflict between the demands of conservation-orientated management and the interests of local communities, especially in respect of employment. In fact, this dichotomy has often been exaggerated and, particularly in recent years, real efforts are being made to reconcile the needs of both sides in the various disputes.

However, the reconciliation of conflicting claims has not been made easier by the great diversity of bodies and individuals who have controlling interests and functions which impinge on the Cairngorms. These include the local authorities and bodies such as Highlands and Islands Enterprise (formerly the Highlands and Islands Development Board), a number of private landowners, corporate landowners including the Royal Society for the Protection of Birds and Scottish Natural Heritage (the successor to the Nature Conservancy Council for Scotland and the Countryside Commission for Scotland), government organizations which give grants or enter into agreements concerning specific activities in forestry, agriculture, tourism, countryside management or nature conservation, and some development companies, such as the Cairngorm Chairlift Company. All of these bodies have direct inputs to the management of the Cairngorms, while in addition there is nation-wide interest and concern on the part of a large sector of the public.

DESIGNATIONS

Among the consequences of growing public awareness of the need to conserve our heritage of wildlife and countryside has been the development of a variety of designations of parcels of land aimed at achieving a degree of protection. In view of the importance of the Cairngorms for a number of different reasons, it is hardly surprising that a high proportion of the area is subject to one or other of these designations, and in parts to several. Much of the central mountain core is a National Nature Reserve, first designated in 1954, of which a relatively small part (about 12 per cent) is owned by Scottish Natural Heritage, the rest being managed jointly under agreements between SNH and private landowners. A substantial additional mountain area, and a number of smaller sites in the surrounding foothills and straths, have been designated over a period from 1949 as Sites of Special Scientific Interest. In addition to these designations which are intended to confer some degree of protection for wildlife and geological features, much of the montane zone of the Cairngorms and an adjacent area covering Lochnagar and Deeside are National Scenic Areas, designated in 1980/81. More recently, international agreements and European Community Directives have led to further, more specialized designations including Ramsar Sites (wetlands of international importance) and an Environmentally Sensitive Area (the Cairngorm Straths) – see Chapter 17. Special Protection Area status, under the EC Directive on the Conservation of Wild Birds, has been conferred on parts of the Cairngorms area, and much of the area is also recommended for listing as a Special Area of Conservation under the EC Directive on the Conservation of Flora, Fauna and Habitats. It is also possible that the Government will nominate the Cairngorms to be a World Heritage Site of Natural Importance.

No doubt in time some simplification of this complex series of designations will emerge, but each is of value in recognizing the significance of the Cairngorms in one of many different respects. Their various functions and the degree of success achieved in meeting their aims will be discussed in later chapters, but here it is important to state the view, held by many conservationists, that even this range of designations and provisions is insufficiently powerful to secure adequate protection of the natural heritage of the area. This is largely because such designations can only prevent damaging operations; they cannot create or do much to encourage sympathetic management to conserve and enhance the landscape, wildlife and social well-being of human communities. Already there are many signs of degradation in the Cairngorms arising from excessive pressures, unwise land use and bad planning, and it is argued that the powers available are insufficient to meet these and future threats. Curry-Lindahl, already quoted, has commented, 'I was surprised by the weak protection given to this outstanding area' (Curry-Lindahl, Watson & Watson, 1982). It is therefore more than ever necessary to achieve integrated management throughout the area to halt ecological deterioration and promote conservation objectives.

THE NEED FOR INTEGRATED MANAGEMENT

Despite the diversity of demands, there has been growing realization in recent years of the urgent need for an integrated approach to the use and management of this exceptionally important and sensitive area. That this is indeed a topical subject is evident from the action of the Government's Scottish Office in setting up in 1991 a 'Cairngorms Working Party', charged with making recommendations for an integrated management strategy for the area and for a structure to bring about its implementation. It reported in 1993 and its recommendation for the establishment of a Cairngorms Partnership was implemented in 1994. The events have created a momentum of discusion and activity which will in various ways influence future land use and management on the one hand, and improve protection of wildlife and landscape on the other. The integration of these objectives in such a way that use and public enjoyment of the Cairngorms countryside can be carried on without detracting from its superb quality, either now or in the future, is the meaning of the concept of 'sustainable' use and management which was one of the Working Party's main principles (Cairngorms Working Party, 1993).

It was with this aim in view that the new British Government, elected in 1997, signified its intention that in due course the Cairngorms area should receive National Park status. Three years later the newly elected Scottish Parliament passed enabling legislation for the establishment of a National Park for the Cairngorms, and it is expected that this may come into being in the year 2003. The principles and management strategies developed by the Cairngorms Working Party and the Cairngorms Partnership will then bear fruit as the new National Park plan is drawn up and implemented.

This book will be very relevant to the work now to be undertaken by a new National Park Authority in meeting its obligation to achieve agreed, integrated and sustainable management plans.

THE AIMS OF THE BOOK

To meet with any measure of success, decision-making in respect of management must clearly be based on a firm foundation of ecological knowledge and understanding, together where relevant with economic and sociological considerations. Fortunately, because of its outstanding scientific value, much ecological research has been focused on the Cairngorms area over a period of at least 60 years. It is the aim of this book to draw on the results of this work and to identify the aspects which should inform and influence all who find delight in the Cairngorms and especially those in whose hands lies their immediate future. The book does not attempt to offer another 'natural history' of the area, so ably accomplished in other publications, but is intended to establish clearly why it is regarded as of such special importance and to underline those features

which should be treated as vital elements of its natural heritage, and then to consider the guiding principles and options for future administration and management.

Part 1 of the book sets out the ecological basis which is fundamental to all aspects of management, covering the environment and the plant and animal ecology of terrestrial and aquatic habitats. Much new information has been assembled by the authors of these chapters, and presented in a way which emphasizes the interactions between habitats, vegetation, fauna and man. In Part 2 a number of 'key issues' are selected for examination, with emphasis both on the impacts of a long history of human occupation and activity in the area and on the pressures of present-day demands on its resources. The final part (Part 3) seeks a vision for the future and makes an attempt to assess the present position and reach an ecological judgement of the options for change in the status and management of the Cairngorms. The needs of people living and working in the area as well as those of visitors and all who have its well-being at heart are addressed in the context of a conservation approach. It is hoped that this will make a constructive contribution to the very topical problem of resolving conflict and reaching solutions which are both realistic and ecologically sound. The conservation of a highly sensitive area, recognized to be of major international importance, is the overall theme.

The several contributors to this volume have been encouraged to adopt their own approaches to their subjects: uniformity of treatment has not been sought. The width of coverage is such that readers may wish to pick and choose those chapters which interest them most. For this reason, each is written so as to be complete in itself, at the risk of occasional repetition.

THE 'CAIRNGORMS AREA' – ZONATION

Definition of the area under consideration (Figure 1.1) has been left almost to the end of this introduction. References have been made to the 'mountain core' and to the surrounding foothills and straths. For the purposes of this book, which is concerned with principles and processes rather than with administrative detail, it is probably unnecessary to indicate a precise boundary to the 'study area'. The important point, however, is that in seeking ecological understanding and interpretation it is not possible to isolate the mountain core from its surroundings. Although the 'montane zone' contains some of the most important and unique plant and animal communities, their composition and structure cannot be adequately interpreted without reference to the gradients in altitude and accompanying environmental factors between the high plateaux and the low ground of the surrounding valleys. The completeness and integrity of this altitudinal sequence and its variations in different parts of the whole contribute some of the most interesting and valuable features of the area, both in terms of wildlife and landscape. The streams

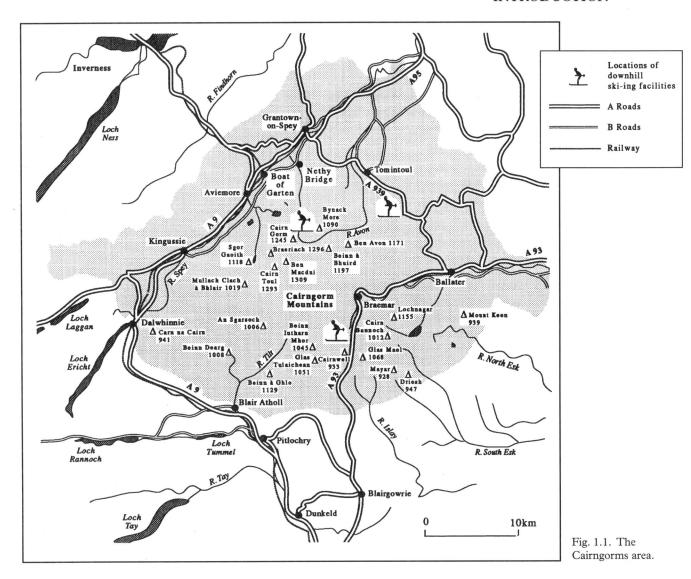

Fig. 1.1. The Cairngorms area.

which rise at high altitudes or issue from high-level lochs and lochans form a continuum with the rivers and low-level lochs of the major valleys. Consideration of the lower altitudes brings the role of man as a determinant of vegetation and landscape into prominence. Hence, whether the intention is to attempt a balanced ecological account or to underpin an integrated management strategy, it is necessary to draw the boundary widely rather than limit attention to the high ground alone.

A similar conclusion has been reached by others, notably the Cairngorms Working Party. The latter outlined (1993) a broad division into three main zones:

1) *The Mountain and Plateau Zone*: essentially the area above the former tree line (about 600 m), comprising the high moorlands, corries, plateaux and peaks;

2) *The Forest and Moorland Zone*: the semi-natural woodlands and planted forests, moorlands and bogs between the Mountain and Plateau Zone and the Valley Zone;

3) *The Valley Zone*: the diverse, largely man-made environments of farmland, meadows, plantation forests and human settlements as well as the more

natural river, loch, moor and semi-natural woodland systems among these (generally lying below 300 m in Strathspey and below 425 m in Upper Avonside/Donside and in Upper Deeside).

To accommodate these linked zones within a reasonably coherent geographical area the Working Party drew a very wide boundary (Fig. 1.1). Leaving aside the arguments as to whether this is manageable for administrative purposes, it seems appropriate to adopt it in this book (without necessarily adhering to detailed limits). In addition to the central Cairngorm massif, the area includes the Badenoch and Strathspey District on its northwest margin, Glenlivet, the Ladder Hills and Upper Donside to the north-east and Upper Deeside in the east. To the south-east it takes in Lochnagar and, in the south, the upper parts of the Angus Glens and Glenshee, while the south-west boundary is formed by the A9 road between Pitlochry and Dalwhinnie. The extent of this area is of the order of 5160 km. In 1996 the Partnership Board enlarged the area by including the Angus Glens and Drumochter Hills. However, the final size and boundaries of the future National Park have yet to be determined, after consultation.

SOME PRECEDING STUDIES

The area has already been featured in many writings both of prose and verse, some of great distinction. This is due not only to its high profile in recent debates on the issues of conservation and development but also to its wide appeal to naturalists, hill walkers, mountaineers, skiers and lovers of wilderness. Many scientific papers and official reports will be cited in subsequent chapters, but special mention may be made here of D. Nethersole-Thompson and A. Watson's book (1981) *The Cairngorms*, which provides an authoritative and unrivalled account of the area, its habitats and natural history. The booklet entitled *The Future of the Cairngorms* (K. Curry- Lindahl, A. Watson and R. Drennan Watson, 1982) drew attention to threats and land-use conflicts arising in the area and made a plea for improved conservation measures. The proceedings of a conference on this subject, held in 1990, were published in *Caring for the High Mountains – Conservation of the Cairngorms*, edited by J.W.H. Conroy, A. Watson and A.R. Gunson (1990). The most recent of many reports on the area is that of the Cairngorms Working Party (1993), already referred to, *Common Sense and Sustainability – A Partnership for the Cairngorms*. A conference entitled *The Environmental History of the Cairngorms* was held in March 1995 and its proceedings were published in 1996 in the *Botanical Journal of Scotland*, Vol. 48, no. 1.

These and other publications all acknowledge the lure of the Cairngorm mountains, the enriching quality of experience to be gained there, the value of the area to science and human welfare, and its susceptibility to damage from a variety of pressures. They are united in the view that this is a 'very special place which deserves and requires special treatment'. Their emphasis and prescriptions may differ, but they agree that there are as yet no sufficient safeguards for the future. They seek 'integrated management', which could be described as management aimed at conserving the special qualities and features of national and international importance, and ensuring that where the land is used for enjoyment or profit its ecological 'health' is sustained. This requires constant use of the results of ecological research and of social, cultural and economic data. It is to this end that it is hoped this book will contribute.

So that the text will be accessible to a wide readership, English names of plants and animals are used where available. However, scientific names are also normally given at the first mention of a species in each chapter, and when necessary to avoid ambiguity.

Scientific nomenclature in Chapter 3 follows Clapham, A.R., Tutin, T.G. & Warburg, E.F. (1981) *Excursion Flora of the British Isles* (Cambridge University Press, 3rd Edition) for vascular plants; Smith, A.J.E. (1978) *The Moss Flora of Britain and Ireland* (Cambridge University Press) for mosses; Purvis, O.W., Coppins, B.J., Hawksworth, D.L., James, P.W. & Moore, D.M. (1992) *The Lichen Flora of Great Britain and Ireland* (The Natural History Museum, London) for lichens.

REFERENCES

Cairngorms Working Party (1993) *Common Sense and Sustainability; a Partnership for the Cairngorms.* HMSO, Edinburgh.

Conroy, J.W.H., Watson, A. & Gunson, A.R., eds. (1990) *Caring for the High Mountains: Conservation of the Cairngorms.* NERC Institute of Terrestrial Ecology and Aberdeen University Centre for Scottish Studies, Aberdeen.

Curry-Lindahl, K. (1982) Preface. In: Curry-Lindahl, K., Watson, A. & Watson, R.Drennan. *The Future of the Cairngorms.* North East Mountain Trust, Aberdeen. p. 7.

Nethersole-Thompson, D. & Watson, A. (1981) *The Cairngorms: Their Natural History and Scenery.* Collins, London.

Ratcliffe, D.A., ed. (1977) *A Nature Conservation Review.* Vol. 1. Cambridge University Press, Cambridge.

PART 1

The Ecological Basis

CHAPTER 2
The Physical Geography

I. M. BROWN AND C. M. CLAPPERTON

THE Cairngorms contain an assemblage of high-altitude physical and ecological features unique not only to the British Isles, but also to western Europe because of their geographical (maritime) location (Fig. 1.1). Set centrally in the heart of the Scottish highlands, the variety of landforms in this massif has evolved under the changing climatic conditions of the late Tertiary and Quaternary geological periods. The most recent and rapidly developing process of landscape change is the degradation of slopes by human activity, a feature of only the past few decades. From a geological and geomorphological point of view, as well as from the ecological perspective, the Cairngorms comprise a very distinctive unit, namely a major granitic massif forming the highest extensive plateau in Britain and separated almost entirely from the surrounding uplands by valleys. To the east there is a more gradual decline in altitude. Consequently, this chapter concentrates on the core area in which most of the unique attributes are found; however, outstanding features outwith the massif are also included where appropriate.

CLIMATE

The climate of the Cairngorms, as elsewhere in Britain, is strongly influenced by the presence and position of the atmospheric polar front – related to the oceanic polar front where polar and tropical waters meet – so that westerly depressions alternate with less frequent more settled spells. The easterly position of the massif in Scotland results in a climate that is less 'oceanic' than the west coast and is more

often influenced by high pressure over Scandinavia. The high latitude (57°N) ensures that there is a large difference between summer and winter with regard to day length and insolation received, which is important for the growing season. The weather on the high plateau is often significantly different from that in the surrounding valleys, usually worse but occasionally better, mainly due to the altitude.

The recent installation of automatic weather stations on the summit of Cairn Gorm, together with the facility on Morrone near Braemar, now provide high-altitude data to complement those received from Braemar, Achnagoichan (Coylumbridge), Balmoral, Glenlivet, Glenmore Lodge and Coire Cas (top and bottom of the chairlift). The longest record is from Braemar and dates back to the time when the Earl of Fife kept a weather diary on his Mar estate at the end of the eighteenth century.

Temperature records (Table 2a) show that both diurnal and annual variation are greater in the Cairngorms area than at the west coast, reflecting a more continental-type regime; for example, the January-July temperature range at Braemar averages 12.5°C (Green, 1981). With increasing altitude, more 'maritime' conditions return, bringing smaller temperature ranges, although there are more air frosts. Temperature usually drops rapidly with altitude although this depends on the prevailing air mass. For example, measurements by Baird (1957) have shown that the average temperature drop from Braemar to Ben Macdui (or Macdhui) is 2.2°C per 300 m, but this is usually greater from April to June due to snow on the high plateau chilling the air. As a result, there is a rapid decline in the length of the

Table 2a Weather data for Braemar (1930 – 1960)

	Temperature (°c)						Precipitation (mm)			Bright Sunshine (hrs)		Rel. Humidity (%)
	Average Daily		Average Monthly		Absolute		Average Monthly Fall	Max fall in 24 hr	Average Days with 0.25 mm or more	Average Monthly Duration	Average % of Possible	Average of Observations at 0900
	Max	Min	Max	Min	Max	Min						
JAN	3.7	−2.5	9.4	−12.9	13.3	−20.6	96	83	19	24	10	85
FEB	4.2	−2.3	9.6	−12.1	13.3	−25.0	66	43	17	56	21	84
MAR	6.6	−1.0	13.6	−10.1	20.6	−21.7	52	24	16	94	26	80
APR	9.4	1.1	15.9	−5.4	21.1	−8.9	55	25	17	129	30	73
MAY	13.3	3.4	21.0	−3.2	27.2	−7.8	62	35	15	167	33	70
JUN	16.4	6.4	24.4	0.4	28.3	−3.3	50	33	15	165	31	69
JUL	17.6	8.6	23.9	3.0	29.4	−0.6	73	33	17	142	27	74
AUG	17.1	8.1	23.5	1.2	27.8	−1.7	75	44	16	124	26	78
SEP	14.4	6.1	20.1	−1.2	23.9	−6.1	72	38	17	104	27	80
OCT	10.5	3.6	16.3	−4.2	21.1	−8.3	101	48	20	66	21	83
NOV	6.8	0.8	11.9	−7.7	15.6	−16.1	96	58	19	31	12	85
DEC	4.8	−0.8	10.1	−10.3	12.2	−21.7	101	40	20	18	8	84
YEAR	10.4	2.6	26.3*	−16.5*	29.4	−25.0	899	83	208	1120	25	79

*Average of highest/lowest each year

growing season with altitude; one rule of thumb is that the rate of decrease is equivalent to one day for every 9 m of altitude.

During winter months frost pockets commonly develop in valleys as dense cold air subsides, resulting in a temperature inversion. This is characteristic of anti-cyclonic weather and the normally high air humidity is much reduced, especially over summits. On such occasions localities such as Braemar, Grantown, Glenlivet or Glenmore Lodge frequently record the lowest temperature in the country, sometimes lower than −27°C.

Precipitation varies from more than 2250 mm/yr on the summits to less than 900 mm/yr in the Spey and Dee valleys (Table 2a); the latter experience a pronounced 'rain shadow' effect, more so than in the narrower valleys in the mountains. Records show that the driest month varies from March in Strathspey (a local anomaly) to June (more common) in the eastern Cairngorms. Precipitation is usually associated with the passing of cyclonic depressions from the west, but a significant proportion comes also with fronts swinging east from the North Sea. During the summer, higher temperatures can trigger convectional rainfall and thunderstorms more commonly than in the west Highlands. These can cause exceptional flooding events, such as the Muckle Spate of 1829 which devastated Moray and the floods of 1956 (Werrity & Acreman, 1985; McEwan, 1993).

The Cairngorms is the snowiest part of Britain and falls are possible throughout the year, although rare in August. May blizzards are a particular feature and snowfalls are more common in June and September than on other mountains in Scotland. Records show that the number of days experiencing snowfall varies from about 90 days/yr at the top of the Coire Cas chairlift to just over 50 days/yr at Achnagoichan; on the summits it is probably well over 100 days/yr (Green, 1981). The annual average of snow-lying days, with snow covering at least half the ground, has been estimated at 60 days/yr on low ground but this has generally declined in recent years; it may reach 200 days/yr on the highest peaks (e.g. Manley, 1971).

Strong winds on the plateau cause severe drifting of snow, often completely scouring the early season cover. Under these conditions snow is deposited in sheltered hollows and corries which become overhung with remarkable cornice structures, sometimes attaining 10–15 m in width, as on Braeriach and Beinn a' Bhuird (Plate 6). The larger drifts tend to accumulate in the shallower corries where gusts and eddies are less prevalent, frequently attaining depths of 20–30 m for example, at Ciste Mhearaid, Cairn Gorm, and north-east of Ben Macdui. Some of these drifts may persist all the year round if the summer is poor (Watson et al., 1994), and the semi-permanent snows of Garbh Choire Mor (Braeriach), which survive most years, are probably the most perennial in the country. Overloading of slopes during snowstorms means that avalanches are frequent, particularly in the twenty-four hours following a snowfall, due to collapse of cornices or soft slab release (Ward, 1984). Lee-side slopes loaded with broken snow crystals, then crusted to form windslab, can release at any time and are notoriously unpredictable. More predictable are the massive avalanches which occur in spring over areas of slabby rock when meltwater lubricates the base of the snow-pack; the most infamous of these occurs on the Great Slab of Coire an Lochain and approaches alpine proportions.

In addition to snow-losses through scouring and melting, sublimation (direct transfer from solid to vapour) occurs on the plateau. Reverse sublimation is also common, producing hoar frost when temperatures are below 0°C and the hills become enshrouded in mist from super-cooled water vapour. The latter is responsible for the development of frost-feathers (often 50 cm long) on the windward side of objects. Melting of snow means that the lowest level of spring/summer river flow in the Cairngorms is later than elsewhere, with runoff exceeding precipitation in April and May (Ferguson, 1985). Sustained thaws, particularly rain-on-snow thaws which produce very rapid melting, can lead to flooding, especially on Speyside.

With regard to ecology, a significant variable is the degree of potential evapo-transpiration (PE) which represents the amount of water that would be evaporated or transpired if there was an unlimited supply. This is important because it increases with radiant energy and when no water remains to evaporate, the surplus energy supplies heat. In reality, water supply is usually limited and the amount of actual evapo-transpiration is only approximately indicated by the potential. At low levels, values of 40 cm/yr have been estimated, and higher up, despite lower temperatures and reduced radiation, because of frequent cloud cover, the value is probably not much lower owing to the drying effect of strong winds. The seasonal variation of the PE : rainfall ratio is also important because a few days without rain in summer can cause plant dessication. If PE is high, a prolonged dry spell can reduce soil moisture and cause a fire hazard, especially in spring when the dry vegetation is either dead or dormant.

Prevailing winds over the Cairngorms are from the south-west and gales on the plateau are very common. The anemograph on Cairn Gorm has registered a series of record wind speeds since it was installed; the strongest gusts recorded annually from 1979–1987 ranged from 177 to 275 km/hr. Local winds occur too, one of the most notable being the 'wind funnel' effect which develops in Coire Cas on Cairn Gorm during strong south-easterly air-flows. In spring and early summer, during anticyclonic weather, convection systems can initiate strong katabatic winds which whistle down hillslopes into sheltered glens on the lee-side causing almost blizzard-like conditions, whilst a few kilometres away conditions can remain perfectly calm. The exposure to wind has a strong impact on vegetation, notably the tree line which, although generally lower on shady, north-facing slopes, also reflects local variations in wind strength.

There has been much speculation recently about future climatic change and possible global warming. This must be considered, however, against the background of climatic changes that have occurred since the end of the last glaciation (10 000 years ago). At the time of the climatic optimum, about 6000 years ago, tree lines were much higher (Pears, 1968) but since then a steady shift to a cooler, wetter, probably windier climate, in which precipitation exceeds evaporation, has favoured the development of bogland rather than trees. The bleached pine stumps found in the peat of now treeless glens represent the formerly extensive nature of the Caledonian forest, and bear witness to this natural process.

The relatively mild winters of the late 1980s and throughout the 1990s may indicate a distinctive climatic change. For example, the airflows responsible for the prevailing weather over Scotland during winter have recently been dominated by warm maritime westerly air streams rather than by cold easterly air-streams. This may be related to a northerly movement of the atmospheric jet stream, the fast circum-polar air current associated with the polar front (Mayes, 1991). Snowfalls occur in Scotland when cold moist air is advected from sub-arctic or arctic sources. This can be due to cold arctic air or polar continental air arriving from the east or north-east, often associated with an anticyclone to the north extending east to Scandinavia. Heavy falls over north-east Scotland and the Cairngorms occur at this time and it is generally very cold. However, snowfalls also occur when arctic or polar maritime air arrives from between west and north, often related to low pressure over Iceland and high pressure to the west of the British Isles. During such weather, greater snowfalls occur in north-west Scotland, and the east receives little by comparison. In addition, due to the warmer airmass, the 'westerly' snow is wetter than the dry powdery 'easterly' snow, and melts more rapidly. Research suggests that westerly-type weather has prevailed during recent winters and accounts for the comparative lack of snowfalls in the Cairngorms and eastern Grampians (Harrison, 1993). If this situation continues, it is likely that those corries and hollows facing between west and north will see greater snow accumulations at the expense of other areas. Together with the normal variability in seasonal snowfall, this trend could further increase the commercial vulnerability of the skiing industry.

GEOLOGY

The main massif of the Cairngorms consists of a large granitoid mass (Fig. 2.1), which was intruded as the largest pluton in a series of post-tectonic intrusions into the Caledonian metamorphic belt 435–390 million years ago (ma). Previously, the Caledonian rocks had been deformed, uplifted and metamorphosed from pre-existing sediments during the Grampian Orogeny which occurred 550–450 ma. The plutons probably developed late in the orogeny when suitable rocks melted; subsequently, they were intruded upwards to cool and solidify into a mass of interlocking crystals dominated by feldspar, quartz and biotite mica.

It was originally thought that a laccolith (sheet) emplacement could account for the Cairngorm granite but recent interpretations have proposed that upward intrusion of a magma body took place (Harrison, 1986). The granite is composite, but porphyritic and non-porphyritic biotite types predominate; several other minor granite bodies within the massif exhibit cross-cutting relationships within the main unit suggesting pulses of magma injection from a deeper source region. The external contacts of the intrusion with the surrounding country rocks are exposed at a few localities such as Coire Garbhlach (Glen Feshie) or Coire Odhar

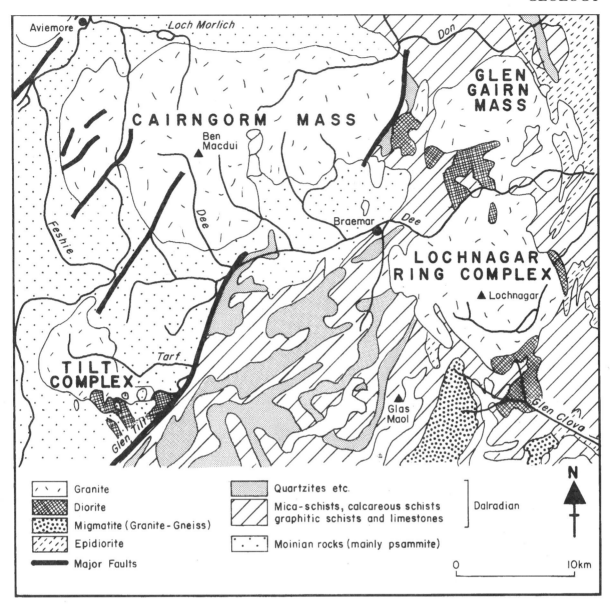

Fig. 2.1. Geological map of the Cairngorms area.

(Glen Einich). These contacts are vertical, discordant and unchilled, probably the remnants of a sub-vertical fracture system created by the upward advance of the magma body. Xenoliths and hornfelsing are very rare, which seems to preclude forcible injection (diapirism) of the granite into the Caledonian mountains, and the absence of disturbance to the foliation of the country rocks provides strong evidence against such a mechanism. At present, therefore, the favoured interpretation (e.g. Harrison, 1986) is that the intrusion into brittle crust occurred at a relatively high level and that stoping took place. In the stoping process, veining along fractures within the stress field of the rising magma caused large blocks of the country rock to become detached and rapidly sink into the rising magma.

The Cairngorms granite is composed of one major unit, known as the Main Granite, and three other minor units (Fig. 2.1). The Glen Avon granite preceded intrusion of the Main Granite whereas the Beinn Bhreac Granite and Carn Ban Mor granite post-dated it. Smaller bodies of fine-grained

porphyritic 'micro-granite' also developed as sheet-like bodies within the Main Granite. These textural variations are important because they may indicate individual pulses of magma during the intrusive episode, although the situation is still far from certain. In addition, porphyritic aplogranites and sheets of very fine-grained aplite and coarse pegmatite crystals developed late in the sequence; the latter are often clearly visible due to the effects of differential weathering. Manganese-rich garnets are locally found in porphyritic granite near the western boundary of the mass. Their distribution is consistent with localized concentrations of volatiles ponded against the walls of the pluton (Harrison, 1988).

Quite rarely, cavities developed in the granitoid mass either as contraction fissures or gas bubbles. During the last stages of crystallization, watery residual volatiles in these cavities adopted their natural crystal shape and minerals grew freely. In particular, very large crystals of quartz developed (sometimes over 60 cm long) and were tinted with impurities to form the characteristic smokey-yellow to dark-brown Cairngorm stones; other impurities allowed good crystals of beryl or topaz to develop. During the last century, much activity went into locating these gemstones, the best sites being Cairn Gorm and Ben Avon (the largest specimen found weighed almost 23 kg. Most of the veins are now worked out although recent excavations in Coire Cas have revealed good specimens. Contraction fissures are usually associated with aplite or pegmatite veins, often accompanied by a milky quartz vein exposed on the surface. The gas cavities (druses) are less easy to detect, and are usually only revealed by careful analysis of scree slopes for broken fragments.

Apart from the granite pluton of the Cairngorms, other smaller intrusions occur around Glen Gairn and at Lochnagar in the east, and around Glen Tilt within the Moine Series to the south. Of these smaller intrusions, that at Lochnagar is the most notable because it is surrounded by a 'ring complex' of metamorphosed rocks which show progressively less alteration away from the intrusion (Oldershaw, 1974; Goodman & Lappin, 1996).

The Tilt complex is very irregular and consists of both diorite and later granite intrusions. Patches of schist within the diorite apparently represent fragments of the roof of the pluton exposed as a result of variations in the form of the intrusion together with differential weathering. The south-east margin of this intrusion is demarcated by the abrupt faultline of Glen Tilt, indicating that this had developed earlier and the intrusion followed a line of crustal weakness. However, the diorite near the faultline is shattered, suggesting that some later movement also occurred.

The Caledonian metamorphic rocks which border the main granite massif of the Cairngorms and underlie the surrounding moors are diverse and complex. Most of the granite massif is bounded by Moine metasediments, mainly psammites (altered sandstones) or semi-pelites (quartz-schists) of the Grampian division; these have a comparatively simple structure with moderate dips, a N–S or NE–SW strike and gentle upright folds together with earlier flat isoclinal folds that have been preserved. Shearing is probably responsible for the characteristic flaggy fabric of these rocks.

At the east end of Glen Avon, more variable Dalradian rocks replace the Moines; these consist of limestones, graphitic schists and semi-pelitic rocks of the Appin group. Further east, intruded basic basalts and dolerites have been metamorphosed into outcrops of epidiorite and hornblende-schist. Unlike the Moine rocks, the Dalradian series have a schistosity and cleavage from crystallization of parallel mica felts, often along the original bedding planes. Dalradian rocks also underlie much of the higher ground south of the Dee, with quartzites and mica-schists dominant. However, south and west of Lochnagar, notably around Glen Clova, coarsely-banded granitic gneiss (migmatite) occurs, and this is well-foliated rather than simply fissile, as with schistose rocks, reflecting great pressure. These mixed rocks probably represent locations where the country rock was partly converted into granite, presumably deep in the palaeo-subduction zone that gave rise to the tectonic origin of the Caledonian mountains.

After the Caledonian orogeny and intrusion of the Cairngorms granite, the rocks were subsequently buried under a great depth of sediments during the late Palaeozoic and Mesozoic eras as denudational processes eroded the mountain chain; the region ultimately sank beneath the waters of shallow shelf seas. At the start of the Tertiary period (about 60 ma), the Highlands were once again elevated above sea level by tectonic movements. For millions of years, weathering and erosion gradually removed the cover rocks (e.g. Cretaceous chalk) and exhumed the old Caledonian mountain roots. Being more resistant, the latter rocks slowly wore down to form elevated plateaux while softer sedimentary rocks formed lowland basins and coastal plains.

Weathering of joints in the exhumed granite has created the distinctive mural cliff-faces of the Cairngorms. Most of the vertical and horizontal joints are contraction features which originated during cooling of the granitoid mass. However, some of the horizontal joints and many of the slabs parallel to valley sides originated as denudation removed the overlying rocks, and pressure release from this unloading caused sheeting structures (dilitation jointing) (Glasser, 1997). This pattern of jointing and sheeting, together with the rounding of exposed blocks, has endowed many cliff-faces with a 'woolsack' appearance (Plate 7); this is particularly notable in Coire an Lochain. Another characteristic of the cliffs here are deep gullies which are usually the lines of small vertical faults or crush-lines containing shattered rock.

PRE-GLACIAL GEOMORPHOLOGY

The landscape of the Cairngorms is dominated by plateaux and smooth, gentle slopes dating from the Tertiary geological period (Plate 8); these have been cut sharply by glacial features developed during the subsequent Pleistocene epoch. The jointing ('sheeting' or 'pseudo-bedding') of upper parts of the granite bedrock tends to conform with undulations of the plateau surface, suggesting that those summit areas experienced very little glacial modification. At the time when the land was periodically elevated above sea level during the Tertiary, a series of stepped erosion surfaces developed over the eastern Grampians and these are well developed on the Cairngorm granite. Concordance of summit altitudes is one indicator of these ancient land surfaces (Fig. 2.2), together with extensive plateau remnants at various levels. A distinctive upper surface at 1100–1300 m is suggested by the Cairn Gorm/Ben Macdui and Braeriach/Cairn Toul plateau. Lower surfaces are evident at 850–950 m on Moine Mhor and Moine Bhealaidh, and at 700–750 m, notably to the north of Glen Avon. Much dispute has centered on whether these features developed due to marine planation or sub-aerial slope retreat. However, recent work has noted the continuation of weathering after uplift, emphasizing the retreat of scarp-slopes due to 'backwasting' and the presence

Plate 1

The extensive high plateau of the Cairngorms mountain core, dissected by glacial valleys. In the foreground are weathered granitic boulders and gravel – May 1989.

Photo: Mike Matthew.

Plate 2

A Cairngorms mountain stream descending through heather-dominated moorland with scree slopes and high plateau in the distance. Glen Clova, May 1974.

Photo: Charles Gimingham.

Plate 3

Glen Clova viewed from Glen Fee – steep glacial valleys in the southern rim of the mountains. May 1973.

Photo: Charles Gimingham.

Plate 4
Snow fields in the
Cairngorms.

Photo: Charles Gimingham.

Plate 5
Icicles on a peat overhang –
the Fir Mounth, November
1982.

Photo: Charles Gimingham.

Plate 6
Large snow cornices
overhang Corrie Bhrochain
on the eastern side of
Braeriach – approaching the
summit from the south.
March 1991.

Photo: Iain Brown.

Plate 7
'Woolsack' jointing and weathering effects on the summit tor of Meikle Pap, Lochnagar. May 1963.

Photo: Chalmers Clapperton.

Plate 8
Gently rolling ancient land surface looking north-west from the south top of Beinn a' Bhuird – summit blockfield is in the foreground. February 1989.

Photo: Iain Brown.

Plate 9
Tors on the summit of Beinn Mheadhoin, showing topographic 'sheeting' structures (dilitation jointing). July 1989.

Photo: Iain Brown.

Plate 10
The Loch Avon trough viewed from the Shelter Stone Crag, looking north-east. Hummocky moraines of the Loch Lomond stadial are evident around the upper (near) end of the loch. June 1990.

Photo: Iain Brown.

Plate 11
The Lairig an Laoigh glacial breach at the head of Glen Derry. Hummocky Moraine in the foreground. July 1989.

Photo: Iain Brown.

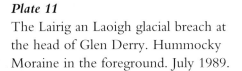

Plate 12
Classic corries cut into the northern flank of Braeriach. The Lairig Ghru glacial breach is on the left.

Photo: Chalmers Clapperton.

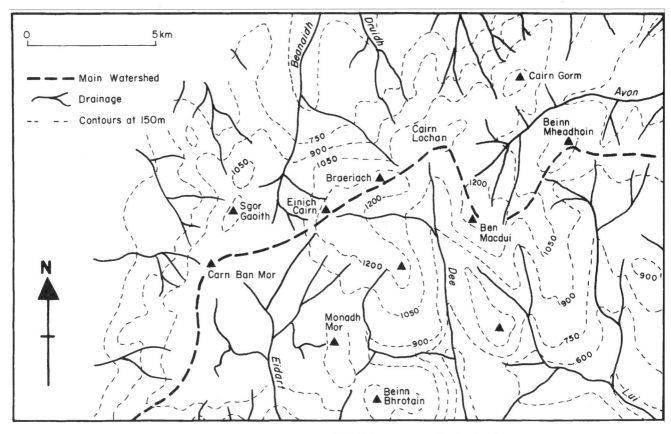

Fig. 2.2. Reconstruction of the pre-glacial Tertiary relief in part of the Cairngorm massif (after Sugden, 1968).

of multiple local levels varying in height due to subsequent tectonic warping (Hall, 1991). In the east of the region, Morven provides a fine example of an isolated residual ('monadnock') rising above the surrounding plateau surface. As the hill occurs within areas of rocks of relatively uniform resistance, it appears that isolation was achieved by encroachment of the surrounding erosion surfaces through inexorable backwasting of their slopes. South of the Dee, Mount Keen is another excellent example and rises above an easterly-tilted plateau; Lochnagar is also a prominent residual fragment of the upper plateau level.

The Cairngorms contain the best array of tors in Britain (Ballantyne, 1993) (Plate 9). These are residual masses of granite bedrock, usually coarse-grained, and occur on plateau summits, hillsides and spurs; they are commonly surrounded by loose boulders and slabs that have weathered out from the bedrock. A fine diversity exists, from long low ridges, for example, at Clach Bhan, Ben Avon, to spectacular stacks reaching 30m high at Barns of Bynack or Clach Bun Rudhtair, Ben Avon. Tors are most common in the east and north-east of the massif, particularly on spurs and slopes facing in these directions. They also occur on the granite of Lochnagar at Meikle Pap.

It is generally accepted that the development of most tors is primarily related to the frequency of jointing in the parent rock since this controlled the differential decomposition by deep chemical weathering during the warm wet climate of the

Tertiary period (Linton, 1955). Most tors have originated where the joint spacing is widest, reducing the depth to which weathering processes could penetrate, so that when the weathered mantle was removed downslope, upstanding blocks of less-weathered granite (tors) remained (Plate 9). Their subsequent survival through several Pleistocene glaciations demonstrates the limited erosive power of ice-sheets over the high plateau summits, and it is notable that most tors occur in sites that were most sheltered from ice flow and associated glacial erosion. It is also possible that some of the smaller tors evolved entirely in a cold (periglacial) climate, similar to the high Arctic. Limited glacial erosion on the Cairngorm plateau is also demonstrated by the survival of residual pockets of deeply-weathered rock (saprolites), for example in Coire Raibeirt, and these also tend to be most common in lee-side sites with respect to former ice flow. Extensive saprolites have also been found in the Gaick Forest within the granites of the Tilt complex.

In some parts of the high plateaux streams have cut steep-sided valleys that remain little modified by glaciation. Most of the bigger valleys lead eastwards across geological boundaries, but in the Speyside area lineations in the Moine rocks have dictated a SW–NE alignment to the drainage. Elsewhere, the easterly trend of the rivers probably relates to tilting of the plateaux during the Tertiary, with the valleys gradually deepening during successive phases of uplift.

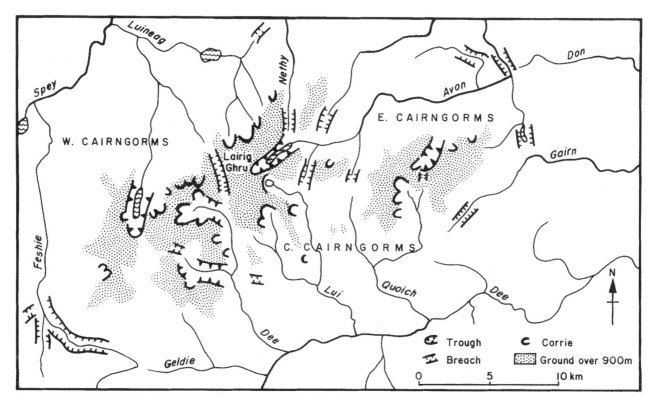

Fig. 2.3   Major elements of linear glacial erosion in the Cairngorms (after Sugden, 1968).

GLACIAL GEOMORPHOLOGY

The more dramatic elements of the Cairngorms landscape were created by a succession of icecaps that developed during cold intervals (stadials) of the Quaternary period (last 2 million years). Sometimes conditions were only just cold enough to allow glacier ice to develop in corries or where wind-blown snow accumulated in sheltered valley heads. But during the colder and more prolonged glacial intervals, ice-caps discharged outlet glaciers down the main valleys. At other times, and probably during the last four major glacial cycles, a large ice-sheet ultimately enveloped the entire region. Hence, there is a great diversity of glacial and pre-glacial landforms in the Cairngorms, and this makes it such an important site for investigating geomorphological processes. Some workers have considered that the survival of pre-glacial elements – tors and deeply-weathered rock – means that the Cairngorms remained as an ice-free enclave during glaciations (e.g. Linton, 1955). Nowadays, this is very difficult to sustain both on theoretical grounds and from empirical evidence, although the hypothesis has never been fully refuted with field evidence. Some of the plateau tors show signs of having been glacially streamlined (Sugden, 1971) but the problem has not yet been fully investigated.

With regard to the last glacial interval, empirical evidence favours the presence of a large ice-dome over the Cairngorms, while the massif was surrounded by the main Scottish ice-sheet flowing from source areas in the west. This is probably why there are no Moine schist 'erratics' in the interior of

the main granite massif, although such rocks are found on the Sgoran Dubh range in the western Cairngorms (Sugden, 1968). It is also consistent with evidence from striations on rocks and other larger forms of glacial erosion suggesting that vigorous ice streams from the west were diverted around the main massif into the Spey and Dee valleys. Moreover, 'erratics' of Cairngorm granite can be found close to the summit of Morven (850 m) in the east, and by extrapolation of the required ice-surface gradient necessary to transport these to this altitude, a local ice-dome over the Cairngorms seems necessary on at least one, and probably more occasions during the last glaciation.

The survival of much of the pre-glacial landscape can most readily be attributed to the Cairngorm ice-cap being cold-based. This means it was frozen to the substrate because it was relatively thin and extremely cold; as such it lacked basal meltwater which is fundamental in causing glacial erosion (Sugden, 1971). Such a model is compatible with the much lower precipitation here compared to the West Highlands, as predicted in ice-sheet models (Gordon, 1979). As a result, the rate of snow accumulation would have been slower and the movement of ice less vigorous. At present, however, the exact relationship between pre-glacial elements and the spatial attributes and activity of the Cairngorm ice-cap have yet to be established. Nevertheless, there is little doubt that where pre-existing topography allowed localized confluence of large volumes of ice, as at valley heads, fast-flowing, warm-based ice-streams evolved and effected considerable erosion (Glasser, 1995). Modern analogues exist in the northern Scandinavian mountains.

Ice-sheet erosion features clearly cut across the pre-glacial landscape (Fig. 2.3), and are nearly always attributable in their present form to the most recent glaciation which ended about 10 000 years ago. However, it is likely that many such landforms were initiated during previous glaciations. *Roches moutonnées* are 'classic' erosional landforms that provide evidence of the former direction of ice movement. Their characteristic asymmetrical profile consists of a smooth, ice-scoured bedrock hill shaped like a whale's back, with an abrupt scarp on the lee-side; this scarp evolved where differential stress on the bedrock above and below a lee-side cavity at the ice bed fractured the rock, while refreezing of the meltwater allowed blocks to be 'plucked' off along joint-lines. These landforms are particularly common where the ice streamed down the Dee and Spey valleys (Sugden *et al.*, 1992), and sometimes exceed 100 m in height. Notable examples include Craigendarroch (Ballater) and Craig Leek (near Braemar) in the upper Dee valley.

Probably the most spectacular elements of glacial erosion are the deep troughs which formed where ice converged into pre-existing valleys, leaving a steep headwall – often related to jointing in the granite – over which the ice descended from the plateau surface. Loch Avon in the centre of the massif is an outstanding example (Plate 10). It is notable that the eastern end of this rock basin terminates adjacent to the col of The Saddle where a diffluent ice-stream diverged from the confines of Glen Avon to flow down Strath Nethy, thereby reducing the erosive power of the ice in Glen Avon. Other fine examples of glacial troughs include Glen Einich, Glen Geusachan and the Slochd Mor between Beinn a' Bhuird and Ben Avon, while those radiating from the Grampians plateau, Glen Callater, Glen Muick and Glen Clova, are equally impressive.

Other remarkable features of the Cairngorms are the glacial breaches which cut through the massif across the watershed. Generally, they are orientated S–N or SW–NE and follow fault lineaments. The most famous of these is the Lairig Ghru, but other excellent examples include the one followed by the Lairig an Laoigh at the head of Glen Derry (Plate 11), the through valley of Glen Builg in the east, and further south, the remarkable breaches of Glen Tilt and the Gaick. The origin of these features remains uncertain and awaits further study. Sugden (1968) suggested that external ice may have been involved because it was difficult to relate local ice to the breaching of the high ground. However, this is not consistent with the presence of a local ice-cap and it is possible that the Lairig Ghru was created by local ice nourished in upper Glen Dee and forced north through a pre-existing col due to the pressure of external ice to the south (Linton, 1951). At some localities glacial breaches provide excellent illustrations of river 'capture', for example, where the Feshie has captured the upper Geldie, or at Inchrory where the Avon has captured the upper Don (Linton, 1949, 1954). In both cases the 'pirate' river makes a spectacular right-angled bend where the capture occurs, whereas the river that has been 'beheaded' has been left as a sluggish 'misfit' stream in an anomalously broad valley.

The corries of the Cairngorms are another obvious facet of glacial erosion (Fig. 2.3, Plate 12). Many contain lochans as at Coire an Lochain, Cairn Gorm or Coire Uaine, Ben Macdui, and often a blocky boulder moraine near the lip represents the most recent occupation by glacier ice (Plate 13). Corries indicate a phase of mountain glaciation, when climatic conditions were only marginal for the formation of glaciers. They formed in hollows on the shady lee-side (in terms of prevailing winds) of massifs where blown snow could accumulate and be protected from insolation; hence, most face between north and east. At some localities, several corrie glaciers combined at a valley head to form a larger glacier which had the erosive power to gouge out a deep trough; An Garbh Choire, between Cairn Toul and Braeriach, is an excellent example of this. It has been proposed that different generations of corrie can be recognized in the Cairngorms, principally on the basis of their size, the largest corries being the oldest features (Sugden, 1969). Clearly, the corries evolved to their present size before the most recent glaciation because moraines on the corrie floors have an insignificant volume compared to the volume of the corrie.

Further erosion took place during the waning stages of the ice-sheets and mountain glaciers when meltwater facilitated the development of fluvioglacial landforms. These are most evident from the period of deglaciation of the last ice-sheet (the Late-glacial), but again many of these features may have been initiated during earlier glaciations, notably those carved out of bedrock. Numerous fine examples of meltwater channels are found in the Cairngorms, the channel now being completely dry or occupied by an insignificant misfit streams (Plate 14). The orientation of channels often reflects the direction of former ice movement, therefore these landforms are useful for ice-sheet reconstruction and modelling. As subglacial meltwater is confined under hydrostatic pressure, it can flow uphill, following a gradient from high to low pressure in the direction of ice movement. Consequently, meltwater channels often cut across the topography, commonly across spurs which were transverse to the direction of ice flow, as in the Dee valley between Braemar and Ballater. Because the meltwater would seek out the route of lowest pressure, cols were the favoured route across spurs. A whole series of channels exists on the north side of the Cairngorm massif (Fig. 2.4) between the northern end of the Lairig Ghru and the massive channel of the Eag Mhor of Dorback, reflecting the power of ice flow down the Spey valley forcing meltwater to the north-east across confining spurs. Elsewhere, meltwater was responsible for carving deep gorges in pre-existing valleys, as at the Water of Ailnack, near Tomintoul, and in some cases, erosion of a meltwater gorge has caused a diversion of drainage and ultimately river 'capture' at Water of Caiplich, Glen Avon. Many channels also follow

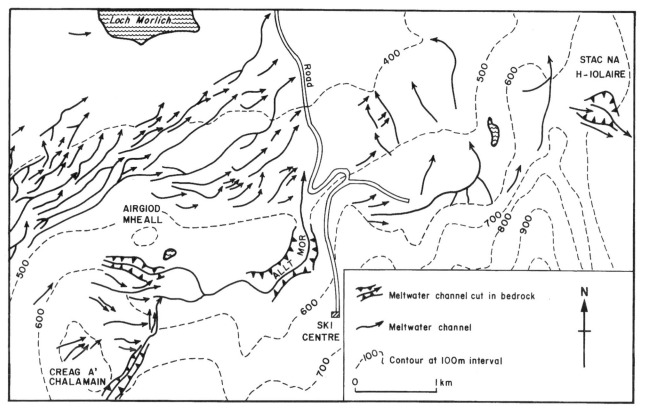

Fig. 2.4   The pattern of glacial meltwater channels on the northern slopes of Cairn Gorm (after Young 1974).

faultlines which would have contained shattered rock that facilitated erosion – Clais Fhearnaig (Glen Quoich) is a good example. The erosive power of subglacial meltwater in these channels can be seen at The Vat near Dinnet where a massive pothole 18 m across and at least 15 m deep has been scoured out of the granite.

When water flow in these fluvioglacial channels began to decline, immense quantities of stratified sediments were deposited as winding ridges known as eskers – smaller fragments and deposits related to other glacier cavities such as crevasses are often referred to as kames. Streams at the ice margin also dumped poorly sorted sediments, and in some cases retreat of the ice margin left bench-like features on the hillside (kame terraces) where sediments had accumulated against the ice edge. The pattern of sedimentation at the ice margin was frequently complicated by buried ice blocks which gradually melted out, causing reworking of sediments and inversion of relief to create a landscape referred to as 'hummocky moraine' or 'kame and kettle topography'. Kettle-holes represent the sites where ice blocks melted out to leave enclosed hollows, often infilled with water, as at Loch Morlich and Loch Garten. Excellent examples of all of these landforms occur around the Muir of Dinnet in the east of the region, where a large outwash plain also formed during a temporary halt of the glacier (Brown, 1992); the area around Loch Morlich on Speyside also contains good examples (Young, 1974). Although 'pockets' of stagnant ice were undoubtedly isolated by the decaying ice-sheet, recent research has emphasized that glaciers

remained dynamically active during retreat ('backwasting'), rather than large masses of ice becoming glaciologically 'dead' and thus 'downwasting' (Brown, 1993, 1994; Brazier *et al.*, 1998).

The vast amount of sediment liberated during deglaciation often caused obstructions on valley floors which allowed lakes to develop upstream. Eventually, sediment infill and the cutting of a deeper outlet through the obstruction reduced the size of the lake so that most are now marshy hollows, as in Glen Derry (Plate 15).

By careful mapping and analysis of sediments, it is possible to reconstruct the waning stages of the last glaciers during recession of the last ice-sheet stage. Also, by comparison with biological evidence (pollen, fossil bettles, etc.), conclusions may be drawn about the climate at the time. For example, it now appears as though much of the early ice decay (18–14 ka) took place when the climate was still extremely cold, suggesting that the lack of snowfall might have been a major cause of glacier recession (Brown, 1993). Considerable controversy has also been generated in the past over the scale of glaciation during the short-lived cold interval which occurred at 11 000–10 000 yr BP following deglaciation of the last ice-sheet. This renewed growth of glacier ice is known as the Loch Lomond Readvance after the type-site in the   south-west Highlands where it has been clearly demarcated and dated. In the Cairngorms, debate has centred on whether it was restricted only to corries (e.g. Sugden, 1980), where it is clearly indicated by boulder moraines (Plate 16), or whether it extended from some of these source areas on to valley floors as indicated by areas of hummocky moraine (Sissons, 1979). Analysis has shown that, although these areas of hummocky moraine may at first appear to be unordered (see Plate 10), a distinctive lineation is generally present (Bennett & Glasser, 1991). However, development of this landform type may have occurred during ice-sheet deglaciation as well as during recession from the Loch Lomond Stadial; resolution of this problem awaits further investigation.

Much of the sediment released during deglaciation ended up as thick deposits of outwash on valley floors. The wide variation in meltwater flow regime (seasonally and diurnally) due to the varied melt-rate, together with the large sediment load, meant that braided rivers developed as the most effective means of transport. Today, the River Feshie represents probably the best example of the residual stages of such a river (Plate 17). In addition, crustal rebound of the land, when the overburden of ice was removed, caused a relative drop in sea level. Combined with a subsequent decline in sediment load after deglaciation, this meant that rivers began to cut into their outwash deposits forming stepped terrace systems on the valley sides, as in the Dee and Spey valleys, and also in smaller valleys such as Glen Feshie and Glen Einich as tributary streams became adjusted to the new level of the main valley.

When the Loch Lomond Stadial ended about 10 000 years ago, glacier ice finally disappeared from Scotland, but the Cairngorms presently remain within about 2°C of developing glaciers again. Indeed, Sugden (1977) suggested on the basis of lichen size on boulders within certain corries that some of the moraines could have been formed by glaciers 150–300 years ago, during the cold interval known as the 'Little Ice Age'. However, analyses of pollen in sediment cores and radiocarbon dating from some of these corries has firmly disproved Sugden's hypothesis (Rapson, 1985). An intriguing exception, however, could have been Garbh Coire Mor of Braeriach which might just have developed a small glacier. As discussed earlier, this corrie contains probably the most perennial snowpatch in Britain at present. Comprehensive reviews of Quaternary glaciation in Scotland are contained in Gordon & Sutherland (1993), Gordon (1997) and Clapperton (1997).

PERIGLACIAL GEOMORPHOLOGY AND CONTEMPORARY GEOMORPHIC PROCESSES

During cold intervals like the Loch Lomond Stadial, when limited glacier build-up occurred throughout the higher massifs in Scotland, periglacial processes operated on the exposed ground and on rocks that remained ice-free. On the Cairngorm plateau cryogenic weathering, mainly through frost-shattering and granular disintegration of rocks, modified tors and broke up exposed rock surfaces into extensive blockfields (see Plate 8). The most widespread activity was probably downslope movement of the regolith caused by solifluction. This process is associated with permanently frozen ground 0.5 m or more below the surface, above which an 'active layer' undergoes a seasonal thaw and becomes waterlogged, facilitating movement on even the gentlest of gradients. Solifluction was responsible for the flat-topped boulder lobes (typically 10–30 m across) (Plate 19) which are so common on hillslopes: these features usually represent the lobate extension of more widespread solifluction sheets. The boulder lobes are believed to date from the time of the Loch Lomond Stadial when freeze-thaw was very active, exploiting the jointing in the granite bedrock to produce massive scree slopes below cliffs. As previous scree slopes would have been removed by successive ice-sheets, and a much more restricted development has occurred since (as evidenced by the vegetated nature of many scree slopes), the geomorphological potential of frost during even this short cold spell (1000–1500 years) is clearly evident. In fact, some cliffs have now been replaced entirely by screes as at Coire Beanaidh, Braeriach.

A result of the rapid rate of rockfall during the Loch Lomond Stadial, was that protalus ramparts developed where fallen boulders accumulated as ridges at the foot of perennial snowpatches. They are particularly common in the Cairngorms, generally at 650–950 m (Ballantyne and Kirkbride, 1986), notably in the Lairig Ghru. A related feature, again at its most common in this region, is rock glaciers (Sissons, 1979), which probably formed at the same time, and usually consist of step-like boulder accumulations at the foot of talus slopes; a fine example exists in Coire Beanaidh of Braeriach. These features moved at a very slow rate, probably by deformation of interstitial ice, and indicate a climatic regime which was very cold with low precipitation.

Some periglacial processes still occur at present on the high plateau, making the Cairngorms the primary area in the country for their study. Continued frost-wedging has probably been responsible for recent large rockfalls on the over-steepened slopes of glaciated valleys, as at Carn Etchachan. Solifluction activity still occurs intermittently, although at a much reduced rate, with the front edge of active lobes ('risers') rarely exceeding 1.0 m in height. 'Ploughing' boulders are widespread on vegetated moist slopes above c.650 m, and their origin has been attributed to a variety of possible causes, including frost creep, freezing and thawing of water under boulders, or sliding over a frozen substrate during a thaw.

On exposed ground above 450 m, niveo-aeolian features such as unvegetated gravel lags or wind-stripes occur. The latter are generally 1m wide or more and at least 2–4 m long and result from the combined action of needle ice growth and wind deflation (King, 1971b). Often the presence of people or deer has exacerbated these features, although the larger gravel patches on the summit plateaux of Beinn a' Bhuird, Ben Avon and Braeriach are undoubtedly due to the great exposure and the winnowing away of any fine-grade material. On slopes, soil creep has produced a stepped profile, consisting of steep well-vegetated risers and bare treads, as a result of needle ice growth and wind erosion. Many of the terraces are horizontal, but others dip steeply upwind on otherwise vegetation-free slopes, often stabilized on the lee-side of boulders.

Another common characteristic of periglacial regimes (which still appear to be active) are stone nets or 'polygons' (King, 1971a). These consist of a ring of stones up to two metres in diameter, with finer material forming a small mound in the interior due to the differential movement of particles of various sizes caused by frost heaving; some of the best examples are found on the plateau north of Ben Macdui. Although the larger features are relict it is not uncommon to see smaller unvegetated examples, particularly on wet corrie floors above about 1000 m, implying present-day activity. On slopes, the sorted clast pattern becomes stretched out to form stone stripes, usually in parallel rills that have been incised downslope.

In contrast to granitic terrain, a different suite of landforms has developed on areas of schistose rocks, which have broken down to give a regolith composed mainly of frost-susceptible fine sand. For example, on the high plateau east of Glen Feshie, small-scale earth hummocks, often over 20 cm high, analagous to the *thufur* of Iceland are present. These landforms are also well developed on the plateaux south of the Dee, notably in the vicinity of Glas Maol. They tend to be absent on granite and appear to be relict features (Ballantyne, 1984). In high-arctic environments such features form as a result of frost heaving in areas of plentiful moisture.

Running water and high wind velocities are probably responsible for the most potent geomorphic processes of the modern environment, but avalanches and rockfalls also cause local erosion and downslope movement of material. Many hillslopes are extremely fragile, consisting of gravel or till (glacial drift) which is incoherent and which may overlie over-consolidated till. On steep slopes (30–35°), heavy rain can saturate and fluidize the regolith (Plate 18), causing gullying and the development of debris flows. The sides of many glaciated valleys in the region are scarred in this way, notably Glen Geusachan and the Lairig Ghru (Luckman, 1992). In some cases, as at upper Glen Feshie, paths or roads have been swept away as a result of heavy prolonged rainstorms. Exceptionally large floods like the Muckle Spate of 1829 or those of August 1956 (Baird and Lewis, 1957) can cause massive changes in the landscape, such as debris flows on hillsides, diversion of rivers and the dumping of vast gravel spreads like those on various reaches of the rivers Dee, Spey and Feshie. The rigorous climate of the summit plateau inhibits soil development and vegetation growth, so that wind action constantly removes detritus loosened by weathering or by human and animal disturbance. These tops are therefore an extremely dynamic, ecologically unique and fragile environment. Burning, overgrazing and construction activity can all disturb the dynamic equilibrium which exists between natural forces, tipping the balance towards instability and hence degradation of the natural environment.

SOILS

The main factors governing soil formation are climate, topography, nature of the parent rock and living organisms. As most of the high plateau is underlain by granite, which weathers to coarse sand and fine gravel due to chemically resistant grains of quartz and feldspar, soils are generally incohesive, porous and barren. Where Moine and Dalradian rocks crop out, notably mica-schists or base-rich rocks, as with epidiorite on Morven or diorite at Crathie and the Moine Bhealaidh, a finer more compact soil results which is less free-draining, more cohesive and more resistant to erosion. At a few localities, calcareous mica-schists occur, which weather readily to give more fertile soils due to the lime content as found in Coire Garbhlach, Glen Feshie and Caenlochan. In addition, there are a number of significant local outcrops of limestone, notably near Braemar on Morrone and north-east of Invercauld, on Ord Ban (near Aviemore) and at Inchrory (Glen Avon). These produce the most fertile soils in the area, and are often demarcated by lush grass which contrasts strongly with the surrounding drab brown heather (see also Chapter 3). On a much smaller scale, locally anomalous lime-rich patches occur even in the granite. Cavities and fissures within the granite may contain minerals such as calcite or epidote which when released can greatly enrich the soil below. This is especially pronounced in the area of shattered rock at the boundary between the Caledonian meta-sediments and the granite, as at the head of Glen Einich. Another influencing factor may be the distribution of glacial drift. This forms a thick cover on most valley floors but the hillsides contain only a thin veneer due to the transport of finer material downslope by solifluction and hillwash. In certain areas, glacial transport of schist or diorite rocks on to granite bedrock has provided more nutrients than would normally be available.

In general, Arctic-type soils are found on the plateaux with pockets of more fertile soil in sheltered corries. Lower down, podsols are predominant in the pine-woods and much of the ground is covered by blanket peat or is peat-hagged. Between these extremes, there is a variety of soil transitions. The generally coarse sandy parent material means that chemical nutrients are in short supply and the cool climate ensures that chemical weathering is very slow; nutrients are thus released very slowly. Leaching and soil creep also remove nutrients, except on waterlogged ground or around springs and lime-rich 'flushes' where groundwater allows accumulations of vital minerals.

Soils in Scotland have been forming for about 10 000 years since the glaciers disappeared, but the pedogenic processes did not reach their present rates of operation until about 7 500 years ago. As a consequence, soils of the Cairngorms are quite young, predominantly mineral soils (Fig. 2.5). They consist mainly of inorganic matter, including large rock particles, with perhaps a surface layer of undecomposed humus on which dead plant litter accumulates. On gentler slopes or in hollows, the

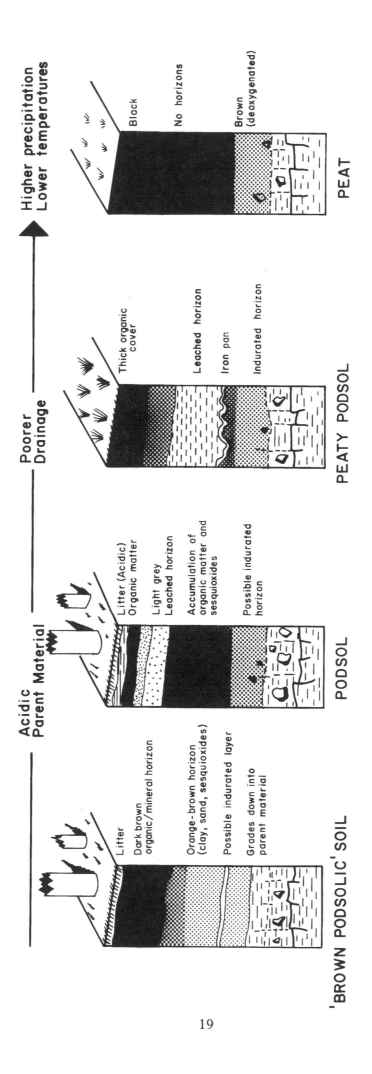

Higher precipitation
Lower temperatures

Poorer Drainage

Acidic Parent Material

PEAT

Black

No horizons

Brown
(deoxygenated)

PEATY PODSOL

Thick organic cover

Leached horizon

Iron pan

Indurated horizon

PODSOL

Litter (Acidic)
Organic matter

Light grey
Leached horizon

Accumulation of
organic matter and
sesquioxides

Possible indurated
horizon

'BROWN PODSOLIC' SOIL

Litter

Dark brown
organic/mineral horizon

Orange-brown horizon
(clay, sand, sesquioxides)

Possible indurated layer

Grades down into
parent material

Fig. 2.5.   A continuum of upland soil profiles reflecting the influence of parent material, topography and local climate on pedogenesis.

19

humus tends to build up and when it reaches a depth greater than 30 cm, the mineral material beneath usually becomes inaccessible to plant roots leading to the development of an organic soil and ultimately peat. The waterlogged nature of peat, which causes expansion in the soil, together with its thickness means very little nourishment is available for plants. Podsolization occurs when the soluble products of raw humus and plant litter transport iron and aluminium oxides (sesquioxides) from the upper to the lower soil horizons. This process is very important at lower levels, but above about 650 m it generally becomes very weak. The threshold altitude varies according to factors such as aspect, exposure and vegetation cover, but it is often used to distinguish between upland and mountain soils.

With regard to the alpine mountain soils, cold conditions now and in the past have impeded their formation. Freeze-thaw processes tend to dominate soil development and structure at high altitudes, hence they are often termed cryosols (Birse, 1980). Aeolisols, soils depending on the distribution of wind-blown material, also occur at these altitudes. The most immature soils have formed on scree, boulder slopes, gravel and bare rock and are colonized only by bacteria or lichens. Where the parent material is less stony and free-draining, and higher plants have been able to colonize, more mature soils have developed although they are invariably strongly leached.

Frost action causes the upper parts of mountain soils to be very loose and the spartan wind-swept vegetation means that it is rare for clear soil horizons to develop. At the highest level, a soil profile characterized by black or organic stained granite beneath surface grit and underlain by red/brown gritty loams is common (Heslop, 1981). At lower levels (below *c.*1050 m), the presence of more vegetation produces a covering of litter (often partly decomposed) to accompany the surface grit, beneath which red-brown humus accumulates with bleached mineral grains. Continuing down the profile, a third horizon of black or dark red/brown sand characterized by mineral grains coated with colloidal humus is further succeeded by horizons of brown gritty sand in which stones have caps of silt leached from above; the thickness of organic matter in the third horizon tends to decrease with height, reflecting the lesser degree of plant cover. The presence of bleached mineral grains in the second horizon together with the downward movement of humus (and occasionally iron) is evidence for weak podsolization. Where mat grass (*Nardus stricta*) predominates – a general indicator of long-lying snow patches – soil profiles often have a thicker and more complete surface organic layer and the second horizon is more grey in colour with less organic matter present due to severe leaching from the spring thaw. Similar soil profiles develop over acidic schists, but the colour is more yellow-brown reflecting the differing parent material, and the coarse gritty texture characteristic of granite soils is absent.

Below about 650 m, upland-zone soils predominate. Most of these are free-draining, leached and podsolized and are generally associated with heather moorland. However, at lower altitudes, it is not uncommon for leached soils to be only weakly podsolized, for example, in the birchwoods on the slopes of Glen Feshie where schists and base-rich rocks prevail. As a consequence, so-called brown podsolic soils have developed, named after their predominantly brown mineral horizons. These soils have a significant decrease in acidity from the upper layers (pH 4–4.5) to the parent material below (pH approx. 5). More podsolized soils are characterized by a surface layer of raw humus, underlain by an ash-coloured mineral horizon and then the lower horizons which have gained aluminium and iron oxides, often with humus, by leaching from above. In the natural pinewoods of Rothiemurchus and Glen Feshie, humus-iron podsols have commonly developed. These are characterized by a humus-enriched dark horizon between the mineral horizon and the ochre horizon in which the sesquioxides have accumulated, and also by a paler, indurated horizon below (just above the parent material) which forms a barrier to plant and tree roots (FitzPatrick, 1977).

In the heath communities above the pine woods, peaty podsols are the typical soils, with a very thin (or absent) humus-enriched horizon or organic layer. In addition, the surface layer of black raw humus is thicker than 10 cm and a thin iron pan of iron oxides forms below the ash-coloured mineral horizon, sometimes succeeded by an iron-enriched horizon. With altitude, the presence of this iron pan or an indurated horizon becomes very slight, so that they are rare above 600 m. Most podsols, except the brown podsolic soils mentioned earlier, have an acidity which varies from pH 3.5–4 in the surface organic horizon to 4.5–5 in the parent material; nutrients are generally concentrated in the organic surface layer. The slow rate of decomposition of organic material means that carbon to nitrogen ratios are in the region 20–30:1.

Peat has developed in waterlogged areas, in both upland and mountain zones. The main area of blanket peat formation lies between 550–750 m and is associated with peaty podsols. At higher levels, extensive areas of peat also occur, as on the Moine Mhor and the Moine Bhealaidh. The peat has often been eroded into hags and gullies by the action of water combined with wind, freeze-thaw activity and, at some sites, deer. In hollows, where the soils have developed into pure peat, pH values of less than 4 and C:N ratios greater than 30:1 reflect the extremely slow rate of decomposition.

OVERVIEW

It has been emphasized in this chapter that the Cairngorm plateau is the remnant of a much older low-lying landscape of gentle slopes and wide river valleys. This was the product of prolonged weathering and drainage development under warm temperate bioclimatic conditions that prevailed for millions of years during the Tertiary geological period. It is remarkable that residual elements of such an ancient landscape remain in view of the severe ravages of subsequent glaciation within and around the massif. Geologically recent uplift and deep fluvial dissection isolated the Cairngorm plateau, due in part to its relatively resistant rocks. This provided relative protection from rapid denudation, thereby enhancing the preservation of old elements of the original landscape. Drainage lines evolved during the later part of the Tertiary in response to tectonic uplift – regional responses to large-scale tectonics in the W. Europe/North Sea basin – and the fall in global sea level consequent upon the build-up of the Antarctic ice-sheet more than 14 million years ago. The broad-scale geometry of this landscape evolution still dominates the Cairngorms and surrounding highlands.

In detail, however, the dramatic scenery of the Cairngorms is due to the sharply etched features of glaciation that were incised ruthlessly into the ancient rolling landscape. For at least the last 800 000 years, glacial-interglacial cycles, each lasting about 100 000 years, have influenced landscape development in the Scottish highlands. For about 80 per cent of each cycle, conditions colder than now prevailed. Since it would take a fall in mean annual temperature of only 2°C to produce permanent beds of snow and ice in the Cairngorms today, it seems very likely that the massif has contained glaciers for 70–80 per cent of the last 800 000 years, and possibly for much longer. In other words, throughout recent geological time, permanent snow and glaciers have normally been present in the Cairngorms and the modern ice-free conditions are anomalous.

The effect of glaciation in the Cairngorms is more dramatic than anywhere else in Britain because of the high relief and the sharp incision of the rolling plateau by corries and troughs. Also, a unique combination of circumstances has helped preserve wide areas of the ancient landscape elements on the summit plateaux. High altitude and geographical position (comparatively dry and extremely cold) during glacial intervals led to the growth of thin ice caps that were frozen solid, that is cold-based, to the underlying rocks, meaning that very little sliding, abrasion and effective erosion took place. This afforded relative protection of the summit plateau and the older landforms that had developed there in pre-glacial times. Moreover, the Cairngorm massif is one of the few parts of mainland Scotland not to have been overrun by the larger Scottish ice-sheet, at least during the last glaciation. An independent Cairngorm ice-dome, combined with high altitudes, inhibited invasion by 'external' ice which flowed around the massif at lower levels. Thus interplay between local and external ice has created a remarkable assemblage of glacial and pre-glacial features unique to the Cairngorms area. For this reason alone, it is of national and international importance for the study of Tertiary-Quaternary landscape evolution.

The combination of altitude and maritime climate exposes the Cairngorm summits to extreme wind and frost processes. Frequent gales shift much surface detritus loosened by weathering and, in places, shape the micro-relief on which soils and plants must develop, and in which some of the fauna must survive. Periodic freezing and thawing of the ground (geocryogenic activity) breaks up rock at scales from individual crystals to large slabs and enhances both vertical and downslope movements of the regolith. Multitudes of lobate, terraced and bouldery landforms mantling the Cairngorms owe their origin to vigorous geocryogenic activity during past cold periods following the last glaciation. Such dynamism operating at and close to the ground surface makes it highly susceptible to permanent disfiguration if the fragile plant and soil cover is broken (Plate 18). Some disturbance has probably occurred periodically during the past 10 000 years due to natural climatic changes, but it has been enhanced catastrophically in places by human activity within the past few decades. It would take another interval of global cooling, with a permanent capping of snow and ice over these mountains, to protect the unique features of the Cairngorms from human disturbance.

REFERENCES

Baird, P.D. (1957) Weather and snow on Ben Macdhui. *Cairngorm Club Journal*, **17** 147–149.

Baird, P.D. & Lewis, W.V. (1957) The Cairngorm floods, 1956: summer solifluction and distributary formation. *Scottish Geographical Magazine* **73**, 91–100.

Ballantyne, C.K. (1984) The Devensian periglaciation of upland Scotland. *Quaternary Science Reviews* **3**, 311–343.

Ballantyne, C.K. (1993) Scottish landform examples, 10: The tors on the Cairngorms. *Scottish Geographical Magazine* **110**, 54–59.

Ballantyne, C.K. & Kirkbride, M.P. (1986) The characteristics and significance of some Late glacial protalus ramparts in upland Britain. *Earth Surface Processes & Landforms* **11**, 659–671.

Bennett, M.R. & Glasser, N.F. (1991) The glacial landforms of Glen Geusachan, Cairngorms: a re-interpretation. *Scottish Geographical Magazine* **107**, 116–123.

Birse, E.L. (1980) Suggested amendments to the world soil classification to accommodate Scottish mountain and aeolian soils. *Journal of Soil Science* **31**, 117–124.

Brazier, V., Kirkbride, M.P. & Gordon, J.E. (1998). Active ice-sheet deglaciation and ice-dammed lakes in the northern Cairngorm mountains, Scotland. *Boreas*, **27**, 297–310.

Brown, I.M. (1992) Deglaciation of the Dee valley, NE Scotland. Ph.D. thesis, University of Aberdeen.

Brown, I.M. (1993) The pattern of deglaciation of the last (Late Devensian) Scottish ice-sheet: evidence from the Dee valley, NE Scotland. *Journal of Quaternary Science* **8**, 235–250.

Brown, I.M. (1994) Former glacial lakes in the Dee valley: origin, drainage and significance. *Scottish Journal of Geology* **30**, 147–158.

Clapperton, C.M. (1997) Greenland ice cores and North Atlantic sediments: implications for the last glaciation in Scotland. In: Gordon, J.E., ed., *Reflections on the Ice Age in Scotland*. Scottish Natural Heritage & Scottish Association of Geography Teachers, Glasgow. pp. 48–58.

Ferguson, R.I. (1985) High densities, water equivalent and melt rates of snow in the Cairngorm Mountains, Scotland. *Weather* **40**, 272–276.

FitzPatrick, E.A. (1997) Soils of the native pinewoods of Scotland. In: Bunce, R.G.H. & Jeffers, J.N.R., eds, *Native Pinewoods of Scotland*. Institute of Terrestrial Ecology, Merlewood. pp. 35–41.

Glasser, N.F. (1995) Modelling the effect of topography on ice-sheet erosion, Scotland. *Geografiska Annaler* **77A**, 67–82.

Glasser, N.F. (1997) The origin and significance of sheet joints in the Cairngorm granite. *Scottish Journal of Geology* **33**, 125–132.

Goodman, S. & Lappin, M.A. (1996) The thermal aureole of the Lochnagar Complex: mineral reactions and implications from thermal modelling. *Scottish Journal of Geology* **32**, 159–172.

Gordon, J.E. (1979) Reconstructed Pleistocene ice-sheet temperatures and glacial erosion in northern Scotland. *Journal of Glaciology* **22** (87), 331–344.

Gordon, J.E., ed. (1997) *Reflections on the Ice Age in Scotland.* Scottish Natural Heritage & Scottish Association of Geography Teachers, Glasgow.

Gordon, J.E. & Sutherland, D.G., eds (1993) *Quaternary of Scotland.* Chapman & Hall, London.

Green, F.W.H. (1981) Weather. In: Nethersole-Thompson, D. & Watson, A., eds, *The Cairngorms.* Collins, London.

Hall, A.M. (1991) Pre-Quaternary landscape evolution in the Scottish Highlands. *Transactions of the Royal Society of Edinburgh, Earth Sciences* **82**, 1–26.

Harrison, T.N. (1986) The mode of emplacement of the Cairngorm Granite. *Scottish Journal of Geology* **22**, 303–314.

Harrison, T.N. (1988) Magmatic garnets in the Cairngorm Granite, Scotland. *Mineralogical Magazine* **52**, 359–368.

Harrison, S.J. (1993) Differences in duration of snow cover on Scottish ski-slopes between mild and cold winters. *Scottish Geographical Magazine* **109**, 37–44.

Heslop, R.E.F. (1981) Soils. In Nethersole-Thompson, D. & Watson, A., eds, *The Cairngorms.* Collins, London.

King, R.B. (1971a) Boulder polygons and stripes in the Cairngorm Mountains, Scotland. *Journal of Glaciology* **10**, 375–386.

King, R.B. (1971b) Vegetation destruction in the sub-Alpine zones of the Cairngorm Mountains. *Scottish Geographical Magazine* **87**, 103–115.

Linton, D.L. (1949) Some Scottish river captures re-examined. *Scottish Geographical Magazine* **65**, 123–132.

Linton, D.L. (1951) Problems of Scottish scenery. *Scottish Geographical Magazine* **67**, 65–85.

Linton, D.L. (1954) Some Scottish river captures re-examined. III. The beheading of the Don. *Scottish Geographical Magazine* **70**, 64–78.

Linton, D.L. (1955) The problem of tors. *Geographical Journal* **121**, 470–487.

Luckman, B.H. (1992) Debris flows and snow avalanche landforms in the Lairig Ghru, Cairngorm Mountains, Scotland. *Geografiska Annaler* **74A**, 109–121.

Manley, G. (1971) Scotland's semi-permanent snows. *Weather* **26**, 458–471.

Mayes, J.C. (1991) Contrasting weather in Northern Scotland 1988–1990 in relation to regional airflow types. *Weather* **46**, 16–21.

McEwan, L.J. (1993) The magnitude and frequency of exteme rainfall within north-east Scotland over an historical timespan. *Scottish Geographical Magazine* **109**, 75–86.

Oldershaw, W. (1974) The Lochnagar granitic ring complex, Aberdeenshire. *Scottish Journal of Geology* **10**, 297–310.

Pears, N.V. (1968) Postglacial treelines in the Cairngorm Mountains. *Transactions of the Botanical Society of Edinburgh* **40**, 361–394.

Rapson, S. (1985) Minimum age of corrie moraine ridges in the Cairngorm Mountains, Scotland. *Boreas* **14**, 155–159.

Sissons, J.B. (1979) The Loch Lomond Advance in the Cairngorm Mountains, Scotland. *Scottish Geographical Magazine* **95**, 66–82.

Sugden, D.E. (1968) The selectivity of glacial erosion in the Cairngorm Mountains. *Transactions of the Institute of British Geographers* **45**, 79–92.

Sugden, D.E. (1969) The age and form of corries in the Cairngorms. *Scottish Geographical Magazine* **85**, 34–46.

Sugden, D.E. (1971) The significance of periglacial activity on some Scottish mountains. *Geographical Journal* **137**, 388–392.

Sugden, D.E. (1977) Did glaciers form in the Cairngorms in the 17–19th centuries? *Cairngorm Club Journal* **97**, 189–201.

Sugden, D.E. (1980) The Loch Lomond Advance in the Cairngorm Mountains. *Scottish Geographical Magazine* **95**, 66–82.

Sugden, D.E., Glasser, N. & Clapperton, C.M. (1992) Evolution of large roches moutonneés, Deeside, Scotland. *Geografiska Annaler* **74A**, 253–264.

Ward, R.G.W. (1984) Avalanche activity in Scotland: I & II. *Applied Geography* **4**, 91–133.

Watson, A., Davidson, R.W. & French, D.D. (1994) Summer snow patches and climate in NE Scotland. *Arctic and Alpine Research* **26**, 141–151.

Werrity, A. & Acreman, M.C. (1985) The flood hazard in Scotland. In: Harrison, S.J., ed., *Climatic hazards in Scotland.* Geo Books, Norwich. pp. 25–40.

Young, J.A.T. (1974) Ice wastage in Glenmore, upper Spey valley, Inverness-shire. *Scottish Journal of Geology* **10**, 147–157.

CHAPTER 3
Vegetation

C.H.GIMINGHAM

INTRODUCTION

The ecology of the plant communities of the Cairngorms area is a subject of both scientific and practical concern, and one with much potential for further research. On the one hand, in the straths and lower slopes the role of man in determining the landscape and vegetation is very apparent, while on the other the unsurpassed range and extent of almost undisturbed high-altitude communities give scope for the study of vegetation processes in places where the influence of the physical environment is not masked by the effects of human activities (Plate 21). Knowledge and understanding of the structure, composition and dynamics of the plant communities, and their affinities with equivalent types in other countries, is fundamental in assessing the importance of the area for nature conservation and in devising appropriate management strategies. This chapter will review some of the findings of ecological studies within the Cairngorms area and will discuss some of the more important lines of current research.

Perhaps the most striking features of the Cairngorm mountains, distinguishing them from other mountain systems in Britain, are the extensive high-level plateaux, with their accompanying crags and corries (Chapter 2). Consequently, the tundra-like plant communities of fell-field, rock debris, montane heath and grassland cover large areas and are among the most distinctive and ecologically important components of the vegetation. While they clearly relate to communities of similar habitats elsewhere in Europe, particularly Scandinavia, they possess unique features for which the highly oceanic nature of the British climate is often responsible.

Because much of the mountain massif is composed of granite or other acidic rocks some of the communities are not especially rich in species, but where outcrops of calcareous mica-schists, diorite, or limestone occur as, for example, at Creag an Dail Bheag, Morrone, Coire Garbhlach, Glen Callater, Caenlochan, the Cairnwell (Plate 22), or where the granite contains minerals such as calcite or epidote, the Cairngorms have their share of the calcicolous or basiphilous mountain flora, numerous species of which are noted rarities in Britain (see Ferreira, 1959).

STUDIES OF THE PLANT ECOLOGY OF THE CAIRNGORMS

The pioneer work of the Smith brothers (R.Smith, 1900; W.G.Smith, 1904, 1911) was probably the earliest to adopt a consciously ecological approach to Scottish mountain vegetation. Following this, however, there was little systematic ecological research in the Cairngorms, but that neglect was impressively remedied in 1938 and 1939 by two expeditions from the Botany School of the University of Cambridge involving 23 participants (Plates 19, 20). Much of the vision which inspired the work of this team came from Dr A.S.Watt, who at an early stage took on the leadership of the project. The four papers which reported the results (Watt & Jones, 1948; Metcalfe, 1950; Burgess, 1951; Ingram, 1958) not only laid a fine foundation for subsequent studies in the Cairngorms but were 'classics' in their own right, presenting new ideas on mountain ecology and vegetation dynamics.

From that base, Poore and McVean (1957) later developed their 'new approach to Scottish mountain vegetation', making it possible to relate the plant ecology of mountain systems such as the Cairngorms not only to the rest of Scotland but also to Scandinavia. These authors began the task of describing and classifiying the plant communities of the Highlands of Scotland, and paved the way for the Nature Conservancy's monograph on the subject (McVean & Ratcliffe, 1962). This extensive survey included species lists from sample stands (relevés) in numerous locations in the Cairngorms and provided for the first time a phytosociological scheme into which the plant communities of the area could be fitted. This has been widely used for descriptive purposes and as a reference-base for research projects. It was a forerunner for more comprehensive community classifications covering lowland as well as upland vegetation, first by Birse (1980, 1984) and Robertson (1984) for Scotland and then most recently for the whole of Britain in the volumes of *British Plant Communities* (Rodwell, 1991a, 1991b, 1992, 1994, 2000), which include valuable ecological accounts of each community type recognized. This chapter draws on these accounts where they relate to communities occurring in the Cairngorms area.*

Data collection to provide the foundation for these phytosociological classifications involved the examination of large numbers of samples, many of them from the Cairngorms. However, as Bayfield, Penny and Moyes (1982) pointed out, this did not amount to a systematic survey of the vegetation of the whole Cairngorms area. These authors used a stratified random sampling system and a numerical classification which divided the vegetation into 16 groups. Though failing to identify rare associations, this produced a broad grouping of plant communities useful, for example, for mapping the distribution of the major vegetation types throughout the area (Table 3a).

There is no better or more comprehensive descriptive account of the vegetation of the Cairngorms than that by Ratcliffe (1974). This can be taken as background for the present chapter, the purpose of which is to concentrate on recent ecological studies rather than duplicate what has already been done so well.

VEGETATIONAL HISTORY

The outlines of vegetational history at the lower altitudes have been established by analysis of pollen, spores, seeds, etc. in peat profiles at localities including Abernethy forest (altitude 221 m), Loch Garten (220 m), Loch Pityoulish (210 m), Loch Kinord (167 m) and Morrone (425 m) (Durno, 1959; Bennet, 1996; Birks, 1970; Birks, 1996; Birks & Mathewes, 1978; Huntley, 1994; O'Sullivan, 1974, 1975, 1976, 1977; Vasari & Vasari, 1968). Following the retreat of glaciers in the late Devensian period (the last glacial stage), the area was probably

---

* The categories and reference numbers of the National Vegetation Classification (NVC) will be used as appropriate in this chapter. Relevant categories are: W (woodlands), M (mires), H (heaths), CG (calcicolous grasslands), U (calcifugous grasslands and montane communities).

Table 3a Classification of vegetation of the Cairngorms into sixteen groups.

Group 1	Moor mat-grass 'heath'[1]
Group 2	Species-rich grass heath
Group 3	Species-poor grass heath
Group 4	Ruderal grass heath (i.e. with species of open habitats often associated with agricultural practice)
Group 5	Dry heather[2] heath
Group 6	Damp heather heath
Group 7	Heather – deer-grass[3] heath
Group 8	Heather – bell heather[4] heath
Group 9	Heather – cotton grass[5] bog
Group 10	Heather – *Dicranum* moss heath
Group 11	Heather – *Cladonia* lichen bog
Group 12	Heather – *Hypnum* moss heath
Group 13	Crowberry[6] – moss-rich heath
Group 14	Crowberry – lichen-rich heath
Group 15	*Racomitrium* heath
Group 16	Species-rich *Racomitrium* heath

Notes: Groups 15 and 16 include stands of three-leaved rush (*Juncus trifidus*).

[1] *Nardus stricta*	[4] *Erica cinerea*
[2] *Calluna vulgaris*	[5] *Eriophorum vaginatum*
[3] *Trichophorum cespitosum*	[6] *Empetrum nigrum*

Data from Bayfield & Moyes, 1982.

---

first colonized by plants from 13 000 years BP (before present). A pioneergrass-sedge vegetation formed patches on the bare moraines (Birks & Mathewes, 1978), and among the species present at that time were alpine saxifrage (*Saxifraga nivalis*), other saxifrages, meadow rue (possibly the alpine meadow rue, *Thalictrum alpinum*), moonwort (*Botrychium lunaria*), interrupted club-moss (*Lycopodium annotinum*), fir club-moss (*Huperzia selago*) and sorrel (probably the mountain sorrel *Oxyria digyna*). Most of these require open habitats with much bare ground, some indicate a relatively high soil-base status, and many are plants described today as arctic-alpines. Later, the grass-dominated vegetation may have been replaced to some extent by a shrub-tundra composed mainly of crowberry (*Empetrum nigrum*) and dwarf birch (*Betula nana*), probably occupying poor, well-drained sandy substrata. During a time of renewed climatic cooling (the 'Loch Lomond readvance') towards the end of the Devensian, around 11 000–10 000 BP, the shrub-tundra gave place again to a more diverse assemblage of plants including mugwort (*Artemisia* sp.), moss campion (*Silene acaulis*) (Plate 26), alpine mouse-ear (*Cerastium alpinum*), sea pink (*Armeria maritima*), least willow (*Salix herbacea*), rock rose (*Helianthemum* sp.) and several saxifrages (Huntley *et al.*, 1997).

Many of these species are components of the present-day vegetation of the high plateaux, which at that time were still blanketed with permanent snow and ice. With the onset of warmer conditions in the early part of the Flandrian period (from about 10 000 BP) and the upward retreat of the snow-line, suitable habitats for these communities became available at progressively higher altitudes, to which they were later confined when woodland or bog took over at lower levels. Thus the fell-field and tundra-like communities of today's high plateaux, with their leached acidic surface debris, are the descendants of the more acid-tolerant elements of the late glacial flora, while the more base-demanding species are now confined to the outcrops of calcareous or other base-rich rocks and nutrient-rich flushes. They survive as extremely important though somewhat reduced versions of similar communities in corresponding habitats in the mountains of Europe and Scandinavia, and at lower elevations in the arctic.

From about 9500 BP onwards, at the lower altitudes, the tundra was relatively rapidly replaced, first by scrub and later by forest, probably of a quite open character with patches of bog, heath and other types. Woodland cover was complete in the lowlands within a few centuries. The history of these changes is outlined in Chapter 9.

STUDIES ON VEGETATION WITHIN THE POTENTIAL FOREST ZONE

The native pinewoods (Plates 64, 69, 96). Chapter 9 deals also with the structure, status and general ecology of the native pinewoods of the Cairngorms area and considers their future, so only brief mention will be made here. The first comprehensive account of the remaining fragments of native pinewoods, dominated by Scots pine (Pinus sylvestris), appears in Steven and Carlisle's (1959) *Native Pinewoods of Scotland*. These authors listed nine woods in the Cairngorms as satisfying their criterion of 'descent from one generation to another by natural means', and divided them into a Deeside group and a Speyside group. Together, these constitute an eastern group of pinewoods (Bunce, 1977), characterized generally by the predominance of podsolic soils and a heathy ground vegetation in which heather (Calluna vulgaris), blaeberry* (Vaccinium myrtillus), cowberry (V. vitis-idaea), crowberry and wavy hair-grass (Deschampsia flexuosa) are often present, together with a rich moss flora. In the National Vegetation Classification (Rodwell, 1991a) this is listed as W18, Scots pine – Hylocomium splendens woodland. Birch, mainly silver birch (Betula pendula) in the eastern pinewoods, rowan (Sorbus aucuparia) and juniper (Juniperus communis) are also present, but when compared with native pinewoods in other parts of Scotland birch seems to be rather poorly represented. Three of the sub-communities recognized by Rodwell (1991a) are well seen in the Cairngorm woods: the bell-heather (Erica cinerea) – creeping ladies' tresses (Goodyera repens) sub-community in which wavy hair-grass is generally prominent and there is often a very well-developed moss layer, the blaeberry – cowberry sub-community characterized by abundance of the ericaceous subshrubs (Plate 64), and the hairy woodrush (Luzula pilosa) sub-community which usually includes a wide range of grass species and mosses, some of them typical of the rather richer soils. Several attractive and rare plants are to be found in the Cairngorm pinewoods, such as the

twin-flower (Linnaea borealis) (Plate 23), the one-flowered wintergreen (Moneses uniflora) and the handsome pinnately branched, golden-coloured moss Ptilium crista-castrensis.

A recent study (Watson & Birse, 1991) has drawn attention to another type of pinewood community, described as 'lichen-rich pinewoods', occurring in areas of relatively dry climate and very freely drained soils both in the east near Dinnet and in Glen Derry, and in Speyside near Loch Morlich, in Abernethy forest and near Kingussie. These woods, including both 'native' pinewoods and plantations, are unlike most others in Scotland because of the carpet of grey and white lichens, many of them forming large cushions. Species of Cladonia are dominant, notably C. ciliata, C. portentosa, C. furcata, C. gracilis and C. uncialis, often with C. arbuscula, C. rangiferina, Coelocaulon aculeatum, Cetraria islandica and various others. There is a distinct resemblance to the flora of widespread lichen-rich coniferous forests in northern Scandinavia and throughout the circumpolar boreal zone. The ground vegetation is very sensitive to disturbance, especially by trampling and, in view of the fact that it occurs here at its extreme climatic limit, is of special interest and conservation value.

The structure of the surviving woods affords evidence that they have been significantly affected by direct or indirect human influence. Birch, rowan, juniper, aspen (Populus tremula) and other species are less abundant than they probably were in the former forest, though here and there in the least disturbed woods juniper is still important as the only significant component of a tall shrub layer. Natural regeneration has in many instances been severely curtailed by factors such as increased deer browsing and the development of dense stands of heather following the opening up of the former forest canopy. However, in some areas such inhibitions have been at least partially lifted in recent years and the conditions for renewed regeneration restored.

Among these conditions are suitable habitats for seed germination and seedling establishment. These have been the subject of recent experimental studies (Edwards, 1981). Regeneration will not take place under the shade of a dense pine canopy but requires gaps, openings or the light conditions of wood margins (Dunlop, 1983). Similarly, dense heather will inhibit seedling establishment though it can occur where gaps develop in old, degenerate bushes. A dense moss mat is also unfavourable. Disturbance of various kinds is therefore often a factor promoting regeneration, whether it be natural disturbance such as death of old trees, windthrow, lightning-induced fire, or artifical disturbance such as felling, logging, screefing or prescribed burning. Seed germination is best where the ground layer of vegetation has been removed, exposing the surface of the humus layer. Birds and rodents cause loss of seeds and young seedlings may succumb to slugs or desiccation, but in a good seed year, which usually occurs at 3–6 year intervals, numerous seedlings may become established. Survival thereafter depends very largely on the intensity of grazing (see Chapter 11).

---

* *Vaccinium myrtillus* has many common names, including bilberry and whortleberry, but the name used throughout Scotland, blaeberry, is preferred here.

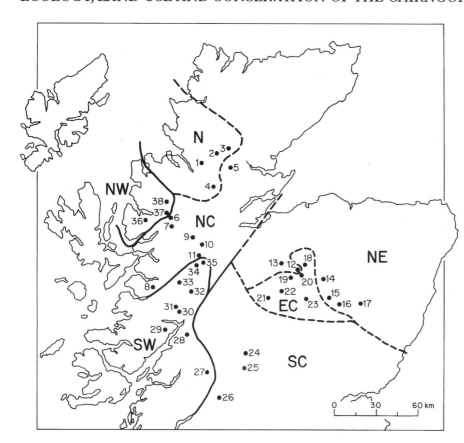

Figure 3.1   Native Scots pine (*Pinus sylvestris*): boundaries of regions of biochemical similarity (indicating genetically distinct populations), according to Dr Ian Forrest. N, North; NC, North Central; NE North East; EC, East Central; SC, South Central; SW, South West; NW, North West. From *Native Pinewoods – Grants and Guidelines*, Forestry Commission, 1989.

A recent development of importance in relation to the management and possible expansion of the remaining woods has come from analyses of the terpene compounds present in the leaves of pine trees in the native stands (Forrest, 1980). These have shown that the populations of the eastern woods are genetically distinct from those of other parts of Scotland (Fig. 3.1). This finding has important implications, both in understanding the derivation of these populations and also in emphasizing the need to ensure that where seed is to be used for restoring or expanding the native woodlands it is always obtained from local sources, if genetic integrity is to be maintained.

Birchwoods and other broadland woods. The flora of some of the birchwoods in the Cairngorms area resembles that of the Scots pine – *Hylocomium splendens* woodland (W 18), often with abundant blaeberry and cowberry. Other birchwoods, especially around the fringes of the mountain massif and in some of the valleys, have a grass-dominated ground flora with species such as common violet (*Viola riviniana*), primrose (*Primula vulgaris*) and sometimes wild strawberry (*Fragaria vesca*). Such communities may be ascribed to the sessile oak (*Quercus petraea*) – downy birch (*Betula pubescens*) – wood-sorrel (*Oxalis acetosella*) woodland community (W 11), though there are now few examples containing oak, except here and there in the major river valleys (Mountford & Peterkin, 2000).

Birchwood soils, especially those of the second type, tend to be brown soils, less podsolized than under pine or heather. Where birch has replaced former pine-birch wood or heather moor it may have

promoted depodsolization (Miles, 1985). Elsewhere, however, long established birch and other broadleaved trees may have 'protected' pockets of brown soils from the podsolizing effects of surrounding heath or moorland.

Both species of birch (silver birch, *Betula pendula*, and downy birch) are abundant in the Cairngorms area, but it has been shown by Forbes and Kenworthy (1973) that in Deeside silver birch is the chief species in the lower reaches of the valley while above an altitude of about 350 m it gives place to downy birch (Fig. 3.2). There is, however, a substantial overlap area. This relationship probably obtains elsewhere in the area as well but the position is further complicated by much morphological variation within both species, and uncertainty as to the extent of hybridization between them (Brown & Tuley, 1971; Forbes & Kenworthy, 1973).

Birches are rapid colonists of bare or disturbed surfaces if soils are favourable. Thus while some upland birchwoods are relicts of former pine-birch woodland, often prevented from regenerating by sheep or deer grazing to which birch is very vulnerable, others represent a successional stage following colonization of former moorland or grassland (Plate 24). While birch cannot readily invade intensively managed heather moor in which stands are kept in the vigorous building phase by regular burning and/or grazing, an occasional fire creates an ideal seed bed, especially where mineral material is exposed or covered only with a thin humus layer. Dinnet Moor provides a clear example: intensive management was discontinued in the late 1940s but, with an abundant input of seed from nearby old birchwoods, occasional fires in the

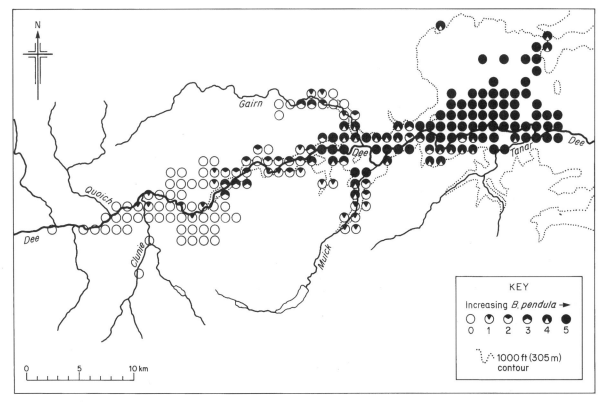

Figure 3.2 Distribution and relative abundance of silver birch (*Betula pendula*) and downy birch (*Betula pubescens*) on upper Deeside. Open circles, *B. pubescens*; closed circles, *B. pendula*; partially filled circles, mixtures of the two species in varying proportions, as shown in the key. From Forbes & Kenworthy, 1973.

succeeding years promoted the establishment of successive cohorts of young birch. These are now developing into pure birchwoods, but it would be reasonable to assume that in the course of time other species may enter. Pollen analysis (Vasari & Vasari, 1968) and other evidence indicates that oak was formerly quite abundant here though today only a very few individuals remain in the area, in inaccessible places. If sufficient seed parents were available oak might spread into the birchwood, but with pine abundant on adjacent slopes this is the more likely species to appear now amongst the birch. Aspen, once a regular component of the valley woodlands, still forms dense stands in scattered locations, while alder (*Alnus glutinosa*) and willows (*Salix* spp.) are common on damp ground and around loch margins at Dinnet and elsewhere.

In places juniper forms a discontinuous shrub layer in the birchwoods, where it has escaped destruction by fire or grazing. Birch-juniper woods are scattered in the Dee valley, with a notable example on the slopes of Morrone near Braemar, and are rather more numerous in Speyside. Some are relicts of former pine-birch woodland in which juniper was an integral component. Sometimes juniper alone survives as dominant of a scrub community.

Bracken (*Pteridium aquilinum*) is often dominant below the canopy of the older birchwoods, and large stands of bracken are common on many of the more freely-drained lower hill slopes, invading both grassland and heath, to the exclusion of heather.

Heaths and Grasslands. The semi-natural vegetation which replaced the forest in the Cairngorms after its destruction includes both heaths and grasslands, the former occupying by far the larger area owing partly to the predominance of freely drained acidic soils and partly to use and management. Heather is the chief dominant, especially on the northern and eastern side of the Cairngorms and Grampian mountains, and the slopes of the major glens and valleys where the soils are podsolized. Often in association with bell heather, it dominates the heather – blaeberry heath community (H12, Rodwell, 1991b) (Plate 25). This is widespread in the northern and upland parts of the British Isles (Fig. 3.3a), and among its most characteristic species are several with predominantly northern patterns of distribution, including for example chickweed wintergreen (*Trientalis europaea*) and lesser twayblade (*Listera cordata*) as well as the subshrubs blaeberry, cowberry and crowberry. Similar vegetation, sometimes named Vaccinio – Callunetum, occurs in Scandinavia and on north-facing slopes or at higher altitudes further south, but the British version often includes species typical of our oceanic climatic conditions such as the hard-fern (*Blechnum spicant*), the heath spotted orchid (*Dactylorhiza maculata* ssp. *ericetorum*) and the moss *Plagiothecium undulatum*.

'Oceanic' elements, including for example the ribbed sedge (*Carex binervis*), are often a feature of a related heath type, the heather-bell heather heath community (H10). This belongs more to western

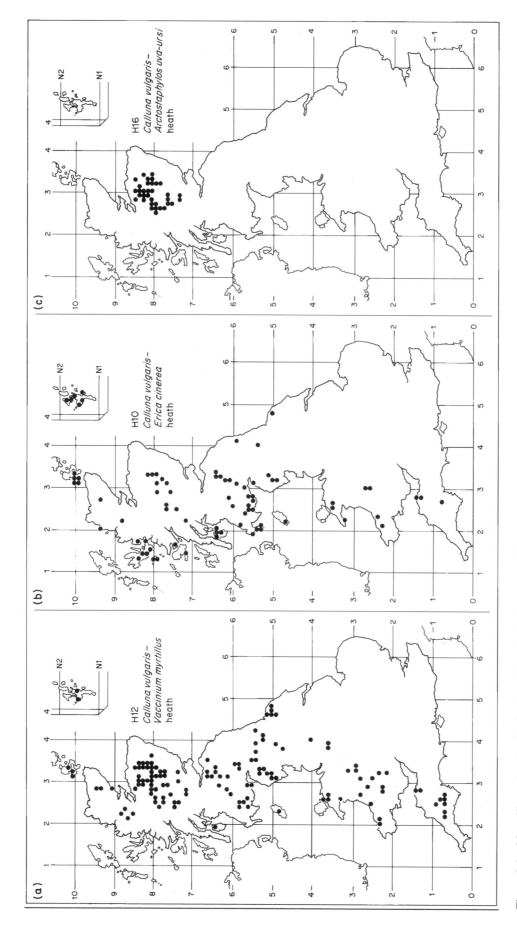

Figure 3.3 Maps illustrating the distribution of certain heath communities in the British Isles: (a) H12, heather – blaeberry heath (*Calluna vulgaris – Vaccinium myrtillus*); (b) H10, heather – bell heather heath (*Calluna vulgaris – Erica cinerea*); (c) H16, heather – bearberry heath (*Calluna vulgaris – Arctostaphylos uva-ursi*). From Rodwell, 1991b.

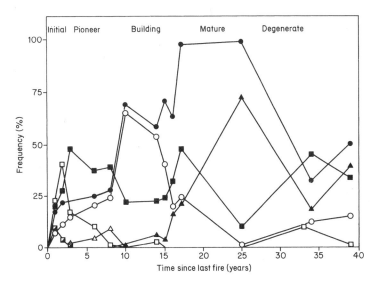

Figure 3.4   Relationship between stand age and composition of major species categories in species-rich heath in north-east Scotland. Percentage frequency of occurrence of each category in 128 subplots (each 10 × 10 cm) in each stand. ○ bearberry (*Arctostaphylos uva-ursi*); ● heather (*Calluna vulgaris*); ■ bell heather (*Erica cinerea*); ◨ forbs; □ grasses; △ lichens; ▲ mosses. From Hobbs *et al.*, 1984.

Scotland, but has outlying stands in the Cairngorms (Fig. 3.3b) generally at low altitudes and on the warmer slopes. Blaeberry, cowberry and crowberry are much less abundant than in the previous type. There are many stands intermediate in composition between H10 and H12, while regular burning and grazing often results in almost pure stands of heather with very few associated species, which may be imposssible to assign to one or other type.

A third type of dry heath community, however, is particularly characteristic of the Cairngorm area, occurring in the main valleys from low levels to moderate altitudes, on soils of somewhat higher base status than in the general run of heath and moorland. This is the heather-bearberry (*Arctostaphylos uva-ursi*) heath (H 16), which has a very restricted distribution centred on the eastern uplands of Scotland, including the Grampians and Cairngorms massif and neighbouring parts of Tayside and Inverness-shire (Fig. 3.3c). It is a most attractive, species-rich heath in which heather and bearberry form a mosaic together with bell heather, cowberry, crowberry and a number of herbaceous plants such as slender St. John's wort (*Hypericum pulchrum*), intermediate wintergreen (*Pyrola media*), bitter vetch (*Lathyrus montanus*), petty whin (*Genista anglica*), cat's foot (*Antennaria dioica*), and numerous mosses and lichens. Among the mosses is one which is scarce in Britain but appears to belong almost exclusively to this community: *Dicranum spurium*. Related vegetation types occur in western Norway, Sweden and Denmark, but they differ in the presence of other species with more continental affinities. The environmental factors responsible for the distribution of the heather – bearberry heath and its very constant species composition have been the subject of research (Ward, 1970, 1971a, 1971b), as have the dynamic interactions between heather and bearberry (Watt, 1947; Metcalfe, 1950; Hobbs *et al.*, 1984) (Fig. 3.4).

The extensive dry heaths of these three types have been maintained and prevented from returning to forest largely because of their value, first for grazing domestic animals, notably cattle and sheep, and second, more recently for purposes of field sports. Heather is the major component of the diet of the red grouse (*Lagopus lagopus scoticus*), and provides a substantial proportion of the winter grazing for red deer (*Cervus elaphus*). The heather hills of the east Grampians and parts of the Cairngorms are famous as grouse moors while red deer are the mainstay of many sporting estates (Chapters 11 and 12). For these reasons the heather has been managed by regular burning over the past two centuries, and probably on a more irregular basis well before that. Hence, the wide stretches of heather-covered hills for which the Cairngorms area is renowned represent a relatively recent man-induced landscape. However, very heavy grazing by red deer in recent years, especially in the valley bottoms, has led to replacement of heather by grass swards, for example in Glen Feshie, Glen Cluny, Glen Einich and Glen Derry.

Where drainage is impeded and a deeper layer of peaty humus has accumulated at the surface of the soil, the typical vegetation is a wet heath in which heather is accompanied by, or in the wettest sites replaced by, cross-leaved heath (*Erica tetralix*) with cotton-grass (*Eriophorum vaginatum*), deer-grass (*Trichophorum cespitosum*), other sedges, rushes and grasses in varying amounts (deer-grass – cross-leaved heath wet heath M 17 and cross-leaved heath – *Sphagnum compactum* wet heath M 16), merging into patches of peat-bog with abundant *Sphagnum* moss.

With the increasing rainfall towards the west of the area the proportion of heather in these semi-natural communities declines, while sedges, rushes and acidophilous grasses increase. These 'wet grass moors' give a green tinge to the landscape – or russet in autumn where deer-grass is abundant – rather than the brown or purple of the heather, and in the same way flushed areas on heather slopes often stand out as bright green streaks because of the abundance of grasses such as creeping bent-grass (*Agrostis stolonifera*) and of

Sphagnum spp. and other mosses. On the other hand, peaty hollows or channels where moor mat-grass (*Nardus stricta*) may be dominant often show up as whitish areas contrasting with the brown moorland. The balance between these several species is a delicate one and strongly influenced by grazing intensity, whether of sheep or deer. On wet soils the competitive vigour of heather is reduced and grazing readily shifts the balance in favour of sedges and grasses. Although occurring patchily in other communities on peaty soils, in the Cairngorms area moor mat-grass is essentially a species of the higher altitudes, and lower-level grasslands dominated by this species (moor mat-grass – heath bedstraw (*Galium saxatile*) grassland, U 5) are uncommon, though they occur in some of the surrounding hill areas such as the Monadh Liath and Clova hills (Ratcliffe, 1974).

Towards the margins of the Cairngorms area there are places where the soils are derived from base-rich rocks. Here the drier slopes support bent-fescue pasture (*Agrostis* spp. with sheep's fescue *Festuca ovina*, and viviparous fescue *F. vivipara* at the higher altitudes). These communities (mainly U4, sheep's fescue – common bent-grass (*Agrostis capillaris*) – heath bedstraw (*Galium saxatile*) grassland, but also on calcareous soils examples of CG 10, sheep's fescue – common bent-grass – wild thyme (*Thymus praecox*) grassland, and CG 11, sheep's fescue – common bent-grass – alpine lady's mantle (*Alchemilla alpina*) grass-heath are productive and provide valuable grazing. They occur also on low ground which, though freely drained, receives inputs of nutrients from periodic flooding. Although accounting for only a small proportion of the total area, some of these grasslands are rich in herbs such as quaking grass (*Briza media*), spring sedge (*Carex caryophyllea*), lady's mantle (*Alchemilla* spp.), white clover (*Trifolium repens*), field gentian (*Gentianella campestris*) and rock rose (*Helianthemun nummularium*). Scattered localities contain dense stands of small orchids, notably the fragrant orchid (*Gymnadenia conopsea*) and the small white orchid (*Pseudorchis albida*), offering a brilliant display in early summer.

Another vegetation type now found only in a very few isolated mountain ledges where it is free from grazing and other disturbance, is the basiphilous tall herb community (U17). This occurs abundantly in equivalent habitats in Scandinavia, and was probably once much more widespread in the Cairngorms.

Wetlands. Throughout much of the altitudinal range, waterlogged depressions and hollows of varying size lead to the development of peat-forming vegetation. In the surviving areas of native pinewood, forest bogs interrupt the tree cover, with abundant *Sphagnum* moss, cross-leaved heath, cotton-grass (*Eriophorum vaginatum* and E. *angustifolium*) and deer-grass. Many of the shallower bogs here are characterized by the presence of scattered stunted pines, often many years old but only two or three metres high. On the deforested hills and at higher altitudes, even gentle slopes and

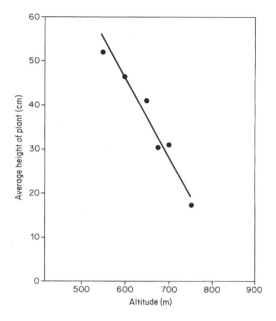

Figure 3.5 Graph showing the relationship between average height of heather (*Calluna vulgaris*) and altitude on the NNE-facing slope of An t'Aonach, Cairn Gorm. (Regression line: altitude = 855m – 5.49cm average height; correlation coefficient = –0.970.) Figure by S. Warren.

flats may become waterlogged, especially on broad saddles between summmits. Here wet heath (M16) or blanket bog vegetation develops, the latter dominated by heather, cotton-grasses and deer-grass (M19), frequently accompanied by cloudberry (*Rubus chamaemorus*).

Peat erosion and gullying is a common feature on the hills, sometimes resulting in conspicuous 'peat hags'. These deep clefts in the peat often reveal buried stumps, branches and roots of birch and pine, providing direct evidence of the former extent of woodland. Stages in the slow recolonization of exposed peat surfaces or redeposited peat fans illustrate the progress of secondary successions.

ALTITUDINAL ZONATION

The heaths and moors. Destruction of the original forest cover has obliterated certain aspects of altitudinal zonation of the vegetation. Because of the lack of woodland the slopes often present an appearance of an unbroken sweep of heather extending from the lower levels to altitudes of about 900 m (Plate 21). However, there are progressive changes of community structure and composition with increasing altitude. As the effects of strong winds become more pronounced the height of the heather canopy declines, except where the terrain affords shelter (Fig. 3.5). There is an accompanying change in the associated flora, for example bell heather and cross-leaved heath are no longer abundant above about 600 m. However, the most pronounced changes in community composition take place at altitudes between about 650 and 700 m, that is at and just above potential tree limit. Here species such as deer-grass, the moss *Hypnum jutlandicum* and the lichens *Cladonia portentosa* and *Hypogymnia physodes* decline while species of the montane heaths appear, for example stiff sedge (*Carex bigelowii*), trailing azalea (*Loiseleuria procumbens*) and hermaphrodite crowberry (*Empetrum nigrum* subsp. *hermaphroditum*).

The tree limit and sub-alpine scrub. Under natural conditions and on the acid soils this landscape of open heath and moorland stretching from the valleys up to the potential tree limit would instead have been one of forest, consisting largely of pine and birch, clothing the lower slopes and thinning out into a scrub zone at the treeline between about 610 and 680 m. However, where pockets of soils of higher base status (brown podsolic or brown forest soils) occur, birch would have played a bigger part and towards the tree limit would have been the chief species of a sub-alpine birch woodland. Some clue as to its appearance and composition is given by the upper parts of the Morrone birchwood near Braemar which is the sole surviving example of a sub-alpine birch-juniper wood in the Cairngorms (Huntley & Birks, 1979a, 1979b).

This wood today extends up to an altitude of about 500 m, above which there is a band of basic rocks, metamorphosed limestone and calcareous schists. As a result the soils range from podsols to brown earths, the latter occurring where the calcareous influence is strong, with gleys in poorly-drained sites. On the podsols, birch and juniper are accompanied by abundant cowberry, sometimes with wavy hair-grass, while on the brown earths the community is richer in species including plants such as meadowsweet (*Filipendula ulmaria*), wood crane's bill (*Geranium sylvaticum*), dog's mercury (*Mercurialis perennis*) and in places viviparous bistort (*Polygonum viviparum*). Although much modified by very heavy deer grazing this wood provides a unique insight into the nature of what was once a more widespread feature of the vegetation of the Cairngorms close to the tree limit.

In one place on the northern flank of the Cairngorm mountains there is a fragment of pine wood which extends upwards to around 648 m and shows all the signs of reaching an altitudinal limit unaffected by forest clearance. Here, on Creag Fhiaclach, the trees become sparse, stunted and knarled, as in the krummholz zone of European mountains (Plates 62, 63). Scattered low-growing juniper bushes occur amongst the pines. From evidence provided by tree stumps and branches buried in peat (Plate 20), Pears (1968, 1970) has shown that tree limits in the Cairngorms have varied in the past in relation to climatic changes. At the post-glacial climatic optimum (late Boreal period, *c.* 7000 BP) it probably reached around 790 m, and after a retreat rose again to around 701 m in the Sub-Boreal period (*c.* 3000 BP). However, recent studies (McConnell & Legg, 1995) based on pollen data from samples at altitudes spanning the present treeline on Craig Fhiaclach indicate that it has been relatively stable at about 640–650 m for a considerable period of time, except perhaps in more sheltered situations where it may have reached just over 700 m in the recent past – Craig Fhiaclach is an exposed western spur.

Elsewhere, the natural upper margins of forest have been obliterated by factors such as grazing, fire and other human interference. However, isolated, dwarfed pines and seedlings can be found at quite high altitudes, even above 850 m. Where there have been reductions in the intensity of grazing by red deer, natural regeneration of pine at the upper margins of native woods is gradually extending the forest in the direction of the potential tree limit. This is seen on the slopes of some of the 'northern corries' to the west of the Cairn Gorm ski development, where disturbance has kept the deer away. Both pine and juniper are establishing amongst the heather (Miller & Cummins, 1982), and it may be that in such places the forest might again reach its natural altitudinal limit. The possibility of encouraging its redevelopment in other places as well is under active consideration by ecologists and conservationists (Miller, 1986; Mardon, 1990). Conservation measures are likely to require exclusion of grazing animals, mainly sheep and deer, at least until such time as an overall reduction of grazing pressure can be achieved.

Where calcareous substrata outcrop at altitudes around the potential tree limit, as for example in Glen Clova, at Coire Sharroch (Caenlochan Glen) and Coire Garbhlach (Glen Feshie), there are a few surviving fragments of montane willow scrub which give some indication of what the sub-alpine scrub zone may have been like in these habitats (Mardon, 1990). The W 20 community, downy willow (*Salix lapponum*) – greater woodrush (*Luzula sylvatica*) scrub (Rodwell, 1991a) may have included species such as woolly willow (*Salix lanata*), myrtle-leaved willow (*S.myrsinites*) and juniper, now in the main represented by small numbers of individuals only.

Higher altitudes. The plant communities here, while not entirely free from human influence, may be regarded as very largely natural in respect of structure and composition. In the low alpine zone (*c.* 700–1100 m), montane heaths and grasslands give more or less continuous cover. The generally low base status and acidity of the substratum over much of the high ground maintains a rather constant edaphic habitat, though small pockets of calcite or epidote occur within the granite, bringing in some unexpected species, such as tufted saxifrage (*Saxifraga cespitosa*) on Ben Avon and Beinn a'Bhuird.

Heather-dominated heath communities continue upwards from the potential tree limit and scrub zone to altitudes of around 900 m. Heather, however, reacts unfavourably to prolonged snow lie and is replaced by other dominants such as moor mat-grass and blaeberry on sheltered slopes and where snow cornices linger near the tops of corrie faces. On the other hand on exposed west-facing slopes

31

which are often blown free of snow, heather-dominated heath may reach over 1000 m and scattered heather plants can be found up to 1095 m (Watt & Jones, 1948). Common associates of heather in the low-alpine heaths include blaeberry, bog whortleberry (*Vaccinim uliginosum*) where snow tends to accumulate, hermaphrodite crowberry usually in the more exposed places, and bearberry. The latter belongs mainly to middle altitudes to about 790 m while the others extend upwards beyond the limit of heather as a dominant. On the drier exposed sites, usually above the limit of bearberry, trailing azalea is often abundant. In the wetter locations, especially where there is lateral water movement in the surface, deer-grass is conspicuous.

With increasing altitude, a 'dwarf *Calluna* heath' community (H13) becomes widespread, in which the heather forms a compact low mat or carpet often only a few centimetres high. In very exposed places this mat may be interrupted by wind-erosion, producing open patches of bare ground. The lichen component of this vegetation is described by Gilbert and Fox (1985) as 'spectacular', being rich in species of *Cladonia* together with the sulphur-yellow *Cetraria nivalis*, luxuriant *Alectoria sarmentosa* subsp. *vexillifera*, *Thamnolia vermicularis* on bare gravel surfaces, and many others.

Above the limit of heather, the nature of the zonation is increasingly influenced by the degree of exposure or shelter and the length of snow-lie. Watt and Jones (1948) were the first to draw up a simplified scheme to illustrate these effects, which was later refined by Poore and McVean (1957) (Fig. 3.6). At the one extreme, moor mat-grass may be dominant to altitudes of about 1200 m where snow lies longest (especially in persistent snow patches, p. 34), and is commonly associated with stiff sedge and heath bedstraw (moor mat-grass – stiff sedge grass heath, U 7). In places on the Braeriach – Cairn Toul and the Cairn Gorm – Ben Macdui plateaux there are also small patches of a community dominated by wavy hair-grass which may be related to a similar association of late snow beds in Norway (McVean & Ratcliffe, 1962).

Under medium conditions of snow-lie, mat-grass becomes less abundant, and blaeberry, cowberry, hermaphrodite crowberry and lichens (notably (*Cladonia arbuscula*) together form a widespread low heath community (H 19) which is strongly centred on the Grampian mountains and Cairngorms (Rodwell 1991b). As greater exposure leads to shortening of the period of snow cover, the moss *Racomitrium lanuginosum* becomes increasingly abundant, often in asociation with the stiff sedge (U 10). In well-drained places of medium exposure and relatively little snow, *Racomitrium* may form a dense carpet known as Racomitrium heath (or stiff sedge – *Racomitrium* moss-heath, U 10). In the Cairngorms this is best represented in the wetter western part of the massif, but is rather scarce towards the east.

The most extreme conditions are experienced on the exposed summit plateaux and windy slopes at high altitudes, where snow is blown off and cannot accumulate. Here the environment is too severe for closed vegetation which is replaced by an open 'fell-field' with clumps of three-leaved rush (*Juncus trifidus*) scattered across wide expanses of coarse gravelly and stony debris (Plate 28). This community (U 9) is especially characteristic of the northern Cairngorms. At equivalent altitudes but in more sheltered places where the snow lies longer it merges into patchy mat-grass with stiff sedge, the mosaics of mat-grass and three-leaved rush faithfully delineating the pattern of winter snow-lie.

Many of the montane heaths described above are rich in lichen species which in places, especially between about 730 and 790 m on the granite, dominate the communities, as for example on certain hills in Glen Feshie, in parts of the Monadh Liath, Carn Dearg Mor and Geall Charn Mor, and in the Ladder Hills to the east of the Lecht. The high ground of the Cairngorms supports 134 lichen species, of which 25 per cent have their main areas of distribution in Britain centred on the Cairngorms plateau (Gilbert & Fox, 1985).

Above about 1160 m the vegetation is always discontinuous and much of the surface consists of bare rock and rock debris. Arctic-alpine species capable of occupying scattered niches here include three-leaved rush, viviparous fescue, least willow, dwarf cudweed (*Gnaphalium supinum*), moss campion (Plate 26), trailing azalea, and various mosses and liverworts. Among other species encountered in this zone are sea pink and wavy hair-grass.

Base-rich rocks at high altitudes, mainly calcareous schists and limestones restricted largely to the southern and eastern fringes of the area and certain other localities (pp. 23, 31), support a distinctive flora. Patches of mountain avens (*Dryas octopetala*) heath with rock sedge (*Carex rupestris*), hermaphrodite crowberry, viviparous bistort, yellow mountain saxifrage (*Saxifraga azoides*) etc., occur in a few places such as Creag an Dail Bheag and the Cairnwell (Plate 22). Alpine grasslands and rock ledges in those areas provide habitats for calcicolous rarities such as alpine milk vetch (*Astragalus alpinus*), alpine saw-wort (*Saussaurea alpina*), alpine meadow-rue, alpine cinquefoil (*Potentilla cranzii*) and *Sibbaldia procumbens*. Springs and flushes often stand out because of the bright green or yellowish green of the mosses, along with several saxifrage species – yellow mountain saxifrage, mossy saxifrage (*S. hypnoides*), starry saxifrage (*Saxifraga stellaris*) and other arctic-alpines of wet habitats such as alpine willow-herb (*Epilobium anagallidifolium*).

PATTERN AND PROCESS AT HIGH ALTITUDES

Some plant communities on the high plateaux, such as the *Racomitrium* heath, may form extensive uniform carpets, but much of the vegetation shows pronounced patterns at various size scales. Some of these patterns relate to the micro-environmental gradients created by topographical features such as solifluction lobes and terraces, or hollows and depressions which hold snowbeds. Other patterns

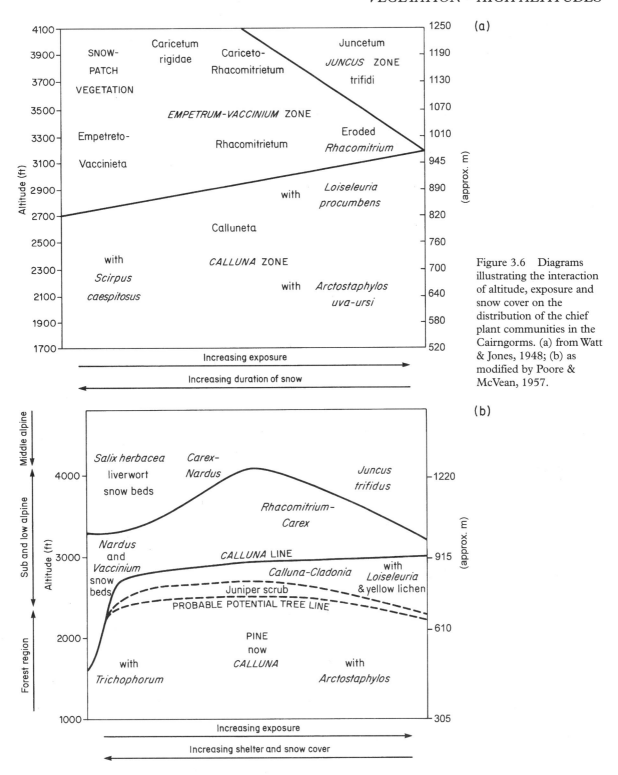

Figure 3.6 Diagrams illustrating the interaction of altitude, exposure and snow cover on the distribution of the chief plant communities in the Cairngorms. (a) from Watt & Jones, 1948; (b) as modified by Poore & McVean, 1957.

are more obviously dynamic, taking the form either of expanding circles or 'waves' progressing over level areas or gentle slopes: these are the result of interactions between the physical environment (especially wind) and the growth behaviour of the species concerned.

Terraces. Solifluction lobes and small-scale terraces are especially well developed in the Cairngorms, notably on many of the northern slopes (see Chapter 2). Their profound effects on

vegetation pattern were first examined by the Cambridge expeditions (Plate 19) and described by Watt & Jones (1948), Metcalfe (1950) and Burgess (1951). They consist usually of a platform of relatively uniform slope, composed of sandy and gravelly material overlain by a layer of peaty humus of varying thickness, with a retaining bank of stones (Fig. 3.7). The brow of the terrace is most exposed to wind, while the more sheltered part is the angle between the bank and the platform. There is also a repeated gradient in soil wetness, the lower part of

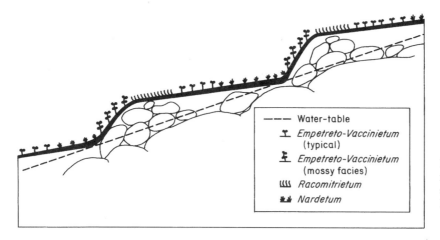

Figure 3.7 Diagram showing the four main habitats on an idealized small-scale 'terrace'. From Burgess, 1951.

the platform, the brow and steep bank of the terrace being freely drained, while rain and meltwater may emerge at the surface in the angle between the bank and the upper part of the platform. These factors result in a small-scale vegetational zonation such as that shown in Figs. 3.7 and 3.8.

Snowbed vegetation. As indicated above, the duration of snow cover is a factor of major importance in determining the composition of plant communities at high altitudes, so it is no surprise that where topography results in patches of long-lasting snow only specialized communities can occur. The centre of such patches, where snow persists for much of the year, may be entirely bare of vegetation, while on passing from this inner core concentric zones are occupied by 'chionophilous' species ranging from bryophytes tolerant of prolonged cover to communities typical of the margin of the patch where duration of snow-lie is only slightly longer than in the surrounding areas.

Communities which are widespread in areas of prolonged snow cover, such as the stiff sedge – *Polytrichum alpinum* sedge-heath (U 8), may occupy snowbeds in more exposed habitats (Fig. 3.9), but there are several communities belonging only to snowbeds at high altitudes in the colder parts of the mountains. Characteristic of the Cairngorms are the *Polytrichum sexangulare – Kiaeria starkei* (U 11) and the least willow – *Racomitrium heterostichum* (U 12) snowbed communities. Their relationships with

other communities which form part of snowbed zonations are illustrated in Fig. 3.10.

Lichens play an important part in snowbed vegetation, as shown by Gilbert and Fox (1985). They recorded numerous species contributing to the zonation within and around snow patches (Fig. 3.11), and found four species new to Britain, one hitherto undescribed species, *Micarea viridiatra* (Coppins, 1985), and many rarities. Transects through the snowbeds gave a clear indication of the relationship between lichen zonation and duration of snow-lie, and revealed a number of 'snowbed specialists', for example two rare *Cladonia* species, *C. maxima* and *C. stricta*, also *Lecanora leptacina*, *Miriquidica (Lecidia) griseoatra*, and others.

Linear and radial vegetation patterns. The Cambridge expeditions carried out detailed studies of the dwarf heather communities in the Cairngorms, associated with altitude and exposure. Metcalfe (1950) described the uniform, wind-clipped mat seldom exceeding 5 cm in height, in

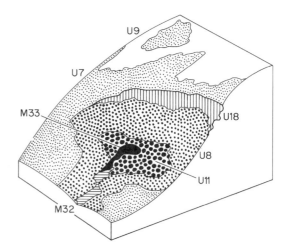

Figure 3.10 Complex of vegetation types around a late snowbed in the Cairngorms. From Rodwell, 1992. U7, *Nardus – Carex* grass heath; U8, *Carex – Polytrichum* sedge – heath and, within, a U11 *Polytrichum – Kiaeria* snow-bed; U9, *Juncus – Racomitrium* rush – heath; U18, *Cryptogramma – Athyrium* fern community; M32, *Philonotis – Saxifraga* community with M33, *Pohlia* spring at its head.

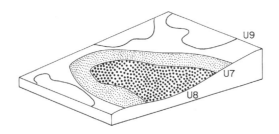

Figure 3.9 A vegetational pattern in and around a snowbed at high altitude in the Cairngorms. From Rodwell, 1992. U7, *Nardus – Carex* grass – heath; U8, *Carex – Polytrichum* sedge – heath; U9, *Juncus – Racomitrium* rush – heath.

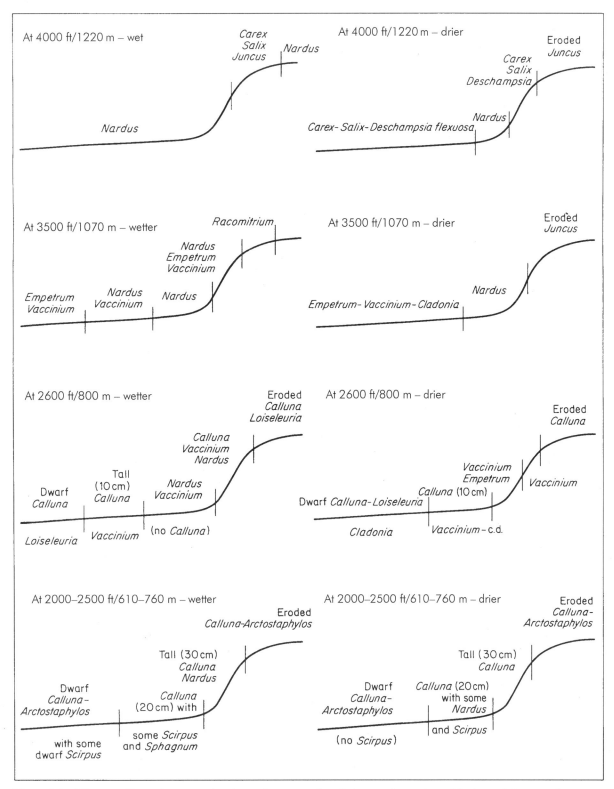

Figure 3.8   Diagrams illustrating vegetational zonation on small-scale 'terraces' at various altitudes and degrees of wetness in the Cairngorms. From Watt & Jones, 1948.

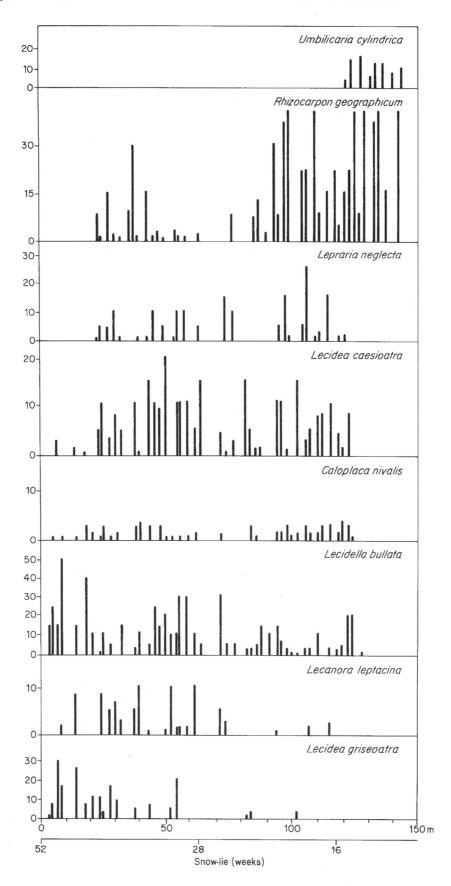

Figure 3.11   Transect data showing the distribution of lichens across a snow patch near the summit of Cairn Gorm. From Gilbert & Fox, 1985. The vertical axes are percentage cover.

Plate 13
Boulder moraines of the
Loch Lomond stadial interval
of glaciation (11 000 to
10 000 years ago) in Coire
nan Clach, Beinn a' Bhuird.
February 1989.

Photo: Iain Brown.

Plate 14
Eag a' Chait, a subglacially-
cut meltwater channel
breaching the spur west of the
Coire Cas car park, Cairn
Gorm. June 1965.

Photo: Chalmers Clapperton.

Plate 15
Glen Derry and Beinn a'
Chaorainn, looking over the
site of a former lake.
September 1992.

Photo: Iain Brown.

Plate 16
View north from the
summit of Lochnagar,
showing the arcuate boulder
moraines (Loch Lomond
stadial) enclosing the lochan
of the great northern corrie.

Photo: Iain Brown.

Plate 17
View up Glen Feshie from
Carnachuin, illustrating the
immature braided nature of
the post-glacial river
channel. May 1991.

Photo: Iain Brown.

Plate 18
Results of extreme rainfall
events on the fragile soils and
vegetation of the Cairn
Gorm, Allt Mor valley in
1963.

Photo: Chalmers Clapperton.

Plate 19
Boulder lobes and terraces – solifluxion terrace system at *c.* 3500 ft (1070 m) – on the north-west slope of Snap Coire na Spreadhe. Cambridge University expeditions 1938/39. Photo: A.S. Watt Collection, University of Aberdeen Library.

Plate 20 *(right)*
Buried pine stumps exposed by peat erosion and indicating former high-level woodland. Shore of Loch Einich, 1938/39. Photo: A.S. Watt Collection, University of Aberdeen Library.

Plate 21 *(below)*
Aspects of vegetation of the northern Cairngorms – a view from Rothiemurchus. In the foreground, *Calluna vulgaris* heath giving place to semi-natural *Pinus sylvestris* woodland. In the distance, heather-covered slopes rise to the mountain plateau. June 1985.

Photo: Roy Dennis.

Plate 22
Mosaic of heath and species-rich alpine grassland overlying outcrops of limestone - the Cairnwell.

Photo: Charles Gimingham.

Plate 23 (right)
Twin-flower *(Linnaea borealis)* in Abernethy Forest.

Photo: Charles Gimingham.

Plate 24 (below)
Invasion of heather-bearberry *(Calluna vulgaris - Arctostaphylos uva-ursi)* heath by birch at Dinnet Moor. January 1979.

Photo: Charles Gimingham.

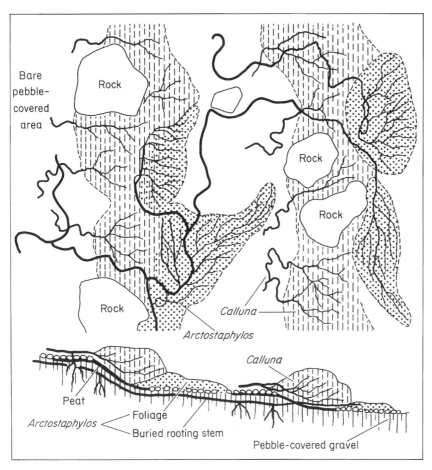

Figure 3.12 Drawings of the prostrate branch systems of heather (*Calluna vulgaris*) and bearberry (*Arctostaphylos uva-ursi*) in two successive stripes or 'waves'. The old heather stems are exposed on the surface. From Metcalfe, 1950.

which the 'individual plants of *Calluna* are straggling and often fantastically contorted', with the woody stems prostrate, rooting adventitiously, and the groups of leafy shoots quite far removed from the original crown and point of anchorage of the plant (Fig. 3.12). Where conditions are not too severe these plants may straggle in all directions, forming a more or less dense mat. However, on the most windswept plateaux and gentle slopes heather grows only into its own windshadow, always in the direction of the prevailing wind. Very often wind-scour erodes away accumulated debris and humus as well as dead shoots and branches behind the living 'front', leaving only the exposed woody stems trailing back to the original anchorage. On very exposed hill shoulders towards the altitudinal limit of heather, this pattern of growth produces striking stripes or 'waves' separated by troughs of bare ground (Bayfield, 1984) (Plate 27).

The green shoots of the heather form a leading edge to each stripe behind which the densely packed branches build a 'crest' of the wave, up to about 4–5 cm above the level of the trough (Bayfield, 1984). This cushion of branches remains attached to the prostrate woody stems which can often be traced back across the bare zone, frequently lying underneath the next wave which has overgrown them. The distance betwen crests of successive stripes varies from 85 to 138 cm in different locations. The whole wave moves slowly in the direction away from the source of the prevailing wind, at an average rate of about 9 mm per year (Bayfield, 1984). On gentle slopes the movement may be downhill, across the slope or even uphill,

according to the direction of the prevailing wind. The stripes arrest particles of sand and gravel which move in the same direction, and so form miniature steps or terraces.

Burgess (1951), Metcalfe (1950) and Watt (1947) also note that various species in addition to heather may be part of this system. For example, bearberry (Fig. 3.12) or hermaphrodite crowberry may occupy the leading, leeward edge of the stripe, growing in the same direction immediately in advance of the heather cushion, while *Racomitrium lanuginosum* and a variety of lichens may find a foothold among the shoots and stems of heather towards the rear. At altitudes above the limit for heather, similar waves may be constructed by hermaphrodite crowberry, sometimes associated with blaeberry (Fig. 3.13).

The question arises as to how the system of stripes originated over such wide areas. Bayfield recorded the presence of heather seedlings at or near the leading edge of the waves, but their mean survival time was no more than 8.8 months (maximum 31 months). Regeneration by seedling establishment must therefore be an extremely rare event under current conditions, though it is possible that these have not always been as severe as they are at present. However, Bayfield suggests that 'ripples' or 'miniature dunes' of sandy ground might have been created on the relatively smooth surfaces even without the intervention of vegetation. Heather might then have colonized in the sheltered parts of troughs, given a favourable run of climate, initiating the stripe system.

Above the altitudinal limit of heather and in conditions too exposed for the development of

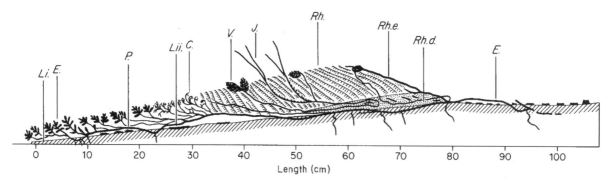

Figure 3.13   Diagram of a transect through a vegetation 'wave' in eroded *Racomitrium* heath at about 1070m on the northern slopes of Cairn Gorm. From Watt, 1947 – figure by N.A. Burgess. Li, Lii, P, communities of liverworts and mosses; E, crowberry (*Empetrum hermaphroditum*); V, blaeberry (*Vaccinium myrtillus*); J, three-leaved rush (*Juncus trifidus*); Rh, moss (*Racomitrium lanuginosum*); Rh.e, eroded face of *Racomitrium*; Rh.d, dead *Racomitrium*.

blaeberry – crowberry or *Racomitrium* heath, tussocks of the three-leaved rush are widely scattered over expanses of bare gravel and stones (Plate 28), where a few lichen species are almost the only other plants (p. 32). Open vegetation of this kind may extend to the highest altitudes, well above 1300 m (Ratcliffe, 1974). Three-leaved rush grows in small, dense clumps, based on the radial growth of short rhizomes. New tillers are always formed on the periphery of the clump, while those in the centre die away, leaving a ring of living shoots continuing to expand slowly (Fig. 3.14). Often the ring is disrupted and partially eroded, leaving only a crescent which maintains clonal growth and may move slowly across the terrain, driven by the prevailing wind. Twenty-eight lichen species have been recorded from these old, degenerate tussocks (Gilbert & Fox, 1985).

A recent detailed investigation by Pryor (1986) has indicated an annual radial growth increment of 2–3 mm of these circular clones, confirming the estimate of 2 mm by Ingram (1958). New tillers are produced each year at the end of the short growing season and overwinter in a dormant state, elongating in the following spring when the previous year's tiller dies away. Growth is thus sympodial and the number of nodes on a primary rhizome indicates the age of the tussock. The most vigorous clumps are those betwen 20 and 30 years old, but a maximum age is difficult to determine owing to death of the central parts of the rhizome system. The largest, however, may be more than 150 years old. The overall pattern is an apparently random scatter of circles, a majority of which have a radius of between 45 and 75 mm, at a mean density of 4.4 per square metre in typical sites. The plant builds up a substantial soil seed bank of up to 1300 germinable seeds per square metre and seedlings are quite numerous on open gravelly substrata (e.g., 4.3 per square metre in typical sites), having a survival rate of 33 per cent in the first year. However, both germination and rate of development decline with increasing altitude.

While these observations reveal the nature of the characteristic pattern created by the three-leaved rush in these extremely exposed situations, they leave open the question as to whether the present vegetation has developed as a result of the colonization of previously bare ground or of the erosion of a former more continuous plant cover. Islands of stiff sedge – *Racomitrium* heath (U 10) are quite often to be seen in the three-leaved rush stands and may be relics of a previously more continuous vegetation, which possibly suffered under the influence of past climatic change (perhaps at the time of the 'little ice-age', from about AD 1550 – 1750). At all events it would seem that the small-scale cycling is likely to persist under present conditions.

THE LARGER FUNGI OF THE MOUNTAINS

Fungi of the montane zones of the Cairngorms have not yet been thoroughly studied, but in recent years much has been added to our knowledge, especially by Watling (1987). The fungus flora of the Cairngorms is, in fact, very diverse and includes a number of arctic-alpine elements, most of which are rare in Britain. The distribution of many of these fungi is determined by the occurrence of vascular plants or plant communities on which they may be dependent as hosts or associates. A key vascular

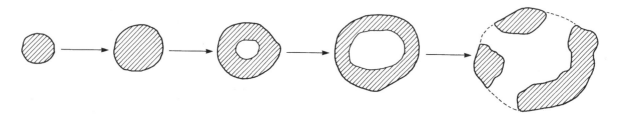

Figure 3.14   Schematic diagram of changes in tussocks of three-leaved rush (*Juncus trifidus*) from immature to degenerate age-states. Shaded areas are those producing green tillers, unshaded areas are bare patches. Figure by P. Pryor.

species in this context is the least willow, an ectomycorrhizal plant which is quite widespread both on acid and basic substrata in the Cairngorms. As with the vascular flora, the fungi are most diverse in the relatively restricted base-rich habitats, such as the Cairnwell where numerous species have been found associated with the least willow. Examples include *Amanita nivals* (a snowbed agaric, exclusively associated with least willow), four species of *Russula* (*R. nana*, *R. norvegica*, *R. pascua* and *R. persicaria*), *Cortinarius norvegicus* and many others. Even on acidic substrata, as for example on Cairn Gorm, the fungal flora may be quite rich.

DISTURBANCE AND RESTORATION

Because of the severe climatic conditions and often unstable substrata, mountain vegetation is notoriously susceptible to damage and disruption. In these habitats erosion is a natural process and in the more exposed areas at high altitudes vegetation mats are frequently subject to local disruption and wind-stripping. Such processes may set up long-term cycles of patchy erosion and recolonization. This may amount to a 'dynamic equilibrium', but when other disturbance factors come into play and cause more extensive erosion, there may be little possibilty of unaided recovery. Such disturbance factors include heavy deer grazing and trampling, repeated passage of walkers or skiers, and high altitude camping.

The most obvious signs of damage to mountain vegetation caused in this way are the expanding margins of heavily used footpaths and the destruction of vegetation with consequent surface erosion which has occurred between the topmost station of the Coire Cas chair-lift and the summit of Cairn Gorm. Certain components of the vegetation, notably heather, *Sphagnum* spp., and some *Cladonia* lichens (especially when dry) are highly susceptible to trampling. Bearberry and hermaphrodite crowberry are also susceptible (Bayfield, 1979; Pryor, 1986; Bayfield *et al.*, 1981), whereas the growth habit of deer-grass appears to confer upon it a capacity to recover more quickly from this kind of damage. Moderate resistance is also shown by blaeberry, bog whortleberry, bell heather, cross-leaved heath and *Racomitrium lanuginosum*. The resistance of *Racomitrium* heath is unexpected: its thick carpet perhaps cushions the impact. Most resistant of all are plants with a very rigid, tussock growth form including moor mat-grass, stiff sedge, three-leaved rush and wavy hair-grass.

The more susceptible species such as heather and lichens show little recovery from heavy trampling (e.g. 80 footfalls or more) even after 23 months (Fig. 3.15; Bayfield, 1979). However, most of those mentioned except *Sphagnum* will eventually recover over a period of 2–8 years if damage is not repeated (Bayfield, 1979; Pryor, 1986; Bayfield *et al.*, 1981).

Disturbance caused by the construction of chair-lifts, ski-tows, buildings or vehicle tracks in the mountains often leaves areas of mineral soil exposed. The surface material is then easily shifted and eroded by wind and water, and may be deposited over otherwise undamaged vegetation. Communities such as crowberry – *Racomitrium* heath may be severely damaged by burial in this way, and fail to survive if depths exceed about 7 cm (Bayfield, 1974). Certain species may recover by sending shoots upwards through sediments of up to 2–5 cm in depth, but there is decreasing recovery from greater depths.

Thus, damage can be caused both to vegetation and soil by a variety of human influences, including trampling and the use of fire and machinery such as bulldozers. It is a matter of great concern that the organic matter which has taken centuries to accumulate can be lost within a matter of days once the vegetation has been disrupted.

In recent years much attention has been devoted to the restoration of damaged or denuded areas at high altitudes, in order to mitigate the most unsightly effects of ski developments, footpath expansion and bulldozed tracks. Because of the severe environment, regeneration of native species and hence natural recolonization is generally extremely slow. However, several of the grass species of which seed is readily available are tolerant of conditions up to about 1100 m and can stabilize the surface, preventing erosion, especially if their establishment is aided by the use of lime and fertilizer and a surface binder such as bitumen. Although the result is a plant community which is both unnatural in composition and also, because of its light green colour, conspicuous against the darker greens or browns of the surrounding vegetation, this is a way of healing the scars created by exposure of the soil surface. Furthermore, most of the introduced species have a limited life-span under the severe conditions, allowing native species to begin to recolonize. First to come are mosses, followed in appropriate habitats by heather which benefits from prolific seed production and a substantial soil seed bank. Other vascular species present in the surrounding vegetation may return more slowly.

NEW PLANT ECOLOGICAL RESEARCH IN THE CAIRNGORMS

As this chapter has shown, plant ecologists have been at work in the Cairngorms for a number of years, but recently activity in this field has increased. In part this is due to the setting up of a 'Cairngorms Project' following up the Report of the Cairngorms Working Party. The task of producing an integrated management strategy (Chapters 16 & 17) is drawing attention to a lack of ecological knowledge on a variety of topics, and this has also become evident as management aimed specifically at nature conservation has been introduced over an increasing proportion of the area (Chapter 15). In addition, it has become apparent that there are exceptional opportunities here for investigating the impacts of atmospheric pollution and global warming on plant and animal communities.

An obvious requirement is a fuller inventory of the flora and fauna and other ecological assets, and this currently has high priority. As well as adding to knowledge of high altitude vegetation and animal

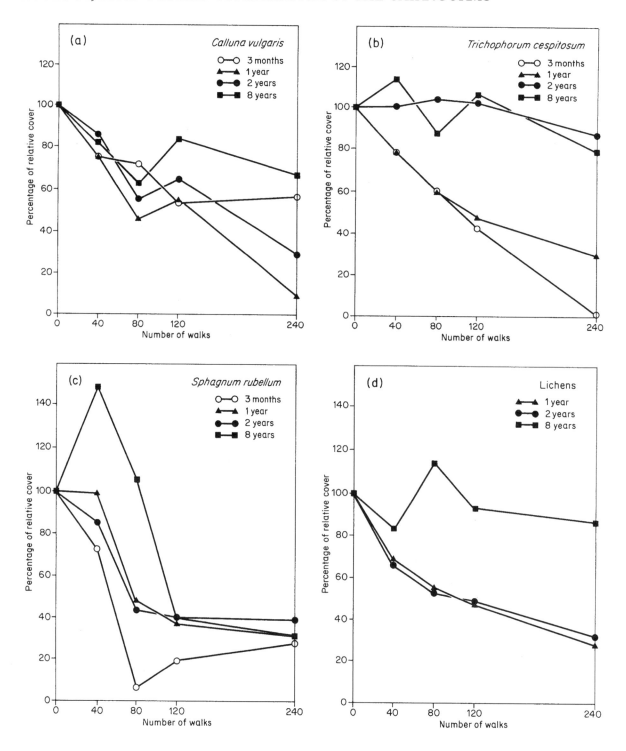

Figure 3.15   An example of the effects of experimental disturbance in lichen-rich heather – deer-grass (*Calluna – Trichophorum*) heath on Cairn Gorm. The graphs show proportions of relatively intact cover of each species at various times after disturbance by trampling. From Bayfield, 1979.
(a) Heather (*Calluna vulgaris*): die-back does not show up until more than 3 months after treatment, but with heavy trampling damage is severe. Substantial recovery has taken place after 8 years.
(b) Deer-grass (*Trichophorum cespitosum*): initially damage is severe, but there is effective recovery after 2 years.
(c) *Sphagnum rubellum*: severe damage and little recovery, even after 8 years.
(d) Lichens: severe damage at first, substantial recovery after 8 years.

populations, emphasis is placed on improving the records of ancient and long-established woodlands, including the broadleaved woodlands of the floodplains in the major valleys. There is a need for better understanding of vegetational history, which is being met by refined pollen analytical techniques and by studies of changes which have taken place in the diatom flora of high-level lochs. Further investigation of past fluctuations in the altitudinal tree limit is also being carried out, as well as of the reproductive biology of plants of high altitudes.

In view of the strong interest in conserving and extending the area of natural and semi-natural pine and birch woods, it is essential to obtain reliable data on the effects of reducing the deer population on the natural regeneration of pine and other trees. Monitoring programmes are being set up for this purpose, and also to follow changes in the structure and relative proportions of heather and grass-dominated communities. The whole question of monitoring vegetation and populations of plants and animals is very much to the fore, because of the possibility of changes due to acid rain, other forms of pollution and climatic change. Through its involvement in the 'Cairngorms Project' Scottish Natural Heritage is playing a leading part in this effort. To establish a base-line against which changes in biodiversity can be examined, records are being made in a large number of permanent sites in the Cairngorms and these will be repeated at intervals and compared with changes in satellite imagery of the terrain. The UK Environmental Change Network has a monitoring site in the Cairngorms, which has also been adopted (both as a terrestrial and an aquatic site) in Alpine and Scandinavian climate change networks ('Gloria' and 'Scannet' respectively.)

High altitude plant communities are likely to be valuable indicators of climatic warming because of their sensitivity to the duration of snow cover. As shown on p. 34, there is often a clear zonation of vegetation from the rim to the centre of snowbeds, caused by the gradual centripetal melting of the snow. Both the temperature regime and the amount of snow are implicated in determining the length of time any particular spot is free from snow each year. Long-term monitoring of changes in the positions of the zones, and of the survival or loss of species which belong to areas of longest snow-lie, is therefore being started as a possible source of evidence for the effects of global warming.

Snowbeds also offer possibilities for direct assessment of some of the effects of atmospheric pollution. Under present conditions snow falling in the mountains is contaminated to varying degrees with pollutants, and deposits of 'black snow' containing a pulse of contamination are not infrequent (Davies *et al.*, 1984). The physiological effects of the deposition of pollutants on snowbed plants by melting snow, and their capacity for recovery, are also under investigation both *in situ* in the mountains and under experimental conditions.

REFERENCES

Bayfield, N.G. (1974) Burial of vegetation by erosion debris near ski lifts on Cairngorm, Scotland. *Biological Conservation* **6**, 246–251.

Bayfield, N.G. (1979) Recovery of four montane heath communities on Cairngorm, Scotland, from disturbance by trampling. *Biological Conservation* **15**, 165–179.

Bayfield, N.G. (1984) The dynamics of heather (*Calluna vulgaris*) stripes in the Cairngorm mountains. *J. Ecol.* **72**, 515–527.

Bayfield, N.G., Penny, M.G. & Moyes, S.M. (1982) An indicator species analysis of map squares and vegetation in the Cairngorms. *Trans. Bot. Soc. Edinb.* **44**, 35–47.

Bayfield, N.G., Urquhart, U.H. & Cooper, S.M. (1981) Susceptibility of four species of *Cladonia* to disturbance by trampling in the Cairngorm mountains, Scotland, *J. Appl. Ecol.* **18**, 303–310.

Bennet, K.D. (1996) Late-quaternary vegetation dynamics of the Cairngorms. *Botanical Journal of Scotland* **48**, 51–63.

Birks, H.H. (1970) Studies in the vegetational history of Scotland. I. A pollen diagram from Abernethy Forest, Inverness-shire. *J. Ecol.* **58**, 827–846.

Birks, H.H. & Mathewes, R.W. (1978) Studies in the vegetational history of Scotland. V. Late Devensian and early Flandrian pollen and macrofossil stratigraphy at Abernethy forest, Inverness-shire. *New Phytol.* **80**, 455–484.

Birks, H.J.B. (1996) Palaeoecological studies in the Cairngorms – Summary and future research needs. *Botanical Journal of Scotland* **48**, 117–126.

Birse, E.L. (1980) *Plant Communities of Scotland. A Preliminary Phytocoenonia.* Macaulay Institute for Soil Research, Aberdeen.

Birse, E.L. (1984) *The Phytocoenonia of Scotland. Additions and Revisions.* Macaulay Institute for Soil Research, Aberdeen.

Brown, I.R. & Tuley, G. (1971) A study of a population of birches in Glen Gairn. *Trans. Bot. Soc. Edinb.* **41**, 231–245.

Bunce, R.G.H. (1977) The range of variation within the pinewoods. In: Bunce, R.G.H. & Jeffers, J.N.R., eds, *Native Pinewoods of Scotland.* NERC Institute of Terrestrial Ecology, Cambridge. pp.10–25.

Burgess, A. (1951) The ecology of the Cairngorms, III. The *Empetrum-Vaccinium* zone. *J. Ecol.* **39**, 271–284.

Coppins, B.J., (1985) A new *Micarea* from the Scottish Highlands. *Lichenologist* **17**, 99–101.

Davies, T.D., Abrahams, P.W., Tranter, M., Blackwood, I., Brumblecombe, P. & Vincent, C.E. (1984) Black acidic snow in the remote Scottish highlands. *Nature* **312**, 58–61.

Dunlop, B.M.S. (1983) The natural regeneration of Scots pine. *Scottish Forestry* **37**, 259–263.

Durno, S.E. (1959) Pollen analysis of peat deposits in the Eastern Grampians. *Scot. Geogr. Mag.* **75**, 102–111.

Edwards, I.D. (1981) The conservation of the Glen Tanar native pinewood near Aboyne, Aberdeenshire. *Scottish Forestry* **35**, 173–178.

Ferreira, R.E.C. (1959) Scottish mountain vegetation in relation to geology. *Trans. Bot. Soc. Edinb.* **37**, 229–250.

Forbes, J.C. & Kenworthy, J.B. (1973) Distributions of two species of birch forming stands on Deeside, Aberdeenshire. *Trans. Bot. Soc. Edinb.* **42**, 101–110.

Forestry Commission (1989) *Native Pinewood Grants and Guidelines.* Forestry Commission, Edinburgh.

Forrest, G.I. (1980) Genotypic variation among native Scots pine populations in Scotland based on monoterpene analysis. *Forestry* **53**, 101–128.

Gilbert, O.L. & Fox, B.W. (1985) Lichens of high ground in the Cairngorm mountains, Scotland. *Lichenologist* **17**, 51–66.

Goodier, R. & Bunce, R.G.H. (1977) the native pinewoods of Scotland: the current state of the resource. In: Bunce, R.G.H. & Jeffers, J.N.R., eds, *Native Pinewoods of Scotland.* NERC Institute of Terrestrial Ecology, Cambridge. pp. 78–87.

Grace, J. (1997) The oceanic tree-line and the limit for tree growth in Scotland. *Botanical Journal of Scotland* **49**, 223–236.

Hobbs, R.J., Mallik, A.U. & Gimingham, C.H. (1984) Studies on fire in Scottish heathland communities. III. Vital attributes of the species. *J. Ecol.* **72**, 963–976.

Hobbs, R.J. & Gimingham, C.H. (1987) Vegetation, fire and herbivore interaction in heathland. In: Macfadyen, A. & Ford, E.D., eds, *Advances in Ecological Research*. Vol.**16**, Academic Press, London. pp.87–173.

Huntley, B. (1994) Late Devensian and Holocene palaeoecology and palaeoenvironments of the Morrone Birkwoods, Aberdeenshire, Scotland. *Journal of Quaternary Science* **9**, 311–336

Huntley, B. & Birks, H.J.B. (1979a) The past and present vegetation of the Morrone Birkwoods National Nature Reserve, Scotland. I. A primary phytosociological survey. *J. Ecol.* **67**, 417–446.

Huntley, B. & Birks, H.J.B. (1979b) The past and present vegetation of the Morrone Birkwoods National Nature Reserve. II. Woodland vegetation and soils. *J. Ecol*, **67**, 447–467.

Huntley, B., Daniell, J.R.G. & Allen, J.R.M. (1997) Scottish vegetation history – the Highlands. *Botanical Journal of Scotland* **49**, 163–175.

Ingram, M. (1958) The ecology of the Cairngorms. The *Juncus* zone: *Juncus trifidus* communities. *J. Ecol.* **46**, 707–737.

McConnell, J. & Legg, C. (1995) Are the upland heaths in the Cairngorms pining for climate change? In: Thompson, D.B.A., Hester, A.J. & Usher, M.B., eds, *Heaths and Moorland: Cultural Landscapes*. HMSO, Edinburgh. pp. 154–161.

McVean, D.N. & Ratcliffe, D.A. (1962) *Plant Communities of the Scottish Highlands*. HMSO, London.

Mardon, D.K. (1990) Conservation of montane willow scrub in Scotland. *Trans. Bot. Soc. Edinb* **45**, 427–436.

Metcalfe, G. (1950) The ecology of the Cairngorms, II. The mountain Callunetum. *J. Ecol.* **38**, 46–74.

Miles, J. (1985) The pedogenic effects of different species and vegetation types and the effects of succession. *Journal of Soil Science* **36**, 571–584.

Miller, G.R. (1986) *Development of subalpine scrub at Northern Corries, Cairngorms SSSI*. Institute of Terrestrial Ecology, Banchory.

Miller, G.R. & Cummins, R.P. (1982) Regeneration of Scots pine *Pinus sylvestris* at a natural tree-line in the Cairngorm mountains, Scotland. *Holarctic Ecol.* **5**, 27–34.

Mountford, E.P. & Peterken, G.F. (2000) Growth, mortality and regeneration in Craigellachie, a semi-natural birchwood in the Scottish Highlands. *Botanical Journal of Scotland* **52**, 187–211.

O'Sullivan, P.E. (1974) Two Flandrian pollen diagrams from the East-central Highlands of Scotland. *Pollen et Spores* **16**, 33–57.

O'Sullivan, P.E. (1975) Early and Middle Flandrian pollen zonation in the Eastern Highlands of Scotland. *Boreas* **4**, 197–207.

O'Sullivan, P.E. (1976) Pollen analysis and radio-carbon dating of a core from Loch Pityoulish, East-central Highlands of Scotland. *J. Biogeogr.* **3**, 293–302.

O'Sullivan, P.E. (1977) Vegetation history and the native pinewoods. In: Bunce, R.G.H. & Jeffers, J.N.R., eds, *Native Pinewoods of Scotland*. NERC Institute of Terrestrial Ecology, Cambridge. pp. 60–69.

Pears, N.V. (1968) Post-glacial tree-lines of the Cairngorm mountains, Scotland. *Trans. Bot. Soc. Edinb.* **40**, 361–394.

Pears, N.V. (1970) Post-glacial tree-lines of the Cairngorm mountains, Scotland: some modifications based on radiocarbon dating. *Trans. Bot. Soc. Edinb.* **40**, 536–544.

Poore, M.E.D. & McVean, D.N. (1957) A new approach to Scottish mountain vegetation. *J. Ecol.* **45**, 401–439.

Pryor, P.J. (1986) Disturbance Studies on Open *Juncus trifidus* heath and other Cairngorm vegetation. Unpublished Ph.D. thesis, University of Aberdeen.

Ratcliffe, D.A. (1974) The Vegetation. In: Nethersole-Thompson, D. & Watson, A., eds, *The Cairngorms. Their Natural History and Scenery*. Collins, London. pp. 42–76.

Robertson, J.S. (1984) *A Key to Common Plant Communities of Scotland*. Macaulay Institute for Soil Research, Aberdeen.

Rodwell, J. (1991a) *British Plant Communities. Vol. 1. Woodland and Scrub*. Cambridge University Press, Cambridge.

Rodwell, J. (1991b) *British Plant Communities. Vol. 2. Mires and Heaths*. Cambridge University Press, Cambridge.

Rodwell, J. (1992) *British Plant Communities. Vol. 3. Grasslands and Montane Communities*. Cambridge University Press, Cambridge.

Rodwell, J.S. (1994) *British Plant Communities. Vol. 4. Aquatic Communities, Swamps and Tall Herb Fens*. Cambridge University Press, Cambridge.

Rodwell, J.S. (2000) *British Plant Communities. Vol. 5. Maritime Communities and Vegetation of Open Habitats*. Cambridge University Press, Cambridge.

Smith, W.G. (1911) Arctic-alpine vegetation. In: Tansley, A.G., ed., *Types of British Vegetation*. Cambridge University Press, Cambridge. pp. 288–329.

Smith, R. (1900) Botanical Survey of Scotland. Part II. North Perthshire. *Scot. Geogr. Mag* **16**, 441–467.

Smith, W.G. (1904), Botanical Survey of Scotland. Part III. Forfar and Fife. *Scot. Geogr. Mag.* **20**, 617–628.

Steven, H.M. & Carlisle, A. (1959) *The Native Pinewoods of Scotland*. Oliver & Boyd, Edinburgh.

Vasari, Y. & Vasari, A. (1968) Late- and post-glacial macrophytic vegetation in the lochs of Northern Scotland. *Acta bot. fenn.* **80**, 120pp.

Ward, S.D. (1970) The phytosociology of *Calluna-Arctostophylos* heaths in Scotland. I. Dinnet Moor, Aberdeenshire. *J. Ecol.* **58**, 847–863.

Ward, S.D. (1971a) The phytosociology of *Calluna-Arctostophylos* heaths in Scotland. II. The north-east Scottish heaths. *J. Ecol.* **59**, 679–696.

Ward, S.D. (1971b) the phytosociology of *Calluna-Arctostophylos* heaths in Scotland. III. A critical examination of the Arctostaphyleto-Callunetum. *J. Ecol.* **59**, 697–712.

Watling, R. (1987) Larger arctic-alpine fungi in Scotland. In: Lauresen, G., Ammirati, J.F. & Redhead, S.A., eds, *Arctic and Alpine Mycology, 2*. Plenum, New York. pp. 17–45.

Watson, A. & Birse, E.L. (1991) Lichen-ripe pinewood, *Cladonia ciliata – Pinus sylvestris* community in north-eastern Scotland. *Botanical Journal of Scotland* **46**, 73–88.

Watson, A. & Nethersole-Thompson, D. (1974) *The Cairngorms. Their Natural History and Scenery*. Collins, London.

Watt, A.S. (1947) Pattern and process in the plant community. *J. Ecol.* **35**, 1–22.

Watt, A.S. & Jones, E.W. (1948) The ecology of the Cairngorms, I. The environment and the altitudinal zonation of the vegetation. *J. Ecol.* **36**, 283–304.

CHAPTER 4
Birds and Mammals

Roy Dennis

The Cairngorms area has been recognized as a very special region for breeding birds for a long time. The altitudinal variation and the diversity of habitats ensure a wide range of species while the relatively dry climate, the cold spring weather, the long-lasting snow fields and the hot summers encourage rare species to remain and breed. The best examples in Britain of arctic-alpine mountain plateaux, native pine forests and northern fens occur in the area. Mammals are well represented but, unlike the birds, there are no species which are restricted to this area within their British range.

BIRDS

About 235 species have been recorded in the Cairngorms area and about 150 of these breed or have bred. Harvie-Brown's series of vertebrate faunas at the turn of this century (1895, 1906) provide early information on birds in the Cairngorms and recent county avifaunas have been published for Badenoch and Strathspey (Dennis, 1984, 1985), north-east Scotland (Buckland, Bell and Picozzi, 1990) and Moray and Nairn (Cook, 1992). There are four chapters on the birds of the Cairngorms in the monograph on the Cairngorms by Nethersole-Thompson and Watson (1974). This chapter does not set out to duplicate earlier accounts and readers are directed towards those books. Instead it aims to highlight those species, habitats and issues of particular interest.

Table 4a illustrates the ornithological importance of the Cairngorms for rare breeding birds and this fact is recognized by the number of species which

are listed on Schedule 1 of the *Wildlife and Countryside Act* 1981 and on Annex 1 of the EC *Birds Directive*. The EC Council *Directive on the Conservation of Wilds Birds* was adopted in 1979 and came into force in 1981. All member states are required to take measures to protect wild birds and to preserve sufficient diversity of habitats for all species naturally occurring within their territories, so as to maintain their populations at an ecologically and scientifically sound level. Species whose status is a cause for some concern are specially identified in Annex 1 for special conservation measures and member states are required to classify the most important areas for these species as Special Protection Areas (SPAs). Nine such sites have been designated or proposed for the Cairngorms area.

Fifty-four species identified in the *Red Data Book* for Britain breed or have bred in the Cairngorms. This list was prepared by the Nature Conservancy Council and the Royal Society for the Protection of Birds in 1990 and drew attention to the need for active conservation of a total of 117 breeding or wintering species which were rare, threatened and important in Britain.

Since the last ice age there have been many changes in the avifauna of the Cairngorms and the changing fortunes of individual species have continued until the present time. During the long period of human influence on the Cairngorms area, those species of open moorland, such as red grouse *Lagopus lagopus* and meadow pipit *Anthus pratensis*, and associated with farmland and habitation, such as lapwing *Vanellus vanellus* and house sparrow *Passer domesticus*, flourished while those of true

43

Table 4a   Rarer species of birds which breed regularly in the Cairngorms area

	Wildlife and Countryside Act 1981 Schedule 1	EC Directive Annex 1	UK Red Data Book
Red-throated diver	★	★	★
Slavonian grebe	★	★	★
Greylag goose	★		★
Wigeon			★
Teal			★
Pintail	★		★
Shoveler			★
Goldeneye	★		★
Hen harrier	★	★	★
Goshawk	★	★	★
Golden eagle	★	★	★
Osprey	★	★	★
Merlin	★	★	★
Red grouse			★
Black grouse			★
Capercaillie		★	★
Grey partridge			★
Spotted crake	★	★	★
Oystercatcher			★
Ringed plover			★
Dotterel	★	★	★
Golden plover		★	★
Purple sandpiper	★		★
Dunlin			★
Curlew			★
Redshank			★
Greenshank	★	★	★
Wood sandpiper	★	★	★
Barn owl	★		★
Redwing	★		★
Crested tit	★		★
Twite			★
Scottish crossbill	★	★	★
Snow bunting	★	★	★

The species listed under Schedule I are protected by special penalties under the *Wildlife and Countryside Act* 1981. The habitats of the species listed under Annex 1 of the EEC Directive should be protected and managed.

forests such as capercaillie *Tetrao urogallus* and Scottish crossbills *Loxia scotica* decreased in line with the destruction of the native forest and its replacement by moors and farmland. A few species such as red grouse and house sparrow have now declined from peak numbers early in this century.

During Victorian times, species such as birds of prey, which may have conflicted with man's interests, were persecuted and in some cases exterminated, for example red kite *Milvus milvus* and osprey *Pandion haliaetus*. In recent decades most of these species have recovered and recent losses, such as those of corncrake *Crex crex* and corn bunting *Miliaria calandra*, have been on a regional scale as opposed to complete extinction throughout the whole country. It is likely that the red kite will return to breed once more following the successful re-introduction of the species to the northern highlands. The only bird species still lost to the avifauna which was present several centuries ago is the crane *Grus grus*. Table 4b lists the main species which have been lost as breeding species or have noticeably declined.

Table 4b   Species which have declined or ceased to breed in the Cairngorms area, and dates of last breeding when appropriate

Grey heron	Nightjar (1960)
Red kite (1892)	Greenshank
Red grouse	Willow tit (1950s)
Black grouse	Raven
Capercaillie	House sparrow
Grey partridge	Twite
Moorhen	Yellowhammer
Corncrake (1970s)	Corn bunting (1970s)
Lapwing	Black-headed gull
Golden plover	

MOUNTAINS

The high tops of the Cairngorms are very special. For the naturalist it is a chance to visit the Arctic! To be mysteriously transported 2500 kilometres to the north. To experience the wild, to be in places where man's influence is not easily visible and really to feel small in the face of the elements. This can be a very dangerous place with snow storms in any month of the year. Yet at other times, under clear blue skies, one can see the length and breadth of Scotland and feel on top of the world.

The mountains either side of the Larig Ghru are the highest and most extensive area of arctic landscape in Scotland. Surrounding four of the five highest mountains in Britain are wide expanses of high level plateaux dominated by short vegetation, gravel and boulder fields and snow beds. To the south and west, the mountains are gentler with broad summits and plateaux of a more grassy nature where the underlying rocks are richer in nutrients. All of these areas are very important for wildlife especially for birds.

The three most important species are dotterel *Charadrius morinellus*, ptarmigan *Lagopus mutus* and snow bunting *Plectrophenax nivalis*. A handful of commoner species regularly breed at high altitude. Golden plovers *Charadrius apricaria* and dunlin *Calidris alpina* are scattered across the grassier areas and peat bogs with common sandpiper *Actitis hypoleucos* and common gulls *Larus canus* nesting in small numbers by some high level lochans. Meadow pipits, skylarks *Alauda arvensis* and wheatears *Oenanthe oenanthe* breed in small numbers throughout the high mountains, and in a few places ring ouzels *Turdus torquatus* haunt the high slopes and cliffs.

Evidence of the Arctic nature of the high tops is shown by the occurrence of birds which are normally only winter visitors or migrants to Scotland. The beautiful snowy owl *Nyctea scandiaca* has occurred on these mountains in recent decades, with birds living for months at a time in some summers. Both sexes have been identified and more than one bird has been seen in a single season but there has been no evidence of breeding or even the establishment of a pair. Purple sandpiper *Calidris maritima*, shore lark *Eromophila alpestris* and lapland bunting *Calcarius lapponicus* have nested and several other northern birds have been observed. A pair of sanderlings *Calidris alba* in summer plumage were seen on 9 June 1974, a pair of ringed plovers *Charadrius hiaticula* of the northern race *tundrae* were seen briefly by Lochan Buidhe on 12 June 1979, and single long-tailed skuas *Stercorarius longicaudus* were seen near Drumochter on 18 June 1974 and another found dead near Bridge of Brown on 4 June 1975. The main difference for predatory birds, like snowy owl and long-tailed skua, between the Cairngorms and the Arctic is the absence of lemmings which is their main prey for successful breeding. Thus the chance of them becoming regular breeders is most unlikely.

Ptarmigan (Plate 29). Of the three special birds, the ptarmigan is an all year resident of the highest mountains. This bird is very well adapted to life in a harsh climate. It is unusual in the fact that it moults in autumn into a beautiful white winter coat, which provides a high degree of insulation from the cold as well as camouflage in the snow from predators. The Cairngorms area is the stronghold of the species in Scotland and a recent report (Pritchard *et al.*, 1992) gave an estimate of 1500 pairs for the proposed Cairngorms Special Protection Area (SPA) alone. The Scottish population is estimated at 10 000 pairs.

Ptarmigan have been studied for many years in the Cairngorms by Adam Watson and his counts indicate that peak numbers occur in cyclic patterns with an average periodicity of ten years on the infertile granites of the Cairngorms. In contrast, on geologically richer mountains to the south, cycles are more frequent and irregular. Densities in these hills are higher than in other places studied in the world. Since 1989, Stuart Rae started more intensive studies of ptarmigan, and the species is also a feature of research by the mountain plateau ecology project run by Scottish Natural Heritage (SNH). In 1990, a density of 50 adults per square kilometre was recorded with two young per adult being reared (Watson & Rae, 1993). The research at present under way should in the next few years improve our knowledge of this species and its present status in relation to the condition and use of the Cairngorms area.

Dotterel (Plate 30). This is a magical bird. Its beautiful plumage, fascinating life style and its wild, arctic nesting grounds in the high mountains make this a speciality for British bird-watchers and many of them make pilgrimages to the Cairngorms to observe it. It is a species which has attracted attention for decades, in fact centuries. For hundreds of years it was hunted as a delicacy and latterly its bright feathers were esteemed for the tying of fishing flies. A monograph was written (Nethersole-Thompson, 1973) and more recently it has also been the subject of research by the mountain plateau ecology project run by SNH.

The majority of the British population nest within the Cairngorms area and this is the most important area for them. A 1987–88 survey by the Nature Conservancy Council estimated the British population at 840 pairs, although it may have been as high as 900 pairs. These figures suggest a considerable change in numbers since the 1960s when the population was estimated at 100 pairs. A study in the mid-1980s estimated a total of 600 pairs (Watson & Rae, 1987) and it was suggested that the differences were due to better survey techniques. This view was not held universally and it was believed a genuine increase had occurred. Breeding densities have doubled on some hills and more hills are being used for breeding in Scotland. It is now accepted that a genuine increase has occurred due to three factors: numbers on passage in Britain have increased since the 1950s, the British climate cooled in the 1960s and 1970s and there has been an extension of snow-lie in Norway in the last 30 years which has forced birds to move south to Scotland (Thompson & Whitfield, 1993). It is likely that the Cairngorms area assumes even greater significance for this species when population levels are lower in periods of climatic amelioration.

Research has revealed some very important features in dotterel breeding in Scotland. In general there is low adult site fidelity and also a low incidence of return by first-time breeders to their natal sites. Some mountain areas produce relatively fewer young per year than other sites and there are clear differences in density and breeding success which are not solely linked to the productivity of the underlying rocks. Thus the productive sites export birds to other hills and on the best sites males, which look after the eggs and young, are more site faithful from year to year. Females are highly mobile and it has been proved than some females nest in Scotland and subsequently in the same season in Norway. This link with Norway suggests that the whole population may ebb and flow in line with climatic conditions. Breeding success is affected by severe weather, nest trampling by red deer and people, disturbance by dogs, by predators and probably by habitat change due to overgrazing (see Table 4c).

Snow bunting (Plate 31). The third of the special species is the snow bunting. This is the most hardy passerine in the world with breeding regularly occurring in the most northerly lands of the Arctic. Those breeding in Scotland represent the most southerly population in Europe. Although numbers are now higher the bird is still one of the most rare and elusive in Britain. Its haunts are the highest corries and boulder screes of the mountains, especially those close to long-lying snowbeds where the birds often search for insects.

Once again, this Cairngorms-oriented bird is the subject of a monograph (Nethersole-Thompson, 1966). Recently it has been studied by Rik Smith (1995). In the 1950s and 1960s numbers of breeding birds were very low in Scotland, in fact always below ten pairs. In line with other species which increased during the period of colder weather in Scotland from the mid-1960s, the snow bunting has established a larger population. Present estimates suggest a Scottish population in excess of

50 pairs, with the majority in the Cairngorms area. The birds nesting in Scotland show the plumage characteristics of the Icelandic birds while breeding success, survival and site fidelity of native birds are sufficient to maintain the small Scottish population (Smith, 1995). The size of the Scottish population is mostly influenced by climatic change rather than human threats.

MOORS

Heather moorland is a very important habitat in the Cairngorms area although it is, of course, the end result of centuries of burning and grazing. Active management of heather moors by the sporting estates has created a unique environment in world terms. The reason for all this effort is the red grouse which is a popular gamebird in this area although much decreased on many moors especially in the west. This species is the main subject of Chapter 12. Nevertheless it is pertinent to mention here that this is a most distinctive and interesting bird. At one time it was recognized as a species endemic to the British Isles but is nowadays treated as a distinct endemic sub-species of the willow grouse.

Many of the moors have areas of birch and willow scrub as well as adjoining hill farms and rough grazing. These form a favoured habitat of black grouse *Tetrao tetrix*, a species that is still well distributed throughout the Cairngorms area but sadly has declined in the last forty years. Raven *Corvus corax* and twite *Carduelis flavirostris* which also inhabit the moors have declined and some of these changes are almost certainly due to the cessation of traditional agriculture on hill farms, especially the growing of oats, the resulting stubble fields and the old style of animal husbandry. A variety of waders also breed on the moors, especially golden plover and snipe *Gallinago gallinago*. Greenshanks *Tringa nebularia* still occur throughout the area but have decreased since the 1950s due to natural regeneration of trees and afforestation.

Heather moorlands are an important habitat for raptors, including golden eagle *Aquila chrysaetos*, peregrine *Falco peregrinus*, hen harrier *Circus cyaneus* and merlin *Falco columbarius*. Short-eared owls *Asio flammeus* also favour this habitat but are not as common as on the grassy uplands further south in Scotland. In some areas, raptors are still illegally persecuted. Heather management is essential for the future of some of these species, especially hen harrier. There is clearly a need to encourage areas of excellence for heather moors where management is undertaken to a high standard and the integrity of very large areas of contiguous moors is safeguarded. The Cairngorms Working Party (CWP) recommended that the east part of the Cairngorms area should be one such area.

DIURNAL RAPTORS

The Cairngorms area has always held an exciting variety of birds of prey. The mountains are home to golden eagle and peregrine, the moors to hen harrier, kestrel *Falco tinnuculus*, peregrine and

Table 4c Impacts of various factors on montane birds in the Cairngorms area

	Dotterel	Ptarmigan	Snow bunting
Grazing pressure	+	+	?
Trampling pressure	+	+	–
Visitors & infrastructure	+	+	–
Hill tracks	+	+	–
Crows & gulls	+	+	–
Climatic change	*	*	*
Pollution	?	?	?

+ can have deleterious effects on population; * likely to have major effects, either increase with a colder climate or decline with amelioration; – no discernible impacts.

merlin, while the forests and lochs hold buzzard *Buteo buteo*, sparrowhawk *Accipiter nisus* and osprey. In the past persecution of these species has been intense and during the latter part of the last century several species were exterminated as elsewhere in Scotland. Those that disappeared completely were white-tailed eagle *Haliaetus albicilla*, red kite, osprey, honey buzzard *Pernis apivorus* and goshawk *Accipter gentilis*.

Nowadays seventeen species can occur in this area; nine of them breed regularly, two irregularly, two used to breed and may recolonize from populations re-introduced elsewhere in Scotland. The hobby *Falco subbuteo* may breed in the future while three species occur as rare visitors, two of them in summer and one in winter. Table 4d details these species; it also indicates recent trends in breeding numbers and the degree of persecution which, sadly, still takes place despite special protection under the law.

Table 4d   Status of diurnal raptors in the Cairngorms area

Species	Status	Trends	Persecution
Hen harrier	breeds	decrease	serious
Goshawk (scarce)	breeds	increase	yes
Sparrowhawk	breeds	increase	
Buzzard	breeds	increase	yes
Golden eagle	breeds	stable	yes
Osprey	breeds	increase	
Kestrel	breeds		
Merlin	breeds	decrease	
Peregrine	breeds	increase	yes
Honey buzzard	rare visitor, occasional breeder		
Red kite	extinct breeder; migrant from re-introduced population		
White-tailed eagle	extinct breeder; migrant from re-introduced population		
Marsh harrier	summer migrant; has bred (1996)		
Rough-legged buzzard	rare winter visitor		
Red-footed falcon	rare summer visitor		
Hobby	rare summer visitor; may breed in future		
Gyrfalcon	rare winter visitor		

The **golden eagles** (Plate 32) of the Cairngorms area have been one of the best studied populations in the world. From the time of Macpherson's book on the homelife of the golden eagle (1909) and Seton Gordon's first studies (1925), this great bird has thrilled a succession of ornithologists. The golden eagle population in the Cairngorms is a very important one. It was the least affected by toxic pesticides, such as dieldrin, during the 1960s and 1970s when eagles elsewhere suffered from serious reductions in breeding success. The Cairngorms area eagles, which live to a greater extent on live prey, such as red grouse, ptarmigan and blue hare, continued to rear young which could move out of the area and bolster populations elsewhere in the highlands.

Despite careful protection by some landowners in the Cairngorms area, golden eagles have suffered from serious persecution and even in the recent decade birds have been killed at the nest or poisoned. In this special area this illegal activity should cease and if it did it is likely that some long extinct home-ranges in the eastern half of the area would be re-occupied. In the western parts of the area there is some evidence that a few home-ranges have been abandoned due to a paucity of live prey caused by long-term overgrazing by sheep and red deer. At least one traditional eyrie site in the central Cairngorms has been abandoned through increased visitor disturbance, and at another a pair of eagles have been encouraged to move into a quieter part of the forest by the provision of artificial nests built in suitable trees.

The **peregrines** of the Cairngorms area also fared better than most of the British population during the pesticide era of the 1960s and 1970s. More young were reared in this area than on average elsewhere despite the fact that some evidence of contamination was present. Peregrines also suffered persecution on grouse moors in this area but since the 1970s the population has increased and more pairs now nest than in the past hundred years, although there is now a worrying resurgence of persecution and some recent evidence of a decline. This is an area where the birds principally feed on wild prey of a wide variety of species rather than on feral pigeon as in many areas of the UK. This fact makes this population of particular value and worthy of special conservation.

Merlin and hen harrier occur on heather moors throughout the area. Merlins are often associated with the forest edge, especially in scattered mature Scots pines, where they lay their eggs in abandoned nests built in previous seasons by crows. There is still a healthy population of merlins but there is concern that the species fluctuates from year to year and declines have been noted in some locations. It is the subject of detailed survey at the present time.

Hen harriers occur in the Cairngorms area but are often persecuted on grouse moors. Recent studies by Etheridge and Summers (1993) show that although clutch and brood size were higher on managed grouse moors in Scotland and Wales than on other heather moorland and afforested land, the clutch and brood survival were the lowest. Annual productivity was only 0.8 chicks per pair compared to 2.4 on other moorland and 1.7 in afforestation. Information on the scale of direct persecution of adult harriers is difficult to obtain but it is possible that persecution in the Cairngorms area is having a deleterious effect on the population. Hen harriers are known to kill red grouse and this subject is covered in the chapter on grouse. In such a special area management must be aimed at managing heather moorland to the best advantage for red grouse without killing protected raptors.

Following its extermination as a breeding bird in Scotland in the early years of this century, the **osprey** (Plate 33) returned to breed in Strathspey where the eyrie at Loch Garten has become world famous as a symbol of nature conservation (Brown

& Waterston, 1962). Since then the population has risen until over 146 pairs were recorded in Scotland in 2000. During the early years all nesting attempts were in Strathspey but from 1966 pairs started to colonize new areas. Badenoch and Strathspey with its lochs, rivers and the fish farm at Aviemore remains one of the strongholds of the species in Scotland but birds nest in at least three other parts of the Cairngorms area as well as in other groups throughout Scotland.

The raptor community in the Cairngorms is of particular importance within the British Isles and Europe. It has a high number of species living together within a large area of native habitats ranging from the rivers to the mountain tops. In general they live principally on live wild prey with little evidence of toxic chemical contamination. In continental terms they are of interest because the effects of the oceanic climate allow some species, such as golden eagle and peregrine, to remain in their home-ranges throughout the whole year whereas in colder areas they move in winter. Most species have shown an increase in numbers and success in recent decades. The future for some would be even better if all persecution ceased and at least two species which were exterminated in the past may return to breed. The raptor population in this area should be specially protected and should continue to be monitored as a very long-term study.

NATIVE WOODLANDS

Native Scots pine forest is one of the most special habitats in Scotland and the remnants are some of the best examples of semi-natural woodland in Britain. Strathspey and Deeside hold the most important remaining areas of native pine forests. They are the stronghold of three birds, namely capercaillie, crested tit *Parus cristatus* and the endemic Scottish crossbill. A variety of other species, such as chaffinch *Fringilla coelebs*, siskin *Carduelis spinus*, coal tit *Parus ater* and sparrowhawk, also live in these forests, while deciduous woodlands of birch, aspen, rowan and, in some places, oak are important for wood warbler *Phylloscopus sibilatrix*, redstart *Phoenicurus phoenicurus*, tree pipit *Anthus trivialis* and woodcock *Scolopax rusticola*.

Following the last ice age natural forests colonized Scotland and in the Scottish Highlands the ancient wood of Caledon, characterized by Scots pine, covered much of the land. Its greatest extent, about 6000 years ago, has been estimated at 1.5 million hectares. Much has been written about this ancient forest (see Chapters 9 and 10): here attention may be drawn to the fact that this great northern forest was a mosaic of Scots pine and native deciduous trees such as birch, alder, oak, aspen and willows.

There was great variation due to the underlying geology and soils as well as to topographic features such as lochs, bogs, rivers, cliffs and mountains and to natural events such as fires, storms, floods and large herbivores. Additionally over the millennia, there were changes in species dominance and extent due to climatic changes.

Our forest has been compared to the great boreal forests of Scandinavia and Russia, but it should be noted that native spruces are absent and that the close proximity of the Atlantic Ocean creates a maritime climate, with rapid changes in temperature even in the middle of winter.

The inventory carried out by Steven and Carlisle (1959) revealed that genuinely native pinewoods in Scotland had shrunk to 35 principal remnants covering a total area of about 16 000 hectares. 99 per cent of the original forest had been destroyed by man; an unpalatable statistic for western nations alarmed by the present-day destruction of the rain forest.

The history of exploitation of the pinewoods is detailed in Chapters 9 and 10. Between 1957 and 1987 a quarter of the remnants of native pine forest identified by Steven and Carlisle was destroyed by felling or underplanting. About 12 000 hectares of native woodland now remain and over half of that is scattered pine. For comparison, conifer plantations in Scotland amount to approximately a million hectares so the native woods represent only 1 per cent of the conifer woodlands of Scotland

Several of the most important remnants occur in Strathspey and Deeside. These are the richest for fauna and flora. Despite the fact that most sites are designated as Sites of Special Scientific Interest (SSSIs) and a Native Pinewood Grant Scheme was introduced in 1978 the ecological health of most woods continued to decline due to various factors including a lack of regeneration and a scarcity of broadleaved trees and shrubs caused by overgrazing by deer (Chapter 11).

In recent years there are signs of real hope that the tide is changing and the native forests are being given the status they deserve. The Forestry Commission has new grant schemes for the protection and enhancement of native pinewoods. The RSPB has embarked on a major restoration project at Abernethy Forest based on natural regeneration through reduction of deer numbers and the removal of sheep. There are already excellent signs of recovery. SNH have undertaken similar measures and private owners are also involved in pinewood regeneration.

These changes are of great significance to the birds of the native pine forests, especially the three key species. The **Scottish crossbill** (Plate 34) is Britain's only endemic species. It is the subject of the monograph by Nethersole-Thompson (1975). Recent research by the RSPB includes an examination of the genetics of this bird through DNA analyses, but much is to be learned about its ecology and movements. Problems of distinguishing this species from the smaller common crossbill *Loxia curvirostris* make study difficult and to make matters worse the even larger billed parrot crossbill *Loxia pytyopsittacus* has been identified in Abernethy Forest since 1983. On 17 May 1991, at least 1083 crossbills were counted by RSPB staff in that forest; the majority were common crossbills which had arrived the previous summer from Scandinavia but there were also ten parrot crossbills. Breeding of this species was proved that summer as well as in a previous year.

The Scottish crossbill is most influenced by the cone crop on Scots pine which has an irregular pattern. In years of plentiful seed, such as 1991, Scottish crossbills are well distributed in the old woods, with up to 75–100 pairs in Abernethy Forest. This is believed to represent 25 per cent of the world breeding population (Pritchard *et al.*, 1992). The species is also present in the Deeside woods as well as in other old Scots pine woods within the Cairngorms area. The smaller-billed common crossbill is more often found in mixed conifers, especially spruces. There is some concern that the presence of maturing spruce plantations within the core areas of native pine may encourage common crossbills to breed within the main range of Scottish crossbill. This may lead to dilution of the endemic bird through hybridization. Proposals for major pine forest expansion and the removal of exotic conifers would be advantageous for the endemic Scottish Crossbill.

The nominate race of the **crested tit** is distributed as a sedentary breeding species from central Fenno-Scandia east across central Russia to the Urals, and south across the greater part of central Europe to southern Spain, northern Italy and Greece (BOU, 1971). A distinctive sub-species *scoticus* is resident in northern Scotland as an endemic race. The headquarters of this bird are the pine forests of Strathspey where it was first identified in 1789. During this century it has spread north and east into the Moray Plain and north to Sutherland. It has never been known to breed in the Deeside forests and the unusual distribution of this species is of interest. Why are they restricted to the pine woods north of the Cairngorm mountains? Is this due to the destruction of pine forests in past centuries or to unusually exacting ecological requirements or even a relict population from an ancient refugium? Cook, 1982, gave a population estimate of 900 pairs for Scotland but noted that severe winters can cause a major reduction in numbers. The old pine forests of Abernethy and Rothiemurchus provide the ideal conditions for crested tits. These are large trees with an extensive needle canopy, plentiful side branches near the ground or an understorey of young pines, a high growth of heather and a good supply of dead trees for nest sites. Positive management for native pine forest will benefit this species.

The indigenous **capercaillie** (Plate 35) became extinct in Scotland in the latter part of the eigthteenth century due to forest destruction and persecution. The species was re-introduced from Sweden from 1837 and successfully recolonized much of its former range. In the 1960s it was a common species in pine woods throughout the Cairngorms area and was actively hunted as a pest by foresters and for food by locals. Since the 1970s there has been a serious decline in numbers and distribution in Scotland.

The main pine forest remnants in the Cairngorms area are still the chief haunts of the species in Scotland as its preferred habitat is mature Scots pine forest with broad-topped trees, a relatively open canopy allowing a rich ground layer of blaeberries for feeding and long heather and juniper for nesting and hiding. Considerable research has been undertaken on the species by Robert Moss and colleagues at ITE Banchory and in recent years by the RSPB at Abernethy. A voluntary ban on shooting was promoted in 1989 and considerable efforts to enhance the breeding success of the present population through habitat management, predator control and research have been undertaken.

The exact causes of decline are uncertain but the loss of native pine forest and its conversion to conifer plantations is regarded as significant. Other reasons include wetter weather in June, over-grazing of the forest understorey by red deer, mortality due to deer fences, increased numbers of crows and foxes as well as overshooting.

The present Scottish population is estimated at under a thousand birds. Proposals to extend and enhance the native pine forests of Strathspey and Mar will undoubtedly help this species. Additionally expansion and merging of the presently fragmented remnants will create a larger forest ecosystem which should benefit this true forest species.

LOCHS, RIVERS AND MARSHES

Three major rivers flow out of the east or north-east of the Cairngorms area and several smaller rivers run to the south into Angus and Perthshire. The Dee and the Spey are of particular importance. They are two of the least polluted or modified major rivers in Britain. They are of international significance for nature. The middle section of the Spey contains some very attractive lochs for birds; some of which are surrounded by native pine forest and give one a real feeling of Scandinavia. There are a number of high altitude lochs in the mountains but these are often rather birdless.

One of the most interesting waterfowl in the Cairngorms area is the **goldeneye** *Bucephala clangula*. This attractive duck has always been a relatively common winter visitor from Scandinavia. A pair first bred near Aviemore in 1970, in a nesting box erected by the RSPB some ten years previously as part of a project to encourage this hole-nesting duck to remain in Scotland and breed. This first nesting attempt which involved a female seen with four ducklings in July was the forerunner of a successful colonization. The original pair bred in 1971 and 1972, there were three nests in 1973, 12 nests by 1978, 47 nests by 1983 and 95 nests by 1990 (Dennis, 1987 & 1993). The population is now well over a hundred pairs in natural sites as well as nest boxes.

Often more than one female will lay in a nest so the true size of the breeding population is difficult to judge and the above totals are a minimum. Annually between 22 and 33 per cent of clutches are not incubated but 80 per cent of the incubated clutches hatch successfully. The mean brood size leaving the nests is between 7.85 and 9.86 per year and about one third of young survive to fledge. Despite the fact that the population is growing fast only small numbers have moved to nest elsewhere in Inverness-shire and once in Perthshire; most prefer to remain in Badenoch & Strathspey and as yet none has bred in Deeside.

Three other waterfowl of note are **Slavonian grebe** *Podiceps auritus*, red-throated diver *Gavia stellata* and goosander *Mergus merganser*. The Slavonian grebe colonized Strathspey in 1971 (Dennis, 1984) and a small population of up to ten pairs has become established, which represents a significant proportion of the British population, but they have declined in recent years. **Red-throated divers** have been colonizing a few hill lochs within the Cairngorms area in recent years and it is likely that this will continue. It is of interest that the parent birds fly to the Moray Firth to catch fish for their young. Finally the **goosander** is well distributed through the river systems of the Cairngorms area as a breeding bird. Roosts occur on some lochs such as Loch Garten in Strathspey and may peak at over 100 birds. Sadly this bird is still heavily persecuted on salmon rivers despite the fact that serious damage to fish stocks has not been proved. This should cease and greater attention should be paid to the ecological condition of the rivers and their catchments instead of blaming fish shortages on goosanders.

Most of the marshes which were once present in the flood plains of the rivers in the Cairngorms area were altered for agricultural use over the centuries. In a few places small marshes associated with lochs and rivers are still present, while in Badenoch one of the most important flood plain mires in Britain defeated earlier drainage schemes and is now an important nature conservation site.

The Insh Marshes have been recognized as an area of outstanding value for birds since at least 1960. It is the largest and most northerly flood-plain mire of the poor fen type in Great Britain. To the ornithologist, it is reminiscent of the large boreal mires of Scandinavia with its distinctive array of northern breeding bird species.

The area is so outstanding that it was declared a SSSI in 1963 by the Nature Conservancy. The ornithological importance was further recognized in 1972 when the RSPB purchased a major section of the marshes from the Forestry Commission. The Insh Marshes Nature Reserve was established in 1973. Further leases and purchases have emphasized the outstanding nature of the area's bird life. The site was re-notified as a SSSI in 1986 under the *Wildlife & Countryside Act* 1981, while its outstanding value for birds was internationally recognized by its listing as a Ramsar site and a SPA.

The ornithological importance is principally centred on its breeding communities of wildfowl, waders and wetland breeding species. Of particular significance are very rare breeding species which have a northern distribution in Europe. They include species such as osprey, goldeneye, spotted crake *Porzana porzana* and wood sandpiper *Tringa glareola*. Insh Marshes is recognized as the most important site for spotted crake in Great Britain as well as one of the three best sites for wood sandpiper.

The wildfowl and wader populations are extraordinarily rich and a detailed survey in 1992 by the RSPB (Bhatia, 1993) gives the latest information on the numbers and variety present. Ten species of wildfowl were breeding in 1992; mute swan *Cygnus olors* (2 pairs), greylag goose *Anser anser* (7 pairs), wigeon *Anas penelope* (37 pairs), teal *Anas crecca* (86 pairs), mallard *Anas platyrhynchos* (275 pairs), shoveler *Anas clypeata* (4 pairs), tufted duck *Aythya fuligula* (37 pairs), goldeneye (30+ pairs), red-breasted merganser *Mergus serrator* (2 pairs) and goosander (5 pairs). Of particular significance are the numbers of wigeon (approx 10 per cent of the British breeding population) and goldeneye (approx 30 per cent of the British population). In some years pintail *Anas acuta* has also bred in the marshes and this is a very rare breeding species in Britain with a population of less than 50 pairs. Additionally the Insh Marshes hold an internationally important wintering population of Icelandic breeding whooper swans. This site is particularly important for the swans because here they feed principally on natural aquatic vegetation; elsewhere in the UK many of the larger flocks are more associated with farmland.

Eight wader species nested on the area in 1992 with the commoner species being oystercatcher *Haematopus ostralegus* (66 pairs), lapwing (96 pairs), snipe (224 pairs), curlew *Numenius arquata* (129 pairs) and redshank *Tringa totanus* (159 pairs). These totals along with the numbers of breeding wildfowl probably make the Insh Marshes the most important site in mainland Scotland for breeding waterfowl. The Insh Marshes also hold important populations of water rails *Rallus aquaticus*, black-headed gulls *Larus ridibundus*, reed buntings *Emberiza schoeniclus*, grasshopper warbler *Locustella naevia* and sedge warblers *Acrocephalus schoenobaenus*. Additionally the water areas on the marshes provide important fishing sites for breeding ospreys and in winter there is a nationally important hen harrier roost site.

The bird communities of the Insh Marshes are inextricably linked to the unique quality of the mire habitat, which includes lochs, pools, rivers, ditches, marsh, drier land, riverine scrub and fringing woodland interspersed by wet flushes and low-intensity farmland. The key component is the water regime, which is subjected to periodic flooding but maintains throughout the spring and summer a high water table in the marshes. Most of the important birds are reliant on the aquatic conditions prevailing at Insh Marshes; they are birds of wet meadows and marshland.

In 1993, a local public inquiry was held into proposals to lower the water levels in Loch Insh and the surrounding marshes. On other occasions, suggestions have been made to return the marshes to more intensive agriculture but in present-day terms such ideas are not economic nor in line with the requirements of the natural environment. The latest proposals involved a lowering of the water table by 27 cm which is well in excess of the 20 cm level recognized as crucial to breeding waders. The case put forward by SNH and the RSPB convinced the Reporter that the drainage proposals should not go ahead.

FARMLAND AND SETTLEMENTS

Farming is an integral part of the countryside in the Cairngorms area and has been in varying ways for over four thousand years. Nowadays, livestock rearing of suckled calves and store lambs is the principal enterprise, with the better land used for the production of winter fodder such as silage, hay, rape and turnips. The natural heritage of the Cairngorms has been influenced by farming practices since early Neolithic times when man first arrived with his flocks of celtic shorthorns, sheep and pigs. At this time, the original wild ox were still living in Scotland and the forest ecosystem naturally included these large herbivores. Land under cultivation and grazing gradually increased through the millenia in line with the slow increase in human population. By the twelfth to fourteenth centuries, the clan system was involved in corn and livestock production as well as cattle stealing from the richer lowlands. But life for the peasantry was extremely difficult with meagre food supplies, and the weather-related famine of 1690 wiped out half the rural population.

Major agricultural advances in the eighteenth century included the arrival of potatoes, turnips, planted hay crops and improved oats. By the end of the eighteenth century much of the land was used for livestock grazing and cultivation, with summer shielings in the remotest glens, such as Loch Avon. These were the times of the highest rural population in the area and the use and modification of the land was intense. A dramatic rise in sheep rearing for wool took place at the end of the century and this involved major changes in land use. To accomodate the sheep, not only were people displaced but huge tracts of land were burned and cleaned up for sheep grazings. Subsequently, as a plentiful supply of wool was imported from the colonies, sheep walks were converted to sporting estates. This century has seen a decline in upland farming as crofts and hill farms were abandoned, amalgamated and mechanized. Many of the old practices, such as stooking and threshing of corn, became redundant. Now, a slimmed-down farming scene is nevertheless still an important feature of the landscape.

Farming in the Highlands has been part and parcel of our landscape for so long that some species are now found here only in association with farmland, for example grey partridge *Perdix perdix*. Despite the serious conflicts in recent decades between wildlife and agriculture, farmland in the Cairngorms area is an important nature conservation habitat.

When man first cleared forested land for cultivation and grazing, birds of the open ground like skylark *Alauda arvensis*, meadow pipit *Anthus pratensis*, curlew and red grouse, as well as mammals like brown hare and field vole, took advantage of the new situation. In general birds of open land have benefited and forest species have declined in numbers and distribution as the forests have shrunk over the centuries. Herds of domestic cattle often created ideal grassland for species like curlew and lapwings, while birds such as jackdaws *Corvus*

monedula and starlings *Sturnus vulgaris* found plentiful insect food in the cattle dung. Over time many such associations have built up.

The extensive network of oat fields in the hill districts in the last century was of great benefit to small seed-eating birds like twite, yellowhammer *Emberiza citrinella* and corn bunting. The latter is now extinct in the area and the other two are scarce birds. Gamebirds, such as red and black grouse and grey partridges also frequented the oatfields and the whole process of cutting, stooking sheaves, building stacks and wintertime threshing created ideal feeding conditions for many birds and small mammals. Cultivation and wet grazing land provided ideal habitats for a whole range of birds including waders, gulls, thrushes and finches, while the old hay meadows were used by corncrakes, sadly no longer a feature of our farms.

It would be incorrect to give the impression that old style agriculture was totally benign to nature. There were considerable losses of native woodland, scrub and wetland, and there was the direct pressure on sensitive species. The introduction of large hirsels of sheep into the Highlands at the end of the eighteenth century had dramatic effects on the native vegetation. After a century of burning and heavy grazing, woodland and scrub regeneration had been curtailed and the selective grazing by sheep was changing the composition of plant communities. More recently, some improved farming practices have damaged wildlife interests, for example improved drainage, chemical sprays and fertilizers and intensive silage grassland.

Nevertheless, compared to most of the British Isles the farmed environment of the Cairngorms area remains rich and diverse. The new ESA schemes introduced in 1994 should enhance this resource which is still rich in wildlife and flora. The recent Red Data book of birds in Britain (Batten, L. *et al.*, 1990) lists 117 species whose populations in Britain are threatened or of conservation significance. Thirty-nine of them occur on farm holdings in the Cairngorms area and a further 17 of 30 species in a second tier of candidate species also occur. Over 130 species of birds regularly occur on farm holdings in the area, which illustrates its importance for birds.

In general traditional farming systems as practised in the Cairngorms area are valuable for nature conservation especially because of their close association with native woodland and moorland. Of particular value for natural heritage are extensive cattle grazing as well as outdoor feeding which, along with the retention of stubbles and the growing of turnips, provide feeding grounds for finches, buntings, thrushes, wildfowl and birds of prey in winter. Spring ploughing provides an important food resource for gulls, waders and passerines prior to egg laying. Rotational cropping and the use of dung enhance soil invertebrates while oat crops are beneficial for a wide variety of wildlife and plants. Field margins and hay meadows are important for flowering plants, insects and birds, such as grey partridges, and wet grazing pastures are crucial for breeding waders.

51

RARE BIRD COLONISTS

The Cairngorms and the glens surrounding the high mountains have been renowned as a place where the most exciting rare birds from northern lands might remain and breed. Usually these species are winter visitors to Scotland or migratory species and the generally accepted view is that the period of cooling climate in the late 1960s and 1970s has encouraged some of them to breed here in habitats which are similar to their more usual haunts in Scandinavia.

These birds make the area very special for bird-watching and there is always the possibility of finding a new breeding species for Scotland. Crane, smew *Mergus albellus*, spotted redshank *Tringa erythropus*, waxwing *Bombycilla garrulus*, great grey shrike *Lanius excubitor* and marsh warbler *Acrocephalus palustris* have all been seen in the spring in suitable nesting habitats, while thrush nightingale *Luscinia luscinia* and river warbler *Locustella fluviatilus* are other potential colonists. Red-necked phalaropes *Phalaropus lobatus* nested for several seasons in Strathspey in the 1980s. These occurrences of rare northern breeders (Table 4e) also give us the opportunity to study the movement of breeding species on the very edge of their range and to try to understand the influence of climatic changes on bird species.

Table 4e   Rare bird species which have colonized, attempted to colonize or re-colonized Scotland and the first time of breeding in the Cairngorms area

Temminck's stint 1934	Lapland bunting 1977
Osprey 1954	Red-backed shrike 1977
Green sandpiper* 1959	Purple sandpiper 1978
Bluethroat 1968	Brambling 1979
Wood sandpiper 1968	Parrot crossbill 1991
Wryneck 1969	Icterine warbler 1992
Goldeneye 1970	Scarlet rosefinch 1992
Shore lark* 1973	

* indicates species which have bred nowhere else in UK

MAMMALS

Thirty-four species of mammals occur in the Cairngorms area but seven of these are of introduced or feral species. Unlike the bird fauna, some of the most impressive and ecological important species were exterminated in Scotland. European beaver *Castor fiber*, brown bear *Ursus arctos*, wolf *Canis lupus*, lynx *Felis lynx*, elk *Alces alces*, wild boar *Sus scrofa*, wild auroch *Bos taurus*, reindeer *Rangifer rangifer* and polecat *Mustela putorius* have all long since disappeared although a small herd of feral reindeer has been established in the Cairngorms, while ferret/polecat ferrets have escaped and are breeding in the wild in a few places. Introduced species include rabbit *Oryctolagus cuniculus*, grey squirrel *Sciurus carolinensis*, american mink *Mustela vison*, sika deer *Cervus nippon* and feral goat *Capra hircus*.

At the present time the most influential wild mammal in the Cairngorms area especially in relation to the natural environment is the red deer *Cervus elaphus*. The population has increased markedly this century and is having a serious effect on tree regeneration. This species is examined in detail in Chapter 11. Roe deer *Capreolus capreolus* are widespread and their numbers are also too high in many areas and are affecting the species diversity of the woody plants of the forest floor.

Many of the rodents commonly found in the British Isles occur in the area but two species which are of interest and require further study are water vole *Arvicola terrestris* and water shrew *Neomys fodiens*. The clear streams in the hills may be important habitats for these species, especially the former which is becoming scarce elsewhere. Strathspey, upper Donside, the Dee valley and the glens in the south and west of the area are all inhabited by the commoner three species of bats. A great deal of recent survey has been undertaken into the distribution of pipistrelle *Pipistrellus pipistrellus*, Daubenton's *Myotis daubentoni* and brown long-eared bats *Plecotus auritus*, while Natterer's bat *Myotis nattereri* has also been recorded. Mountain hare *Lepus timidus* (Plate 36) numbers are still very high in the east and south of the Cairngorms area but in the west the animal has declined during this century. Red squirrels *Sciurus vulgaris* (Plate 37) are still plentiful in the pine forests and numbers fluctuate with the cone crops on the Scots pine. Some initial studies are being undertaken in Abernethy Forest but like many of the smaller mammals rather little detailed study has been undertaken. In contrast badgers *Meles meles* and otters *Lutra lutra* have been intensively researched in both Strathspey and Deeside. Hans Kruuk and his colleagues from ITE studied the badgers in the area from Glen Feshie in Badenoch to Tulloch in Strathspey between 1975 and 1981. Their pioneering work on badger populations and their ecology in the Cairngorms area was published in the book, *The Social Badger* (Kruuk, 1989). Badger distribution and populations in the Cairngorms area have been surveyed recently.

Wild cats *Felis silvestris* are thinly distributed throughout the area although some of the highest densities are lower down in the glens where rabbits are plentiful. There was evidence of an increase in numbers and a spread in distribution in the 1950s after many decades of persecution. Numbers have increased since that time but persecution is sadly still widespread. Hybridization is taking place with domestic cats and there is concern over the genetic purity of Scottish wildcat (Easterbee *et al.*, 1991). Nevertheless it is still possible to observe wildcats which have all the visual characteristics of the species. Considering the length of time that domestic cats have been present it is surprising this relative purity remains. It is unacceptable that this superb animal is still actively persecuted and this should cease. There should be an attempt to establish areas free of feral domestic cats, where people keeping house cats should be encouraged to have them neutered to prevent chance breeding with wild cats.

Plate 25 *(left)*
Heather-blaeberry *(Calluna vulgaris - Vaccinium myrtillus)* heath community. Culblean Hill near Dinnet. Photo: Charles Gimingham.

Plate 26 *(above)*
Moss campion *(Silene acaulis)* on Cairn Gorm. August 1987. Photo: Charles Gimingham.

Plate 27
Heather 'stripes', or waves, on an exposed slope above Coire na Ciste, Cairn Gorm *(left)*, and close up *(above)*. July 1981.
Photos: Charles Gimingham.

Plate 28
Exposed plateau with three-leaved rush *(Juncus trifidus)*. Beinn Mheadhoin and Beinn a' Bhuird on skyline. September 1964.
Photo: Charles Gimingham.

Plate 34 *(left)*
Scottish crossbill. Found only in Scotland, where it inhabits the older Scots pine woods. Photo: S. Rae.

Plate 35 *(centre)*
Capercaillie. A characteristic species of coniferous forest reintroduced to Scotland in 1837 after it had become extinct. Photo: S. Rae.

Plate 36 *(below left)*
Mountain hare. White-coated in winter, mountain hares are abundant in parts of the Cairngorms. Photo: Roy Dennis.

Plate 37 *(below right)*
Red squirrel. Although its range in Britain has been severely reduced, the red squirrel is still fairly plentiful in the pinewoods of the Cairngorms. Photo: Brian Staines.

Plates 38–41 *(above, left to right)*: some Red Data Book insects of the Cairngorms.

Plate 38 *Coccinella quinquepunctata* Linn. (Coleoptera, Coccinellidae) – five-spot ladybird. Widely distributed, but local, associated mainly with river shingle on the River Spey. Photo: Iain MacGowan.

Plate 39 *Rhadiurgus variabilis* (Zett.) (Diptera, Asilidae). Almost confined to the eastern Highlands where it occurrs on river shingles and within conifer woodlands. Photo: Iain MacGowan.

Plate 40 *Callicera rufa* Schummel (Diptera, Syrphidae). Fairly widespread in coniferous woodlands, requiring rot holes in living trees or water pockets on cut stumps for larval development. Photo: Iain MacGowan.

Plate 41 *Spiriverpa lunulata* (Zett.) (Diptera, Therevidae). Usually on river shingles in the central Highlands. Photo: Iain MacGowan.

Plate 42 *(above, far right)*
The emperor moth *Saturnia pavonia* (Linn.) (Lepidoptera). Larvae feed on heather, and the moth is common on heaths and moors. Photo: Iain MacGowan.

Plate 43 *(centre)*
A 'Malaise trap' – one of the methods available for studying insects. Photo: Iain MacGowan.

Plate 44 *(below)*
Sap run on a pine tree – one of the microhabitats which are importants for rare insects. Photo: Iain MacGowan.

Plate 45 *(below)* River shingle habitat, River Feshie – a type of habitat associated with rare communities of insects, especially Diptera and Coleoptera (see also Plates 38, 39 and 41 above). Photo: Iain MacGowan.

In recent years, there have been increasing numbers of pine martens *Martes martes* in the Cairngorms area and the species is now breeding in Badenoch & Strathspey and in upper Banffshire. It is likely to continue its southwards expansion. It is encouraging to see the recovery of some predatory mammals which were extensively persecuted and reduced in numbers in the last two centuries. In such vastly changed times and with such an interest in re-establishing large areas of native forests, the restoration of the whole ecosystem is foremost in our minds. Now the question is whether some of the larger mammals, like beaver, wild boar and lynx, should be returned to play their part in restoring the real ecological health of these very special habitats. In my view they should, for without the full range of species it is difficult to see how the special areas of the Cairngorms and its forests can be classed as fully recovered.

REFERENCES

Batten, L. *et al.* (1990) *Red Data Birds In Britain.* Poyser, London.

Bhatia, Z. (1993) Breeding waterfowl of Insh Marshes. RSPB, Sandy.

BOU (1971) *The Status of Birds in Britain and Ireland.* Blackwell, Oxford.

Brown, P. & Waterston, G. (1962) *The Return of the Osprey.* Collins, London.

Buckland, S.T., Bell, M.V. & Picozzi, N. (1990) *The Birds of North-East Scotland.* North-east Scotland Bird Club, Aberdeen.

Cook, M.J.H. (1982) Breeding status of the crested tit. *Scot. Birds* **12**, 97–106.

Cook, M. (1992) *The Birds of Moray and Nairn.* Mercat Press, Edinburgh.

Dennis, R. (1984) *The Birds of Badenoch & Strathspey.* Inverness.

Dennis, R. (1987) Boxes for Goldeneyes. *Conservation Review* **1**, 85–87.

Dennis, R. (1993) Goldeneye. In: Gibbons, D.W. *et al.*, eds, *The New Atlas of Breeding Birds in Britain and Ireland: 1988–91.* Poyser, London. pp 88–89.

Dennis, R. (1995) *The Birds of Badenoch and Strathspey.* Colin Baxter, Grantown-on-Spey.

Easterbee, N., Hepburn, L.V. & Jefferies, D.J. (1991) *Survey of the Status and Distribution of the Wildcat in Scotland, 1983–1987.* Nature Conservancy Council for Scotland, Edinburgh.

Etheridge, B. & Summers, R.W. (1993) Nest survival and productivity of Hen Harriers breeding in different habitats. Paper read at Ecology and Conservation of Harriers Symposium. Canterbury.

Gordon, S. (1925) *The Cairngorm Hills of Scotland.* Cassell, London.

Harvie-Brown, J.A. & Buckley, T.E. (1895) *A Vertebrate Fauna of the Moray Basin* (2 vols). Douglas, Edinburgh.

Harvie-Brown, J.A. (1906) *A Vertebrate Fauna of the Tay Basin and Strathmore.* Douglas, Edinburgh.

Kruuk, H. (1989) *The Social Badger.* Oxford University Press, Oxford.

Macpherson, H.B. (1909) *The Home-Life of a Golden Eagle.* Witherby, London.

Nethersole-Thompson, D. (1966) *The Snow Bunting.* Oliver & Boyd, Edinburgh.

Nethersole-Thompson, D. (1973) *The Dotterel.* Collins, London.

Nethersole-Thompson, D. & Watson, A. (1974) *The Cairngorms. Their Natural History and Scenery.* Collins, London.

Nethersole-Thompson, D. (1975) *Pine Crossbills.* Poyser, Berkhamsted.

Pritchard, D.E. *et al.* (1992) *Important Bird Areas of the United Kingdom.* RSPB/JNCC, Sandy.

Smith, R.D. (1995) Snow buntings: the behavioural ecology and site use of an itinerant flock species in the non-breeding season. Unpublished thesis, University of Glasgow.

Steven, H.M. & Carlisle, A. (1959) *The Native Pinewoods of Scotland.* Oliver & Boyd, London & Edinburgh.

Thompson, D.B.A. & Whitfield, D.P. (1993) Dotterel. In: *The New Atlas of Breeding Birds.* Poyser, London. pp. 166–167.

Watson, A. & Rae, S. (1987). Dotterel numbers, habitats, and breeding success in Scotland. *Scot. Birds* **14**, 191–198.

Watson, A. & Rae, S. (1993) Ptarmigan. In: *The New Atlas of Breeding Birds.* Poyser, London. pp. 128–129.

CHAPTER 5
Insects of the Cairngorms

M.R. YOUNG AND K.R. WATT

There has been only one substantial account of the insects of the Cairngorms, that of Welch (1974), and it is disappointing to report that in the succeeding years little extra information has been published. Welch concentrated on cataloguing the rare and characteristic species of the Cairngorm habitats, rather than reporting on ecological studies, for the very good reason that such studies did not then exist. That position has hardly changed. This chapter sets out to provide an update of the status of some of the rarer species but mainly to review the small number of recent studies that have included some ecological work.

The dramatic environmental extremes of the Cairngorms, especially on the plateau, have a greater impact on insects than on most other groups of animals, because their cold-bloodedness and small size mean that they are especially susceptible to adverse conditions and can only be active for very limited periods. The second part of this circular argument is that they often show particularly interesting adaptations that allow them to operate effectively even in difficult circumstances. They do not, however, show one of the predominant behavioural responses of mammals and birds: there is probably not a single example of an insect species that migrates to lower ground in winter, but breeds on the plateau in the summer.

In a general sense insects show a set of features that influence the life-style that they must lead. These include small size; potentially short generation times with no 'resistant' stages; high reproductive and mate-finding ability but little

emphasis on mate selection; highly specific 'niches' usually with a very restricted foodplant range; and rather high mobility for their size (Young, 1992). In consequence they are often very localized by foodplant and micro-climate; show wide and rapid population changes in response to short-lived environmental conditions (with relatively frequent local extinctions and re-colonizations); and require a continuity of conditions from year to year to accommodate their short generation time. Such conditions are best provided by extensive areas of semi-natural habitats, as is so effectively provided by the Cairngorms. The insect communities of the main habitat types are specialized, of long standing and are undoubtedly of major national significance. Although the species richness is constrained by the low number of plant species present and by the extreme climate, the importance of the insect assemblages cannot be overstated.

The presence of known rarities attracts many visiting entomologists but it is still true, as lamented by Welch (1974), that most revisit well-known localities, generally near Aviemore, so our knowledge of the wider distribution of the Cairngorm specialities is depressingly limited. Some parts, such as the hills south of the Feshie and Geldie streams, have hardly ever been worked, whereas Cairn Gorm itself and the northern corries are comparatively well studied. Each year brings a small harvest of new distribution records and there have been a few intensive surveys of specific locations in the last 20 years, as reported below, but research studies have been very scarce, with the notable exception of the recent work of members of the Malloch Society, who have studied Diptera both on the plateau and those associated with dead wood of aspen, birch and pine in woodlands. Smith (1997) has recently made an intensive study on the crane-flies of the plateau around Glas Maol. There are obvious reasons for this relative dearth of new information, for insects can be surveyed and studied only in equable weather conditions and so visiting entomologists may find that the whole of their stay passes without a single suitable day for upland field work. Such problems encourage concentration on lowland habitats, where the weather has less effect, and the precious few hours of good weather are understandably spent at localities already known to be rich in rare species.

INSECTS OF THE HIGH TOPS

There have been many brief visits to the plateau by entomologists since 1974 but only four studies that included repeated visits and only three of these can be regarded as having an ecological input.

MacAlpine (1979) reports on an extensive survey carried out from March to September 1976, late July and August 1977 and mid-August and early September 1978, when he ran portable light traps at eight locations in Cairngorms NNR and also spent many hours searching for Lepidoptera. Most of his trap sites were at low levels but he also included higher altitudes, when conditions allowed, and certainly netted specimens on the plateau; however all his recording was done from the Speyside side of the Cairngorms and in the northern part of the reserve. He accumulated records for 387 species, compared to the previous total of 115, indicating that even for well-studied groups, like moths and butterflies, our knowledge is far from complete.

Amongst MacAlpine's captures were several species known to be restricted to the plateau, such as the 'grass' moth *Crambus furcatellus*, but he did not record any rare species as new to the general area and his only captures of listed rarities were at lower elevations, except that he comments particularly on the capture in 1976 of specimens of the black mountain moth *Psodos coracina* on Cairn Gorm, noting that this should have been the 'wrong' year for them. This draws attention to a regular feature in the life history strategy of montane and northern insects, namely that they may take more than one year to complete their larval growth and development, in the cool, short northern seasons, and may then emerge in synchrony every other year. It seems to be true that many northern Lepidoptera show this feature and there are certainly other upland examples, although they do not necessarily show synchronous emergence (Young, 1997).

A related life history trait is for the pupal stage to last a variable time; in the case of the Kentish glory moth *Endromis versicolora* this may be as long as seven years, with the obvious advantage in a northern climate that not all adults will emerge into what might be an impossibly inclement year. Tutt (1902) refers to this and Leverton (1993) regards it as a common strategy in northern Lepidoptera, even at low elevations, and he is steadily accumulating breeding records which bear this out.

Recently, there here has been a substantial attempt to study the higher Diptera of Scotland's mountains (Horsfield & MacGowan, 1998). These workers used 174 sample sites, many of which were from the Cairngorms and all above the putative tree line. From these they collected many species of larger flies but some were obvious strays from below or were species found widely on moors at all altitudes. They identified 21 which they believe are found only on the high tops (linking them to three others which they did not find but which are similarly identified in the literature) and of these, nine are widespread on mountains throughout Britain; six are found widely on Scottish mountains; three are western in distribution; and six seem to be localized to the Grampian mountains, three being further restricted to the Cairngorms, namely *Wiedemannia impudica*, *Alliopsis albipennis* and *Delia pilifemur*. (However, these three were also the ones not found in the present study and they may eventually be discovered to be more widespread.)

None of the characteristic species is endemic to the Scottish mountains, most are reasonably widely distributed elsewhere and their ranges are variously boreal, arctic, boreo-alpine and alpine, indicating a unique breadth in the origin of the Cairngorm fauna – but there is little further known of the ecological requirements of these species. Horsfield and MacGowan found that the greatest diversity and abundance of the insect catches was from mid-May to June, in some cases closely following the snow melt, and this is in strong contrast to the July peak in the lowlands. This may be to allow the resultant larvae to have a sufficiently long growing season, before the advent of winter, to have accumulated enough food reserves to survive, but this is merely speculation at present. They also suggest that it is the low mean summer temperatures that act to limit the distribution of these montane flies in Britain but, without knowledge of the eco-physiological adaptations of the species concerned, this remains speculative.

Smith (1997) and Smith *et al.* (2001) investigated the ecology of the crane-fly *Tipula montana* on the summit plateau of Glas Maol. He found that the larvae have a two-year development period but that there is not complete synchrony, so that some adults emerge each year. Many larvae become 'trapped' on snowbeds in spring and they, and adults, are clearly important prey for upland birds.

It was noted above that many of the insects caught on the plateau actually originated at lower altitudes and this phenomenon has been reported frequently, especially with reference to organisms becoming stranded on snow patches. Watson and Stroyan (1984), for example, found aphids in sufficient numbers to form a scum on pools and to discolour snow patches, and in this case they were able to relate that to migration from the summer hosts by the aphids, which were then blown on to the Cairngorms by uphill breezes in calm, warm weather. Ashmole *et al.* (1983) report a detailed and unusually comprehensive study of insects and spiders stranded on snow fields in the Cairngorms, and concluded that the great majority were strays from below. These represent a significant input of organic matter to the plateau, providing food for many upland predators, from snow buntings to mites, and they even found that some widespread predatory flies were moving to the snow fields to take advantage of the food available. Of the 130 species that they collected, only 10 were true montane inhabitants and even fewer were species that live on, below or at the margins of snow. These accumulations of specimens are also of interest for what they tell us about migration in insects and spiders, and they indicate that we tend to underestimate this greatly.

In contrast, Owen and Thaxton (1994), who used pitfall traps to study beetles on A'Choinneach and Ben Macdui in 1987, found only one species, out of their total of 25, which was an obvious stray from below and they categorized 15 of their total as montane. A distinctive feature of their results was that only three species were common to both mountains, despite their proximity and the general similarity of the vegetation. The exact site on A'Choinneach was very slightly sheltered, compared with the Ben Macdui locations, and Owen and Thaxton suggest that this is the most probable reason for the lack of complementarity. Amongst their captures were four species that are boreal in general distribution, including *Amara alpinus*, which is found almost exclusively above 900 metres.

INSECTS OF WOODLANDS

The birch woodlands of Speyside and Deeside are renowned for their rare insects but these have never been fully studied, merely recorded. Currently there is concern that mature and over-mature birches may be becoming less common, even on Speyside, and that this may then adversely affect the insects which depend on them. A symbolic species for these old woods is the Rannoch sprawler moth *Brachionycha nubeculosa*, which emerges in the early spring and has for years been found in the Aviemore area. It is one of the few species that has not also been found on Deeside and the usual, anecdotal explanation is that the birches of Deeside never achieve sufficient age and size, as do those on Speyside. Recently this moth seems to have become less common, although it has still been seen near Kincraig, and this supposed scarcity has been ascribed to the loss of old birch. Despite this concern, no-one has yet studied the Rannoch sprawler and its ecological relationship to the old birch woods. From the scattered literature and by analogy with aspen (see below), there is no doubt that there are many rare species of insect associated with overaged and dead birch trees and with the fungi that help rot them. These await further study.

Equal anxiety has been expressed about the lack of regenerating birch and there has been a study of a characteristic insect of this type of woodland, namely the Kentish glory moth *Endromis versicolora*. This species no longer occurs in Kent but is now restricted to the eastern highland valleys (Young, 1991) and it is only found at all commonly on Speyside and Deeside. The supposed explanation for this was a requirement for extensive areas of regenerating birch, now absent from the old southern haunts of this moth, and this hypothesis was tested by Barbour and Young (1993), who studied the ecology of the species amongst the varied birch woodland at Muir of Dinnet NNR. They found that the female moths choose to lay their egg batches predominantly on the side twigs of birches less than three metres high, when these are in a sheltered but open matrix, as so typically provided by birch regenerating on heathland. By transferring eggs from their usual sheltered position at around one metre, to less protected twigs at three metres height, and then observing the fate of the larvae as they hatched and grew, Barbour and Young showed that the larvae were dislodged and killed from the higher, more exposed positions (see Table 5a). The Kentish glory is a large moth but the females seem to have limited dispersal powers and so, to survive, the species needs a continuity of extensive birch regeneration in contiguous areas and it is to be hoped that this can be accommodated in the Cairngorm valleys in future. The progressive extinction of this moth in other parts of its British range seems to mirror the gradual loss of such regenerative birch.

Table 5a   Characteristics of egg batch sites for the Kentish glory moth and survival of larvae at different heights at Muir of Dinnet NNR, Deeside, in 1989 (Data from Barbour & Young, 1993)

Egg site characteristics (24 batches)

Mean height above ground	1.20 m	(range 0.75–2.10 m)
Mean height of tree used	2.08 m	(range 1.20–3.75 m)
Mean distance from twig tip	0.07 m	(range 0.01–0.20 m)

Survival of larvae at various heights

	Wild larvae	Experimental larvae	
		1m above ground	3m above ground
% hatching	95	78	57
% surviving from hatch			
to 15 June	90	86	47
to 22 June	50	57	25
to 16 July	6	10	0

Owen (1989a and 1989b) recently carried out an exhaustive and highly successful survey of the beetles of the pine woodland in the Loch Garten area and found many of the characteristic rarities of such woods, as well as a water beetle *Agabus wasastjernae* new to Britain (Owen *et al.*, 1992). He has recorded 868 species of beetle from the area so far and is still finding new species each year (Owen, *in litt.*). Amongst these are a number of rare species and in many cases these are more common than originally thought, but the sampling effort needed to produce this impressive result was very great. Owen also made the point that to find each species often needs a precise collecting technique, so that the full assemblage of beetles cannot be adequately surveyed in a general way. He searched blossom, sieved birds nests, used pitfall traps, collected from dead wood and basically searched in every way available. This is undoubtedly reflected in his final total, much greater than the total produced by Young, Armstrong and Edgar (1991) for beetles collected using a standardized and generalized sampling routine at Abernethy (see Table 5b). The specificity of the habitat requirements of many of the Loch Garten beetles underlines the need to conserve the full range of microhabitats found in native woodlands (Plate 44).

In places the remaining pinewoods now have a managed nature, being either young plantations or rather uniform old stands and Young, Armstrong and Edgar (1991) set out to establish whether such managed areas have a value in terms of their insect fauna. Matched plantations, mature but uniform, and semi-natural stands were selected at Abernethy (Speyside) and Glen Tanar (Deeside) and pitfall and water traps (and to a lesser extent many other methods (Plate 43)), were used to collect insects over two seasons. Such methods collect only a limited sub-set of the full insect community but the replicated nature of the sampling allowed reliable, quantitative conclusions to be drawn from the study. In the context of these managed stands being part of very extensive and inter-mixed native pinewoods at Abernethy and Glen Tanar, it was found that they actually added to the richness of the insect fauna, without detracting from it (see Table 5b). The plantations seemed to offer a sheltered environment, which was used beneficially by many species in windy weather, although some of these species bred only in the semi-natural stands; and the mature

uniform zones also harboured their full share of insects. It seems unlikely that isolated commercial woodlands could have the same value but, from the insects' point of view, it is clear that some managed plots can be accepted in extensive native forests. However, this study did not use collecting techniques specifically aimed at saproxylic species and so those are under-represented. It is known that many rare species depend on old and decaying wood and these will thrive only in 'semi-natural' stands. Many examples of such species are listed on pp. 59–63.

Recently Malloch Society members have been studying the flies and beetles associated with old aspen stands and their results are summarized by MacGowan (1993). By concentrating their attention on specific collecting techniques and visiting many aspen stands that had not been collected from before, they located many rare species, often extending the known range of these considerably and even finding a previously undescribed species of fly, *Ectaetia christii* (Rotheray & Horsfield, 1997). Of special interest is *Hammerschmidtia ferruginea*, which is a rare and renowned indicator of ancient aspen, previously only found near Speybridge. Its larvae live under the bark of large, fallen aspen trunks, feeding on the bacteria and fungi which are decaying the wood, and a particular search was made for these larvae. The result was that several new sites were discovered, even beyond the Cairngorms area, but always still in stands of very old trees. This study has also demonstrated that there is a recognizable 'community' of fly species associated with old aspens and that there are a limited number of woodlands where these still occur. These woodlands are of crucial significance for the conservation of the characteristic insects of aspen.

INSECTS OF LOWLAND HEATHLANDS

The abundant heaths on acidic soils in the Cairngorms, dominated by ling heather *Calluna vulgaris*, harbour an insect community that is obvious, from the abundance of such visible species as emperor moths *Saturnia pavonia* (Plate 42) or common heath moths *Ematurga atomaria*, but this community does not differ from that of similar heaths anywhere else in upland Britain. In contrast there are distinctive and rare insect species which are associated with species-rich bearberry *Arctostaphylos uva-ursi* heaths (NVC H16, both *Pyrola* and *Vaccinium* sub-communities; Rodwell, 1991), where these occur at low altitudes, and together they comprise a highly localized and scarce assemblage, which is predominantly found on Speyside and Deeside and is of national significance. Regrettably there have been no ecological studies specifically concerned with this assemblage, but there have been some distribution surveys which serve to shed a little light on the natural history of the rarer species (Young, 1989).

An interesting distinction can be drawn between those insect species, such as the netted mountain moth *Semiothisa carbonaria*, whose larva feeds on bearberry itself, which extend at least up to 700 m, and the more common pattern of restriction to the

Table 5b The number of insect taxa recorded in standardized samples from a series of plots at Forest Lodge NNR, Abernethy, Speyside, in 1986 and 1987

	Stand type			
	Plantation	Uniform mature	Semi-natural mature (2 stands)	
Number of taxa	417	382	358	359
Overall number of taxa		592		

Data from Young, Armstrong & Edgar, 1991

heaths of the valley floors, as exemplified by the larval case-bearing moths *Coleophora arctostaphyli* and *C. genistae*, whose foodplants are bearberry and petty whin *Genista anglica* respectively. It is the lowland assemblage that is so localized and rare and there are no known examples of insects of *Arctostaphylos* that are exclusively upland. It would be most interesting to compare the ecology of *S. carbonaria* with that of a lowland inhabitant, such as the small dark yellow underwing *Anarta cordigera*, both of whom emerge as adults in May.

The composition of this distinctive fauna seems to be controlled principally by the bearberry itself, for most of the rare insects use it directly as a food resource. The associated plant species, however, do have some role, for, apart from the petty whin referred to above, bitter vetch *Lathyrus montanus* also hosts rare insects, notably the moth *Leucoptera orobi*, very recently rediscovered at Tulloch, some years after its apparent loss from Britain.

THE DEFOLIATION OF UPLAND HEATHLANDS BY MOTH LARVAE

A most interesting but worrying recent occurrence on some areas of mid-altitude heath has been defoliation of heather and blaeberry *Vaccinium myrtillus* by the larvae of the winter moth *Operophtera brumata* (Hartley, 1993). The winter moth is a frequent defoliator of deciduous forest trees (and has recently begun to eat spruce as well), but the addition of heather takes the species into an entirely new habitat. Outbreaks have been observed in other parts of Scotland, including Orkney, but the problem has recently been studied in the Cairngorms, with the aim of determining which factors encourage the moths to begin feeding on ling and whether control is a realistic option. Infected areas of heather may be severely checked and killed and Kerslake *et al.* (1996) suggest that this may allow grass to become established instead.

RARE INSECTS IN THE CAIRNGORMS

Prior to the advent of the Biological Records Centre in the 1960s, our knowledge of the status and distribution of even our large and highly visible insect species was haphazard and incomplete and this applied with special force to remote places like the Cairngorms. The work of the various distribution schemes began to improve matters and this process was focused on and continued by the Nature Conservancy Council and its successor bodies, particularly by the Joint Nature Conservation Committee. The important end-products of this attention are the Red Data Book (Insects) (Shirt, 1987) and the series covering various orders called collectively 'A Review of the Scarce and Threatened . . .[Order Name] . . .of Great Britain' (Falk, 1991a and 1991b; Hyman and Parsons, 1992; Kirby, 1992).

These publications list those species which are found in fewer than a given number of 10 km National Grid squares, or only a known number of localities, under a series of categories ranging from Red Data Book (RDB1), for species which are

Table 5c   A summary of the numbers of rare insects found in the Cairngorms

Overall no. of RDB1 – RDB3 found in Cairngorms (plus Notables found only in Cairngorms)		262
These comprise:	RDB1 (Endangered)	25
	RDB2 (Vulnerable)	26
	RDB3 (Rare)	80
Representation by order:	Diptera	105
	Coleoptera	97
	Lepidoptera	30
	Hemiptera	9
	Hymenoptera	15
	Odonata	2
	Trichoptera	2
	Ephemeroptera	1
	Plecoptera	1
Representation by habitat:		
	Montane	54
	Wetlands	68
	Grasslands	29
	Heaths	31
	Woods overall	129
	pine	36
	birch	13
	aspen	10

(RDB=Red Data Book)

exceedingly rare and threatened, to Notable for those which are merely scarce and local. Each Order account also collates briefly what is known of the ecology of each species, whether they are declining and the nature of the threats they face. Whilst these lists represent a dramatic advance on the anecdotal evidence of the past, they are only as good as the survey information that they summarize and this is still rather thin and unequal in its coverage. The apparent authority of the lists must not be allowed to suggest that our knowledge of Cairngorm insects is anything other than patchy and incomplete. A selection of the rarest species has recently been listed (Anon, 1995) for inclusion in *Biodiversity: the UK Steering Group Report*. As part of the Government's response to the Biodiversity Convention, signed at the 'Rio Summit', these species are each having a 'species action plan' prepared to assist their conservation. These fall into two groups: 'Priority Species' and 'Species of Conservation Concern'. A further recent development is that the Cairngorms Partnership is preparing a 'Biodiversity Action Plan' for the Cairngorms area and, as a preliminary to this, Leaper (1998) has produced a species audit, recording the scarce species in the area.

We have extracted the data that apply to the Cairngorms from these sources (and from Ackland, 1989; Ball and Morris, 1992; Drake, 1991; Edwards, 1933; Rotheray and Robertson, 1993; and Stubbs, 1992); have consulted widely amongst other entomologists and have summarized the data in

Provisional list of rare and notable Cairngorm species of insects

(Note that for ease of reference this list is arranged alphabetically within Orders and Families)

ORDER/FAMILY	SPECIES	STATUS		HABITAT
COLEOPTERA				
Carabidae	*Agonum quadripunctatum* (Degeer)	R1	+	woodland, heath
	Amara alpina (Paykull)	R3	+ c	montane, grassland, wet heath
	Dyschirus angustatus (Ahrens)	R3	+ p	
	Elaphrus lapponicus Gyllenhal	Nt	+	montane, wetland
	Leistus montanus Stephens	Nt	+	montane
	Nebria nivalis (Paykull)	Nt	+	montane, moss & lichen heath
	Pelophila borealis (Paykull)	R3	+	wetland, moorland
Cerambycidae	*Leptura sanguinolenta* Linn.	R3	+	woodland (pine)
	Tetropeum castaneum (Linn.)	R3		woodland
Chrysomelidae	*Cryptocephalus decemmaculatus* (Linn.)	R2	+ p	woodland (sallow, birch)
	Cryptocephalus coryli (Linnaeus)	R1(ext.)	+ c	woodland (decid.)
	Donacia aquatica (Linn.)	R3	+ p	wetland
	Phyllodecta polaris Schneider	R3	+	montane in *Racomitrium* moss
Cisidae	*Cis coluber* Abeille	R3	+	woodland (decid.), fungus or under bark
	Cis dentatus Mellie	R3	–	woodland (conif.)
	Rhopalodontus perforatus (Gyllenhal)	R3	+	woodland (birch), fungus
Cleridae	*Thanasimus rufipes* (Brahm)	R3	+	woodland (pine)
Coccinellidae	*Coccinella quinquepunctata* Linn. (Plate 38)	R3	+	river shingle
Cryptophagidae	*Atomaria badia* Erichson	R?	–	woodland (pine)
	Atomaria bella Reitter	R?	–	woodland (pine)
	Atomaria hislopi Wollaston	R?	+	woodland (conif.)
	Atomaria ornata Heer	R?	+	woodland (pine)
	Atomaria procerula Erichson	R?	+	woodland (decid. & conif.)
	Cercyon alpinus Vogt	R?	–	woodland (pine)
	Cryptophagus badius Sturm	R?	–	woodland (squirrel dreys)
	Cryptophagus lapponicus Gyllenhal	R?	–	woodland (squirrel dreys)
	Micrambe bimaculatus (Panzer)	R?	+	woodland (conif.)
	Micrambe lindbergorum (Bruce)	R?	+	woodland (pine)
Cucujidae	*Uleiota planata* (Linn.)	R2	–	woodland (beech, birch, pine)
Curculionidae	*Dorytomus affinis* (Paykull)	R2	–	woodland (aspen)
	Lepyrus capucinus (Schaller)	R(ext.)	–(S)	wetland, woodland (*Salix*)
	Pissodes validirostris (Sahlberg)	R3	+	woodland (pine)
	Rhynchaenus testaceus (Muller)	R2	+ p	woodland (alder)
Dytiscidae	*Agabus wasastjernae* Sahlberg	R?	–	woodland (pine), wetland
Elateridae	*Ampedus tristis* (Linn.)	R2	+	woodland (pine)
	Negastrius pulchellus (Linn.)	R2	+	wetland, shingle
Hydrophilidae	*Cercyon alpinus* Vogt	R?		woodland (pine), deer dung
Lathridiidae	*Corticaria latipennis* (Sahlberg)	R?	–	woodland (pine)
	Corticaria longicollis (Zett.)	R?	+	ancient woodland (oak)
	Enicmus rugosus (Herbst)	R2	–	woodland
Leiodidae	*Agathidium arcticum* Thomson	R?	+	woodland, fungus
	Catops nigriclavis Gerhardt	R?	+	mole nests
	Colon angulare Erichson	R?	+	woodland
	Colon viennense Herbst	R?	+	grassland, woodland (decid.)
	Leiodes flavescens (Schmidt)	R?	+	subterranean fungus
	Leiodes picea (Panzer)	R?	+	woodland (decid.), subterranean fungus
	Leiodes silesiaca (Kraatz)	R?	–	subterranean fungus
Melandryidae	*Abdera affinis* (Paykull)	R1	–	woodland (birch), fungus
Nitidulidae	*Epuraea silacea* (Herbst)	R3	+	woodland (birch), fungus
	Epuraea terminalis (Mannerheim)	R?	+	woodland (birch), sap
	Epuraea variegata (Herbst)	R?	+	woodland, fungus
Oedemeridae	*Chrysanthia nigricornis* (Westhoff)	R1	–	woodland (pine)
Peltidae	*Ostoma ferrugineum* (Linn.)	R1	–	woodland (pine)
Pselaphidae	*Euplectus bescidicus* Reitter	R?	+	woodland (mixed)
	Euplectus decipiens Raffray	R?	+	woodland
	Euplectus punctatus Mulsant	R3	+	woodland (birch & pine)
Ptiliidae	*Ptiliolum caledonicum* (Sharp)	R?	–	woodland (pine)
	Ptiliolum schwarzi (Flach)	R?	–(S)	woodland (decid.)
	Ptinella limbata (Heer)	R?	+	woodland (decid. & conif.)

ORDER/ FAMILY	SPECIES	STATUS		HABITAT
Rhizophagidae	*Rhizophagus parvulus* (Paykull)	R3	–	woodland (decid.), sap, fungus
Scarabaeidae	*Melolontha hippocastani* Fab.	R?	+	woodland (hawthorn)
Scolytidae	*Pityophhorus lichtensteini* (Ratzburg)	R3	+	woodland (pine)
	Tomicus minor (Hartig)	R3	+	woodland (pine)
Scraptiidae	*Anaspis bohemica* Schilsky	R?	–	woodland (pine)
	Anaspis septentrionalis Champion	R(ext)	–	woodland
Scydmaenidae	*Scydmoraphes sparshalli* (Denny)	R?	+	grassland
Sphaeritidae	*Sphaerites glabratus* (Fab.)	R3	+	woodland, under bark, sap, dung
Staphylinidae	*Aleochara fumata* Gravenhorst	R?	+	woodland, fungus
	Atheta boletophila (Thomson)	R?	–	woodland, fungus
	Atheta clintoni Kevan	R?	–	pastureland
	Atheta procera (Kraatz)	R?	–	woodland, carrion
	Atheta puberula (Sharp)	R?	+	wetland
	Atheta spatuloides Benick	R?	+	woodland
	Atheta sylvicola (Kraatz)	R?	+	wetland, shingle
	Bledius arcticus Sahlberg	R?	–	wetland, shingle
	Bledius terebrans (Schioedte)	R?	+	wetland
	Eudectus whitei Sharp	Nt	+	montane, summit
	Euryporus picipes (Paykull)	R?	+	woodland, moorland
	Gabrius scoticus Joy & Tomlin	R?	–	montane, moss
	Gyrophaena pulchella Heer	R?	+	woodland, fungus
	Hydropora cunctans (Erichson)	R?	+	wetland, heath
	Hydrosmecta delicatula (Sharp)	R?	+	wetland, shingle
	Lathrobium dilutum Erichson	R3	+	wetland, shingle
	Mycetoporus bimaculatus Bois. & Lac.	R?	+	grassland
	Neohilara subterranea (Mulsant & Rey)	R?	+	wetland, woodland (pine)
	Olophrum assimile (Paykull)	R?	–(S)	montane, wetland (moss)
	Paranopleta inhabilis (Kraatz)	R?	+	woodland (conif.)
	Phyllodrepa salicis (Gyllenhal)	R?	+	woodland, squirrel dreys, carrion
	Schistoglossa benicki Lohse	R?	–	moss
	Scopaeus gracilis (Sperk)	R?	+	wetland, shingle
	Staphylinus ophthalmicus Scopoli	R3		wetland
	Stenus glacialis Heer	R?	+	montane, wet moss & dry moss
	Stenus incanus Erichson	R?	+	wetland, shingle
	Tachinus rufipennis Gyllenhal	R3	+	woodland
	Tachyusa scitula Erichson	R?	+	wetland, riverside
	Thinobius major Kraatz	R?	+	wetland, riverside
	Thinobius newberyi Scheerpeltz	R?	+ p	montane, wetland, shingle
Tenebrionidae	*Bolitophaga reticulatus* (Linn.)	R3	+	woodland (birch), fungus

DIPTERA

ORDER/ FAMILY	SPECIES	STATUS		HABITAT
Anisopodidae	*Mycetobia pallipes* Meigen	Nt	+	woodland
	Mycetobia gemella Mamaev	New to GB	–	woodland (pine)
	Mycetobia obscura Mamaev	New to GB	–	woodland (pine, lime, oak)
Anthomyiidae	*Botanophila gentanae* (Pandellé)	New to GB		grassland, upland & lowland
	Delia pilifemur (Ringdahl)	R1	–	montane, heath
	Hydrophoria spiniclunis (Pandelle)	R3	+	montane, grassland, moss heath
	Alliopsis albipennis (Ringdahl)	R1	–	montane summit
	Alliopsis atronitens (Strobl)	R?	+	montane, moss heath, grassland, *Calluna* heath
	Alliopsis similaris Fonseca	R?	–	montane
	Pegohylemyia apicseta (Ringdahl)	R?	+	montane
	Pseudomyopina moriens (Zett.)	R2	+	montane, moss heath, grassland
Asilidae	*Laphria flava* (Linn.)	R3	+ c	woodland (pine)
	Rhadiurgus variabilis (Zett.) (Plate 39)	R3	+	river shingle, pinewood sandy areas
Calliphoridae	*Calliphora alpina* (Zett.)	R3	+	montane, moss heath
Chironomidae	*Pseudorthocladius pilosipennis* Brundin	R?	–	montane, upland
Chloropidae	*Chlorops triangularis* Becker	Nt	+	wetland, wet grassland
Culicidae	*Culiseta alaskaensis* (Ludlow)	R?	–?	
Dolichopodidae	*Dolichopus maculipennis* Zett.	R2		montane, wetland, bryophyte flush, flushed grassland
	Hydrophorus rufibarbis Gerstaekert	Nt	+	montane, aquatic

60

ORDER/FAMILY	SPECIES	STATUS		HABITAT
	Medetera inspissata Collin	R3	+	woodland (aspen)
Empididae	*Clinocera nivalis* (Zett.)	R3	+	montane, moss heath flushes
	Hilara barbipes Frey	R3		wetland
	Hilara setosa Collin	R2 endemic to GB		river shingle [now common]
	Rhamphomyia hirtula Zett.	R3	+	montane, moorland, grassland, moss heath
	Symballophthalmus pictipes (Becker)	R3		
	Weidemannia impudica Mik	R1	–	montane, aquatic
	Weidemannia phantasma Mik	R3	+	lochside
Ephyridae	*Scatella callosicosta* Bezzi	R1		
Heleomyzidae	*Scoliocentra scutellaris* (Zett.)	R3	+	montane, moss heath, grassland
	Suilla oxyphora (Mik)	R2	–	wetland
Hybotidae	*Oedalea hybotina* (Fallen)	R1		woodland (decid.)
	Platypalpus alter (Collin)	R3	+	river shingle
	Platypalpus pallidicoxa Frey	R2	+	wetland
	Tachydromia acklandi (Chvala)	R1		river shingle
	Tachydromia halidayi (Collin)	R3		
	Tachypeza heeri Zett.	R1	+	woodland (aspen, birch)
Lauxaniidae	*Peplomyza litura* (Meigen)	new to S		woodland (decid.)
Micropezidae	*Calobata stylifera* Loew	R3	–	wetland
Muscidae	*Phaonia colbrani* Collin			endemic to S
	Phaonia lugubris (Meigen)	Nt	+	montane, heath, grassland
	Phaonia meigeni	Nt		
	Phaonia subfuscinervis (Zett.)	Nt	+	montane, grassland, heath, wetland
	Spilogona triangulifera (Zett.)	Nt	+	montane, grassland, moss heath
	Thricops hirtulus (Zett.)	Nt	+	montane, moss heath
Mycetophilidae	*Bolitophila bimaculata* Zett.	R2	–	
	Dynatosoma nigromaculatum Lundstroem	R3	–	
	Mycetophila bohemica (Lastovka)	R2	–	
	Sciophila rufa Meigen	Nt	?	woodland (birch)
Otitidae	*Homalocephala albitarsis* Zett.	R1	+	woodland (aspen)
	Homalocephala biumbrata (Wahlberg)	R1	+	woodland (aspen)
Scathophagidae	*Cordilura similis* Siebke	R3	–	wetland
	Ernoneura argus (Zett.)	R2	+	wetland, aquatic
	Gonatherus planiceps (Fallen)	R3	+	montane, grassland, wet heath, moss heath
	Microprosopa pallidicauda (Zett.)	R3	–	wetland
Scatopsidae	*Ectaetia christii* Rotheray & Horsfield	sp. n		woodland (aspen)
Sciomyzidae	*Antichaeta analis* (Meigen)	R3	+	marsh
	Ectinocera borealis (Zett.)	R3	+	woodland (conif.)
Strongylophthalmidae				
	Strongylophthalmyia ustulata (Zett.)	R1	+	woodland (aspen)
Syrphidae	*Blera fallax* (Linn.)	R1	– p	woodland (pine)
	Callicera rufa Schummel (Plate 40)	R3	+	woodland (pine)
	Chamaesyrphus caledonicus Collin	R1	+	woodland (pine)
	Chamaesyrphus scaevoides (Fallen)	R3	+	woodland (pine)
	Cheilosia chrysocoma (Meigen)	R3	+	wet areas (phytophagous)
	Cheilosia sahlbergi Becker	R2	+	montane, grassland
	Cheilosia sp. B. Stubbs & Falk	R1	–	riverside
	Criorhina ranunculi (Panzer)	Nt	+	woodland (decid.)
	Eupeodes lapponicus (Zett.)	Nt	p	
	Hammerschmidtia ferruginea (Fallen)	R1	+ p	woodland (aspen)
	Melanostoma dubium (Zett.)	Nt	+	montane
	Parasyrphus nigritarsis (Zett.)	R1	+ c	woodland (willow)
	Platycheirus melanopsis Loew	R3	+	montane, heath, wet heath, moss heath
	Sphegina sibirica Stackelberg	R?	+	woodland (mixed), damp
	Xanthandrus comtus (Harris)	Nt	+	woodland (decid.)
Tabanidae	*Hybomitra lurida* (Fallen)	R3	+	wetland, woodland
Tephritidae	*Campiglossa argyrocephala* (Loew)	R3	+	wetland
Therevidae	*Spiriverpa lunulata* Zett. (Plate 41)	R3	+ p	river shingle
	Thereva handlirschi Krober	R3	+	dry heath
	Thereva inornata Verrall	R3	+	dry heath

ORDER/ FAMILY	SPECIES	STATUS		HABITAT
	Thereva lunulata Zett.	R3	+ p	dry heath
Tipulidae	*Dicranota guerini* Zett.	Nt	+	montane, upland
	Dicranota simulans Lackschewitz	R3	+	montane, wetland
	Erioptera meigeni (Zett.)	R3	−	montane, wetland
	Erioptera sordida Zett.	R3	−(+1)	marsh
	Limonia caledonica (Edwards)	Nt	+	montane, seepages
	Limonia consimilis (Zett.)	R3	−	wetland
	Ormosia fascipennis (Zett.)	new to GB		montane
	Limonia omissinervis (deMeijere)	R2	−(S)	wetland
	Lipsothrix ecucullata Edwards	R3	+ p	woodland, seepages
	Molophilus czizeki Lackschewitz	R3	−?	woodland, wetland
	Molophilus pusillus Edwards		c	
	Nephrotoma aculeata (Loew)	R2	−	wetland
	Pedicia claripennis (Verrall)	R?	+	montane
	Pilaria decolor (Zett.)	R?	−	swamp
	Rhabdomastix hilaris Edwards	R3	−(S)p	wetland
	Rhabdomastix inclinata Edwards	R2	−(S)	wetland, woodland
	Tipula alpium Bergroth	R?	+	montane, upland
	Tipula bistilata Lundstroem	R2	−	wetland
	Tipula cheethami Edwards	Nt	+	montane, upland
	Tipula gimmerthali Lackschewitz	R3	+	montane, wetland
	Tipula grisescens Zett.	R3	+	montane, bogs
	Tipula laetabilis Zett.	R2	−	wetland
	Tipula marginata Meigen	R3	−(S)	damp heath, fen
	Tipula montana Curtis	R?	+	montane, upland
	Tipula nodicornis Meigen	R3	+	wetland
	Triogma trisulcata (Schummel)	R3	+	montane, wetland, upland streams
Xylophagidae	*Xylophagus cinctus* Degeer	R3	+	woodland (pine)
	Xylophagus junki Szilady	R1ext.	−	

EPHEMEROPTERA

	Heptagenia longicauda (Stephens)	+	p	rivers

HEMIPTERA

ORDER/ FAMILY	SPECIES	STATUS		HABITAT
Aphididae	*Macrosiphum scoticum* Stroyan	R1	−	wetland
Aradidae	*Aradus betulae* (Linn.)	R3	+	woodland (birch)
Cicadellidae	*Ebarrius cognatus* (Fieber)	Nt	−	montane, grassland
	Emelyanoviana contraria (Ribaut)	Nt	+	montane (rock rose), grassland
Cimicidae	*Xylocoris formicetorum* (Boheman)	Nt	−(S)	ant nests
Delphacidae	*Paraliburnia litoralis* (Reuter)	R1?	−	wetland
Lygaeidae	*Eremocoris abietis* (Linn.)	R3	+	woodland (pine), leaf litter, juniper
	Eremocoris plebejus (Fallen)	R3	+	woodland (conif.), moorland (moss)
Miridae	*Zygimus nigriceps* (Fallen)	Nt	−	juniper

HYMENOPTERA

ORDER/ FAMILY	SPECIES	STATUS		HABITAT
Apidae	*Bombus distinguendus* Morawitz		+ p	(not since 1960), grassland
Chrysididae	*Chrysura hirsuta* (Gerstaeker)	R2	+ p	montane, moorland
Diprionidae	*Monoctenus juniperi* (Linn.)	R?	+	juniper
Eumenidae	*Ancisatrocerus antilope* (Panzer)	R3	+	various
Formicidae	*Formica exsecta* Nylander	R1	+ p	heath, woodland (pine)
	Formica aquilonia Yarrow		+ p	woodland (pine)
	Formica lugubris Zetterstedt		+ p	
Megachilidae	*Osmia inermis* (Zett.)	R2	+ p	montane, base rich upland pasture
	Osmia uncinata Gerstaecker	R2	−(+1)p	woodland (pine)
Sphecidae	*Pemphredon wesmaeli* (Morawitz)	R3	+	woodland (pine)
Tenthredinidae	*Allantus basalis caledonicus* Benson	Nt?	−?	
	Amauronematus abnormis (Holmgren)	R?	−	montane, willow
	Amauronematus arcticola (Dalla Torre)	R?	−	montane, willow
	Amauronematus semilacteus (Zaddach)	R?	−	woodland (willow)
	Nematus reticulatus Holmgren	R?		montane, willow

LEPIDOPTERA

ORDER/ FAMILY	SPECIES	STATUS		HABITAT
Coleophoridae	*Coleophora arctostaphyli* Meder	Nt	−	heath

ORDER/ FAMILY	SPECIES	STATUS			HABITAT
Cossidae	*Cossus cossus* (Linn.)		+	c	open woodland
Ethemiidae	*Ethmia pyrausta* (Pall.)		–		montane
Endromidae	*Endromis versicolora* (Linn.)	R3	+	c	woodland (birch)
Geometridae	*Chesias rufata* (Fabr.)		+	c	open woodland
	Coenocalpe lapidata (Hubn.)		+	c	grassland
	Dyscia fagaria (Thunb.)		+	p	heathland
	Epione paralellaria (Denis & Schiff.)	R3	+	p	woodland (aspen)
	Lycia lapponaria scotica (Harrison)	R3	+		heath
	Psodos coracina (Esper)	R3	+		montane
	Rheumaptera hastata (Linn.)		+	p	wet heath
	Semiothisa carbonaria (Clerck)	R3	+	p	heath
Lycaenidae	*Aricia artaxerxes* (Fabr.)		+	p	grassland
Lyonetiidae	*Bucculatrix capreella* Krogerus	Nt	–		grassland
	Leucoptera orobi (Stt.)		+		grassland
	Paraleucoptera sinuella (Reutti)	R2(ext)	–		woodland (aspen)
Noctuidae	*Anarta cordigera* (Thunberg)	R3	+	c	heath
	A. melanopa (Thunb.)		+	c	montane
	Brachionycha nubeculosa (Esper)	R3	+	c	woodland (birch)
	Noctua orbona (Hufn.)		+	p	open woodland
	Paradiarsia sobrina (Dup.)		+	p	woodland
	Xestia alpicola (Zett.)		+	p	montane
	Xylena exsoleta (Linn.)		+	p	grassland
Nymphalidae	*Boloria euphrosyne* (Linn.)		+	p	open woodland
Oecophoridae	*Depressaria silesiaca* Heinemann	Nt	–		grassland
Pyralidae	*Catoptria permutatella* (Herrich–Schaffer)	Nt	–		woodland (mixed)
Sphingidae	*Hemaris tityus* (Linn.)		+	p	grassland
Tineidae	*Archinemapogon yildizae* Kocak	Nt	–		on bracket fungus
	Myrmecozela ochraceella (Tengstrom)	Nt	–		woodants nests
Tortricidae	*Eana argentana* (Clerck)	R3	–		grassland
	Gypsonoma nitidulana (Leinig & Zeller)	R1(ext.)	–		woodland (aspen)
Zygaenidae	*Zygaena exulans subochracea* White	R3	–	c	montane

ODONATA

Coenagridae	*Coenagrion hastulatum* (Charpentier)	R2	+	c	wetland
	Leucorrhinia dubia (Linden)		+		wetland

PLECOPTERA

	Brachyptera putata (Newman)		+	p	rivers

TRICHOPTERA

Limnephilidae	*Nemataulius punctatolineatus* (Retzius)	R1	–(S)		wetland
Phryganeidae	*Hagenella clathrata* (Kolenati)	R1	–(S)		wetland

KEY

R1	Red Data Book 1 Endangered
R2	Red Data Book 2 Vulnerable
R3	Red Data Book 3 Rare
Nt	Notable
R?	RDB status unknown
ext.	thought to be extinct
+	Cairngorms + other Scottish sites
–	Cairngorms only sites
–(S)	In Scotland only recorded from the Cairngorms; however also taken in England or Wales
p	priority species
c	species of conservation concern

Table 5c and the list on pp. 59–63. It is immediately apparent that there are discrepancies between this and the account of Welch (1974) and some of these reflect the extra knowledge that has been gathered recently. However some are merely different interpretations of the status of species, based on inadequate data, and we must expect other interpretations in the future, as more records accumulate. Our Table and list must be regarded as provisional.

We have found 264 species that are either RDB 1 to RDB 3 (and include the Cairngorms in their range), or are Notable and are mainly found in the Cairngorms in Britain. This represents about 10 per cent of the rarest insects in Britain. Around 90 are apparently restricted to the Cairngorms area but of course it is very likely that some of these will eventually be found elsewhere in the Highlands. The great majority are either Diptera (true flies) or Coleoptera (beetles), but it is not clear whether this is a true reflection of the real situation or whether these orders have received more survey attention in the Cairngorms. Both are known to be well represented in northern Britain, as distinct from Orthoptera, for example, which is a southern group with no Cairngorms specialities. Both are also amongst the most species-rich Orders in Britain, but this also applies to the Hymenoptera (bees, wasps, ants and saw flies) and yet there are only 15 of these on our list. Hymenoptera, especially the very numerous parasitic species, are notoriously difficult to identify and so are known to be very under-recorded. Only 32 Lepidoptera are included, and yet, in contrast to the Hymenoptera, these are the most well known and comprehensively studied of Britain's insects. Perhaps it is really true, therefore, that flies and beetles are specially well represented in the Cairngorms.

Little is known of the habitat requirements of a substantial number of these rare species but for most we have at least some idea of the general areas in which they are found. As set out in Table 5c, most are associated with woodlands, with roughly equal numbers from wetlands (Plate 45) and the montane zone and others from heaths and grasslands. With the proviso that some of the montane species also favour upland heathlands, this division seems to accord broadly with the proportionate extent of the habitats in the Cairngorms area. The characteristic local habitats, such as pine woods, rich heaths and the plateau, all have their own specialities but, whereas over half of the woodland species are restricted in their British distribution to the Cairngorms and this applies to around a third of the montane species, as few as 10 – 13 per cent of the heathland and grassland species are so restricted. Perhaps this emphasizes the particular importance of the montane zone and the woods within the Cairngorms.

Enough is known to illustrate the national importance of the Cairngorm insects, but it is also clear that our true knowledge of the fauna is still poor, even for the best worked habitats, such as pine woods, and the best studied orders, like the Lepidoptera. This emphasizes the need to encourage well planned and intensive surveys of the Cairngorm insects, including little visited areas and under-recorded groups (and this must surely apply with even greater force to the other even less well-known invertebrate groups!).

THREATS TO INSECTS IN THE CAIRNGORMS

There are few substantial threats to the insects that inhabit the Cairngorm plateau, except for such wide-ranging factors as climate change and acid deposition (see Table 5d which summarizes the threats to Cairngorm insects). The features that are so alarming for the amenity of the area and for the larger wildlife, such as the degree of human disturbance adjacent to tracks and tourist facilities, will have only a small and localized impact on insects. If extensive soil erosion develops from increased trampling, then this will have an effect, but overall it is difficult to see this being really significant.

If there is a definite change to the climate, or to pollution deposition, however, this will have a profound effect, for the plateau insects are certainly critically adapted to the extreme conditions and even a small change in temperature or precipitation will produce serious consequences. Since we know almost nothing about the precise requirements of the insects, however, we cannot yet make sensible predictions about the changes that will result, beyond the obvious observations that species already living at the highest altitudes will have no further place to retreat to, if the climate warms.

In contrast, there are serious threats to the insect fauna of the moors and woods. The lack of regeneration, the reduction in area and the increasing fragmentation and isolation of the woods will all have an impact on their characteristic fauna. Insects, even more than other animals, are prone to local extinctions and so need to have a mosaic of

Table 5d   The threats to Cairngorm insect communities

Habitat types	Critical problems	Threats
Plateau	Climate change/acid deposition (These are also threats to other habitats)	Trampling and disturbance
Pine/aspen woods	Lack of regeneration /overgrazing	Fragmentation/ isolation
Birch/mixed woods	Grazing/lack of regeneration/loss of dynamic shift	Removal of old trees/change to commercial forestry
Upland heaths	Overburning plus sheep grazing Underburning	Trampling and disturbances
Lowland heaths	Woodland invasion/ Overgrazing Underburning	Loss to agriculture

habitats available, from which recolonization is possible. It is difficult to see how this could work effectively if a species was lost from one of the fragments of the pinewoods at Mar, for example, now that the surviving remnants are so small and isolated. Furthermore, the specific requirements of insects are such that within each wood the actual effective habitat area may be substantially smaller than the overall area of the wood, so that habitat size may be more critical than appears at first. For example, the number of suitable rot holes in pine or freshly fallen large aspen trees may be very limited, even if the wood is quite large. Another point is that the woodland insects may actually be associated with non-tree features, such as a particular structure of herb layer, and this may be adversely affected before there is any actual loss of woodland area. The heavy grazing that eventually leads to a loss of woodland, by preventing regeneration, will earlier have eliminated many of those insect species which live in the lower layers of the forest. Each age and style of woodland also has its own assemblage of insects and whereas in lowland Britain it is generally species of older, over-mature trees that are now most threatened, in the highlands it may be insects of both old and young woodland that are at risk.

The dynamic nature of birch woods means that they change in nature and location quickly and the insects found in them may also have to have relatively high mobility. Despite this there is concern that there is currently a lack of both over-mature and young regenerating birch woodland around the Cairngorms fringe, so threatening the insects of these habitats. Sufficient space must be available to allow for continuing regeneration, close enough to existing woodlands to allow invasion by insects, in the way described above for *E. versicolora*. The use of birch woodlands for providing sheltered grazing for stock may have contributed to woodland retention in the short term, by giving them a value to farmers, but such grazing prevents regeneration and removes the shrub and herb layer, so that the insect assemblage is adversely affected and the woodland becomes senescent and sparse. An area may seem to be well stocked with birch but close inspection can reveal that the value of the woodland to wildlife is low. Until recently a further threat was the replacement of birch by commercial plantations and the removal of birch from these plantations as a competing 'weed' species. This threat is now receding.

Threats to the highest heathlands are similar to those for the plateau but at intermediate altitudes, where heaths have either been managed for sheep or grouse, the insect communities have become adapted to the management regimes. In places all management has recently been withdrawn and the consequent slow 'maturation' of the heaths will certainly have been accompanied by unnoticed changes in the relative abundance of different insect species. Of more consequence has been the change from the mosaic of small-scale fires, which favour grouse, to the use of more extensive fires, with subsequent sheep grazing, resulting in more grass and less dwarf shrub cover. The resultant changes in the insects present are readily observed and

unarguable, but it is not yet clear whether any rare species have been adversely affected. Time will tell if the winter moth will also have a widespread effect!

Concern about the threats to insects of lowland heaths are focused on the bearberry moors. Their importance to insects has been stressed above and they are now becoming rapidly depleted, first by conversion to agricultural land and more recently both by woodland regeneration and by increased grazing. Granish Moor, on Strathspey, was formerly regarded as a rich lowland heath for insects but heavy grazing pressure has changed it to a short, grassy heath of little entomological value. Its successors, Tulloch Moor in Strathspey and Dinnet Muir on Deeside, have also both changed in recent years. At Dinnet the extensive birch regeneration (so welcome in its own right) has greatly reduced the area of open moor, leaving only one extensive section where burning and cutting are used to sustain the bearberry heath, and at Tulloch there has been too little burning, so that the heathland has become rank and birch is invading. Such heaths require traditional, small-scale muirburn to sustain their entomological interest but there now seems to be little commercial incentive for this and the future of critically rare species, such as the moth *Coleophora arctostaphyli*, seems to be in jeopardy.

A crucial last point is that there is currently no systematic monitoring of the status and distribution of most insects in the Cairngorms and this is highly regrettable. Without it, it will be very difficult to assess the extent and significance of future changes and so it is most important that some suitable monitoring schemes are put in place.

In summary, the insect communities of the plateau and highest moors are threatened by such general factors as climate change, whereas those of mid and low-altitude heaths and woods will require sympathetic management of their habitats if they are to survive.

CONCLUSIONS

It has been most disappointing to have so few ecological studies of Cairngorms insects to describe (although most other upland areas of Scotland are even less well known). The obvious interest of the area, both because of its extreme conditions and because of the intrinsic value of the insect communities, make it surprising that so little has been attempted and it is surely particularly important that the Cairngorms plateau is studied, so that the role insects play in the overall functioning of this ecosystem is better understood. In another twenty years time it is to be hoped that a very different and more informed account of Cairngorms insects can be written.

REFERENCES

Ackland, D.M. (1989) Anthomyiidae (Dipt.) new to Britain, with a description of a new species of *Botanophila* Lioy. *Entomologist's Monthly Magazine* **125**, 211–230.
Anon. (1995) *Biodiversity: The UK Steering Group Report. Vol. 2.* HMSO, London.

Ashmole, N.P., Nelson, J.M., Shaw, M.R. & Garside, A. (1983) Insects and spiders on snowfields in the Cairngorms, Scotland. *Journal of Natural History* 17, 599–613.

Ball, S. & Morris, R. (1992) *Diptera Recording Schemes Field Meeting Report – 1992 – Stirling*. Joint Nature Conservation Committee.

Barbour, D.A. and Young, M.R. (1993) Ecology and conservation of the Kentish Glory moth (*Endromis versicolora* L.) in eastern Scotland. *Entomologist* 112, 25–33.

Drake, M.C. (1991) *Provisional atlas of the Larger Brachycera (Diptera) of Britain and Ireland*. NERC Institute of Terrestrial Ecology.

Edwards, F.W. (1933) Some Perthshire Diptera. *Scottish Naturalist* 45(92) 113–117.

Falk, S. (1991a) *A Review of the Scarce and Threatened Bees, Wasps and Ants of Great Britain*. Joint Nature Conservation Committee, Peterborough.

Falk, S. (1991b) *A Review of the Scarce and Threatened Flies of Great Britain (Part 1)*. Joint Nature Conservation Committee, Peterborough.

Hartley, S. (1993) Insect pests on heather moorland. *9th Annual Report of the Joseph Nickerson Moorland Restoration Project*. pp. 46–47.

Horsfield, D. & MacGowan, I. (1998) An assessment of the distribution and status of montane Brachycera Diptera in Scotland. *Malloch Society Research Report* 3. 73pp.

Hyman, P.S. & Parsons, M.S. (1992) *A Review of the Scarce and Threatened Coleoptera of Great Britain*. Joint Nature Conservation Committee, Peterborough.

Kerslake, J., Kruuk, L., Hartley, S. & Woodin, S. (1996) Winter moth (*Operophtera brumata*, Lepidoptera: Geometridae) outbreaks on Scottish heather moorlands: effects of host plant and parasitoids on larval survival and development. *Bulletin of Entomological Research* 86, 155–164.

Kirby, P. (1992) *A Review of the Scarce and Threatened Hemiptera of Great Britain*. Joint Nature Conservation Committee, Peterborough.

Leaper, G. (1998) *The Biodiversity of the Cairngorms Partnership Area*. Cairngorms Partnership, Grantown-on-Spey.

Leverton, R. (1993) *Dicallomera fascelina* L. (Lep.: Lymantriidae) with two year life cycle. *Entomologist's Record and Journal of Variation* 105, 219–220.

MacAlpine, E.A.M. (1979) The Lepidoptera of the Cairngorms National Nature Reserve. *Entomologist's Record and Journal of Variation*. 91, 1–6, 65–70, 213–216, 242–244.

MacGowan, I. (1993) The entomological value of aspen in the Scottish Highlands. *Malloch Society Research Report I*.

Owen, J.A. (1989a) A preliminary account of the beetles of the RSPB Loch Garten Reserve. *British Journal of Entomology and Natural History* 2, 17–28.

Owen, J.A. (1989b) Beetles from pitfall-trapping in a caledonian pinewood at Loch Garten, Inverness-shire. *British Journal of Entomology and Natural History* 2, 107–113.

Owen, J.A., Lyszkowski, R.M., Proctor, R. & Taylor, S. (1992) *Agabus wasastjernae* Sahlberg (Col.:Dytiscidae) new to Scotland. *Entomologist's Record and Journal of Variation* 104, 225–230.

Owen, J.A. & Thaxton, R.W. (1994) Beetles from pitfall-trapping at high altitudes in the Cairngorms. *Entomologist's Record and Journal of Variation* 106, 51–54.

Rodwell, J.S., ed. (1991) *British Plant Communities 2. Mires and Heaths*. Cambridge University Press, Cambridge. 628 pp.

Rotheray, G.E. & Horsfield, D. (1997) *Ectaetia christii* sp.n., a Scottish species similar to *Ectaetia clavipes* (Diptera, Scatopsidae). *Dipterists' Digest* 4, (i).

Rotheray, G.E. & Robertson, D.M. (1993) Insects from shingle banks and riverside habitats in Strathspey. *Malloch Society Research Report 2*.

Shirt, D.B., ed. (1987) *British Red Data Books: 2 Insects*. Nature Conservancy Council, Peterborough.

Smith, R. (1997) *Ecology of the crane-fly* Tipula montana *in an upland environment*. Unpublished Ph.D. thesis, University of Aberdeen.

Smith, R., Young, M.R. & Marquiss, M. (2001) Bryophyte use by an insect herbivore: does the crane-fly *Tipula montana* select food to maximise growth? *Ecological Entomology* 26, 83–90.

Stubbs, A.E. (1992) *Provisional atlas of the long-palped craneflies (Diptera: Tipulinae) of Britain and Ireland*. NERC Institute of Terrestrial Ecology.

Tutt, J.W. (1902) *Practical Hints for the Field Lepidopterist II*. Elliot Stock, London.

Watson, A. & Stroyan, H.L.G. (1984) Unusual concentrations of aphids at high altitudes in the Cairngorms. *Entomologist's Monthly Magazine* 120, 145–149.

Welch, R.C. (1974) *Insects and Other Invertebrates*. In: Nethersole-Thompson, D. & Watson, A., *The Cairngorms*. Collins, London. 286 pp.

Young, M.R. (1989) *A survey of the insects of Arctostaphylos heaths*. Contract Report to Nature Conservancy Council, Edinburgh.

Young, M.R. (1991) Endromidae. In: Emmet, A.M. & Heath, J., eds, *The Moths and Butterflies of Great Britain and Ireland* Vol. 7(2). Harley Books, Essex.

Young, M.R. (1992) Conserving insect communities in mixed woodlands. In: Cannell, M.G.R., Malcolm, D.C. & Robertson, P.A., eds, *The Ecology of Mixed Species Stands of Trees*. BES Special Publication 11. Blackwell Science, Oxford.

Young, M.R., (1997) *The Natural History of Moths*. Poyser, London.

Young, M.R., Armstrong, G. & Edgar, A. (1991) *A survey of the invertebrates of native pine woods*. Contract Report to Nature Conservancy Council, Edinburgh.

CHAPTER 6

Ecology of Aquatic and Sub-aquatic Habitats

M.B. Davidson, R.P. Owen and D.W. Mackay

AQUATIC ECOLOGY

AQUATIC HABITATS OF THE CAIRNGORMS

The aquatic habitats of the Cairngorms are of importance for many reasons in regional, national and world contexts. They have an intrinsic value within the landscape and indeed the streams and rivers are major forces in the erosion, sediment transport and general reworking of the post-glacial morphology (Bremner, 1912). The relatively unpolluted waters of the Cairngorms area have considerable economic importance for fishing, whisky distillation, tourism and recreation (Cairngorms Working Party Report, 1993).

In this chapter, we consider the aquatic habitats within the upper parts of the Spey, Don, Dee, Esk and Garry catchments using the boundary proposed by the Cairngorms Working Party. Scientific investigation of the aquatic habitats in this area has been rather limited and focused on a few aspects of the ecology. In the 1930s and '40s, R.M. Neill of Aberdeen University collected macroinvertebrate samples from the River Dee using an early 'Hess' sampler and artificial substrates. Neill was interested in fish food and feeding (Neill, 1938), and fishery management and improvement have been the motivation behind much of the research in this area (e.g., Morrison & Harriman, 1992; Gardiner & Mackay, this volume, Chapter 13). Some biological surveys have been carried out in relation to habitat assessment for nature conservation or to specific environmental problems such as acidification. In the

past the uplands have been seen as marginal, from an economic point of view, and therefore ecological research on the aquatic habitats has received little funding or encouragement. The realization that they are important, not only as part of our natural heritage, but also as ecological monitors of long-term environmental change, is modifying this attitude.

PHYSICAL INTERACTIONS

Running waters. The nature of the watercourses and standing waters of the Cairngorms and neighbouring areas is largely determined by the montane character of the region. Rivers and streams draining these mountains have some of the highest sources in Britain, the Dee, for example, rising on the Braeriach plateau at about 1220 m (Plate 47). Extensive tracts of high ground contribute to the catchment areas of the major watercourses of the Tay, Spey, Dee (Plate 48) and Don, all of which are amongst the largest rivers in Scotland. These four drainage basins, together with the North and South Esks draining to the south-east, form the hydrological boundaries of the area.

The drainage direction of the major basins is controlled by the strike and varied resistance of the underlying geology, although the eastward flowing Dee and Don present some anomalies (Bremner, 1912). Exploitation of weaker rock types by some rivers appears to have led to the capture of some headwater streams of adjacent catchments (e.g., the upper Don by the Avon). Subsequent glacial action has considerably modified the topography of the Cairngorms and superimposed a number of features. The wide and straightened valleys of the upper Dee, Don and Spey allow these rivers to assume winding courses across extensive river terraces. Numerous hanging corries, many with lochans in deepened basins, give rise to high gradient streams and gorges where post-glacial rivers have cut through rock lips.

The rainfall, influenced by orogenic climatic effects, is high and varies in relation to altitude so that annual means range from 800 mm at the boundaries of the area to more than 2000 mm in the mountains (Warren, 1985). Winter accumulations of snow account for a significant proportion of stored precipitation (Plate 54) and contribute to river flows in a complex manner whenever warmer air masses arrive, especially in the spring. The influence of snow cover on hydrology and hydrochemistry has been discussed by Soulsby *et al.* (1997) who highlight the implications of climate change.

High catchment runoff rates reflect the relatively large proportion of high gradient slopes and thin soils. However smaller watercourses greatly outnumber the larger ones and the thousands of kilometres of small streams, as well as the many seeps and flushes, are an intrinsic feature of the Cairngorm landscape (Plate 50).

Stream gradient dominates many aspects of the physical environment of watercourses, having consequences for current velocity, sediment transport, substratum composition and some aspects of chemistry. In the core montane zone the majority of streams are of high gradient, lessening quite sharply with loss of altitude. Nevertheless, the lower gradient running waters contain important aquatic habitats, as in the meanders and pools of some larger rivers (e.g., the Dee in upper Glen Dee) and the innumerable rivulets, flushes and seepages so characteristic of upland heaths. High gradients and flows result in the transport of all but the coarsest materials resulting in bouldery stream beds with, as slopes lessen, greater proportions in sequence of cobbles, pebbles, gravel, sand and silt. However, even in these armoured, bouldery river beds (Plate 53) pockets of finer material can be found at sites protected from the current. Tributaries of the major rivers transport large volumes of sediment derived from crystalline granites, schists and gneisses, especially during storm events, which accumulate downstream at lower gradients. These outwashed materials can form extensive alluvial fans and braided streams (e.g., lower Feshie).

An interesting and important contrasting feature of the Spey is provided by its relatively low gradient (*c.* 2.6 m/km) for 40 km upstream of Grantown. The broad, alluvial flats, meandering river, marshes and open water of Loch Insh occupy an extensive flood plain and give the area the largest fenland in Britain outside the Norfolk Broads.

Standing waters. There are relatively few lochs of any size in the area though ten are within the largest

Table 6a Classification of Spey Valley lochs according to method of formation

		No.	% of total
Glacial	Kettlehole	18	34.5
	Morraine Dam	5	9.5
	Scoured by ice	8	1.5
Flood plain	Meander	5	9.5
	Marsh Pool	18	34.5
Groups of Lochs in Kettleholes		5	9.5
Man-made Lochs		4	7.5

Source: Charter, 1988a

two hundred by volume of Scottish lochs (Murray & Pullar, 1910; MacDonald *et al.*, 1975) and Loch Muick is ranked thirty-sixth. There are many smaller lochans (Plate 51) and temporary pools providing an abundance of still water habitats. All the lochs of the Cairngorms have been formed by glacial action with the larger ones, Lochs Muick (Plate 52) and Einich (Plate 54), occupying scoured depressions in glaciated valleys and dammed by morainic material while others, Morlich (Plate 49) and Insh, are kettleholes in origin or are high corrie lochans such as Dubh Lochan (Plate 51), Lochnagar and Coire an Lochan (Table 6a).

Loch Muick (surface area 2.20 km²; mean depth 35.45 m) stores about 48 per cent of the total standing water in the eighteen major lochs (i.e. volumes $>600 \times 10^3$ m³) of Grampian Region and, at an altitude of 400 m, is one of the highest of the large Scottish water bodies. Within the montane zone there are several lochs above 900 m and one small lochan on the Braeriach plateau at about 1215 m is reputedly the highest in Scotland. Not surprisingly, ice cover on some of these still waters may last from October through to June or later.

Morphological characteristics of the Cairngorm lochs vary widely from steeply shelving glacial troughs with very narrow littoral zones at Loch Avon, to shallow basins supporting wide, marginal areas of soft sediment at Lochs Insh and Davan (Plate 46). Many of the corrie lochans have rocky or bouldery beds and their catchments are dominated by bare rock and screes although thick layers of sediment can accumulate in their deepest holes. Many of the still waters in the montane area have generally harsh conditions for fauna and flora.

CHEMICAL CHARACTERISTICS

In the Cairngorm area, unlike many other large tracts of land where anthropogenic emissions have much greater effect, underlying geology has the greatest influence on aquatic chemistry. The main mountain masses have been formed by intruded granites while the surrounding country rock is comprised in the main of schists, gneisses and quartzite. Importantly, there are significant outcrops

Table 6b Chemistry of Dee headwater streams and geology (mean values from monthly surveys, Jan-Dec 1992; all units in mg/l unless indicated otherwise)

	Baddoch Burn	*Allt Darrarie*	*Allt an Dubh Loch*
National Grid Reference	NO 134833	NO 309852	NO 253823
Altitude (m)	410	410	590
Catchment Area (km^2)	23	15	15
Conductivity (uS/cm)	57	51	26
Alkalinity	16	12	<1
Calcium	5.9	3.4	0.9
pH (units)	7.2	7.0	5.5
Total Oxidized Nitrogen	0.22	0.21	0.20
Soluble Reactive Phosphorus	0.002	0.003	<LOD
Silicate	1.85	4.40	1.24
Dominant Catchment Geology	Calc. Schists	Gneisses Granite	Granite

of other rock types, including calcareous rocks, which influence the chemistry of any waters flowing over them.

Chemical monitoring carried out by the North East River Purification Board (NERPB) shows how stream chemistry can vary. Table 6b compares three headwater streams of the Dee catchment during 1992, each with different catchment geology.

All three streams are similarly deficient in plant nutrients, reflecting the thin soils and upland heath of their catchments, but the most obvious differ-

ences are in their relative calcium concentration, alkalinity and acidity. The low leaching rate of minerals from granitic rocks leads to poor buffering capacity and, since these upland, peaty soils are usually strongly acidic (Gorham, 1957), also to more acid waters than in streams with less resistant geologies. Alkalinity is a good indicator of the ability to buffer against increases in acidity. A survey of 82 relatively accessible headwater streams in the Spey and Dee catchments, in August 1983, indicated that nearly one-fifth of the streams had very low alkalinity and were, thus, 'at risk' from acid deposition (Pugh, 1985). It is likely that this is an underestimate of the proportion of poorly buffered streams draining the central mountain area.

Not surprisingly, many of the standing waters in the montane area are strongly acidic with consequently poor fish populations (Morrison & Harriman, 1992). In Lochnagar, a high altitude corrie lochan, it appears that an increase in acidity began in the mid-nineteenth century, coinciding with a rapid rise in the level of airborne pollutants. Concomitant increases in carbonaceous materials and in some heavy metals are also apparent in their sediments (Patrick *et al.*, 1989).

Rivers and lochs outside the mountain areas are more likely to be richer in salts because of less resistant bedrocks, thicker overlying deposits and catchment soils which support greater plant productivity and agricultural activities. The Scottish Environment Protection Agency (SEPA) has monitored several of the larger lochs to assess trophic status and these are compared in Table 6c.

In general these lochs are poor in dissolved salts and nutrients while at the same time being somewhat acidic. Of these waters Loch Davan, on the edge of the Cairngorms area, has the most intensive agricultural activity in its catchment reflected in much higher mean conductivity and mean nitrogen concentrations. The productivity of these standing waters is likely to be primarily determined by the availability of nutrients.

Table 6c Chemical characteristics of standing waters (mean annual concentrations in mg/l unless otherwise indicated)

	Muick	*Morlich*	*Insh*	*an Eilein*	*Garten*	*Kinord*	*Davan*
Conductivity	26	40		46	88	106	206
Alkalinity	2	11	16	5	7	14	28
pH (units)	5.9	6.3	6.2	6.8	6.5	6.6	6.8
Total Oxidized Nitrogen	0.21	0.06	0.08	0.06	0.11	0.09	1.06
Soluble Reactive Phosphorus	0.002	0.002	0.003	0.002	0.003	0.006	0.007
Silicate	1.41	2.01	1.94	2.49	2.69	2.75	2.55
Total Organic Carbon	2.1	2.8		2.3	11.6	4.4	4.5
Period of Data	1983–93	1980–93	1993	1988–91	1989–91	1989–93	1989–93
No. Samples	117	69	11	21	18	41	44

ZONATION

Rivers. The physical and chemical characteristics of the Cairngorm river systems largely determine the composition of the biological communities which inhabit them.

Rivers are difficult to classify because they normally change in nature from source to mouth, both physically and in trophic status, imposing modifications on fauna and flora with distance from source. The concept of river zonation is a useful one and has been discussed by many authors (e.g., Hawkes, 1975; Hynes, 1970) and applied, using both plants and animals, to the rivers of the Cairngorms area. This has led to various attempts to classify whole river systems and their constituent reaches using their fauna or flora (Holmes, 1983, Wright *et al.*, 1984). Within the Cairngorms area, all the rivers are firmly within the salmonid zone. The headwaters lose altitude rapidly, most notably in the Dee, 850 m in 20 km, and coalesce to form erosive, cold, stenothermal, oligotrophic watercourses with high oxygen concentrations. The pH and alkalinity are often low, and the invertebrate fauna is dominated by stoneflies and the more acid-tolerant mayflies and caddis. Bryophytes and algae grow where the current permits.

Useful as the concept of zonation is, the biological communities in a river generally form continua, unless there are clear environmental boundaries or barriers, such as an instream loch, or a sharp change in geology of the river bed.

The Don is probably the only large river in the area which includes upland headwaters, middle reaches and a lowland zone, with a transition from oligotrophy in the highlands to eutrophy in its lower reaches. However, its eutrophic status is due to agricultural and industrial pollution and its natural status should be no more than mesotrophic and therefore similar to the Spey.

The Dee is described by Ratcliffe (1977) as being the best example in Britain of a large, oligotrophic river. This characteristic is maintained, almost to the sea, due to the lack of a lowland reach and the resistant nature of the underlying rocks throughout its length. At most, this river achieves mesotrophic status in its lowest reaches.

Due to the existence of an instream loch, at Insh, the River Spey becomes mesotrophic much more quickly than the Dee. Loch Insh, like all loch outflows, increases the secondary productivity of the river. Much larger populations of filter-feeding blackfly are to be found below Loch Insh than elsewhere in the river (Coupland, 1990) and the combination of lotic and lentic species makes the area of great conservation interest (Maitland, 1991; Wright & Furse, 1990).

The catchment of the Garry is much altered by hydroelectricity schemes and the presence of various dams and the movement of water from within and outwith the catchment must significantly alter the natural conditions.

A river is generally considered as a water-filled channel bounded by two banks and a bed, possibly with aquatic plants adding to the physical structure.

It may erode its banks and, on a longer time-scale, meander within its flood plain but at any point in time it appears to have quite definite physical boundaries. From an ecological point of view this is quite far from the truth. The submerged river bed and banks are not entirely separate entities, but zones of interaction. Water can flow either in or out of the river, through the substratum. The bed material provides a three-dimensional habitat for a wide variety of animals from the micro to macroscopic. The river bed is in effect an extension of the soil and another example of a habitat continuum. The Enchytraeid worms, which are very common in well oxygenated oligotrophic upland river sediments, are in effect inhabiting waterlogged gravelly soils, much as they do in saturated ground elsewhere.

River shingle. Already recognized as botanically interesting, shingle banks have recently been found to be very important for a large number of invertebrates. Forster & Green (1985) noted the importance of shingle as a habitat for plants typical of the uplands, but able to establish themselves in this dynamic habitat. By means of seeds and vegetative parts, plants such as northern bedstraw (*Galium boreale*), yellow saxifrage (*Saxifraga azoides*), mountain sorrel (*Oxyria digyna*) and northern rock-cress (*Arabis petraea*) are able to colonize the coarse sediments of shingle banks. Marren (1982) records the history of the invasion of the Dee by the Nootka lupin (*Lupinus nootkatensis*) from North America. It is now characteristic of the river shingles in this area.

In relation to a threatened flood alleviation scheme, a review of information and a survey were carried out by Stubbs (1991) on the Feshie fan. This is the largest intact shingle fan in Britain. Maitland (1991) assessed the aquatic fauna as consisting of the common cleanwater types able to recolonize quickly after catastrophic flood events. Intimately associated with the river channel is a series of habitats which depend on its dynamic processes for their continued existence. River shingle is just one of these habitats.

At first sight this would appear to be an unpromising habitat for non-aquatic invertebrates due to the frequency and unpredictability of flooding. However, the Spey is considered to be the best river in the Scottish highlands for shingle/sandbank flies (Stubbs, 1991). Many species of fly, beetle and spider specialize in using this habitat and several of those occurring in the Feshie fan are Red Data Book or Nationally Notable species. Stubbs emphasized the importance of the Feshie fan for conservation and cites the example of the cranefly fauna. The species considered have aquatic or semi-aquatic larvae. All are river specialists, and they include four Red Databook entries.

Organic flood debris, incorporated in the sediments, provides a food supply for burrowing fly larvae. Predatory beetles and spiders have a variety of food sources including invertebrates living within the shingle, emerging aerial forms of aquatic insects and terrestrial species flying in or falling off overhanging vegetation.

River shingles rely on the activity of the river for their continued existence. Any alteration of the river, particularly to channel morphology, could have drastic effects on the ecology of these dynamic habitats.

Hyporheic zone. The interstitial environment within the sediments of watercourses, the hyporheic zone, has been well described by Williams (1989). Berthelemy (1966) showed that larval leuctrid stoneflies were able to inhabit the spaces deep within a stream bed and a considerable portion of the invertebrate fauna may be living within, rather than on, the substratum. The existence of such a habitat explains how many animals appear to be able to avoid the effects of floods and even brief flushes of pollutants such as acid rain events. Hyporheic animals are found down to depths of 1m in some rivers. Dredging activities seldom take account of the structure of the resulting substratum and the effects on the fauna.

Chemically, the hyporheic zone can be quite different from the surface waters. Within the sediments, pH may be up to one unit lower, carbon dioxide concentrations are higher and oxygen lower, while the temperature remains lower in the summer and higher in the winter.

The hyporheic zone can thus afford some protection to benthic organisms from extreme conditions. Surface water temperatures recorded for flowing water at the Linn o' Dee in February 1979 were as low as $-1.5°$ C (Davidson & Young, 1979). Water as cold as this freezes instantly on being slowed and ice forms on the bottom sediments. Undoubtedly, under these conditions, most of the invertebrates are likely to be living within the sediments where the interstitial water remains unfrozen and they are safe from ice scour.

Riparian zone. The nature of the vegetation in the area bordering a watercourse can be of great importance, particularly in the uplands. During the autumn and winter, leaves provide a ready source of food for detritus-feeding invertebrates (Cummins et al., 1973), becoming more palatable as they are entrapped in the sediments and degraded by saprophytic micro-organisms. Terrestrial invertebrates have also been shown to be an important source of food to fish, particularly in low productivity waters (Morrison & Harriman, 1992).

The riparian vegetation of the Cairngorm headwater streams, being typically treeless, of low pH and with reduced microbial activity (Chamier, 1987), provides little feeding for invertebrates and consequently for fish.

Standing waters and wetlands. In the same way that river zonation has been used to describe the downstream evolution of a river, the concept of hydroseral succession has been applied to standing waters. The Cairngorm lochs have evolved at different rates since the end of the ice age.

Sedimentation rates have varied greatly (Jones et al., 1993) even amongst the high altitude lochs which have generally remained in a juvenile stage. Lochs on lower ground have been subject to a greater influx of sediment and, where this has consisted of finer, peaty material, it has allowed the development of a more abundant marginal vegetation (Charter, 1988a) (Plate 55). Under conditions of increasing sedimentation or falling water level, the marginal vegetation will encroach on the open water area until a quaking mat forms. The transformation of open water to wetland and finally dry land is a natural process, but the rate at which it occurs is greatly influenced by the activities of man.

AQUATIC AND WETLAND FLORA

Lower plants. Aquatic algae are discussed in some detail later in relation to the flora of standing waters and the problems of acidification and eutrophication.

There has been very little systematic survey work on the algal flora of the area but various surveys have included information on the larger forms (e.g., Holmes, 1985).

Locally, calcitic rocks can have a dramatic effect on the algal flora of a stream. In catchments such as the Deskry (Don) and the Baddoch/Clunie (Dee), particularly during periods of low flow when ground water has more influence on water chemistry than surface waters, a thick macroscopic mat of the stalked diatom *Gomphonema* develops.

Although authors such as Holmes (1983) have recorded some lichens associated with streams (e.g., *Dermatocarpon fluviatile*), they have not been surveyed in detail. Lichens have proved to be of great value as indicators of atmospheric pollution and this may apply to those associated with streams, particularly in the uplands, in relation to compounds associated with acid deposition.

The Bryophytes (mosses and liverworts) are probably the most obvious and characteristic components of the aquatic flora of the Cairngorms. They live largely on the nutriment provided by the water which they trap, which seeps through them or in which they are submerged. The greatest diversity of bryophytes will be found in the springs and wet flushes, including species such as *Cratoneuron commutatum* and *Philonotis fontana*.

Bryophytes are the major components of the aquatic flora of the Cairngorm river systems. Mosses and liverworts such as *Hygrohypnum ochraceum* and *Scapania undulata* are able to survive on rock surfaces from the splash zone to the stream bed even in the most nutrient-poor situations and provide a habitat for a community of other organisms.

Light and Lewis Smith (1976) recorded 16 species of bryophytes (8 mosses and 8 liverworts) at depths ranging from 1–20 m in four high altitude lochs in the Cairngorms (Loch Avon, Loch nan Eun on Lochnagar, Lochan an Uaine on Ben Macdhui and Loch Coire an Lochain on Braeriach; altitudes 730 m, 890 m, 950 m, and 990 m respectively). All these lochs are covered by about 1 m of ice and varying depths of snow for up to 7 months of the year. A few of the species were represented only by isolated shoots which might have survived from material washed or blown into the lochs, but most were firmly attached to the substratum and had formed dense stands. Several (e.g., *Oligotrichum hercynicum*, *Thuidium* cf. *tamariscinum*, *Pohlia* sp.) are not typically aquatic but had evidently become adapted to the stable deep-water environment. Prior to this study bryophytes had not been found in Britain at depths exceeding about 12 m. Clearly the bryophyte flora of high altitude lochs would repay further research.

Macrophyte distribution. The macrophyte flora (flowering plants and fern allies such as quillwort *Isoetes lacustris*) of the aquatic habitats of the Cairngorms area is characteristically impoverished. There are a number of reasons for this, including the relatively recent glaciation of the area, the climate and the oligotrophic nature of most of the waterbodies. A richer flora occurs where lime-rich rocks outcrop, in base-rich springs and flushes, and in lochs and rivers with finer substrata.

The macrophytes are poorly represented in the area but tend to be most common in still water situations where there is some opportunity for the build-up of a suitable substratum for rooting and a nutrient reservoir. What the area lacks in abundance and diversity, it makes up for with relict species and rarities such as pillwort (*Pilularia globulifera*), least water-lily (*Nuphar pumila*), awlwort (*Subularia aquatica*) and slender-leaved pondweed (*Potamogeton filiformis*).

River vegetation surveys. A national survey of aquatic river vegetation by Holmes (1983), which developed into a classification scheme, included the Spey, Dee and Don, but largely ignored the tributaries. Forster and Green (1985) carried out a vegetation survey of the Dee river corridor, concentrating on the terrestrial components but also examining wetter habitats in the riparian zone.

The major aquatic plant communities described by Holmes in the rivers of the Cairngorms area are given in Table 6d. In this classification the Spey and Dee have communities in groups D and C only. Group D is the most oligotrophic community type, based on a lack of flowering plants and the richness of lichens and mosses. Group C is described as oligo/mesotrophic, with most of the sites falling in this group being typical of upland rivers in Scotland.

The Don grades into Group B (meso/eutrophic) in its lower reaches due to agricultural and industrial enrichment.

Ratcliffe's assessment of the Dee was confirmed by Holmes (1985) who classified its flora as oligotrophic throughout most of its length, gradually becoming meso-oligotrophic at its mouth. Based on criteria of naturalness and typicalness of its flora (and other biota), the Dee is considered to be nationally important as a nature conservation site.

Table 6d Major river plant communities of the Cairngorms area

Distribution of Community Types in the Major Catchments

Dee	Don	Spey
D3ii	D1i	D4i
D1i	C4iii	D1i
C4iii	C4ii	C4iii
C4i	C4i	C3i
		C4i

Community	Occurrence
Group C	*Oligo-mesotrophic rivers*
C3i	Upland rivers with fen and bog
C4i	Large oligotrophic Scottish rivers
C4ii	Upland rivers of wide glacial valleys
C4iii	Highland rivers with gravel and peat
Group D	*Oligotrophic rivers*
D1i	Mountain rivers with gravel margins
D3ii	Moorland rivers with boulders and adjacent peat
D4i	Slow-flowing upland rivers

Source: Holmes, 1983

Holmes noted that the upper Dee has a sparse flora because of spate and ice scour and this undoubtedly holds true for the other catchments. Nevertheless, he recorded a variety of liverworts and mosses where the current was less severe, such as *Hygrobiella laxifolia*, *Cephalozia bicuspidata*, *Anthelia julacea* and *Blindia accuta*. On the larger rocks, species such as *Nardia compressa*, *Scapania marsupella*, *Racomitrium aciculare* and *R. aquaticum* are characteristic.

In the early part of the year chrysophytes and diatoms form a film on submerged rocks, while filamentous green algae dominate in the warmer months.

Forster and Green's Dee survey concentrated on vegetation which was directly influenced by river processes, essentially within the river corridor, or managed, for example, in relation to fishing and flood control. The survey extended no further up river than the Whitebridge in upper Glen Dee.

In addition to Holmes's work, Haslam (1982) surveyed the Spey as part of an NCC report on the vegetation of British Rivers. More recently, Murphy & Hudson (1991) examined the Spey and Feshie in relation to proposed flood control schemes. These recent authors noted that the main river channel of the Spey provided little scope for macrophyte development due to its stony substrata, fast flow and spatey nature – these features hold true for all the Cairngorm rivers. They recorded plants such as alternate-flowered water-milfoil (*Myriophyllum alterniflorum*), shoreweed (*Littorella uniflora*) red pondweed (*Potamogeton alpinus*) and intermediate water-starwort (*Callitriche hamulata*). A greater diversity of plants was recorded from the backwaters, due to slacker flows and finer substrates and these included broad-leaved pondweed (*Potamogeton natans*), common water-starwort (*Callitriche stagnalis*) and intermediate bladderwort (*Utricularia intermedia*).

The other river systems of the area are botanically similar in nature and have aquatic floras determined by the same factors of current speed, spatiness and resistant geological conditions.

PLANT COMMUNITIES IN STANDING WATERS

A vegetation survey of fifty-two lochs and lochans in the Spey valley between Laggan and Grantown was completed by Charter in 1985 (Charter, 1988a). This has provided a useful baseline against which to measure the effects of any future changes in land use, climate or pollution. Twenty-five of these lochs are within SSSIs.

The lochs and lochans in the Cairngorms, and Strathspey in particular, have been classified according to their method of formation (Table 6a). This has important implications for their nutrient status and ecology.

Charter recorded 88 species of aquatic and marshland plant during her survey, nine of which are nationally scarce. In addition, a further nine locally scarce species were considered as being worthy of special protection within this area (Palmer & Newbold 1983) (Table 6e).

The plant communities in these lochs vary depending on water depth and substratum. The large lochs tend to have stony shores with sand/gravel and peat in the sheltered bays as at Morlich. These stony shores support species such as lesser spearwort (*Ranunculus flamula*) shoreweed and water lobelia (*Lobelia dortmanna*) while various species of sedge (*Carex*) dominate the finer peaty sediments.

In the deeper water, with silt and gravel, are found quillwort, alternate-flowered water-milfoil, *Nitella* and *Potamogeton* species. Where more peat occurs the white water-lily (*Nymphaea alba*) and the yellow water-lily (*Nuphar lutea*) are common, along with bogbean (*Menyanthes trifoliata*), blunt-leaved pondweed (*Potamogeton obtusifolius*) and mare's-tail (*Hippuris vulgaris*).

Many of the smaller lochans have a floating fringe of vegetation including water sedge (*Carex aquatilis*), marsh-marigold (*Caltha palustris*) and cowbane (*Cicuta virosa*). These lochs have interesting, if not rich, floras which are clearly worthy of conservation due to their unusual species composition and lack of disturbance.

Table 6e Aquatic plants locally worthy of special protection

Plant	No. of Lochs
Apium inundatum	4
Carex limosa	2
C. paniculata	2
C. vesicaria	13
Potamogeton × *zizii*	1
Scirpus lacustris ssp. lacustris	6
Sparganium angustifolium	27
Utricularia intermedia	10
U. minor	7

Source: Palmer & Newbold, 1983

High altitude lochs. The high corrie lochs of the Cairngorms generally have rather sparse macrophytic floras. The harsh conditions, coarse substrata and wave-washed shores allow only a few plants such as awlwort and water lobelia to survive. The main interest of these lochs is to be found in their planktonic algal populations which include many rare and unusual species. The work of Battarbee and his colleagues on the diatom flora of lochs such as Lochnagar and Loch Coire an Lochan, in relation to acidification, is discussed later.

Morrison and Harriman (1992) noted the presence of shoreweed, water lobelia and bulbous rush (*Juncus bulbosus*) in lochs such as Einich and Loch a' Bhanain. Loch Callater, on Deeside, had larger plants such as *Myriophyllum* spp. A much greater diversity of benthic invertebrates is to be found in those lochs with a well vegetated littoral zone.

Other lochs. A recent survey of Loch Davan (Dinnet NNR) by Diers (1994), using a global positioning system, has produced an interesting series of maps showing the distribution of the various species which he recorded (Plate 46). Davan is generally considered to be mesotrophic, contrasting with its oligotrophic neighbour, Loch Kinord, which has a less rich flora and little agricultural land in its catchment.

Most of the central area of Davan is occupied by dense stands of the invasive Canadian pondweed (*Elodea canadensis*) with more scattered plants occupying the east corner and west margin. It is not known when *Elodea* was introduced to the loch but undoubtedly it has had a major impact on the distribution of other species such as curled pondweed (*Potamogeton crispus*), perfoliate pondweed (*P. perfoliatus*) and blunt-leaved pondweed. Other species recorded by Diers include waterwort (*Elatine hexandra*), white water-lily and common club-rush (*Schoenoplectus lacustris*).

Both lochs show evidence of having reduced in open water area during this century. Spence (1964) indicated that up to 20 cm of sediment had accumulated in parts of the north-west corner of Kinord over about 57 years. Marren (1979) presents evidence from aerial photographs of hydroseral shrinkage over the past century.

The exposed shores of these lochs are largely weed free, but elsewhere there are stands of bottle sedge (*Carex rostrata*) and slender sedge (*C. lasiocarpa*) alternating with *Phragmites* swamp. In Kinord, this reed-swamp is up to 400m wide on the silty delta formed by the Vat Burn. A variety of other species appear around the lochs as the reed-swamp becomes fen on the less steep shores.

WETLANDS

The majority of wetlands are of natural origin and as such are valuable conservation sites. They are not discrete entities and generally form part of a continuum from aquatic to terrestrial habitats. The historical changes which have taken place are frequently recorded in the water-logged sediments and peats and can be revealed by palaeoecological studies in a way not usually possible in other habitats.

The Sphagnaceae is the dominant group in the great peat mosses of the area, acting as vast unseen reservoirs slowly releasing the winter's precipitation and snow-melt throughout the drier summer months. Their ability to exchange hydrogen ions for valuable nutrients contributes to the acidification of these waters (Gagnon & Glime, 1992). *Sphagnum* is able to hold many times its own weight in water and such wet moss habitats support many microscopic animals, such as protozoans and tardigrades.

Insh Marshes. This area includes the series of lochans (discussed above) which Charter regarded as the most valuable open waters in the Spey Valley. The semi-aquatic vegetation of this complex site is equally important, and the Insh Marshes constitute the largest flood plain mire outside the Norfolk Broads (Ratcliffe, 1977). Rieley and Page (1991) describe the vegetation of the marshes as being essentially northern in character, containing a strong boreal element of the British flora. However the flora also contains a variety of plants which are near their northern geographical limit.

A complex mosaic of wetland plant communities, including fen, swamp, marsh and bog, has developed in the flood plain between Kingussie and Kincraig and this has been described by various authors (Charter, 1988 a & b; Fojt, 1989; Wood & Evans, 1989). Additional work has been carried out by Murphy and Hudson (1991) and Rieley and Page (1991).

The succession from open water to dry land is affected by minor differences in substratum, water chemistry, flow and depth, producing a mosaic of plant communities. The balance between fen and bog communities will be determined largely by the degree of flooding and the area has been much modified by past control measures such as flood banks and drainage ditches. However, it seems likely that these have increased the diversity of the Insh Marshes. Rieley and Page (1991) concluded that the over-riding factor influencing the aquatic plant communities of the Insh Marshes is the hydrology of the adjacent section of the River Spey and its flood plain, with the frequency and extent of flooding determining the balance between the different communities.

THE FAUNA

Invertebrates. Adaptations to life in torrential upland streams have been well described by numerous authors such as Neilsen (1950) and Hynes (1970). The headwater streams of the Cairngorms present probably the most extreme and hostile unpolluted environment for aquatic invertebrates in the UK. The short summer season and low temperatures throughout the year mean that development of egg and larval stages will be slow and several species of upland insect are brachypterous (short-winged) in their adult stage.

The macroinvertebrates are probably the most studied because of their value as pollution indicator organisms and, as such, have been used by the pollution control authorities and other organizations to monitor long-term environmental changes, such as the effects of acidification on upland catchments (Doughty, 1990).

Morgan, Egglishaw and Mackay (Morgan & Egglishaw, 1964; Egglishaw & Morgan, 1965; Egglishaw & Mackay, 1967), in their classic survey of the bottom fauna of streams in the Scottish highlands, appear not to have included the Cairngorms area. However, many of their findings are undoubtedly applicable to the streams of the Cairngorms. The springtime faunas of the streams they sampled, including largely granite-based catchments, were composed mainly of stoneflies, mayflies and diptera. By contrast, the dominant groups in their summer samples were Chironomidae, mayflies and oligochaetes.

A macroinvertebrate survey of the River Dee was carried out for the Nature Conservancy Council in 1978–9 (Davidson & Young, 1979; Davidson, Owen & Young, 1985) and included samples taken in the headwaters of the Dee and its tributaries. As in Morgan, Egglishaw and Mackay's survey of highland streams, the fauna in the highest streams was dominated by stoneflies. The Allt na Lairig Ghru, at 800 m, and the Allt a' Garbh-Choire, at 605 m, were the only localities where Davidson found *Protonemura montana*, a distinctly upland stonefly, in the Dee catchment. Other upland species recorded at these sites were another stonefly *Diura bicaudata* and the mayfly *Ameletus inopinatus*. The Dee near Corrour Bothy (545 m) was the only site for the stonefly *Capnia vidua*, a species found in small stony streams. Aquatic weeds were uncommon in these high burns but mosses such as *Rhynchostegium riparioides* provided a niche for *Taeniopteryx nebulosa*, a detrital feeding stonefly with dorsal abdominal spines which help it to avoid being washed out.

Other surveys have been carried out by Morrison and Harriman (1992) on the high altitude lochs and headwaters of the Spey and Dee. Wright and Furse (1990) surveyed the Spey, while Maitland (1991) looked at the invertebrates on the Spey, Feshie and Insh Marshes, in relation to the Feshie flood alleviation scheme.

The rivers of the Cairngorms are monitored in relation to water quality trends and specific pollution problems, such as acidification, by the Scottish Environment Protection Agency (SEPA), formerly the North East and Tay River Protection Boards. Relatively few sites are monitored because the area is, rightly, considered to be one of the most pristine in the British Isles. The water quality of the area has been put in a national context in the 1990 and 1995 Water Quality Reviews (Scottish Office, 1992, 1997). All of the watercourses in the Cairngorms area were assessed as being of the highest biological quality (Class A), except for parts of the upper River Dee (Class B) which suffer from the effects of acidification.

Since 1983 the NERPB and SEPA have monitored acidification in the upper Spey and Dee catchments. A large-scale survey of the uplands was carried out by the River Purification Boards during 1986–89, the results of which were recorded by Doughty (1989 & 1990). This puts the Cairngorms sites in a wider Scottish context and identifies invertebrates which may be useful as indicators of acidification.

Invertebrate data from the Spey and Dee, collected by the NERPB, were included in a national classification of running water sites which formed the basis of the *RIV*ers *P*rediction *A*nd *C*lassification *S*cheme (RIVPACS) (Wright *et al.*, 1984).

As Morgan and his colleagues noted, the dipteran larvae, and in particular the Chironomidae, form a major portion of the fauna of upland streams, especially during the summer months. They are important components of the fauna and deserve greater attention from freshwater ecologists.

The most diverse sites for macroinvertebrates in the upper Dee catchment were found to be at boundaries between potamon and rithron zones, where slow flowing stretches became shallow, stony riffles and habitat diversity is greatest. At these places the fauna consisted of a mixture of the characteristic species of both regimes such as the mayflies *Leptophlebia marginata*, *Siphlonurus lacustris* and *Rhithrogena semicolorata*. Similarly, as already noted, the presence of Loch Insh on the Spey significantly increases the secondary productivity of the river downstream.

Loch outflows are important for a variety of specialist invertebrates such as the caddis Neureclepsis bimaculatum, which filter out (in this case using a net) fine planktonic debris, and the stonefly Capnia atra, an inhabitant of shallow loch shores, which is regularly found in the outflow of Loch Muick.

Little work has been done on the benthic macroinvertebrates of the lochs, but a grab survey of Morlich, in 1988, showed that the dominant types were *Pisidium* spp. (pea-mussels) and Chironomids and there is considerable scope for anyone interested in the taxonomy of these groups. Other invertebrates included the caddis *Cyrnus flavidus* and the mayfly *Leptophlebia vespertina*. The highest diversity was found in the area of greatest silt deposition, near the inlet.

Morrison and Harriman (1992) give lists of benthic invertebrates collected from sixteen Cairngorms lochs, including Coire an Lochain, Lochnagar, Dubh Loch and Einich and recorded species such as *Procloeon bifidum* (Ephemeroptera), *Hygrotus novemlineatus* (Coleoptera) and *Holocentropus picicornis* (Trichoptera).

Despite all this monitoring activity, the ecology of the aquatic invertebrates of the Cairngorms is relatively poorly known compared with similar upland areas elsewhere. There is considerable scope in the Cairngorms for more detailed survey work, placing more reliance on the identification of adult insects, both collected and reared.

THREATS TO AQUATIC HABITATS

WATER QUALITY AND POLLUTION

Within the Cairngorms area, there is only a small number of industrial effluent discharges. These include fish farms and whisky distilleries and, in relation to the available dilution and inputs from natural sources, they have little impact on the general water quality.

Treated sewage effluent is discharged from a number of small and medium-sized settlements, and again these have a relatively minor impact. The high ecological quality of the Dee and Spey is recognized by the regulatory authorities, and higher standards are applied to effluents being discharged to these waters than in less sensitive areas. The designation of these rivers as Special Areas of Conservation under the EC Habitats Directive (92/43/EEC) and the implementation of the EC Water Framework Directive (2000/60/EC) will provide additional mechanisms to protect their international status.

Acidification. It is well known that the gaseous effluents of industrial processes, particularly the oxides of nitrogen and sulphur, can be transported long distances in the atmosphere before being deposited as an acidic rain, mist or dust. Immediate effects can be caused by sudden heavy rainfall, or snow-melt, rapidly reducing the pH in a stream and

resulting in the death of fish. On a longer time-scale the acid waters leach cations from the soil, reducing their buffering capacity and releasing aluminium which can be toxic to a variety of organisms.

Acidification of freshwaters can affect their plant communities as well as invertebrates and fish. Kinross *et al.* (1993), studying highland streams, have shown that a fall in pH is accompanied by a decrease in algal biomass and diversity. The benthic and planktonic algal communities react to a progressive decrease in pH with a reduction in abundance of diatoms and rhodophytes and their progressive replacement by cyanobacteria and then filamentous green algae which become increasingly common below pH 6.0. Even the micro-organisms responsible for degradation of organic matter and making it palatable to various invertebrates, are affected by acidification (Griffith & Perry, 1993; Chamier, 1987).

At a first glance the Cairngorms area appears remote from sources of atmospheric pollution but, even as early as the 1950s, Gorham (1957) was speculating that atmospheric pollution was influencing the region's waters. An important factor in determining the effect of acid deposition on freshwaters is the buffering capacity of the local soils. In the Cairngorms, the soils are very base poor, having been derived largely from resistant igneous and

Table 6f   Classification of Cairngorm streams in relation to pH and alkalinity

	Alka-linity	pH	Classification by Doughty as:
Allt an Dubh Loch	1	5.3	Normally acid
Glass Allt	1	5.6	
River Muick	2	5.9	Occasion-ally acid
Allt a'Mharcaidh	2	6.3	
Allt Fearnagan	3	6.4	
Allt Ruadh	3	6.3	
Feith Talagain	4	6.0	
Allt an t'Slugain Dhuibh	4	6.3	
Quoich Water	4	6.4	
River Lui	4	6.5	
Allt Mor	5	6.4	Rarely/never acid
Allt Coire Chaoil	7	6.8	
Allt na Fearna	9	6.7	
Slugain Burn	9	6.8	
Callater Burn	12	7.0	
Allt Darrarie	13	6.8	
Allt na Baranachd	15	6.8	
Baddoch Burn	18	7.2	

metamorphic rocks, and the buffering capacity is low.

The realization that upland catchments, particularly with underlying granite, could be susceptible to acidification prompted the River Purification Board to initiate a long-term monitoring programme in 1983, based on eighteen streams with varying geology. From 1986 to 1989, these sites were included in a Scotland-wide baseline investigation (Doughty, 1990), against which future changes in acidity can be measured. These long-term data are presented in Table 6f giving the mean alkalinity and mean pH of the Caingorm streams, and their classification according to Doughty.

In addition to two normally acid sites, eight were considered to be vulnerable to acid events on the basis that they had alkalinities below 5mg/l. Other streams, such as the Allt Mor (Glen Feshie) with a recorded minimum pH of 4.9, were also apparently at risk from acid events. Doughty found that the most acid waters were those draining granitic rocks, while a strong correlation between the concentration of non-marine sulphate and the Henricksen Acidification Index (Henricksen, 1980) indicated a clear link between acidification and loss of alkalinity. Within Scotland, those sites identified as being susceptible to acidification were found mainly in Galloway, the Trossachs and the Cairngorms.

The invertebrate data showed a general relationship between pH and species richness, with the most acid sites having the lowest numbers of species. Stoneflies were found to be the most tolerant of acid conditions and the physical characteristics of watercourses had a greater influence on their distribution than had the pH.

Despite these general findings, there is often no simple relationship between surface water chemistry and stream biology. Other factors such as the ground water composition, structure of the hyporheic zone and the amount of organic matter will influence the effects of acid events. Using continuous water quality data, Jarvie *et al.* (2001) have indicated that there are large hydrologically active stores of groundwater in the upper Dee catchment. These provide an important contribution to stream flow under summer low-flows, when the biota can have a significant diurnal effect on pH.

A recent review of data for acidified streams around the Cairngorms up to 1994, by Soulsby *et al.* (1995, 1997), showed that despite a significant decline in the concentration of non-marine sulphate in those waters, there was only slight evidence for the recovery of the stream biology. Biological recovery is likely to take place over a longer time-scale. In Canada, Hall and Ide (1987) were able to show changes in faunal composition related to increased acidity over half a century. However, there are no comparable historical data for any Cairngorm site.

The lochs of the Cairngorms have also shown evidence of acidification and this has been investigated by scientists from University College London. They have examined the deposits of animal and plant remains from the bottom sediments of several lochs where they are preserved by the cold, low oxygen, acidic conditions. Of particular interest are the silica shells of diatoms, a type of single-celled alga, which are resistant to decay and relatively easily identified. There are many different species of diatom each with their own ecological niche and preferred pH range. Temporal changes in pH in a loch would be expected to be mirrored by adjustments in the composition of the diatom flora. Jones *et al.* (1993) studied five lochs in the Cairngorms area, four of which show clear evidence of acidification since the mid to late nineteenth century, Lochnagar, Loch nan Eun, Dubh Loch, Lochan Uaine. The diatom assemblages identified at different depths in the cores were compared with modern diatom communities which occur at a known pH, and statistical techniques were used to derive an estimated historical pH.

Studies by Flower and Jones (1989) produced five new diatom taxa from these lochs including *Achnanthes scotica*. The decline of this and several other species, indicated by these studies, has implications for the conservation value of these unique ecosystems.

The results of the analyses indicated that the pH in Lochnagar, the Dubh Loch and Lochan Uaine had decreased by about 0.5 units since the mid to late nineteenth century. The decrease in Loch nan Eun had exceeded 0.5 pH units since the start of the

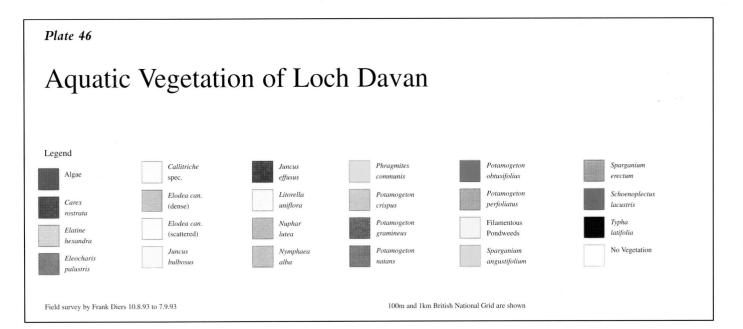

Plate 46

Aquatic Vegetation of Loch Davan

Legend

Algae	
Carex rostrata	
Elatine hexandra	
Eleocharis palustris	
Callitriche spec.	
Elodea can. (dense)	
Elodea can. (scattered)	
Juncus bulbosus	
Juncus effusus	
Litorella uniflora	
Nuphar lutea	
Nymphaea alba	
Phragmites communis	
Potamogeton crispus	
Potamogeton gramineus	
Potamogeton natans	
Potamogeton obtusifolius	
Potamogeton perfoliatus	
Filamentous Pondweeds	
Sparganium angustifolium	
Sparganium erectum	
Schoenoplectus lacustris	
Typha latifolia	
No Vegetation	

Field survey by Frank Diers 10.8.93 to 7.9.93

100m and 1km British National Grid are shown

Computer Cartography at ITE Banchory by Philip Bacon and Frank Diers

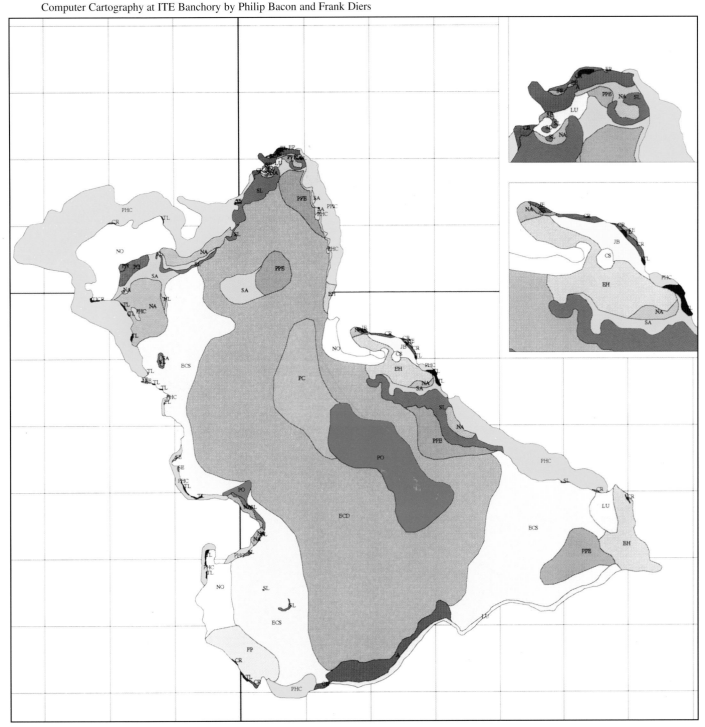

Plate 47 (above left)
Wells of Dee. September 1983.
Photo: North East River
Purification Board.

Plate 48 (above right)
Lairig Ghru and Pools of Dee, July
1989. Photo: Roger Owen.

Plate 49 (centre)
Loch Morlich and the Cairngorms
beyond. Photo: Mike Davidson

Plate 50
Punch Bowl, Glen Quoich,
near Braemar. May 1981.

Photo: Mike Davidson

Plate 51 *(above)*
Dubh Lochan from Beinn a' Bhuird. May 1984.
Photo: Richard Gibbens.

Plate 52 *(right)*
Loch Muick, June 1988. Photo: Mike Davidson.

Plate 53 *(below)*
River Dee – upper stretches of the Linn, July 1990.
Photo: Roy Dennis.

Plate 54
Loch Einich in snow, 1987.

Photo: Mike Davidson.

Plate 55
Loch a' Gharbh-Choire,
Strathnethy, October 1993.

Photo: Mike Davidson.

Plate 56
River Nethy in Abernethy
Forest with semi-natural
pinewood vegetation and
fallen trees, October 1993.

Photo: Mike Davidson

twentieth century while Loch Coire an Lochan showed no change. These changes contrast with lochs in south-west Scotland where the pH has decreased by 1 pH unit.

Eutrophication. Despite the preponderance of nutrient-poor surface waters in the Cairngorms there are anthropogenic and other sources of nitrogen and phosphorus in the catchments of certain waterbodies and, in a few cases, some symptoms of eutrophication are already apparent. Catchment-derived nutrient sources include domestic sewage and fertilizers used to promote forestry and agricultural productivity.

The most often quoted biological manifestation of eutrophication in standing waters is the appearance of phytoplanktonic algal blooms. Loch Garten, surrounded by mature Caledonian pine forest and famous for its ospreys, has no obvious catchment-derived sources of nutrients but has suffered regular, usually short-lived, blooms of phytoplankton over recent years at least. Dominant genera have included the potentially toxic cyanobacteria *Anabaena* and *Microcystis* as well as, at other times, diatoms and green algae. Significantly, there appears to have been a reduction in the number of species of pondweed (*Potamogeton* spp.) since the 1940s. Loch Garten regularly supports a large population of birds of different species and their faecal deposits may well contribute to the availability of phosphorus at times crucial for phytoplankton growth. Bearing in mind the ecological interdependency of ospreys, fish and trophic status, further study of this important loch would be prudent.

Phytoplanktonic blooms are relatively rare in Cairngorm lochs but symptoms of eutrophication might be inferred from the abundance of benthic, mat-forming algal communities, including the potentially toxic cyanobacterium (blue-green alga) genus, *Oscillatoria*, reported from Loch Insh, a well-known centre for watersports activities. Anecdotal evidence is that the quantity of algal material accumulating on lee shores in late summer and early autumn has increased in recent years. The toxicity of these accumulations was demonstrated all too well in 1991 and 1992 by the poisoning of dogs which had consumed the decaying, stranded mats (Edwards *et al.*, 1992). The catchment of Loch Insh receives treated sewage effluents from a number of settlements, including Newtonmore, Kingussie, Lynchat and Insh. Despite this, and the abundance of benthic algae, it would appear from limited chemical monitoring (Table 6c) and relatively low phytoplanktonic biomass that Loch Insh has been classified as oligotrophic (Charter, 1988a). However, it is very likely that the high annual mean flushing rate of over 21 loch volumes per year (Bailey-Watts *et al.*, 1993) severely restricts phytoplankton abundance. More information is needed to assess nutrient loading, especially during peak flows and flood events, and to determine the nutrient chemistry of the loch sediment/algal mat interface.

The disposal of sewage effluent takes place even in the mountain areas. Treated sewage from the many thousands of visitors to the skiing facilities on Cairn Gorm, discharges into mountain streams draining to Loch Morlich. Monitoring of the loch and its catchment, which began in 1980 and still continues, has shown no evidence for any increase in nitrogen or phosphorus. There are, however, recent records of *Oscillatoria* forming light scums on the recreational beach at the east end of the loch. It is not clear whether this is a recent or merely a previously unreported phenomenon.

Loch Davan, which has the highest trophic status of all those waterbodies listed in Table 6c, does not support high phytoplanktonic productivity (Bailey-Watts *et al.*, 1993). This lack of algal biomass demonstrates the importance of a number of other factors controlling the accumulation of algal cells in lochs. The most important in this case are the high flushing rate and an extensive littoral zone supporting dense macrophyte beds.

The quality of a number of Cairngorm lochs is presented within a Scottish classification for standing waters, by Fozzard *et al.* (1999), based on phosphorus, acid neutralizing capacity and toxic substances. Although not specifically in the Cairngorms, Gilbert and Giovarini (2000) have investigated the zonation of lichens in the splash zone around lochs and related the communities to water quality. They also highlight the need for investigation of the effects of artificial alteration of water levels.

ABSTRACTION AND CATCHMENT TRANSFERS

Within the Cairngorms area there are significant abstractions and catchment transfers for power generation, mainly under two schemes. The Scottish Hydro-Electric scheme transfers flows from the Tromie and Truim into the Ericht-Tummel-Tay system, while the British Alcan Scheme diverts upper Spey and Mashie waters into the Pattack-Laggan system. An estimate of the quantities of water transferred out of the Spey catchment is given in Table 6g.

These abstractions together represent a considerable discharge loss to the Spey, being about 42 per cent of the mean daily flow expected from the upper catchment as measured at Loch Insh and 19 per cent of that expected from the whole catchment. There are likely to have been some ecological consequences of these diversion schemes though it would be difficult to assess them in retrospect. Certainly, there must have been a significant loss of potential spawning streams for salmon since about 45 per cent of the Tromie and Truim catchments, some 79.7 km², and the whole of the Mashie, another 26.6 km², became impassable. The remainder of the Tromie and Truim, and the upper Spey catchments have been provided with minimal compensation flows – the Spey Dam provides a dry weather compensation flow of about 1 m³/sec compared to the estimated mean daily diversion of 7.3 m³/sec – and fish ladders at the retaining structures.

These catchment transfers were enabled by various legislative means and capital works executed between 1921 and 1940. The EC Water Framework Directive will introduce controls on

Table 6g   Catchment transfers from the upper Spey

Watercourse	NGR* of Dam	Catchment Area (km²)	Estimated Mean Daily Flow (m³/sec)
a) Scottish Hydro-Electric plc			
Allt Bhran	NN 776894	27.3	1.1
Tromie	NN 764882	56.0	2.7
Allt na Fearna	NN 750894	8.1	0.2
Loch Cuaich	NN 691873	13.1	0.4
Allt a Choire Chais	NN 683865	8.7	0.3
Allt a Chore Chairn	NN 673861	7.3	0.2
River Truim	NN 638835	42.1	2.0
Allt Choire Bhathaich	NN 641838	5.6	0.2
Allt an t-Sluic	NN 635862	8.5	0.3
Caochan an Tuigh	NN 633854	1.1	0.1
Totals		177.8	7.5
b) British Alcan			
Spey	NN 582935	173.8	7.3
Mashie	NN 587909	26.6	0.7
Totals		200.4	8.0
Totals for all Abstractions		378.2	15.5
Long-term gauged flows in the Spey at Kinrara (downstream Loch Insh)		1012.0	21.0
at Boat o'Brig (lowest station)		2861.0	64.3

*NGR is National Grid Reference

water impoundment and abstraction. There is currently little indication of the extent of private abstraction other than Water Orders for Public Supply and Spray Irrigation Orders under the *Natural Heritage (Scotland) Act* 1991.

Another major abstraction in the area is from Loch Einich which has a supply order enabling abstraction of up to 6.82 Ml/d (1991 figure, equivalent to 0.01 m³/sec) of water to the Aviemore area.

FLOOD ALLEVIATION

Upland rivers are characteristically spatey. Heavy rainfall on the hills, or rapid snow-melt, drains quickly to the river valleys. In extreme cases the waters may overtop the banks, inundating the flood plain. Flooding in the highlands has undoubtedly been exacerbated by centuries of deforestation and land drainage, resulting in more rapid runoff and soil erosion.

Historically, there are many records of catastrophic flooding, where life and property have been lost. Calculated from the statistics of recorded flows, the time which would be expected to elapse before such a flood would recur is known as its return period. However, these are probabilities based on

recent past experience, and there is no reason why several large floods should not occur in quick succession and, indeed, this is exactly what has happened in Strathspey, and on the Tay and Dee, in recent years.

Properties built on the flood plain have been affected repeatedly, resulting in danger to life and financial loss. This situation has led to calls for flood alleviation schemes and attention has been focused on the River Feshie at its confluence with the Spey below the Insh Marshes. The Feshie transports large amounts of sediment into the Spey and deposition of this 'plug' of material and the resulting constriction of the channel was seen as one cause of the flooding problem.

The area is of national and international importance for nature conservation. The Insh Marshes and adjacent River Spey constitute a biological SSSI which has been proposed as a Ramsar Site and Special Protection Area. The Feshie SSSI was designated on the basis of its geomorphological importance, being the best example of an active alluvial fan in Britain, and has recently been recognized as an area of considerable biological importance (Stubbs, 1991). Although Loch Insh has no formal designation it is an area of great importance for wildlife and recreation and has considerable influence on the ecology of the River Spey.

Two schemes proposed for flood alleviation in Upper Strathspey were to realign the River Feshie at its confluence with the Spey, or to regrade the main channel of the Spey downstream from Loch Insh. These proposals prompted the Nature Conservancy Council for Scotland (NCCS) to commission a major study by the Institute of Hydrology into the likely efficacy and effects of these two options (Johnson *et al.*, 1991). Experts in engineering, hydrology, geomorphology, and aquatic and terrestrial ecology were asked to consider both schemes, in relation to their impact on the various components of the Spey-Insh-Feshie system. The study brought together a vast amount of pre-existing information about this important river flood-plain ecosystem and the effects that river engineering would have on it. Equally important has been the realization that very little was known about the complex ecology of the Feshie Fan braided stream system (see earlier discussion).

Flood alleviation relies on increasing the amount of water which the channel is capable of moving downstream, either by increasing the cross-section of the channel or by increasing its gradient. These methods are, respectively, analogous to dualling a road and increasing the speed limit. Both result in the traffic, cars or water, getting to their destination more quickly and with greater peak intensity. However, this only moves the problem on to the next settlement.

The reduction of flooding is likely to have the effect of lowering water levels in Loch Insh and the Insh Marshes during drier periods, leading to a reduction in habitat area for a wide range of plants and animals. Channelization of the Feshie would reduce the amount of inundation of adjacent woodland and affect the maintenance of open shingle. In all cases habitat diversity would be reduced.

The agreed compromise was to excavate a new channel for the river through a series of established sediment deposits. Results from a computational model of the river system had shown that the design of this channel would result in a small lowering of flood water levels but little change in dry weather levels in the Insh Marshes, and would therefore minimize impact on the ecology and geomorphology of the river system. Following these modifications little change in the Insh Marshes water levels has been observed but further major flood events have recurred which have seen parts of the Spey returning to its old channel. Such schemes obviously require major capital input to maintain any benefit which does accrue.

It is disappointing that some river managers in Scotland have not learned from the mistakes which have been made, and are now being corrected, in many other parts of the world. It was to the credit of the NCCS (now Scottish Natural Heritage) that it sought expert advice on the situation on the Spey and reached a compromise. The need in Stathspey and other highland river systems is not to prevent flooding but to recognize its ecological importance and to manage it by setting aside areas of the natural flood plain as safety valves. The reality and inevitability of flooding must be recognized by planning authorities who should restrict development to safe areas. Engineering guidance for gravel-bed rivers is given by Hoey *et al.* (1998).

FISH FARMING

The abundance of good quality water is a factor favouring the intensive production of salmonids. However, there are only two fish farms in the area under consideration, both being land-based units abstracting 'from watercourses. The fish farm at Inverdruie, Aviemore, is by far the largest in the north-east of Scotland with an annual production up to 200 tonnes of rainbow trout, taking water from the River Druie and discharging to the Spey. The discharges from these fish farms are controlled by consent conditions designed to protect the Spey from undue organic loading, suspended solids, excess nutrient enrichment or other pollutants, especially during dry weather flows. Escapes of farm fish can have significant impacts on wild populations and disease transmission is also a concern for fishery managers.

FORESTRY

Large areas of the wider Cairngorms, up to the altitudinal growth limit of 500 m, are potentially suitable for afforestation (Towers & Thompson, 1988). Appropriate woodland regeneration, where open pine forest and native deciduous species are encouraged, would certainly enhance the productivity and biological diversity of streams and still waters. However, economic timber production often dictates that more regimented stands of fast-growing, non-native conifers are grown very intensively.

Commercial forestry activities may adversely affect aquatic ecology through poor management in a number of ways. Initial ploughing and planting can cause erosion and increased sediment transport leading to major changes in the substratum composition of stream beds. Erosion of stream banks occurs at later stages of forest development when canopies close over watercourses and shade the marginal and semi-aquatic vegetation whose root systems bind the soils together. The accumulation of sand and silt on coarser materials reduces the abundance and diversity of invertebrate fauna and clogs salmonid spawning gravels. Planting too close to streams also shades out aquatic algae, macrophytes and bryophytes which are essential components of stream ecology.

Forestry fertilization programmes, using materials that release phosphorus and nitrogen, are commonly considered as essential for economic viability on poor soils. Subsequent losses into watercourses of up to five per cent of the applied fertilizer have been measured and leaching of nutrients can occur over long periods (Swift, 1987; Harriman, 1978). The enrichment of streams and upland lochs, particularly those previously oligotrophic, can lead to significant increases in algal productivity and to undesirable ecological change. The quality of upland water supplies could be threatened by afforestation so that the costs of treatment then rise substantially (Critchley, McNaughton & Youngman, 1980).

Afforestation may exacerbate acidification of susceptible streams through the propensity of trees to filter out acid pollutants in the atmosphere, which are then washed down into forest soils (Miller, 1988). However, recent modelling work by Wade *et al.* (2001) indicates that regeneration of Scots pine forest is unlikely to contribute significantly to stream acidification.

TOURISM AND RECREATION

The Cairngorms attract many tourists who indulge in a wide range of land and water-based outdoor pursuits which have direct or indirect effects on the aquatic environment. For example, access to the ski areas, and general road maintenance in the winter, require the use of large amounts of salt and subsequent runoff may affect the fauna or flora of receiving waters (Williams & Feltmate, 1992). A baseline survey of Loch Alvie (NERPB, 1980), in relation to the Aviemore by-pass, indicated that the Loch was unlikely to be adversely affected. However, small streams or ponds, receiving large amounts of runoff may well be damaged. One small road-side pool in upper Donside contains rare water-beetles, such as *Dytiscus lapponicus* and *Gyrinus opacus*, which are at risk because of leaching from salt heaps.

Anecdotal evidence suggests that there has been increased erosion in the Allt Mor catchment on Cairn Gorm due to the ski developments and that there has been increased sediment deposition in Loch Morlich.

The populations of villages such as Braemar and Aviemore fluctuate widely due to influxes of tourists for periods in the summer and winter. Continuing development pressures at Aviemore have resulted in the treatment works rapidly reaching maximum capacity and new facilities are being provided.

CLIMATE CHANGE

It has been recognized for many years that there has been a continuing increase in the average global temperature (Meterological Office, 1982) and that industrialization and world deforestation, through the production of various 'greenhouse' gases, have driven this process.

Potentially, many species would benefit from an extension to their ranges, with a rise in global temperature. However, there may be considerable consequences for upland areas such as the Cairngorms, where even small changes in temperature regime could mean the loss of numerous post-glacial relict species and habitats. Aquatic ecosytems could be badly affected and furthermore, as temperatures rise, peatlands may compound the problem by releasing additional greenhouse gases from their reservoirs of carbon dioxide and methane. The rate of this process may be further accelerated by the deposition of nitrogen and phosphorus from the atmosphere.

These climatic changes will also affect the distribution and quantity of precipitation. It has been predicted that there will be an increase in winter precipitation and runoff, but a reduction in the amount of snowfall and ice. However the mean annual change in precipitation may be quite small due to a reduction in summer rainfall (Hessen, 1993). The implications of these changes on drinking water supplies in catchments such as the Dee and Spey, which rely on surface abstraction, are considerable. Hydroelectricity generation would also be affected.

A temperature increase would have implications for the distribution, reproduction and development

of many species. The flatworms *Crenobia alpina* and *Polycelis felina* live in streams and partition the habitat in relation to temperature. An increase in temperature would presumably move the boundary, between the species, uphill. *Crenobia* may become less common in the benthos of streams, relying more on the cooler subterranean and hyporheic habitats along with a range of other species such as the beetle *Agabus guttatus*.

The lower-lying lochs such as Insh are likely to warm significantly in the absence of the spring snow-melt with consequences for the distribution of arctic charr.

Other indirect effects such as increases in the rate of mineralization of organic matter, winter runoff and erosion of soils may increase the winter phosphorus loadings, with implications for the nutrient status of upland lochs. Hessen and Wright (1993) present evidence, from Norway, of the effects of three consecutive mild winters (1988–90) which indicated significant increases in the phosporus load during the winter months. Much of this phosphorus will be adsorbed to soil particles but Berg and Kalqvist (1990) have shown, using algal bioassay techniques in relation to agricultural runoff, that up to 40 per cent of this phosphorus is available for use by algae. This may have relevance in situations like Loch Insh where benthic algal mats are currently causing problems.

The same authors predict increased acidification of soils and water due to the increased release of nitrogen from the mineralization of peat in areas that are already saturated with atmospheric nitrogen.

Another possible effect of mild winters was observed in Southern Norway during 1989 and 1990, when the pH of an upland stream underwent a significant reduction (Hessen & Wright, 1993). The pH fell from about 6.0 to 5.0, probably because surface runoff had little interaction with the snow-free, but still frozen, soil.

CONSERVATION AND MANAGEMENT OF AQUATIC HABITATS

HABITAT DEGRADATION AND DEFORESTATION

Arguably, the biggest impacts on the aquatic ecology of the Cairngorms have been brought about by degradation of terrestrial habitats and landuse changes. The composition of terrestrial vegetation has suffered considerable modification during the past millennium with undoubted consequences for aquatic habitats.

The post-glacial Caledonian pine forest has disappeared from much of the Cairngorms. Where native woodland once covered about 80 per cent of the land surface, there remains only 10 per cent cover of the area below the natural treeline (Cairngorms Working Party, 1993). The roots of this lost forest are still present in the peat at surprisingly high altitudes in areas such as Glen Geusachan. The

old Caledonian woodlands were probably quite open with a mixture of species, including native broadleaves such as birch and rowan. Aquatic habitats within this forest would have been diverse, ranging from forest mires to open waters. Large-scale forest loss may well have altered temperature regimes in surface waters through removal of a varied degree of shading. Of major effect would be the reduced input of organic matter, particularly leaves and terrestrial invertebrates, thus lowering the productivity of pools and streams. The structure of instream habitats must be quite different in the absence of significant amounts of submerged timber. Even where woodland still exists adjacent to watercourses, fallen trees are often removed to alleviate perceived flooding problems, and to improve access for fishing. However, dead wood provides niches for a variety of organisms, it obstructs flow thereby collecting organic matter, such as leaves and finer sediments, increasing the structural diversity of the habitat (Petts, 2000). The removal of tree cover is known to affect catchment yield and flow regime, and bankside trees play an important role in bank stabilization.

The re-establishment of mixed, open woodland, particularly in upland areas, would have considerable benefits by restoring a degree of aquatic habitat diversity which is now sadly lacking. Areas such as the Nethy catchment, now largely owned by the RSPB, provide important opportunities for the restoration of aquatic habitats to their natural condition (Plate 56). The proposal by Scottish Natural Heritage to reintroduce the Beaver is likely to be beneficial in this respect, if accompanied by significant broad-leaved woodland expansion to support the population.

Acidification. As described previously, acidification has already occurred over a long period in the high lochans and streams, particularly in the Lochnagar area. Measurable effects on fauna and flora include damage to fisheries and to fish food organisms. The freshwater pearl mussel *Margaratifera margaratifera* has undoubtedly suffered a reduction in range and abundance because of acidification. Although this species is protected by law from exploitation it remains vulnerable to environmental change.

Amelioration of acidification by liming has been attempted extensively in Scandinavia, and also in Scotland, for example, at Loch Dee in Galloway (Werritty & Maucotel, 1993). An economic assessment of the effectiveness of liming in an acid Scottish loch showed that secondary productivity could be improved but, in most such cases, annual treatments would be necessary (Owen, 1976). The risks of unpredictable habitat change are probably too great for liming to be used as a large-scale conservation measure in fragile, oligotrophic systems. Foster (1991a) recorded a decline in water beetles after the liming of Loch Fleet though it was not clear how much of this might have been due to the sudden pH change and how much to predation by reintroduced fish.

There have been recent reductions in the atmospheric deposition of sulphur but any reversal of the acidification process may also require lower atmospheric loads of oxides of nitrogen. It is apparent that the only satisfactory solution to the problem of acidification will be further controls at source.

Nutrient enrichment. Even apparently small changes in water chemistry can have major effects on plant and animal communities and lead eventually to the loss of the original ecosystem. The importance of maintaining the trophic status of nutrient poor waters has been recognized by the pollution control authorities and higher standards of effluent treatment are demanded for discharges to the Spey and Dee catchments. Further work is underway, for example, at Loch Insh to find out more about the interaction between sewage effluents and oligotrophic waters. The relation between sediment-derived phosphorus and the occurrence of benthic algal mats in apparently nutrient-poor lochs should be explored.

Other sources of nutrients, including forest fertilization, need to be carefully controlled and the effects of new developments predicted before allowing them to proceed. Lochs with large goose roosts, such as Garten and Davan, are among those identified as having become enriched and the nutrient contribution from birds also needs to be assessed.

PROTECTION MEASURES FOR CONSERVATION

It is debatable whether the conservation of aquatic habitats in the Cairngorms has so far been tackled successfully. Current designations do little to guard or restore the overall ecological balance of the wider Cairngorms area. While some special areas, for instance the Dinnet Lochs and the Insh Marshes, receive some measure of formal protection, many aquatic systems of undoubted conservation value do not. Lists of species of aquatic flora requiring special protection have been published (Palmer & Newbold, 1983). However, without more general powers there is little that can be done to protect those plants occurring outwith sites specially designated under the legislation. The Dee and Spey have been recognized by the Nature Conservation Review (Ratcliffe, 1977) as of particular merit. Nevertheless, the biological communities of these rivers have so far received little practical protection purely for conservation benefit because of the difficulties of designating sites with multiple land-ownership and fishing rights. The proposed designation of the main stems of the Spey and Dee as 'Special Areas of Conservation' is a welcome development in this regard.

There is no inherent reason why appropriate management of rivers for conservation and wildlife should conflict with their use for fishing. Indeed, it is now becoming clear that measures to re-establish more diverse habitats would improve fisheries and raise the quality of the river environment for all users.

Boon (1992) has addressed the issue of flood alleviation schemes on the Spey and Feshie, highlighting the conflict between conservation of the flood-dependent features and the interests of adjacent landowners. Good ecological management demands that the river be allowed to behave naturally, to inundate its flood plain occasionally and, thereby, maintain all its important, diverse features.

The issue of management agreements for whole or substantial stretches of rivers, with grant-aided improvements for conservation, should be more vigorously pursued. The economic benefits of a growth in 'ecotourism' would easily balance the costs of such measures.

The concept of integrated catchment management is gaining favour in the UK, and plans are under development for both the Spey and Dee (Scottish Environment Protection Agency, 1999). The term 'river corridor' has been used to describe the close inter-dependency between the aquatic, semi-aquatic and adjacent terrestrial zones of a river. Methods for surveying river corridors have been developed by the National Rivers Authority (NRA, 1992). Good river corridor management requires maintenance or restoration of the riparian zone, including woodland, and that demands the removal or control of grazing pressure from deer and sheep.

New methods are being developed which attempt to provide objective assessments of the conservation value of aquatic systems. Foster (1991a) has discussed the use of multivariate statistical analysis of species lists and Scottish Natural Heritage has developed a method (SERCON) which assigns scores to features and attributes of rivers (Boon et al., 1996). Care should be taken, however, that conservation scoring does not lead to the protection of a few high-value rivers at the expense of the rest; nor, indeed, should low-value rivers be abandoned but efforts made instead for their rehabilitation.

River Habitat Survey (Raven et al., 1998) is a methodology for assessing the physical character and quality of river habitats, which has been used extensively on the Spey and Dee (Webb et al., 1998). This not only provides physical habitat data for use by SERCON but will prove invaluable for assessing long-term changes in habitat quality, the impact of river modifications and the effectiveness of rehabilitation projects.

KNOWLEDGE AND AWARENESS

Few aquatic invertebrates attract public attention, unless through notoriety, as with blackfly and midges. Dragonflies are the only large and colourful insects associated with water that command wide interest, and reserve managers are able to record different species without necessarily referring to specialists. Indeed, the number of breeding dragonfly species is used as one criterion for SSSI designation of wetland sites. The Muir of Dinnet, Insh Marshes and the pools of Loch Vaa are probably worthy of formal protection on the basis of their dragonflies alone.

Foster (1991b) drew attention to the main blocks to adequate conservation of aquatic invertebrates. These included a lack of enlightenment on the part of landowners or developers; a lack of direction on the part of conservation managers; low public awareness; and ignorance amongst entomologists. This latter point was made especially to highlight the lack of detailed knowledge about life-cycles, habitat and feeding requirements, distribution of host plants, pupation sites and other ecological information.

In general, there has been little systematic survey work in the Cairngorms. Much of the research that has been carried out has concentrated on the few specially protected sites, and most surveys have tackled only the easier taxonomic groups of invertebrates. Water quality assessments using invertebrates are employed by SEPA biologists at large numbers of sites and are useful for the determination of pollutant-induced change. However, coverage of upland rivers and lochs is generally low and the taxonomic levels employed are not always sufficient for conservation purposes.

The priority for freshwater biologists and those responsible for management of the Cairngorms area must be to improve knowledge and understanding of the ecology of the aquatic habitats, their interaction with terrestrial systems and their responses to external influences. In this way, better and more appropriate management of these important resources can be put into practice.

REFERENCES

Bailey-Watts, A.E., Lyle, A.A., Kirika, A. & Gunn, I.D.M. (1993) Sensitivity of Lentic Waters. Report to the Scottish Office Environment Department. Institute of Terrestrial Ecology, Edinburgh.

Berg, D. & Calqvist, T. (1990) Bioavailability of phosphorus from agricultural runoff. A comparison with other sources. NIVA report 2367.

Berthelemy, C. (1966) Recherches ecologiques et biogéographiques sur les Plecoptères et Cleoptères d'eau courante (Hydraena et Elminthidae) des Pyrénées. Annls. Limnol. 2, 227–458.

Boon, P.J. (1992) Essential elements in the case for river conservation. In: Boon, P.J., Calow, P., & Petts, G.E., eds, River conservation and management. Wiley, Chichester. pp. 11–33.

Boon, P.J., Holmes, N.T.H., Maitland, P.S. & Rowell, T.A. (1996) SERCON: System for Evaluating Rivers for Conservation. Version 1 Manual. Scottish Natural Heritage Research Survey and Monitoring Report No. 61. SNH, Edinburgh.

Bremner, A. (1912) The physical geology of the Dee Valley. Aberdeen University Press, Aberdeen.

Cairngorms Working Party (1993) Common Sense and Sustainability: A partnership for the Cairngorms. The Scottish Office, Edinburgh.

Chamier, A.-C. (1987) Effect of pH on microbial degradation of leaf litter in seven streams of the English Lake District. Oecologia 71, 491–500.

Charter, E. (1988a) Survey of Spey Valley Lochs, 1985. Contract Surveys No.16. Nature Conservancy Council, Peterborough.

Charter, E. (1988b) Survey of Spey Valley Lochs, 1985. Annex Evaluation of sites and recommendations for conservation. Contract Surveys No.16. Nature Conservancy Council, Peterborough.

Critchley, R.F., McNaughton, J. & Youngman, R.E. (1980) Afforestation of upland catchments: economic implications for the water industry. WrC Internal Report 19-M. Medmenham.

Coupland, J.B. (1990) The ecology of black flies (Diptera: Simulidae) in the Scottish Highlands in relation to control. Ph.D. thesis, University of Aberdeen.

Cummins, K.W., Peterson, R.C., Howard, F.O., Wuycheck, J.C. & Holt, V.I. (1973) The utilisation of leaf litter by stream detritivores. Ecology 54, 336–345.

Davidson, M.B., Owen, R.P. & Young, M.R. (1985) Invertebrates of the River Dee. In: Jenkins, D., ed., The biology and management of the River Dee. (ITE sysmposium no.14.) Institute of Terrestrial Ecology, Abbots Ripton. pp.64–82.

Davidson, M.B. & Young, M.R. (1979) A Biological Survey of the River Dee (Aberdeenshire) and its Main Tributaries. Nature Conservancy Council (Unpublished).

Diers, F. (1994) GIS – Database of the Muir of Dinnet Nature Reserve and New Vegetation Map of Loch Davan. Institute of Terrestrial Ecology, Banchory.

Doughty, C.R. (1989) Baseline study of acidified waters in Scotland. Final report to the Department of the Environment (Contract No. PECD7/10/104). Clyde River Purification Board, East Kilbride.

Doughty, C.R. (1990) *Acidity in Scottish Rivers, a chemical and biological baseline survey*. Report for the Department of the Environment (Contract No. PECD7/10/104). Scottish River Purification Boards, East Kilbride.

Edwards, C., Beattie, K.A., Scrimgeour, C.M. & Codd, G.A. (1992) Identification of anatoxin-a in benthic cyanobacteria (blue-green algae) and in associated dog poisonings at Loch Insh, Scotland. *Toxicon.* **30** (10), 1165–1175.

Egglishaw, H.J. & Mackay, D.W. (1967) A survey of the bottom fauna of streams in the Scottish Highlands. Part III Seasonal changes in the fauna of three streams. *Hydrobiologia* **30**, 305–334.

Egglishaw, H.J. & Morgan, N.C. (1965) A survey of the bottom fauna of streams in the Scottish Highlands. Part II The relationship of the fauna to the chemical and geological conditions. *Hydrobiologia* **26**, 173–183.

Flower, R.J. & Jones, V.J. (1989) Taxonomic descriptions and occurrences of new *Achnanthes* taxa in acid lakes in the UK. *Diatom Research* **4**, 227–239.

Fojt, W. (1989) *A vegetation survey of the Insh Marshes SSSI*. Nature Conservancy Council, Peterborough.

Forster, J.A. & Green, J. (1985) Vegetation of the valley floor of the River Dee. In: Jenkins, D., ed., *The Biology and mangement of the River Dee*. (ITE Symposium No.14.) Institute of Terrestrial Ecology, Abbots Ripton. pp.64–82.

Foster, G.N. (1991a) Aquatic beetle population changes associated with recreating a trout fishery by liming a lake catchment. *Arch. Hydrobiol.* **122**, 313–322.

Foster, G.N. (1991b) Conserving insects of aquatic and wetland habitats, with special reference to beetles. In: *The conservation of insects and their habitats*. Royal Entomological Society, 15th Symposium. Academic Press, London.

Fozzard, I., Doughty, R., Ferrier, R.C., Leatherhead, T. & Owen, R. (1999) A quality classification for management of Scottish standing waters. *Hydrobiologia* **395/396**, 433–453.

Gagnon, Z.E. & Glime, J.M. (1992) The pH lowering ability of *Sphagnum magellanicum* Brid. *J. Bryol.* **17**, 47–57.

Gilbert, O., & Giovarini, V. (2000) The lichen vegetation of lake margins in Britain. *Lichenologist* **32**(4) 365–386.

Gorham, E. (1957) The chemical composition of some natural waters in the Cairn Gorm – Strath Spey district of Scotland. *Limnol. Oceanogr.* **2**, 143–154.

Griffith, M.B. & Perry, S.A. (1993) Colonisation and processing of leaf litter by macroinvertebrate shredders in streams of contrasting pH. *Freshwat. Biol.* **30**, 93–103.

Hall, R.J. & Ide, F.P. (1987) Evidence of acidification effects on stream insect communities in Central Ontario between 1937 and 1985. *Can. J. Fish. Aquat. Sci.* **44**, 1652–7.

Harriman, R. (1978) Nutrient leaching from fertilized forest watersheds in Scotland. *J.App.Ecol.* **15**, 933–942.

Haslam, S.M. (1982) *Vegetation in British rivers*. Vol.I: Text. Vol.II: River maps. (CST note 32.) Nature Conservancy Council, Banbury.

Hawkes, H.A. (1975) River Zonation and Classification. In: Whitton, B.A., ed., *River Ecology*. Blackwell, Oxford. pp.312–374.

Henricksen, A (1980) Acidification of fresh waters – a large-scale titration. In: Drablos, D. E., Tollan, A., eds., *Ecological impact of acid precipitation*. Proc. Int. Conf., Norway 1980. SNSF project. 68–74, Oslo.

Hessen, D.O. (1993) Climatic changes; effects on aquatic ecosystems. In: J.I. Holten, G. Paulsen & W.C. Oechel, eds., *Impacts of climatic change on natural ecosystems – with emphasis on boreal and arctic/alpine areas*. NINA, Trondheim. pp.151–153.

Hessen, D.O. & Wright, R.F. (1993) Climatic effects on freshwater: nutrient loading, eutrophication and acidification. In: Holten, J.I., Paulsen, G. & Oechel, W.C., eds., *Impacts of climatic change on natural ecosystems – with emphasis on boreal and arctic/alpine areas*. NINA, Trondheim. pp.151–153.

Hoey, T.B., Smart, D.W.J., Pender, G. & Metcalf, N. (edited by Leys, K.) (1998) Engineering methods for Scottish gravel bed rivers. *Scottish Natural Heritage Review* No. 47.

Holmes, N. (1983) *Typing British rivers according to their flora*. (Focus on nature conservation no.4) Nature Conservancy Council, Banbury.

Holmes, N. (1985) Vegetation of the River Dee. In: Jenkins, D., ed., *The biology and management of the River Dee*. (ITE sysmposium no.14.) Institute of Terrestrial Ecology, Abbots Ripton. pp.64–82.

Hynes, H.B.N. (1970) *The ecology of running waters*. Liverpool University Press, Liverpool.

Jarvie, H.P., Neal, C., Smart, R., Owen, R., Fraser, D., Forbes, I. & Wade, A. (2001) Use of continuous water quality records for hydrogen separation and to assess short-term variability and extremes in acidity and disolved carbon dioxide for the River Dee, Scotland. *Sci Total Environ* **265**, 85–98.

Johnson, R.C., Piper, B.S., Acreman, M.C. & Gilman, K. (1991) *Flood alleviation in Upper Strathspey, modelling and environment study*. Report prepared for the Nature Conservancy Council for Scotland. Vol.I Main report. Vol.II Supporting reports. Institute of Hydrology, Wallingford.

Jones, V.J., Flower, R.J., Appleby, P.G., Natkansky, J., Richardson, N., Rippey, B., Stevenson, A.C. & Battarbee, R.W. (1993) Palaeolimnological evidence for the acidification and atmospheric contamination of lochs in the Cairngorm and Lochnagar areas of Scotland. *J. Ecol.* **81**, 3–24.

Kinross, J.H., Kristofi, N., Read, P.A. & Harriman, R. (1993) Filamentous algal communities related to pH in streams in the Trossachs, Scotland. *Freshwat. Biol.* **30**, 301–317.

Light, J.J. & Lewis Smith, R.I., (1976) Deep-water bryophytes from the highest Scottish Lochs. *Journal of Bryology* **9**, 55–62.

MacDonald, M., & Partners (1975) *Regional Water Resources Study*. Vol.III Hydrology and Fisheries. (Report for North East of Scotland Water Board.) Inverness.

Maitland, P.S. (1991) Assessment of impact on aquatic fauna. In*: Flood Alleviation in Upper Strathspey – Modelling and Environment Study*. Vol.II Supporting Reports. Report prepared for the Nature Conservancy Council for Scotland. Institute of Hydrology, Wallingford.

Marren, P. (1979) *The Muir of Dinnet. Portrait of a National Nature Reserve*. Nature Conservancy Council, NE Region (Scotland), Aberdeen.

Marren, P. (1982) *A Natural History of Aberdeen*. Callander, Aberdeen.

Meteorological Office (1982) *Meteorological Office Annual Report 1982*. HMSO, London.

Miller, H. (1988) Forests and acidification. In: *Acidification in Scotland*. Scottish Development Department, Edinburgh.

Morgan, N.C. & Egglishaw, H.J. (1964) A survey of the bottom fauna of streams in the Scottish Highlands. Part I Composition of the fauna. *Hydrobiologia* **25**, 181–211.

Morrison, B.R.S. & Harriman, R. (1992) *Fish populations and invertebrates in some headwaters of the Rivers Dee and Spey, 1983–1985*. Scottish Fisheries Research Report No. 53. HMSO, Edinburgh.

Murray, J. & Pullar, L. (1910) *Bathymetrical survey of the Scottish freshwater lochs*. Vol.II. Challenger Office, Edinburgh.

Murphy, K.J. & Hudson, K.D. (1991) Environmental Assessment of Spey Flood Alleviation Scheme: Potential Impacts on Aquatic Plant Ecology. In: *Flood alleviation in Upper Strathspey – modelling and environment study*. Vol.II Supporting Reports. Report prepared for the Nature Conservancy Council for Scotland. Institute of Hydrology, Wallingford.

National Rivers Authority (1992) *River corridor surveys, methods and procedures*. NRA, Bristol.

Neill, R.M. (1938) The food and feeding of the Brown Trout (*Salmo trutta* L.) in relation to the organic environment. *Trans. Roy. Soc. Edin.* **59**, 481–519.

Neilsen, A. (1950) The torrential invertebrate fauna. *Oikos* **2:2**, 176–196.

North East River Purification Board (1980) *Loch Alvie: the likely effects of road salt*. NERPB, Aberdeen.

North East River Purification Board (1994) *Water Quality Review*. NERPB, Aberdeen.

Owen, R.P. (1976) *An economic and biological assessment of the effectiveness of liming in acid-water lochs*. Ph.D. thesis. University of Stirling.

Palmer, M. & Newbold, C. (1983) *Wetland and riparian plants in Great Britain*. Focus on Nature Conservation No.1. Nature Conservancy Council, Shrewsbury.

Patrick, S.T., Flower, R.J., Appleby, P.G., Oldfield, F., Rippey, B., Stevenson, A.C., Darley, J. & Battarbee, R.W. (1989) *Palaeoecological evaluation of the recent acidification of Lochnagar, Scotland*. Research Paper 34. Palaeoecology Research Unit, University College London.

Petts, G.E. (2000) Wood in world rivers. *Freshwater Biological Association Newsletter* **12**, 1–2.

Pugh, K.P. (1985) The chemistry of the river system. In: Jenkins, D., ed., *The Biology and Management of the River Dee*. (ITE Symposium No. 14) Institute of Terrestrial Ecology, Banchory.

Ratcliffe, D.A. (1977) *A Nature Conservation Review. The selection of sites of national importance for nature conservation in Britain*. Cambridge University Press, Cambridge.

Raven, P.J., Holmes, H.T.H., Dawson, F.H., Fox, P.J.A., Everard, M., Fozzard, I.R. & Rouen, K.J. (1998) *River Habitat Quality: the physical character of rivers and streams in the UK and Isle of Man. River Habitat Survey,* Report No. 2. Environment Agency, Bristol.

Rieley, J.O. & Page, S.E. (1991) Terrestrial Plant Communities. A Botanical Description and Evaluation. In: *Flood alleviation in Upper Strathspey – modelling and environmental study.* Vol. II Supporting Reports. Report prepared for the Nature Conservancy Council for Scotland. Institute of Hydrology, Wallingford.

Scottish Environment Protection Agency (1999) The River Dee: catchment management plan issues. Consultation document.

Scottish Office (1992) *Water quality survey of Scotland 1990.* Scottish Office Environment Department, Edinburgh.

Scottish Office (1997) *Water Quality Survey of Scotland 1995.* Scottish Office Environment Protection Unit, Edinburgh.

Soulsby, C., Helliwell, R.C., Ferrier, R.C., Jenkins, A. & Harriman, R. (1997) Seasonal snowpack influence on the hydrology of a sub-arctic catchment in Scotland, *J. Hydrol.* **192**, 17–32.

Soulsby, C., Turnbull, D., Hirst, D., Langan, S.J. & Owen, R. (1997) Reversibility of stream acidification in the Cairngorm region of Scotland. *J. Hydrol.* **195**, 291–311.

Soulsby, C., Turnbull, D., Langan, S.J., Owen, R. & Hirst, D. (1995) Long-term trends in stream chemistry and biology in North-east Scotland: evidence for recovery. *Water, Air and Soil Pollution* **85**, 689–694.

Spence, D.H.N. (1964) The macrophytic vegetation of freshwater lochs, swamps and associated fens. In: Burnett, J.H., ed., *The vegetation of Scotland*. Oliver & Boyd, Edinburgh. pp.306–425.

Stubbs, A. (1991) Terrestrial Entomology. In: *Flood alleviation in Upper Strathspey – modelling and environment study.* Vol.II Supporting Reports. Report prepared for the Nature Conservancy Council for Scotland. Institute of Hydrology, Wallingford.

Swift, D.W. (1987) *Phosphorus in runoff from Glenorchy Forest – the impact of aerial application of rock phosphate fertiliser.* WrC Report PRU 1699-M. Medmenham.

Towers, W. & Thompson, S. (1988) The potential for further afforestation in the catchment of the River Spey. In: *Land use in the River Spey catchment.* Aberdeen Centre for Land Use, Aberdeen.

Wade, A.J., Neal, C., Soulsby, C., Langan, S.J. & Smart, R.P. (2001) On modelling the effects of afforestation on acidification in heterogeneous catchments at different spatial and temporal scales. *J. Hydrol.* **250**, 149–169.

Warren, J.S. (1985) Hydrology of the River Dee and its tributaries. In: Jenkins, D., ed., *The Biology and Management of the River Dee*. Institute of Terrestrial Ecology, Banchory.

Webb, A.D., Bacon, P.J. & Naura, M. (1998) Catchment stream surveys and the use of GIS for integrated management: DeeCAMP and Deeside Rivers Survey. *Aquatic Conserv: Mar. Freshw. Ecosyst.* **8**, 541–553.

Werritty, A. & Maucotel, S. (1993) Hydrochemistry of lake sediments and the impact of liming Loch Dee. In: *Proceedings of the Loch Dee Symposium.* Foundation for Water Research, Marlow.

Williams, D.D. (1989) Towards a biological and chemical definition of the hyporheic zone in two Canadian Rivers. *Freshwat. Biol.* **22**, 189–208.

Williams, D.D. & Feltmate, B.W. (1992) *Aquatic insects.* CAB International, Wallingford.

Wood, D. & Evans, C. (1989) *A vegetation survey of the Insh Marshes RSPB Reserve.* Royal Society for the Protection of Birds, Sandy.

Wright, J.F. & Furse, M.T. (1990) *The macroinvertebrate fauna of the River Spey.* Report to the Nature Conservancy Council, Peterborough.

Wright, J.F., Moss, D., Armitage, P.D. & Furse, M.T. (1984) A preliminary classification of running-water sites in Great Britain based on macro-invertebrate species and the prediction of community type using environmental data. *Freshwater Biology* **14**, 221–256

Checklists:

Maitland, P.S. (1977) *A coded checklist of animals occurring in freshwater in the British Isles.* Institute of Terrestrial Ecology, Edinburgh.

Stace, C. (1991) *New Flora of the British Isles.* Cambridge University Press, Cambridge.

PART 2

Key Issues

CHAPTER 7
Land Use in the Cairngorms

D.M. SHUCKSMITH

THE EVOLUTION OF LAND USE

Until the early eighteenth century, the Highlands supported a feudal peasant society, based on the clan system. The members of the clan held arable and pasture lands in common: this system of 'run-rig' (see p.98) was perceived by those keen to commercialize Highland agriculture to consist of 'ludicrously small holdings, dispersed strips, ill defined peasant rights, collective practices' (Gray, 1952). Evidence of run-rig may be seen in most Cairngorm glens. It was the basis of commercial stability and of the Highland economy (Hunter, 1976), and custom, tradition and social relationships hinged on the degree of accessibility to the land. In the sixteenth century, ownership of the Cairngorms was in the hands of only four clan chieftains. Following the union of Scotland with England in 1707, however, the Highland economy was transformed from feudalism to capitalism, hastened by the dismantling of the clan system after the Jacobite rebellions and the vesting of property rights in the clan chieftains.

After the 1745 rebellion, in particular, there were dramatic changes in the clan social structure. Roads and bridges were built to allow rapid troop movement, including the military road from Blairgowrie to Grantown, via the Cairnwell, Braemar, Gairn Shiel, the Lecht and Bridge of Brown. Many estates were forfeited and passed to supporters of the Hanoverians. Highlanders were forbidden to hold clan gatherings, to bear arms or to wear tartan.

Apart from the imposition of military rule, these changes emphasized the private ownership of the land resource and specifically the derivation of property income from land. The new landowners and the former clan chiefs adopted English and lowland ways, moving in London and Edinburgh society, and consequently they required large amounts of money to sustain their modish lifestyles. They were thus motivated to exploit their land for profit.

One consequence was an increased exploitation of the timber resources of the Cairngorms. The Napoleonic wars created a demand for timber and timber companies were formed, floating timber down the Spey and Dee (Steven & Carlisle, 1959) for processing elsewhere, and in the early 1860s much of the Rothiemurchus forest was felled to provide sleepers for the Highland railway (Nethersole-Thompson & Watson, 1974 – see also Chapter 9).

Moreover, the Industrial Revolution created high wool prices and the hill lands of the Highlands and Islands offered profitable sheep runs. The outcome in many parts of the Highlands was the notoriously brutal 'clearances' by which communally worked land was expropriated to allow sheep ranching by the landowners: the enforced emigration of the population and the misery it caused has been documented elsewhere (Hunter, 1976; Richards, 1982). The consequence was that 'a labour-intensive, communal economy gave way to a land-intensive, individualistic framework' (Richards,

1982). The Cairngorms Working Party (1993) noted that 'the latter part of the 18th Century saw the spread of sheep farming across the Highlands. Much of the old hunting land [in the Cairngorms] was converted to sheep runs in an attempt to make the Highlands more economically productive . . . By the end of the century sheep prices were starting to fall, however; by the late nineteenth century deer had replaced sheep as the preferred use of some of the uplands.' While large-scale clearances like those in Sutherland were unusual in the Cairngorms, except at Glen Lui (1726) and Glen Ey (1840), there is plenty of evidence of smaller-scale clearances (Plate 60) in favour of deer as much as sheep. Nethersole-Thompson and Watson (1974) report that:

> Around 1850 Karl Marx became very excited about word of new clearances for deer on Gaick, Glenfeshie and Glen Tilt . . . Michie (1908) described a band of 'evicted families from the upper glens of Braemar . . . with sorrow and sadness depicted in every face, and headed by a piper playing 'Lochaber no more' . . . compelled to give up their fields to the deer . . . ' He also described how a proprietor in upper Deeside, exasperated by local people who did little work, served warrants of removal; when they disregarded these, their homes were pulled down about their ears. In Badenoch, too, there were evictions in the late 18th century at Balavil and Kinrara. (pp. 20–21)

In the late eighteenth and in the nineteenth centuries, then, the basis of the rural economy in the Cairngorms was fundamentally different from that before the *Act of Union* and the Jacobite rebellions. Landowners enjoyed considerable wealth as a result of the income from their estates, while at least until the 1820s the peasantry suffered great poverty. According to Nethersole-Thompson and Watson (1974), 'famine killed off half the people in some Deeside parishes', and in Strathspey the situation 'was truly distressing'. Such famines hastened the process of farm amalgamation, especially in the lower valleys, although the process of change was later in the upper straths. Instead of the narrow, scattered strips of run-rig, farms were bigger and fields were enclosed and enlarged. Production was increased by cultivating more land, by rotating crops and through the growing of turnips as winter fodder.

The basis of the rural economy was cattle (Plate 58), which summered on hill pastures and wintered in the valleys, together with oats, barley, sheep (Plate 59) and goats. The black cattle were driven along ancient drove roads, such as the Lairig Ghru and the various routes across the Mounth, to markets in the lowlands until the railways made it possible to transport less hardy (and more profitable) breeds more cheaply. Few areas of the Cairngorms were suited to sheep, however: the granite areas of the central Cairngorms are notably less suited than the lime-rich schists of the Tomintoul moors, for instance.

In the late eighteenth century it appears that the population of many parts of the Cairngorms fell, as mass voluntary emigration and army recruiting began. In the early nineteenth century there was a brief upturn, but since the 1830s numbers have fallen continuously, other than in the towns. The remotest parts were first to lose their population, and these have suffered the greatest losses. During this period the human settlements of the Cairngorms area also evolved. Housing conditions were very primitive, akin to the blackhouses of the crofting areas, formed of loose stones and turf. A number of landowners instituted improvements, however, and the planned villages of Grantown, Tomintoul, Ballater, Kingussie and others resulted.

It was during the nineteenth century that sporting uses of land became important. During the previous century it seems that game was plentiful but that there was little hunting, although in earlier centuries there had been massive deer drives to prearranged killing areas. Nethersole-Thompson and Watson (1974) report that in 1786 few deer were hunted in Strathspey although there was plenty of game, and that after 1745 the Duke of Gordon let most of his deer forests in Badenoch as grazings and from 1788 until 1826 he let Gaick as a sheep farm.

> Rothiemurchus became a deer forest in 1843 . . . In 1843 poaching was common in Strathdon . . . Many people poached game around Crathie in the early 19th century, but some proprietors did not worry about it, a clear sign that the boom in field sports after 1850 had not arrived.

From the middle of the nineteenth century, deer stalking and grouse shooting became status symbols for the wealthy, with important consequences for both land use and employment. According to the Cairngorms Working Party (1993), 'stalking became a popular and socially acceptable pursuit for the moneyed and leisured classes and it became fashionable for such people to purchase or lease estates where they could practise their sport'. Lairds and their tenants employed many keepers, ghillies, stalkers, domestic servants and other staff not only to manage and shoot the game but also to permit the upkeep of their grand houses and shooting lodges. Queen Victoria's purchase of Balmoral intensified this trend. Amenity woodlands were often planted around these houses, but on the hills the main effects have come from muirburn and use as deer forest. Burning, to prevent the regeneration of scrub and forest, became standard practice, and is generally done in strips so as to provide both soft, young shoots for deer and grouse to eat and shelter for the birds in the taller heather. A further landscape impact has been the construction of hill tracks to facilitate access.

Salmon fishing, which had been a communal activity for the purpose of food gathering, also became a status sport for the wealthy, and fishing by fork (the traditional means) was made illegal in 1868. The Dee and Spey, in particular, commanded high rents for fishing as the highest status rivers in Scotland.

Since the 1930s, the employment deriving from sporting estates has declined. The number of gamekeepers employed on deer forests has fallen sharply, as has the number on grouse moors.

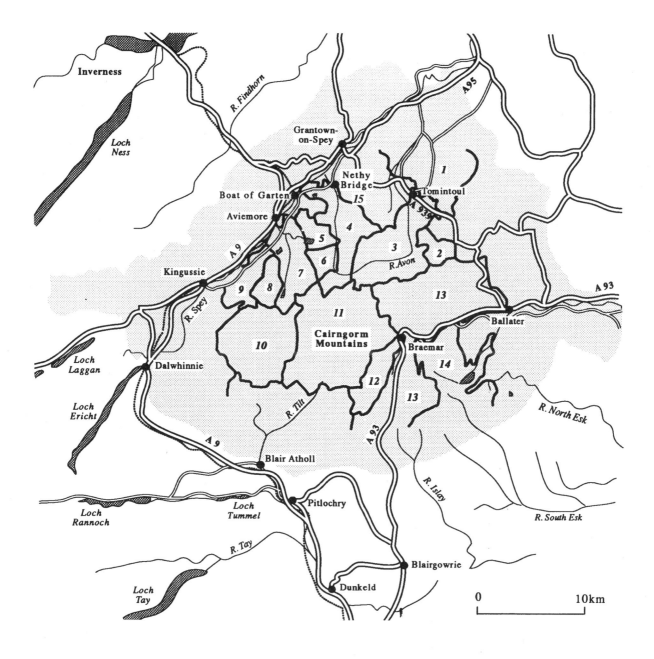

Fig. 7.1.   Ownership of the main Estates in the Cairngorms area (boundaries approximate).

1. Glen Livet: Crown Estates Commission   2. Delnadamph: H.R.H. The Prince of Wales.   3. Glen Avon: Andras Ltd.
4. Abernethy Forest: Royal Society for the Protection of Birds.   5. Glen More: Forestry Commission.
6. Cairngorm Estate: Highlands and Islands Enterprise.   7. Rothiemurchus: J.P. Grant.   8. Invereshie/Inshriach:
Scottish Natural Heritage.   9. Inshriach Forest: Forestry Commission.   10. Glenfeshie: Klaus Helmersen.
11. Mar Lodge: National Trust for Scotland.   12. Mar: Capt. Nicholson.   13. Invercauld: Capt. Farquharson.
14. Balmoral: H.M. The Queen   15. Dorback/Revack: Lady Pauline Grant-Nicholson.

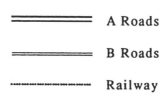

========== A Roads

========== B Roads

············· Railway

88

Domestic servants have become few and far between. Thus, the Mar Lodge Estate, for example, in 1993 employed only 11 full-time staff in total (one per 7000 acres, *c.* 2850 ha.).

The main changes, then, during the period since 1745, have been the vesting of property rights in private owners – not only for land cultivation and grazing but for fishing and hunting as well – and their exploitation for commercial or leisure purposes. There are processes of commoditization, by which is meant 'the extension of markets to new spheres of activity or, more usually in advanced economies, the superimposition of new types of market relation' (Marsden *et al.*, 1993). The transition from feudalism to capitalism brought with it the need to transform new and existing use values into exchange values. This process of commoditization has had major consequences for land use.

LAND USE AND LAND MANAGEMENT TODAY

The pattern of landholding. As a result of the events described in the previous section, land in a large part of the Cairngorms area is held by a few large-scale private landowners, for example in Glenavon (14 000 ha), Rothiemurchus (8000 ha), Invercauld (43 000 ha) and others, illustrated in general terms in Figure 7.1. This sketch map of landownership on Speyside is based on Millman (1969), updated with the assistance of Highland Regional Council, and because of the imprecise data available to the public, is intended to convey only a general impression of the structure of landholding.

Though there has been a steady decline in private ownership of large estates during much of this century, with much of the Cairngorms area passing into the hands of smaller landowners and public bodies, some 65 per cent of the land area is still in the hands of private individuals owning over 400 ha (Callander, 1987). Much of this land is owned by a very few large landowners, though it often constitutes the poorest hill land. Some estates have been purchased by non-traditional owners, such as the Eagle Star Insurance Company, which owns 7500 ha around Rothes and Craigellachie. Several smaller areas are owned by public agencies, such as the Crown Estates (Glenlivet) (Plate 57), Forestry Commission, Highlands and Islands Enterprise (Cairn Gorm) and Scottish Natural Heritage (Craig Meagaidh and Invereshie). Recent purchases of Abernethy Forest by the Royal Society for the Protection of Birds, and the Mar Lodge estate by the National Trust for Scotland, have further reduced the proportion of the area in private ownership. While the largest private estates are predominantly sporting, many of the smaller estates are mixed farming and sporting enterprises. There has also been considerable diversification into forestry and tourism enterprises.

The ownership of the land is not always so stable, and Morris (1993) uses the device of an imaginary visit to the Cairngorms by assessors for world heritage status to illustrate this point and its implications for land use and conservation:

> Entering the Highland Region sector of the Cairngorms, the assessors would note the changing pattern of landownership. Behind the first village, Dalwhinnie, the traditional owners sold in 1992 to new owners from the Netherlands. Disillusioned by a very wet August in 1992, these new owners put the estate back on the market; it now appears to be owned by people from Switzerland. At the next village, Newtonmore, the locally-based family who owned most of the surrounding land sold in early 1993. It is now owned by people from Italy. At the third village, Kingussie, all the land from the village golf course to the summit of the Monadh Liath massif is controlled by Dutch landowners . . . The assessors would be bound to ask whether the legitimate needs of local communities can be met under such a landownership pattern, and whether local councils are properly equipped to apply what few regulations are available to restrict damaging land-use activities.

The land use of the Cairngorms is therefore primarily within the control of the small number of large landowners of private estates, subject to the constraints which are placed upon them by feu burdens and legislative and fiscal measures. Accordingly, the next sections consider in turn the nature of feudal title and its significance, the objectives of private estate owners' land management, and the legislative and fiscal constraints currently operating.

The nature of feudal title. In addition to the property rights held by landholders, within Scotland's system of feudal land ownership there are less obvious property rights which may have been retained by the feudal superior upon disposal of the land. The owners of possession in land do not own their land outright, even if they are owner-occupiers, and their property rights must be placed within the context of Scotland's feudal system. Their management of land is thus constrained not only by the laws of the land, which operate to protect the public interest and the interests of other individuals, but also by the nature of their feudal title to the land.

Scotland's feudal tenure is hierarchical, often with several intermediate levels between the Crown and the occupier of land, who has the *dominium utile*. Under this system, not only are certain rights reserved by the Crown, but in the same way anyone who disposes of land can retain an interest in that land. There is no limit to the number of times that this process of subinfeudation can be repeated over the same piece of ground, and at each stage superiors can limit the extent of possession conveyed by reserving rights to themselves and by imposing additional conditions and burdens on their vassals. The chains of superior/vassal relationships thus created mean that the distribution of property rights in Scotland is infinitely more complex than the mere pattern of landholdings.

The highest level in the hierarchy (below God) is the Crown. The Crown's interests principally consist of the sovereign rights which are held inalienably, for example the ownership of coastal waters, and other property rights reserved to the Crown but capable of being sold, such as the rights to minerals and salmon fishings. The second level consists of the feudal superiors, of which there may be several. The rights commonly reserved by superiors are those associated with minerals and sport, together with rights to pre-empt building and other development by their vassals. The interests of the vassal in possession of the land may, therefore, be considerably restricted. Amongst the three levels of ownership described, the interests of the vassals in possession (i.e. the land-holders in possession shown in Figure 7.1) are thought to represent the least concentrated pattern of land ownership. For example, estates which have sold off land over the years and contracted to a small size may have retained the sporting rights over the whole of their former estate. Thus, the retention of rights by superiors created 'hidden maps' of land ownership that are even more concentrated than the present pattern of landholdings documented by Millman (1969), MacEwen (1977) and others.

The objectives of land management. Of paramount importance to any consideration of land use and land management is an understanding of the objectives of landholders and of the feudal superiors who have reserved sporting and other property rights.

Armstrong and Mather (1983) suggest from their own analysis that the typical Highland landowner is a product of an English public school, followed by Oxford and the Services, in accordance with their popular image. While a large minority has undergone formal training in disciplines related to land management, there is considerable variation in this respect, ranging from highly qualified professionals to untrained 'amateurs'. Most Highland estates, they found, were supported by financial links from external sources. Many landowners have interests in finance, banking and insurance, or in manufacturing, and more than half their sample owned land in other parts of Britain, typically in the south of England, the Midlands or in lowland Scotland. These links may reinforce the orientation towards the south of England already inherent in landowners' educational and social backgrounds.

Armstrong and Mather (1983) also surveyed a sample of Highland estate owners and asked them to indicate their reasons for ownership. Despite the difficulties in such a question, they were able to conclude that

> . . . it seems clear that the principal motives for Highland estate ownership are sport and family continuity. Family continuity is the most widely quoted primary reason for land ownership, and, as might be expected, is afforded greatest priority by proprietors of inherited estates with long family connections . . . Translated into decisions about land use, this thinking highlights survival as a primary objective. Decisions are likely to be fairly conservative and responsive to changing fiscal and other conditions, rather than innovative or experimental.

They also found that

> . . . the popular view of the Highland estate as a sporting retreat is borne out by the findings . . . just under one third of the sample estate owners listed sport as their primary motive for ownership; it is clearly the leading category amongst secondary reasons, and is perceived as being of importance on all but 17% of the sample units. A substantial minority of owners also assigned importance to the estate's role as a holiday home. In almost every case this role was associated with sport.

It might be expected that the importance placed on sporting motives would be even higher in the Cairngorms, given the quality of the fishing in particular, although the extent to which this is reserved for the owner's own pleasure or managed as a profit-oriented business is likely to vary from one estate to another.

Armstrong and Mather found, to their surprise, that

> . . . the major feature of Highland land ownership is the relatively low priority afforded to economic reasons. Whatever else it may be, the estate is not widely seen by its owner as a means of earning a living . . . Capital appreciation and livelihood are each regarded as the primary reason for land ownership by around one fifth of Highland landowners, and a further one third attach at least some significance to economic factors. These motives lag well behind family continuity and sport. It is clear that the typical Highland estate owner is not primarily motivated by economic considerations, but this is not to say that he is unconcerned about all economic aspects of his estate and its management. It is also true to say that reasons for land ownership vary according to the means by which the estate was acquired. Family continuity is the leading motive amongst owners who have acquired their estate by inheritance or gift, while the primary motive amongst purchasing proprietors is probably sport.

This emphasis upon the use value of the land rather than upon its exchange value and potential for capital accumulation is particularly interesting in the context of the earlier commoditization process which followed the break-up of the clan system. While the property rights remain vested in the individual landowners (in contrast to the communal pattern of pre-Jacobite days), the aim of deriving an income appears often to be less important than the enjoyment of the use of land, albeit now for sport rather than for subsistence.

Armstrong and Mather note, quite correctly, that management goals may not always reflect these broader landowning objectives, and they attempt an impressionistic classification of estate management goals on the basis of their survey responses as a whole (Table 7a). The first group ('livelihood') is commercially orientated, aiming to obtain an annual income from the estate and to maintain its viability, while usually also pursuing secondary residential and sporting objectives. Typically these estates are large and diversified, with young, permanently resident owners who are personally active in day-to-day management. Usually the estate is the only source of income or capital.

Table 7a   Goal orientations of estate policy (% of responses to a survey)

Primary orientation	%	Secondary orientation	%
Livelihood	20		
Investment	52	Business	24
		Capital Growth	7
		Sport	20
Sport	28	Investment	19
		Enjoyment	9

Source: Armstrong and Mather, 1983

The second and largest group ('investment') pursues objectives of long-term capital growth or, at least, capital conservation, with an ultimate aim of ensuring that the estate is handed on to the next generation intact. However, they are distinct from the first group in that they are not dependent on annual income from the estate. Three sub-groups are identified within this 'investment' group. The first ('business') tends to share some characteristics with the 'livelihood' group, in that estates are concerned with short-term viability as well as long-term survival, but differs in that external capital is available and plays an important role. The second sub-group ('capital growth') takes a more long-term view and indeed some owners may be regarded as hobby farmers. The third sub-group ('sport') is distinguished by the importance which the (absentee) owner places on his own personal enjoyment of sport and holidays and, while he has little direct input into land management, his values are incorporated into estate policy.

The third group ('sport') consists of estates managed primarily as sporting retreats for 'extremely wealthy industrial families who keep them for the amenities they have to offer and who can afford to a certain extent to disregard profitability' (Sutherland, 1968). Most do pursue secondary commercial objectives, however, and only a minority are managed purely for enjoyment. Their absentee landlords rely on extensive business interests elsewhere.

Armstrong and Mather (1983) conclude that there exists a spectrum of management objectives on Highland estates, from the mainly sporting estates at one extreme whose chief object is the owner's personal and perhaps exclusive enjoyment of his estate, largely regardless of financial consideration, to those estates at the other extreme which are intensively managed to yield a satisfactory income to their proprietors. Between these poles are located the majority of estates, pursuing a multiplicity of objectives with varying emphases. These objectives usually include non-commercial goals, such as the owner's own sport and amenity, in addition to economic viability, long-term capital growth and security, and the prospect of handing the property on to a successor.

It is principally upon these landowners that the wider public must depend for the continued preservation and enhancement of the landscape and scientific value of the Cairngorms, and for allowing and facilitating public access. Yet the Conservative Government Working Party's report on the future of the Cairngorms included no account of land ownership in the Cairngorms nor any discussion of the motivations of estate owners. It asserted that private landowners must be persuaded or induced to pursue land management practices which accord with the wider public interest, albeit with the accompanying threat that 'if these prescriptions do not work, tighter controls will become necessary'. This voluntaristic assumption was again at the heart of the Cairngorms Partnership announced by the Scottish Office in November 1994 with responsibility for conserving and enhancing the Cairngorms. According to one Labour MP, however, 'the landowners are responsible for some of the problems – putting them in charge will not work'* This is also the view of Watson (1977) who argued that 'a national interest such as conservation of wildlife and wilderness in a large area like the Cairngorms region is unlikely to be safeguarded in the long run unless a national conservation body controls the most outstanding parts of the area', and that 'the only way to ensure a long-term conservation policy is for a national conservation body to own those parts of the area that are best for wildlife.' This is still Watson's (1993) view.

These potential conflicts of interest were, however, recognized by the new Labour Government in its consultative paper 'Land Reform: Identifying the Problems' (Scottish Office, 1998). This argued that 'Land is a key resource. The life chances of people living in rural areas depend on how it is used. All too often in the past, the interests of the majority have been damaged by the interests of the few who control that resource'. The paper states that the objective of any land reform pursued by the new Scottish Parliament will be to remove the land-related barriers to the sustainable development of rural communities. However, private land-ownership is not in itself the issue, 'so long as land is used to foster thriving communities'. The Government has established a Land Reform Policy Group to identify means of improving the way in which land is used and its proposals emerged during 1999. Further change in the Cairngorms will come through the establishment of National Parks in Scotland, and detailed proposals have recently appeared (2001). It will be interesting to see if these proposals together can resolve the current conflict of interests regarding land use in the Cairngorms, or at least alter the balance between private and public interests.

Legislative and fiscal influences on land management. The potential conflict between landowners' private interests, others' private interests and the wider public interest is addressed,

---

* Sam Galbraith, quoted in the *Press & Journal*, 9 November 1994. Many other critics have also highlighted this issue of landowners' influence and voluntarism.

at least to some extent, through legislation, regulation and monetary incentives.

The occupier's freedom to manage the land as he chooses is restricted in three main ways. First, occupiers are subject to laws of the State which impose universal constraints on all members of society, such as the 1947 *Town and Country Planning Act*'s nationalization of development rights in land and the 1981 *Wildlife and Countryside Act*'s prohibition of the killing of numerous species of birds and wildlife. Second, a landholder is frequently prevented from infringing the rights of other landholders, for example · by obstructing an established right of access. Of course, many conflicts of interest may arise precisely because of the failure of the law to protect the interests of one landowner from the actions of a neighbour, for example where afforestation interferes with deer management. Third, the landholder is constrained by the nature of his feudal title as described above. Beyond these impositions there may also be constraints which have been accepted by agreement, such as management agreements made under the *Wildlife and Countryside Act* 1981 and nature reserve agreements under the *National Parks and Access to the Countryside Act* 1949. Such agreements are widespread in the Cairngorms, with the Cairngorms National Nature Reserve itself occupying 25 958 ha and being by far the largest in Britain, and many Sites of Special Scientific Interest (SSSIs) also designated. These are discussed in detail in other contributions to this volume.

Physical planning is particularly concerned with land use, and might therefore be seen as especially relevant to this volume, although in reality there are few planning controls over the major rural land uses of agriculture, forestry, fishing and shooting. The Cairngorms Working Party (1993) observes that:

> The role of planning is fundamental to the success of our Management Strategy. It is important, however, to recognise at the outset that the planning system has limitations, and has little influence over many of the matters central to the Strategy such as: land management; most tree planting and felling; agricultural operations such as land drainage, pasture improvement, and hedge and dyke removal; road maintenance work including widening and straightening; roadside clearance; street lighting and road drainage; recreational activities such as skiing (excluding built facilities), biking and sporting events; and temporary land uses such as caravan rallies and rock concerts which though short-lived can nevertheless be controversial.

Some other limited forms of landuse control are exercised in the public interest by other public agencies, however. Changes from agriculture to forestry do not formally require permission, but little private afforestation proceeds without planting grants from the Forestry Commission, whose approval is a condition of payment. The Scottish Executive Rural Affairs Department (SERAD) is normally consulted on such applications, and SERAD is also consulted by planning authorities on the agricultural aspects of any proposed development on prime farmland. Because the

Cairngorms is designated a National Scenic Area, SNH must also be consulted on any planning application, and landholders are prevented (in theory) from making vehicle tracks in the hills without planning consent (p. 187).

These are minor constraints upon the principal rural land uses, however, and would generally allow existing land management practices to continue unhindered. Only where agricultural land, scenic value or conservation importance is threatened by a change of established practices is there likely to be any attempt to constrain private land management in order to safeguard the public interest.

Monetary incentives are more pervasive, on the other hand, especially in relation to agriculture and forestry, even if Highland landowners are not primarily motivated by economic considerations. These incentives are discussed in more detail in Chapter 8, but a few brief points must be noted here.

Agriculture in the Cairngorms is now highly dependent upon the payment of government and EU subsidies to hill farmers. For most farmers in the area, livestock subsidies represent more than 100 per cent of net farm income, rendering them highly vulnerable to any further reductions in these direct payments (Shucksmith, 1993a, & 1993b). The level of these Less Favoured Area (LFA) payments has been cut substantially by the UK Government since 1992. When farmers in the Cairngorms were asked in 1991 (Shucksmith 1993a) how they would react to a substantial fall in their farming incomes, the majority replied that they would either stop farming (38 per cent) or continue as before with a lower standard of living (37 per cent). Only 16 per cent indicated that they would reallocate their efforts and resources in other directions. This unwillingness of farmers to diversify, despite the incentives and exhortations of policymakers, increases their vulnerability to any further cuts in LFA payments. Such a decline in agricultural fortunes might have very serious implications for land use in the Cairngorms, given that 69 per cent of the Cairngorms land area is occupied by agriculture. On the other hand, much of this area is 'rough grazing' including huge areas of deer forest only used occasionally for sheep and cattle. Despite this, the Cairngorms Working Party report (1993) notes that

> . . . From the natural heritage perspective the farmed land stretching from the Spey and the Dee to the high hills contains many semi-natural habitats of great importance for both people and wildlife . . . In general, traditional farming systems as practised in the Cairngorms Area are valuable for the natural heritage, especially because of their close association with native woodland and moorland. The mix of farms and crofts interspersed with woodland and moorland provides attractively varied scenery enhanced by the backdrop of high hills. The farming community is also of crucial importance to the cultural traditions of the area. The wide variety of wildlife depends to a great extent upon the more traditional, low intensity and environmentally friendly farming methods. Nature conservation on the lower ground cannot be separated from farming . . . (p. 30)

Plate 61 *(right)*
Deeside from the Forest of Birse.
Here the landscape of the Cairngorms
is a mosaic of pine-birch regeneration,
mature birchwoods, agricultural land,
scattered settlements and native Scots
pine plantations. September 1985.
Photo: Neil MacKenzie.

Plate 62 *(centre left)*
Scots pine at the natural tree limit,
about 650 m above sea level on Creag
Fhiaclach. The growth of the wind-
shaped seedling in the foreground has
been held back by repeated deer
browsing. October 1993.
Photo: Neil MacKenzie.

Plate 63 *(centre right)*
The dwarf and semi-prostrate
Scots pine (krummholz
condition) on the slopes of
Creag Fhiaclach, one of the few
natural tree lines in the British
Isles. October 1993.
Photo: Neil MacKenzie.

Plate 64 *(right)*
Even-aged stand of Scots pine at
Abernethy with blaeberry
(*Vaccinium myrtillus*) understorey.
This part of the forest has been
managed for timber (selectively
felled) in the past. July 1994.
Photo: Neil MacKenzie.

Plate 65
A moribund birchwood in the Cairngorms. Most trees are dying due to windthrow and old age. There has been no successful regeneration for many decades because of persistent browsing pressure, and this wood will soon disappear. The open areas have already been colonized by dense bracken and the ground flora is impoverished due to intensive grazing by the sheep. May 1993. Photo: Neil MacKenzie.

Plate 66
Timber floating at Rothiemurchus, late nineteenth century. The Scots pine logs, felled and extracted from the forest, were bound together to form rafts of 60 to 80 logs, and were transported by the 'floaters' down the River Spey to the sawmills at Garmouth.
Photo courtesy of the National Museums of Scotland, Edinburgh.

Plate 67
Strathspey - an extract from William Roy's military survey of Scotland (1747-55), showing the natural woodland at Rothiemurchus, Glenmore and Abernethy, as well as Loch Morlich and the River Spey. Areas of settlement and cultivation are coloured red.
Copyright, The British Library.

Plate 68 *(above left)*
A naturally-grown birch of excellent form amongst lodgepole pine at 610m ASL. Photo: Jim Atterson.

Plate 69 *(above right)*
Excellent stem forms in 120-year old naturally regenerated Scots pines at Cur Wood near Dulnain Bridge on the Seafield Estate.
Photo: Jim Atterson.

Plate 70 *(centre)*
High elevation experimental plots (620m ASL) on the west side of the Cairngorms, showing plots of lodgepole pine and Sitka spruce.
Photo: Jim Atterson.

Plate 71
Natural regeneration of Scots pine following reduction of grazing by red deer. Inshriach.
Photo: Charles Gimingham.

For that reason, the Cairngorms Straths have recently been designated as an Environmentally Sensitive Area (ESA). This scheme, which is intended to encourage farming in harmony with the environmental interest in areas of prime environmental importance, offers agricultural occupiers payments for promoting environmentally sensitive management of their land. Some 250 farms, and 150 smaller units, are eligible for payments in return for agreeing not only to protect the area from potentially damaging farming operations but also to undertake positive enhancement of natural heritage features through grazing plans and other measures. The Cairngorms Working Party saw this designation 'as the essential element in achieving our aims for environmentally friendly farming in the Cairngorms', provided that the levels of financial support were sufficiently attractive for farmers to enrol.

In relation to forestry, there has been a fundamental change in the regime of financial incentives since 1988. Until then, private forestry derived its *raison d'être* almost entirely from the fiscal regime, under which substantial tax concessions were offered to investors upon planting, during the growth of the crop and upon harvesting (see Johnson & Nicholls, 1987, for details). The consequence was that most private landowners had a strong incentive to invest in forestry not primarily to earn income but in order to reduce their tax liability on other sources of income and capital. The fiscal treatment of forestry thus tended to promote afforestation of bare land with fast-growing conifers, removing the motive for good husbandry.

Since 1988, however, these fiscal incentives have been replaced with direct grants targeted especially at broadleaves and native-pine species. Payments of £700 per hectare are available under the Woodland Grant Scheme for new conifer planting, with additional supplements also payable in certain circumstances (for example, for community woodlands). The Farm Woodland Grants Scheme offers annual payments instead for up to 40 years to compensate for the loss of agicultural income. The establishment of small woodlands may also attract support from SNH, and this may be particularly relevant for the birchwoods of the Cairngorms. The Cairngorms Working Party called for a substantial expansion of woodland of native species with support from these various grant schemes 'in the region of £1 million per annum, which would create a worthwhile increase in employment throughout the area, quite apart from 'long-term environmental, recreational and timber benefits'. This expansion will require investment from the Forestry Commission as well as relying upon the stimulation of landowner interest. Again, it is unclear whether the majority of landowners will be motivated by such financial incentives, but there is certainly some current enthusiasm amongst members of the Highland Deeside Forest Owners Group.

The responsiveness of private landowners to the various financial incentives and regulations is clearly of critical importance to the resolution of landuse conflicts between private property rights and the public interest according to the voluntary principle through which the Cairngorms are to be managed. The Chairman of the Save the Cairngorms Campaign takes a pessimistic view of the voluntary principle, suggesting (Scott, 1993) that:

> In fact a more accurate description of the measures proposed would be the 'pay massively for even the slightest environmental benefit principle'. It is ripe for exploitation, double-counting and misappropriation and would seem to have no measure of direct public accountability, with funds channelled through many disparate agencies . . . It should not be for the landowner to call the tune, to decide which parts of the Cairngorms heritage to exploit and which to preserve and enhance. And he or she should also be expected to make a substantial voluntary contribution in recognition of his or her privileged position as temporary custodian of part of an international asset.

SETTLEMENTS AND THE LOCAL ECONOMY TODAY

One feature of the Cairngorms Working Party's report was the emphasis placed on achieving a balance between the environmental management of the area and the support of the rural economy to provide a more secure future for local communities. Recent years have seen a reversal of long-established trends of population loss in the Cairngorms area, and especially in Badenoch and Strathspey where 64 per cent of the area's population resides. The total population of the Cairngorms area in 1991 was 17 082, which represents an increase of 7.8 per cent (1240 persons) over the 1981 Census figure.

Grantown-on-Spey, with a population of 3300 is the largest settlement. Apart from this, Aviemore (2405) and Kingussie (1500) are the main settlements on the western side, while Ballater (1260) and Braemar (410) are the primary centres on the eastern flanks of the Cairngorms. Below this tier are a variety of villages with populations of around 250–500 such as Carrbridge, Nethy Bridge, Cromdale and Tomintoul. The size, complex topography and the relatively poor quality of east-west road links mean that the Cairngorms do not have a single 'local economy', but must be considered in sub-parts.

Population trends. The relatively small part of the population which is located in the eastern Cairngorms (Upland Grampian) is very sparsely distributed, with a density of less than 0.1 persons per hectare. The age structure is unbalanced, with few children and young people of working age and more pensioners than elsewhere. In Badenoch and Strathspey the trends are somewhat different, in so far as there has been a much slower long-term decline of population during the twentieth century than in the eastern Cairngorms, and since the 1960s the decline in land-based employment has been more than offset by employment and population growth related to the economic stimulus of tourist development, offering greater opportunities for young people. The age structure is compared with that for Scotland as a whole in Table 7b.

In both the eastern and western Cairngorms, the recent population growth has not been uniform but has been concentrated in the principal settlements and at the expense of the landward areas which have continued to experience depopulation. Between 1971 and 1981 Strathdon, for example, lost 20 per cent of its population. In Strathspey, one can distinguish differentiated patterns, with the high proportion of young people in Aviemore and Kincraig reflecting their employment opportunities in the tourist industry, while the large number of elderly people living in Boat of Garten, Grantown, Kingussie, Nethy Bridge and Newtonmore suggests that these settlements are mainly recipients of retirement migration.

Population projections suggest that a further increase of 4.3 per cent will occur in the area's population to 2001, principally in Badenoch & Strathspey and in Kincardine & Deeside. Significantly, the projection for Badenoch & Strathspey predicts a further decrease in the numbers of people in the 15–39 age group (with a 15 per cent decline in those aged 15–24 in particular), and a large increase in those aged over 75 as retirement migration proceeds.

The rural economy. Clearly, if young working people are predicted to leave the Cairngorms area in such numbers, then the cause is likely to lie in restructuring of the local economy, in restricted opportunities for employment, and in the lack of availability of affordable housing. These are considered briefly in turn.

The Cairngorms are remote from markets and economic activity and have tended towards concentration on primary resources and related manufacturing. Such a slim base is vulnerable to external influences, such as non-local ownership and changes in the national/global economy. For example, many whisky distilleries closed during the early 1980s due to adverse currency movements and weak demand at home: nevertheless, the whisky industry is still an important employer in several remote glens such as Dalwhinnie, Tomintoul and Glenlivet. Forestry has expanded somewhat since the war but, although forestry is a major user of the poorer quality hill land, employment is limited. Agricultural and estate employment is declining rapidly, as both capital-labour substitution and farm amalgamations proceed. Nevertheless, agriculture is still an important employer in the landward areas of Upland

Grampian, albeit a declining one. The extent of the reduction is shown in Table 7c, which presents the employment structure of the Cairngorms in 1981 and 1989 by the standard industrial classification.

Tourism, on the other hand, has become increasingly significant as the economic life-saver of many declining communities especially in the Cairngorms with its superb mountain scenery, as suggested by the increase in those employed in Distribution and Catering from 37 per cent to 50 per cent of the Cairngorms workforce during the 1980s. This has been especially significant in Strathspey, since the development of the Aviemore Centre in the 1960s and the associated ski developments, and on Royal Deeside.

Most activity in Speyside occurs in the Aviemore-Cairngorm corridor, and one of the major criticisms is that remoter parts of the district have benefited little. Tourist accommodation is plentiful, with over 4500 bed-spaces in Speyside, and the suspicion that the market is over-supplied is encouraged by figures showing that occupancy levels for both hotels and self-catering were below the regional average during the early 1980s. Consequently, planning policies restricted further additions to less developed parts of the valley. The Aviemore Centre itself, which is now being redeveloped, has many critics, both in relation to its appearance, and because of its unintended centripetal effect, causing remoter rural areas on Speyside to gain little, or indeed to lose. In 1981, the Highlands and Islands Development Board (HIDB) set up the Newtonmore/Dalwhinnie/Laggan Project to seek to disperse tourist trade to remoter areas.

Much employment is also generated by the skiing developments, especially at Cairngorm and Glenshee, which have a larger capacity than the Lecht. Jobs are generated in the local ski schools, the ski centres themselves, hotels, restaurants and in local services. While conflicts between supporters of ski developments and conservationists have become increasingly acrimonious, skiing-related employment appears set to increase in the future.

Table 7b Cairngorms population age structure, 1991

Age Band	0–14	15–24	25–39	40–59	60+	Total
Cairngorms	17%	14%	19%	26%	24%	100%
Scotland	19%	15%	23%	24%	20%	100%

Table 7c Employment structure in the Cairngorms, 1981 and 1989 (figures are percentages of the Cairngorms workforce)

	1981	1989
Agriculture & Forestry	11	3
Energy & Water	2	1
Manufacturing	9	8
Construction	11	3
Distribution & Catering	37	50
Transport	4	4
Other Services	27	31
Total Employment	4260	4086
Total Self Employed	776	801

To the east of the Cairngorms, the tourist industry is relatively undeveloped except in Upper Deeside where many settlements are heavily dependent on tourism. In Ballater and Braemar, in 1973, seven hotels employed 70 men and 100 women, accounting for a half of all local employment. Generally, the employment opportunities offered by tourism in the Cairngorms have been relatively concentrated, with the central remoter communities not having developed their tourism potential to any great extent. It is also important to note the low-paid, seasonal nature of much of the employment generated* and its vulnerability to changes in external circumstances, for example currency rates.

Unemployment in the western Cairngorms was high in the early 1990s, exceeding 13 per cent in Badenoch and Strathspey in April 1993, due to the impact of the recession of the early 1990s on tourism together with several poor ski seasons. This rate has now fallen to around six per cent as the economy has recovered. In the remainder of the Cairngorms, while rates of registered unemployment tend to be lower, there are relatively low proportions of the population of working age who are economically active, and this is indicative of concealed unemployment.

Taken together, the dependence of the local economy on tourism, the low pay and insecurity of tourism employment, and the high rates of unemployment in the western Cairngorms all contribute to the emigration of young people from the Cairngorm communities. The area's dependence on tourism and the decline in traditional industries seems likely to continue, and it is not clear how incomes and prospects for young people can be improved in this context.

Affordable housing. The pressures for young people to leave are exacerbated by the difficulties they face in finding affordable housing in the Cairngorms area. While there has been a large increase in the housing stock in the last decade, most of it is beyond the means of young local people. 27 per cent of the stock is non-effective, in the sense that the houses are holiday and second homes. Retirement migration has also had a major impact, with 31 per cent of all purchasers in the Cairngorms moving from outside the area.

Less and less rented accommodation is available, partly as a result of a continuing decline in the private rented sector, but mainly as a consequence of the Conservative Government's policy of mandatory council house sales. In Badenoch and Strathspey, the council has sold half its housing stock since 1979, and all new houses built in the past decade have been in the private sector. According to a recent study of the Cairngorms Housing Market (CR Planning/University of Aberdeen, 1993), 'when the shift in tenure is considered in relation to the relatively low waged economy and the higher than average house prices, the key conclusion is that the last decade has seen a reduction in the proportion of accommodation which can be regarded as affordable by local people.' That study concluded that it was essential that public agencies 'promote social housing in key locations, targeted at households on lower incomes who will find it impossible to become home owners.'

CONCLUSIONS

The history of land use in the Cairngorms, then, is one of private property rights often diverging from the public interest, while at the same time new markets have emerged for new uses of land. The late eighteenth and nineteenth centuries saw the vesting of property rights in private owners – not only for land cultivation and grazing but for fishing and hunting as well, as these activities became commoditized and acquired a marketable value. Ironically, it seems that most estate owners today emphasize the use value of the land rather than its exchange value or potential for capital accumulation, being primarily orientated towards sport and family continuity rather than profit. This may blunt the effectiveness of financial incentives designed to induce private owners to manage their land in the public interest.

At the same time, much of the national interest in the Cairngorms stems from the area's unique natural heritage, and it is interesting to note that the voluntary principle now adopted for the protection of this interest relies to a large extent on the commoditization of these natural heritage assets. Owners will be paid to maintain the value of these previously unpriced heritage assets, should they wish to do so, thus deriving income once again from a new market for the use of the land. The local community, also, derives its income from the commoditization of heritage, in so far as the local economy is now heavily dependent on tourism and related services. One major challenge to the new Government and to the Cairngorms Partnership is to find a way of improving opportunities for housing and employment so as to sustain a vibrant rural economy at the same time as protecting and enhancing the environment. Their other major challenge is the resolution of conflict between private owners and the various public interests over the future uses of land in the Cairngorms.

---

* A 1990 survey in Carrbridge for Albyn Housing Association suggested that 75% of respondents had a total annual income of less than £10 000; and a 1993 survey in Upper Donside for Gordon District Council suggested that 55% of respondents there had annual household incomes of less than £11 000. It seems that an hourly rate of between £3.50 and £4.00 is normal in the Cairngorms tourist industry, resulting in monthly incomes of around £500 per month during the season.

REFERENCES

Armstrong, A.M. & Mather, A.S. (1983) *Land Ownership and Land Use in the Scottish Highlands*. O'Dell Memorial Monograph No.13. Department of Geography, University of Aberdeen.

Callander, R.F. (1987) *A Pattern of Landownership in Scotland.* Haughend Publications, Finzean.

Cairngorms Working Party (1993) *Common Sense and Sustainability: A Partnership for the Cairngorms.* The Scottish Office, Edinburgh.

CR Planning and the Department of Land Economy, University of Aberdeen (1993) *Cairngorms Housing Market Study.* Final Report to Scottish Homes.

Gray, M. (1952) The abolition of run-rig in the Highlands of Scotland. *Economic History Review,* Series 2, **5**, 46–57.

Hunter, J. (1976) *The Making of the Crofting Community.* John Donald, Edinburgh.

Johnson, J.A. & Nicholls, D.C. (1987) The value of fiscal measures to the private woodland owner in Britain. In: Merlo, M., Stellin, G., Harou, P. & Whitby, M., eds., *Multipurpose Agriculture and Forestry.* Vauk, Kiel.

MacEwen, J. (1977) *Who Owns Scotland?* Edinburgh University Press.

Marsden, T., Murdoch, J., Lowe, P., Munton, R. & Flynn, A. (1993) *Constructing the Countryside.* UCL Press, London.

Michie, J.G. (1908) *Deeside Tales.* Wylie, Aberdeen.

Millman, R. (1969) The marches of the Highland estates. *Scottish Geographical Magazine* **85**, 172–181.

Morris, D. (1993) World Heritage Status for the Cairngorms. In: Watson, A. & Conroy, J., eds, *The Cairngorms: Planning Ahead.* Kincardine & Deeside District Council, Stonehaven.

Nethersole-Thompson, D. & Watson, A. (1974) *The Cairngorms.* Collins, London.

Richards, E. (1982) *A History of Highland Clearances. Vol. 1. Agrarian Transformation and the Evictions, 1746–1886.* Croom Helm, London.

Scott, M. (1993) A Manifesto for the Cairngorms. In: Watson, A. & Conroy, J., eds., *The Cairngorms: Planning Ahead.* Kincardine & Deeside District Council, Stonehaven.

Scottish Office (1998). *Land Reform – Identifying the Problem.* Scotish Office, Edinburgh.

Shucksmith, D.M. (1993a) Farm Household Behaviour and the Transition to Post-Productivism. *Journal of Agricultural Economics* **44**, 466–478.

Shucksmith, D.M. (1993b) The Effects of European Agricultural Policies on the communities of Upland Scotland: the case of Grampians. *Revue de Géographie Alpine* **53**, 97–116.

Steven, H.M. & Carlisle, A. (1959) *The Native Pinewoods of Scotland.* Oliver & Boyd, Edinburgh.

Sutherland, D. (1968) *The Landowners.* Blond, London.

Watson, A. (1977) Wildlife Potential in the Cairngorms Region. *Scottish Birds* **9**, 245–262.

Watson, A. (1993) A Vision for the Cairngorms and Critique of the Working Party's Report. In: Watson, A. & Conroy, J., eds, *The Cairngorms: Planning Ahead.* Kincardine & Deeside District Council, Stonehaven.

Watson, A. & Conroy, J., eds, *The Cairngorms: Planning Ahead.* Kincardine & Deeside District Council, Stonehaven.

CHAPTER 8
Agriculture

K.J. THOMSON

INTRODUCTION

To agriculture, the Cairngorms present a formidable challenge: located in the northern region of the British Isles, exposed to the influences of Atlantic and Arctic weather, with generally inhospitable soils and temperatures, and remote from major markets, this 'largest self-contained block of truly hill country' in the British Isles (Cairngorms Working Party (CWP), 1993, p.13) offers at first sight few opportunities for the viable production of food. Nevertheless, the hard work and perseverance of its inhabitants, and the operation of the national economy in general and agricultural policy in particular, have established farming as an important land use in the area, especially in the lower parts surrounding the high tops. In these regions, agriculture may be said to have formed the details of the landscape through which all visitors must pass, and in which many remain throughout their stay, and to provide habitats used by many forms of wildlife as well as sheep and cattle. Farming also remains an important economic activity in the wider Cairngorms region, offering directly family-based and year-round employment on the land, and indirectly demand for private and public services over a wide area.

Thus, through its pervasiveness in terms of managing the land over much of the Cairngorms area, many of the issues identified in this and other chapters of this book involve agriculture to a greater or lesser extent. Farming cannot escape entanglement, direct or indirect, in the many detailed local

issues of site conservation and tourist management. Also, as will become clear, farming has for many years been the focus of intense government interest, and this in turn involves difficult and important questions of national policy, with ramifications reaching up to various departments of state and out to questions of international trade, well beyond the confines of the Cairngorms themselves.

HISTORICAL BACKGROUND

The presence of farmers in the Cairngorms area can be traced back several thousand years, through the presence of standing stones and crannogs which prove the existence of substantial and established communities which must have subsisted on local production of food. Clearance of the native forest would have begun at this early stage, on land between the low-lying bogs and the stonier, more exposed heights. Then, as now, farming consisted of a mixture of cropping and husbandry, though the need for virtual self-sufficiency necessitated the production of sufficient grain for human consumption – mainly early varieties of oats and barley, or bere, with some wheat, peas and beans. Cattle and goats formed the bulk of the livestock population and both no doubt were the object of occasional neighbourly depredations.

In early historical times, Scottish farming was based mostly on a complicated feudal system resembling the European manorial pattern (Chapter 7). The general population lived in settlements, surrounded by 'infield' and 'outfield'. The former was under constant cultivation and enrichment through human and animal dung, while the latter was periodically rested under grass (Handley, 1953, p. 37 *et seq.*). Beyond the outfield lay the hill land proper, fit only for rough pasturing. The infield was divided by *run-rig*, characterized by long narrow strips cultivated by one family, and periodically reallocated with much precision. Run-rig remains can be observed in most Cairngorm glens, especially in conditions of shadow or light snow. In highland areas, including the Cairngorms, *transhumance*, or the movement of animals and part of the population up into more mountainous areas to take advantage of summer growth, is testified by the presence of the remains of *shielings* or huts which would be annually repaired and reused. However, numerous varieties of farming systems – both technical and organizational – are reported by all authors. For example, sub-feudal *tacksmen* – middlemen, often of the chieftain's family – were paid rent in services and kind by tenants-at-will, and in Aberdeenshire areas called *faughs* were ploughed in rotation with grass in the outfield. Especially in the remoter and agriculturally more difficult areas, and where the clan system persisted against more organized social forms, farming must have been practised in ways that best accommodated local physical features and social preferences. There is thus little in the way of a unique and traditional 'Cairngorms agriculture', although of course this in no way detracts from the cultural interest of the area.

The eighteenth century saw major change for Scotland, most obviously as a consequence of the Union of the Parliaments, and the subsequent failure of the two Jacobite Rebellions. But in agriculture, as in industry, huge changes were afoot, though they took a considerable time to penetrate some parts of Scotland (Carter, 1979). The turnip transformed the crop-livestock relationship by providing animal feed while cleaning the ground, and the potato became a basic foodstuff for even the poorest families. Many landowners were inspired by advances in England and the Continent and took up progressive farming, with enclosure – less brutal than in England – and experimentation with new varieties of crops, livestock and instruments. In the second half of the century, southern breeds of sheep were imported into the highlands, and new roads greatly improved communications (though not as yet bulk transport), facilitating the emigration of the rural population to the growing towns and overseas. Tree planting became fashionable, with some reversal of the devastating effects of centuries of grazing and logging: the results are still important in the Cairngorms.

By the nineteenth century, the elements of modern Scottish hill farming were in place, with a large-scale landowner-tenant system alongside owner-occupiers on farms of small and medium size (by contemporary standards). Cattle and sheep were being bred for urban markets to the south, and the ancient drove roads were being gradually abandoned as railways and better roads

became available. The condition of most of the human population took longer to improve, but alongside the establishment of the laid-out townships such as Grantown, Ballater, Tomintoul and Kingussie came the building of more substantial farmhouses and their outbuildings for commercial agriculture. Eventually the long-standing problem of poor housing for farm workers was addressed through the widespread cottage improvement movement, and eased by the outflow of population which accelerated during and after the First World War and has continued till recent times.

As British agriculture attempted to survive the depression of the later 1920s and early 1930s, the number of sheep on the lower ground increased, but the ploughing-up campaign of the Second World War reversed this trend. Between 1939 and 1944, by far the most important crop was oats whose area increased markedly, along with much smaller areas of wheat, barley and potatoes, even on hill sheep farms, while leys of grass in rotation correspondingly diminished. Under the supervision of the Agricultural Executive Committees, and with an increased labour force, a general intensification took place, with an increase in the number of cattle and poultry, but decreases in sheep and pig numbers.

There was a general shortage of hired labour, partly due to the low wages payable, and partly to poor housing and remoteness of many units. On the other hand, the smaller farms could hardly afford the cost of additional regular labour, and family labour was relied on, perhaps excessively in some cases. Moreover, the economic position of farming in the Cairngorms seemed worse than elsewhere in Scotland. Lower prices for store cattle, and the need to enlarge the cropped area during wartime, contributed to this position. But also, improvements elsewhere in dairying and mechanization had little effect in this region and, it may be inferred, especially on upland farms.

A survey during the last two years of the war (DAS, 1947) recorded the number of farms in each parish considered to be marginal, that is, not making a satisfactory profit (a worker's wage for the farmer plus interest on capital). The greatest proportions of such farms were found in the upland parishes of Aberdeen, Banff, Moray and Nairn, with a 'hard core' in the area lying south and west of a line from Cawdor in the north, through Huntly in Aberdeenshire, to Kincardine O'Neil in Deeside, plus a small group around the Bennachie and Foudland hills. In the parishes of Glenmuick and Kildrummy, over 30 per cent of the farms were marginal, over 60 per cent in Strathdon and Crathie and Braemar, and over 75 per cent in Glass and Glenbuchat. The proportions lying at altitudes over 250 m (750 ft) were 51 per cent in Aberdeenshire and 97 per cent in Banffshire. However, hill sheep farms accounted for only five per cent of all marginal farms in the north-east region, and mixed farms for the remaining 95 per cent.

It was concluded that 'Marginality in this Region is associated primarily with high altitude, with poor soil conditions, and with small-scale units of production. High altitude and soil conditions have procured a type of farming in which output per acre is relatively low. When this is combined with a small size of unit, a low output per acre becomes a low output per farm. In consequence the returns from farming – to be shared between landlord, farmer and farm labourer – are relatively small. Rents are low, farmers' standards of living are low and there are few hired labourers. Because of the low rents, landlords cannot afford to keep the capital equipment of the farms in repair; because of small profits, farmers generally are short of capital, and are unwilling to undertake expensive repairs or improvements' (CWP, 1993, p.22). To some extent, this has remained the position throughout the post-war period, in the Cairngorms as elsewhere in the upland areas of Britain.

At this time, the large majority (84 per cent) of north-east farms were tenanted, and only 16 per cent owner-occupied, and the balance in the hills and uplands was probably still more uneven (CWP, 1993, p.14). However, the majority (59 per cent) of tenants were sitting on tacit relocation or on a year-to-year basis, reflecting the general uncertainty about future farming prospects. It was reported that 'Owners of the more remote farms are finding it increasingly difficult to obtain tenants even at low rents, and the more enterprising farmers have been tending to leave the upland districts because of the greater attraction of farms in the lowlands, or of other occupations' (CWP, 1993, p.14). At the same time, amenities were often lacking: water was seldom laid on to the house or steading, telephones and electricity were rare, and bad roads and buildings encouraged the desertion of smaller farms. The solution lay clearly in increasing output per man, whether by higher rates of lime and fertilizer, or new and more profitable enterprises, or, as seemed inevitable in any case, a reduction in those occupied in farming.

The much more active government support for hill farming since the 1940s has enabled a larger number of holdings to survive, and for longer, than would otherwise have been the case. During the 1960s, Treasury constraints led to a tightening of such subsidies, and for a time British farming, and especially the sheep sector, went through a difficult period, with the consequence of accelerated structural change involving farm amalgamations and labour outflow to the then-buoyant employment opportunities elsewhere. However, eventually, entry to the European Community (then called the Common Market, now the European Union) secured a different and more prosperous economic

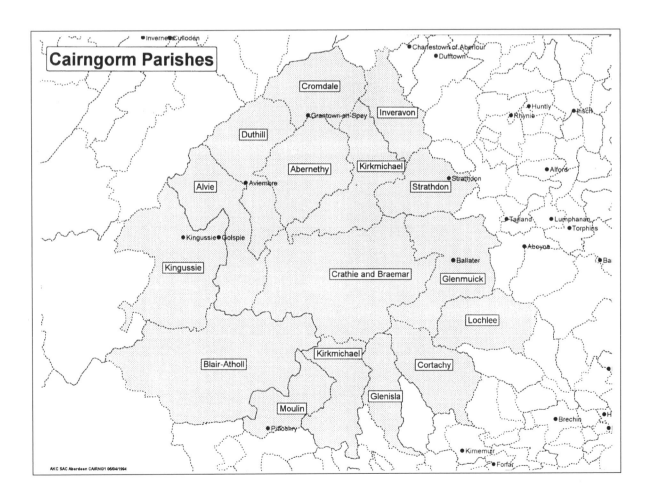

Fig. 8.1. Map of the Cairngorms area showing Parish boundaries.

Table 8a Land use in the United Kingdom, Scotland, the Scottish Highlands[1] and the Cairngorms[2] (thousand ha)

	United Kingdom	Scotland	Scottish Highlands	Cairngorms
Total Area	23 797	7708	3905	544
Forestry	2395	1131	500	n.a.
Rough Grazing[3]	5910	4006	2028	376
Crops and Grass	11 864	1711	283	24
Other (farm woods, roads)	712	141	385	10

1 Highlands and Islands Regions. Forestry data approximate.
2 Sixteen 'core area' parishes: Strathdon, Crathie and Braemar, Glenmuick, Lochlee, Cortachy, Glenisla, Inveravon, Kirkmichael (Banffshire), Abernethy, Alvie, Duthill, Kingussie, Cromdale, Kirkmichael (Perthshire), Blair Atholl and Moulin.
3 Including common grazings.

Sources: June Agricultural Census, 1991, Scottish Office Agriculture and Food Department, Edinburgh; and Highlands and Islands Enterprise, Inverness.

climate, although sheep producers had to await the 1980s before a 'common organisation' was arranged for their commodity. It is this long historical background that has created much of the landscape, and the land-occupation structure, that can be observed today around the central massif of the Cairngorm mountains themselves.

PHYSICAL FEATURES

According to the 1991 agricultural census*, the sixteen Cairngorm parishes (Fig. 8.1 and Table 8a) contain about 410 000 hectares (410 Kha) of agricultural land. This represents an intermediate proportion (69 per cent) of the total superficial area (544 Kha) of these parishes compared to the figures for the whole of Scotland (74 per cent) and the Scottish Highlands as a whole (59 per cent). The agricultural area is almost equally divided between owned and rented land, and thus in the Cairngorms tenanted farmland has a higher share than the national figure of about 40 per cent.

---

* The annual agricultural census in Britain is an invaluable source of data, but lacks information on overall land use and socio-economic aspects. Returns are completed for each agricultural holding, i.e. independently managed unit, rather than actual 'farms', and contain no financial and little social information, e.g. family relationships, tenure details. Data on land use rather than land type are collected, without geographical identity, and with little detail for the more extensive and non-farmed areas. Common grazings are collected separately. Individual returns are not disclosed, but data are published by 'agricultural parish', which may or may not relate closely to the corresponding civil parish according to the (unknown) boundaries of the holdings included. Many of these problems are accentuated in hill areas such as the Cairngorms, where 'holdings' may be very large and incorporate huge areas of deer forest used occasionally for sheep or cattle grazing. Inspection of a series of annual parish statistics often reveals large changes explicable only in terms of ownership changes or the administrative processes involved rather than ground-level developments.

Of the total, 376 Kha are rough grazing†, of which only 5 Kha are common grazings. Thus by far the largest share of land area in Cairngorms agriculture (and in the Cairngorms as a whole, as thus defined) consists of pasture of poor agricultural quality under single management. The remaining agricultural area consists of 4 Kha of crops and fallow (of which about half is spring barley), and 20 Kha of temporary and permanent sown grassland. The remaining 10 Kha is 'other' land within farm holdings, of which about half is classified as 'woodland', probably almost all birch and remnant plantation.

In terms of livestock, there were about 131 000 ewes and 34 000 head of cattle in the 16 Cairngorms parishes in 1991, with negligible numbers of dairy cattle, pigs and poultry. Sheep numbers had increased considerably (up by 16 per cent from 113 000 ewes since 1975, with a 30 per cent increase in lambs over the same period), while cattle had declined by 24 per cent from 45 000 head. A crude stocking rate is thus about 1 livestock unit per forage ha, well below the national average.

The number of agricultural holdings in 1991 was 460, down by 11 per cent from 1975. On these holdings were reported 220 full-time occupiers (down 18 per cent), 127 part-time occupiers (up 21 per cent), and 318 regular and casual workers (down 39 per cent) of which 225 were full-time hired (149) and family (76) workers. These trends are typical of Scotland as a whole.

FARMING SUPPORT

It has already been mentioned that agricultural policy has played a large part in the development of farming in Scotland. During and after the Second World War, the degree of national self-sufficiency in

---

† Land which cannot normally be cultivated or is dominated by poor quality grasses, heather, bracken, etc., including mountain, hill, moor and deer forest situated within the farming unit, whether enclosed or not.

food was the driving force behind major schemes of encouragement towards land and husbandry improvement and direct support of farm product markets and farming incomes. Originally, national measures, such as livestock headage payments, and grants for capital improvements, were introduced with the 1947 *Agriculture Act,* and many of these have persisted in one form or another, to this day. Later, a deficiency payment system, supplementing market returns with direct payments to farmers in order to ensure a minimum guaranteed output price, were introduced, although this system impinged less directly on hill farmers who produced mainly 'store' animals for sale to lowland fatteners for final sale.

Since the 1970s, support for hill farming in Britain has been operated as part of the European Community's Common Agricultural Policy (CAP). At the time of entry, the post-war UK hill farming areas were transformed into the CAP's Less Favoured Areas (LFAs), within which farmers are eligible for enhanced rates of capital investment assistance and direct payments (hill compensatory livestock allowances). All these measures apply in the Cairngorms as in most parts of the Scottish highlands (farms on certain islands receive even higher rates); indeed, nearly 90 per cent of all Scottish agriculture is LFA-classified.

The current extent to which modern hill farming is dependent on subsidies can be measured from the official Farm Accounts Scheme, which shows that total subsidies per holding for upland/LFA farms* in Scotland have averaged about £14 000 at 1990 values over the last 20 years (Thomson, 1993, p.90), and often represent over 100 per cent of net farm income (NFI). This compares with figures of about £1500 per lowground farm between the mid-1970s and 1988 (though with a rise in recent years), corresponding to about 10 per cent of NFI. These calculations exclude indirect support through the protection of EC markets for beef, sheep-meat, etc., and the free or low-cost provision of advice, research and development. Thus it can be seen that farming in areas such as the Cairngorms would be severely pressured were such support to be substantially reduced.

British Government policy in the face of this situation has been multi-stranded. Given the existence of the CAP with its common financing of agricultural expenditure through the EC budget, one natural tendency, fully supported by farmer interests, has been to press for higher CAP payments. This has sometimes run counter to the UK's general advocacy of tighter control of Community expenditure, but the conflict has been reduced in several ways. The long-run depreciation of sterling against the Ecu, in which CAP payments are denominated, has raised their domestic value. British ministers have so far managed largely to avoid 'discrimination' against larger farms, so maximizing the benefit to the UK where such farms

are common. Finally, in 1980 and 1982, Mrs Thatcher negotiated a special UK budget rebate, which has substantially reduced the British share of additional farm expenditure.

In Brussels, the British Government has been concerned to promote 'structural' policy to assist areas of the European Community that need extensive economic redevelopment. Thus it is content to see retirement aids for small farmers in other member states which helps remaining holdings to become more viable, but in the UK it has preferred 'diversification' measures that encourage farmers to find other income-earning enterprises on their holdings, such as tourism and first-stage processing activities.

The difficulties of sustaining economically viable farming in the LFAs, with its crucial role in conserving the traditional environment, have been recognized by government, which has stated that 'financial support for farming in the LFAs must be retained' (MAFF, 1991). However, it is seeking ways in which this support can be more closely linked to environmental benefits.

One substantial opportunity for that approach arose during the negotiation of the 'MacSharry' CAP reforms, which were finally agreed by the European Council of Agricultural Ministers in May 1992, coming into effect over the subsequent three years. These reforms represent a substantial switch from market price support, via intervention (state) purchasing and export subsidization of surplus production, towards direct payments to farmers on the basis of crop areas and livestock numbers. They thus offer the opportunity not only to eliminate some of the inefficiencies of indirect support, but also to tailor the payments to targeted social and environmental goals. More recent policy developments, such as the Uruguay Round agreement on farming support, and further CAP reform (CEC, 1994, 1997), point in the same direction.

The MacSharry reforms, however, represent only a partial success in these respects. Changes in livestock payments, stocking-rate restrictions, and enhanced rates for 'extensive' farming, do not affect Scottish farming greatly, especially in hill areas such as the Cairngorms. Farmers there certainly benefit from the higher payments, but with little need to adjust their farming systems, while other elements of the MacSharry reforms – lower market prices, set-aside of arable land – are negative or largely irrelevant for this group. Since cereal support prices have been cut by over 30 per cent, there has been some reduction in the cost of feedstuffs, but this is likely to benefit lowground lamb and beef producers as much, if not more than, hill farmers for whom the cost of winter feed, and the price of 'store' animals sold for finishing elsewhere, are more important.

Under the Commission's *Agenda 2000* proposals for further CAP reform, more cuts in support prices for cereals and beef took place in the year 2000, in exchange for still higher direct payments for arable areas and livestock numbers. However, in addition, greater freedom was given to the British

---

* LFA Mainly Sheep, LFA Sheep and Cattle, LFA Mainly Cattle and LFA with Arable holdings.

Government – and thus to the Scottish administration and parliament which became responsible for agriculture – to allocate at least some of these expenditures between intensive and extensive forms of farming according to environmental criteria. Moreover, rural development is to take on a higher profile within the CAP, again with national and regional variations. Hence, Cairngorms agriculture faces a future still more dependent on direct subsidies, whose scope and nature will become even more critical to the survival and activities of local producers.

FARMING AND FORESTRY

Mention has been made above to the historical disappearance of most of the natural primeval forest during earlier centuries. Planting, first by landowners in the eighteenth and nineteenth centuries, and in the twentieth century by the Forestry Commission, both directly (Plate 57) and with tax and grant incentives to private landowners, has led to a gradual recovery in land under trees to about 15 per cent for Scotland as a whole. However, the nature of this re-afforestation programme has been very much of a 'top-down' process, led in the private sector by the larger estate owners and by forest management companies acting for city pension funds and insurance companies. Working farmers have tended until recently to be involved only to the extent of planting occasional shelter-belts, and the sale of land to forest interests or the reorganization of tenancies by farming landlords. Thus only 131 Kha of Scottish agricultural holdings in 1994 were recorded as 'woodland', that is 2.5 per cent of the total area. However, this represents a virtual doubling of the figure of some ten years before.

One reason for the recent upsurge in interest by farmers in forestry has been the very substantial changes in the tax/grant situation since 1988, when the tax incentives for new planting were removed. In their place, direct grants have been steadily increased, especially to smaller plantings of broadleaf and native pine species which are considered of particular environmental benefit. Under the standard Woodland Grant Scheme, payments of £700 per hectare for new conifer planting were available from September 1994, with supplements bringing the total well over £1000 for smaller areas. Farm Woodland Schemes carrying annual payments for up to 40 years to compensate for loss of farming income on arable and improved grassland have been available to supplement the normal Forestry Commission planting grants. Similarly, and since 1992 mandatory for all but the smallest arable farms, the set-aside system has included an afforestation option designed to encourage this alternative and semi-permanent land use. Environmental agencies such as Scottish Natural Heritage offer payments for the establishment of small woodlands, and for the preservation and enhancement of endangered birchwoods which are of particular significance in the Cairngorm surroundings. These developments have been supplemented by much research, development and advisory activity, usually with further public funds, in order to improve woodland management and timber marketing.

Despite these efforts, it appears that farmers in general, and hill farmers in particular, have yet to be convinced that afforestation of family holdings is to be undertaken on a substantial scale, perhaps leading eventually to the much more mixed farming/forestry systems found in parts of Scandinavia (Reforesting Scotland, 1994). Part of the problem may be the low but reasonably certain returns to be made from core farming activities: even with fluctuating climatic conditions and product markets, farmers can expect countercyclical policy adjustments and tax arrangements to secure them a modest annual income, albeit one needing to be supplemented by off-farm and sometimes on-farm 'diversification' earnings. Against this, the technical and financial uncertainties of farm woodland enterprises which involve inter-generational production cycles – with loss of land-use flexibility – are less attractive. Recent policy changes, such as the 1992 CAP reforms which gave farmers substantial direct payments for agricultural activities including rotational set-aside, and even the rather frequent upgrading of the forestry grants themselves, may also be engendering a 'wait and see' feeling.

For an area such as the Cairngorms, the policy issue thus involves determining the future relationship between farming and forestry, whether this be one of integrated land management by family farmers, a changed balance on the mixed estates, or a continued separation of the two land uses. Responses to this question in this area will be significantly affected by national and EC policy for agriculture and forestry, unless, by special area designation or otherwise, the Cairngorms are somehow insulated. Otherwise, efforts to neutralize undesired effects of these larger forces, or to promote local initiatives, will prove costly and/or ineffective.

Moreover, not only does the question remain unresolved in the minds of the policy-makers, but farmers and landowners on the ground will have to be convinced of the long-term reliability of the policy and market background before they will be induced to make the necessary decisions. This emphasizes once again the pervasive influences of such apparently remote factors as accession of the Nordic states (Norway, Sweden, Finland) and Austria to the European Union (EU), the success or otherwise of British and EU macro-economic policy, especially as regards interest rates and the sterling exchange rate and, closer to home, the attitude of future UK governments to wealth and landownership.

FARMING AND THE ENVIRONMENT

Increasingly, agricultural policy has been influenced by concern over the environment. At the highest level, both the 1985 Single European Act and various international agreements commit the British

Government at least to take account of such concepts as nature conservation and sustainability. Indeed, the latter concept is explicitly mentioned in the terms of reference for the Scottish Natural Heritage agency. The aims of the Scottish Office Agriculture and Fisheries Department are currently '(i) to promote the competitive efficiency of agriculture in Scotland, (ii) to ensure a proper balance between agriculture and other rural development and interests *including conservation of the environment* (italics added), and (iii) to maintain and develop assistance, where appropriate, for those farming in the Less Favoured Areas' (Scottish Office, 1992). More locally, statutory authorities, such as those for roads and water, have become stricter monitors of farming practices, with a mixture of 'carrots' (e.g. agricultural grants for anti-pollution measures) and 'sticks' (prosecutions of offending farmers).

Farmers have long regarded themselves as 'stewards' of the land (Colman, 1994), and various surveys (e.g., Crabtree & Appleton, 1992) have identified substantial groups of farmers who place environmental conservation and enhancement high, if not highest, on their list of priorities in land management decision-making. The increasing importance of the residential value of land holdings compared with agricultural productivity may be one explanation; in other cases, farmers may feel an attachment to, and (equally important) have an understanding of, local features of natural interest and value. However, the economic imperatives of productive efficiency obviously militate against these influences, at least in the long run, and might be expected to result in a gradual loss of landscape quality and wildlife through drainage and fencing for land 'improvement', the use of agri-chemicals and large-scale farm machinery, and overgrazing by sheep and cattle.

The outstanding environmental qualities of the Cairngorms warrant particular attention to those aspects of agriculture, yet no great public conflicts appear to have arisen in the area between farming and environmental interests. There has been no parallel to the well-known case in Glen Lochay, near Loch Tay, where a large sum was found payable in compensation to a farmer who was hindered in his attempts to convert with grant an area of hill grazing to coniferous plantation. This is not to say that conflicts involving farmland in the Cairngorms do not exist, at least in biological terms. But the major issues appear to involve the large estates rather than local farmers whose image, and often reality, of hard work and a frugal lifestyle hinders criticism that might be directed towards agriculture as such.

In part, the reason is because the more unusual and ecologically sensitive parts of the Cairngorms face no or very low farming pressures. Highly visible erosion on the summit plateaux is caused by walkers and by vehicles used for sport shooting, and on the slopes the effects of skiing developments and insensitive afforestation are similarly obvious, but these are not areas where farmers are the main land users. Lower sites such as those with rare woodland species may be more vulnerable to agricultural

damage but, with reduced farm investment, the dangers at present are small, and not apparent to the casual, infrequent or non-expert visitor.

It is on the lower slopes, along the tourist routes and around the settlements, that farming practices can result in the enhancement or deterioration of the natural environment, and of the built environment in the shape of traditional stone buildings and other constructions. Here, a combination of neglect and physical damage can over time spoil the smaller features of a pleasant countryside, all the more regrettable when these farming areas form part of a wider scene containing more distant forests and mountainsides. To the farmer, the state of gates, dykes, fences, footpaths and shelters may become a matter of growing or total neglect as farming practices adjust to lower labour requirements and different kinds of plant and machinery. To the visitor, these features form environmental assets whose disappearance, decline or damage diminishes the overall experience.

It has not proved easy to tailor agricultural policy to cope with such problems. The foremost local attempt has been the 1992 designation of an Environmentally Sensitive Area (ESA). The Cairngorms Straths ESA, as with the northern extension of the existing Breadalbane ESA into the southern part of the Cairngorm area, and other ESAs elsewhere, seeks 'to support the continuation of farming practices which have helped to create distinctive landscapes and have maintained wildlife habitats and historic features', and 'to encourage measures that will enhance the environment' (SOAFD, 1993). Administered by the Agriculture Department since 1987, ESA designation enables farmers to be paid for the management of land in more environmentally friendly ways, for example by reducing stock numbers to preserve natural woodland, by fencing against deer or rabbits, by restoring stone dykes as field boundaries, by controlling bracken, and by protecting archaeological sites. It has also been suggested that District Councils could play a greater role in grants to farmers in the Cairngorms (Kincardine and Deeside District Council, 1994)

On a wider scale, the 1992 CAP reforms included the 'agri-environmental' Regulation 2078/92, which authorizes EU Member States to introduce further schemes promoting less intensive farming methods, land management for public access, and the conservation or re-establishment of biological and scenic diversity. The potential along these lines is still being explored. However, along with schemes promoted by environmental organizations such as Scottish Natural Heritage and voluntary bodies, and the activities of such bodies as the Grampian Farming and Wildlife Advisory Group, farmers are thus being made increasingly aware of the significance of their holdings and activities to the general public in terms of landscape and wildlife. Together with the wider horizons of the rising generation, it may be hoped that ways will be found to reconcile the financial imperatives of the commodity markets with incentives to maintain and improve the agricultural environment.

FARMING AND THE LEISURE SECTOR

Country leisure pursuits have long been important in the Cairngorms area, from the days of the establishment of the sporting estates, when many areas were cleared of sheep, cattle and people (Plate 60) to make way for deer and grouse. This era probably saw the most drastic historical change to local agricultural patterns. In shooting areas, farming was relegated to a permanent but background activity, secondary to the main interests of landed proprietors. Members of farming families found employment in and around the 'big hoose', especially in season, and henceforth co-existed with a variety of other employees in land management and visitor service, ranging from game-keeping and forestry to tourist shops and bed-and-breakfast accommodation.

The character of visitors to the region has of course changed markedly over the twentieth century. Originally members of the aristocracy (*ancien* or *nouveau*), with occasional foreign guests, were invited to the newly built or restored castles and hotels. Later, especially with the coming of the railway lines up Deeside and down Speyside, members of the rising professional and middle classes, pursuing newly popular outdoor pursuits such as hill-walking, began to arrive for weekends and summer holidays. Neither of these groups would have had much contact with farmers, except occasionally to request basic refreshment, transport or accommodation away from the growing settlements such as Ballater and Braemar – Aviemore had no hotel until late in the nineteenth century.

After the catastrophe of the First World War – which itself terminated many a farming and estate succession – leisure interests took time to recover, but in the 1930s the influence of the motor car and the popularity of camping brought more visitors, and from further afield, into the farming and mountain areas. The arrival of student and other lower-income groups in the countryside, so noticeable in the Pennines and the Glasgow area, was less obvious in the Cairngorms, given their greater distance from the major conurbations, until the 1950s. Only in the 1960s, with the long-term pressures on the rural economy becoming more and more obvious, did public policy and private enterprise turn seriously to tourism and other leisure activities as a possible means of economic support for farming and other households facing decline from improved communications, which reduced the need for localized services, and from lower real prices for primary commodities such as food, wool and timber.

It is, however, only in the last decade or so that farmers have been actively encouraged to consider leisure as a source of household income, through a range of possibilities including overnight and longer-term accommodation in buildings, caravans or tents, covert shooting, 'war games' and orienteering, horse-riding and adventure driving. In the late 1980s, Farm Diversification Schemes were introduced, offering to existing agricultural businesses a range of grants to non-farming enterprises for investment, feasibility studies and marketing. Other rural support agencies, such as the Tourist Boards, Enterprise Trusts, the Countryside Commission for Scotland and the Scottish Agricultural College have also offered financial and advisory assistance to farmers as well as others. For farm households in the Cairngorms area, perhaps the local Area Tourist Boards have been most widely known and used, in connection with visitors in both summer and (for skiing) in winter.

Despite all this official and semi-official activity, and the advent of mass tourism by car and bus in the 1980s and 1990s, only a minority of farmers, certainly in the Grampian Region (Shucksmith & Smith, 1991), have become involved in leisure diversification, especially amongst full-time family businesses. If they seek additional income at all, such farmers are more likely to derive this from such activities as agricultural contracting in the neighbourhood, or from off-farm jobs held by certain members of the household. On the other hand, very small farms, sometimes purchased by 'incomers' with non-farming backgrounds, may rely on diversified enterprises on-farm such as unusual livestock husbandry or on-farm processing, sometimes with roadside visitor attractions, in order to maintain a way of life, while the larger estates, with their greater and more varied resources, are very likely to run leisure enterprises in tandem with farming businesses or tenancies. Shortage of labour, as well as the weekly and seasonal variability of many leisure pursuits, has led some farms and estates not to attempt to exploit opportunities themselves but to rent out, or sell off, assets not required for farming, in the form of cottages and pieces of land wanted for car-parking, picnicking, and so on.

Finally, farms, as occupiers of the bulk of the land outside the high mountains in the Cairngorms area, are experiencing increased levels of countryside access by the general public. On sheep farms especially, this can bring problems with dogs at lambing time, and occasional vandalism, while more generally questions of rights of way and signposting have been raised. So far, these problems seem relatively minor in the Cairngorms area, given its large extent and limited number of visitors compared to the urban fringes or other mountain areas (Crabtree *et al.*, 1992). Also, facilities for walking and picnicking have been provided by the local authorities and others, in co-operation with landowners. However, although the area is wide, the road network is limited and the terrain often vulnerable to erosion, so that continued pressures may force more attention to be paid to the management, education and servicing of the many different groups and individuals seeking leisure in the open air.

THE FUTURE FOR FARMING IN THE CAIRNGORMS AREA

This Chapter has attempted to cover some of the background and issues facing farming in the Cairngorms area. It is hoped that it has been made clear that the economic viability of the sector now depends crucially on direct payments to farmers under the reformed Common Agricultural Policy of the European Union, while various developments in other land uses, such as forestry, nature conservation and leisure activities, are having an increasing if still limited impact on the structure and incomes of farming families and businesses.

Given the relative importance of the estate and forestry interests in the area, the future of many farms will be bound up with the intentions of much larger organizations, whether land-owning family trusts, forest management companies or government agencies. Although 'multiple land use' is not widely practised at an individual level, social pressures, articulated through individual decisions and the substantial policy interventions now being made in rural areas, will increasingly ensure that farmers are forced to take the wider context into account, so that the region as a whole is not unnecessarily damaged by single-minded developments – or absence of development – which detract from the variety and uniqueness of the environment. Both the previous and current Scottish administrations (Scottish Office, 1995, 1997, 1998; Scottish Executive, 2000, 2001) have tried to develop policy debate along these lines, invoking concepts of partnership, sustainable development, land reform and rural development generally.

Repeated policy statements from Edinburgh, London and Brussels have sought to reassure farmers that their role in the upland areas of the countryside is valued and will be maintained against adverse economic forces. However, there must be a limit to this willingness to subsidize otherwise unviable holdings – though much higher payments to remote farms are made in countries such as Norway and Switzerland – and cynics may suspect that the assurances are made only because ministers find it increasingly difficult to justify maintained levels of spending. At best, subsidies for agricultural production *per se* are now becoming increasingly constrained, while 'cross-compliance' with environmental conditions, such as eligibility for hill livestock headage payments becoming dependent on limited stocking rates, and the availability of grants and assistance for 'non-productive' activities on farms, are becoming more common.

So far at least, Cairngorm farmers, as elsewhere in Grampian Region and the Highlands, have indeed benefited from increased farm subsidies, especially since the 1992 devaluation of sterling and the advent of increased livestock payments. These episodes may have reinforced a reluctance already apparent amongst many in the area (Shucksmith, 1993) to face the long-term pressures on the sector. The importance of farmer attitudes and expectations in this situation is of course crucial, since these determine capital and livestock investments, and indeed the succession of farm ownerships and tenancies. Also important are the observable experiences of those farms taking up the new opportunities offered by grants and market openings. If these 'leaders' are seen to survive and succeed, others will be induced to follow; if not, further years will go by as traditional farming families seek to cut

costs and maintain living standards through adjustments to their existing businesses. No great technological changes are on the horizon, although new methods, such as ewe-scanning during ewe pregnancies, embryo transplants for cattle, and improved farm vehicles, are always being introduced. In any case such methods are unlikely to alter the relative position of hill and upland farms within national, European and international competition.

From the point of view of conserving and enhancing the Cairngorms for their qualities of landscape and wildlife uniqueness, farming may be said generally to play a less important role than forestry and leisure management. However, farming shares the land area involved, especially heather moors and herb meadows, and so must be managed in such a way as to preserve these features. Moreover, for their *enjoyment* by the public, the context offered by access through, and often direct use of, the farmland surrounding the most ecologically valuable areas depends on a healthy farming economy.

Agriculture has received attention in the various policy consultations and proposals of the Cairngorms Working Party (CWP) and Cairngorms Partnership Board (CPB), and the more recent moves towards National Park status. In its public consultation paper of May 1992 (CWP, 1992), the role of traditional farming systems in the Cairngorms area was endorsed as a valuable basis for nature conservation and for a variety of socio-economic and cultural activities. Little that was specific, except training schemes and advisory services, was put forward as a way of reversing land management problems such as overgrazing. However, in its December 1992 report to the Secretary of State, the CWP (1993, pp.30–34), in welcoming the establishment of the Cairngorm Straths ESA, requested that the needs of the special natural heritage qualities of the area be 'fully recognized', and that environmental payments be extended beyond the ESA boundaries where heather moorland is under threat. They also saw a need to involve farmers in the planning and management of visitor facilities, and to 'maintain farming as a central activity attractive to the younger generation'. Elements of the CPB's 1996 draft management strategy (CP, 1996) went further, suggesting that the Partnership 'take the lead' in seeking ways to improve agricultural support schemes, promote farm diversification into recreational and other opportunities via financial incentives from local enterprise companies and others, and encourage more advice and training to existing and new farmers. This might be tied in with the 1997 Scottish Countryside Premium Scheme, which offers training in environmentally friendly farming methods. In the biologically crucial montane zone, sheep numbers might have to be managed to ensure recovery of natural habitats and species. The practicalities of such suggestions would, of course, be dependent on the resources and powers made available by central government and (in the case of core farm support) the European Union. The prospect – under active analysis by Scottish National Heritage (SNH) and others at the time of writing – of the Cairngorms becoming a national park raises further opportunities for modifying agricultural policy in the area, again depending on the funding and legal powers awarded to the governing body. It will be essential that any agencies which are set up to protect and enhance the area's many attractions recognize both the high and increasing dependence of farming incomes on direct payments rather than market returns, and the complexities of that dependence between different farms and over time.

Farming in the Cairngorms area must in future expect to depend increasingly on its adaptation to the increased willingness of the public, through its tax, subsidy and regulatory systems, and through its leisure markets for visitors, to reward environmental improvements and to penalize environmental damage. Precisely what comprises 'improvement' and 'damage' in any particular context – and, whether, for example, past damage should be repaired fully at public cost – will have to be determined by a complex system of hierarchical environmental designations and decision-making, from international bodies at one end of the scale, to local officials and land managers at the other. For Cairngorm farmers, accustomed to supplying food in harsh conditions to far-away markets, this will be a new form of an old challenge.

REFERENCES

Cairngorms Partnership (CP) (1996) *Managing the Cairngorms – Consultation Papers: Upper Deeside; Badenoch and Strathspey; The Montane Zone*. Cairngorms Partnership, Grantown-on-Spey.

Cairngorms Working Party (CWP) (1992) *Public Consultation Paper: May 1992*. The Scottish Office, Edinburgh.

Cairngorms Working Party (1993) *Common Sense and Sustainability: a Partnership for the Cairngorms*. The Scottish Office, Edinburgh.

Carter, J. S. (1979) *Farming Life in North East Scotland*. John Donald, Edinburgh.

Colman, D.R. (1994) Ethics and Externalities: Agricultural Stewardship and Other Behaviour. *J. agric. Econ.* 45(3), 299–311.

Commission of the European Communities (CEC) (1994) *EC Agriculture Policy for the 21st Century*. Brussels.

Commission of the European Communities (CEC) (1997) *Agenda 2000: For a Stronger and Wider Union*, DOC/97/6. Brussels.

Crabtree, J.R. & Appleton, Z. (1992) Economic Evaluation of the Farm Woodland Scheme in Scotland. *J. agric. Econ.*, 43(3) 355–367.

Crabtree, J.R., Appleton, Z., Thomson, K.J. & Slee, R.W. (1992) *The Economics of Countryside Access in Scotland*. Report to the Countryside Commission for Scotland. Battleby, Perth.

Department of Agriculture for Scotland (DAS) (1947) *Scotland's Marginal Farms: The North East of Scotland*. Regional Report V. HMSO, Edinburgh.

Handley, J.E. (1953) *Scottish Farming in the Eighteenth Century*. Faber and Faber, London.

Kincardine and Deeside District Council (1994) Response to the Cairngorms Working Party's Report Common Sense and Sustainability. In: Watson, A. & Conroy. J., eds, *The Cairngorms: Planning Ahead*. Proceedings of Conference at Ballater, June 1993. Appendix. KDDC, Stonehaven. pp. 93–109.

Ministry of Agriculture, Fisheries and Food (MAFF) (1991) *Our Farming Future*. MAFF Publications, London.

Reforesting Scotland (1994) *Norway and Scotland: a Study in Land Use*. Ullapool.

Scottish Executive (2000) *Scottish Agriculture: a Guide to Grants and Services*. Edinburgh.

Scottish Executive (2001) *A Forward Strategy for Agriculture*. Edinburgh.

Scottish Office (1992) *Rural Framework*. Edinburgh.

Scottish Office (1995) *Rural Scotland: People, Prosperity and Partnership*. Edinburgh.

Scottish Office (1997) *Towards a Development Strategy for Rural Scotland: a Discussion Paper*. Edinburgh.

Scottish Office (1998) *Land Reform Policy Group: Identifying the Problems*. Edinburgh.

Scottish Office Agriculture and Fisheries Department (SOAFD) (1993) *Cairngorms Straths Environmentally Sensitive Area: Explanatory Leaflet for Farmers*. CS/ESA 1. Edinburgh.

Shucksmith, D.M. & Smith, R. (1991) Farm Household Strategies and Pluriactivity in Upland Scotland. *J. agric. Econ.* 42(3), 340–353.

Shucksmith, D.M. (1993) Farm Household Behaviour and the Transition to Post-Productivism. *J. agric. Econ.* 44(3), 466–478.

Thomson, K.J., ed. (1993) *Scottish Farm Income Trends and the Natural Environment*. SNH Research, Survey and Monitoring Report No. 17. Scottish Natural Heritage, Edinburgh.

CHAPTER 9

The Native Woodlands
History, Decline and Present Status

N.A. MacKenzie

The foothills and straths of the Cairngorms contain some of the finest, and most extensive, naturally-occurring woodland in Britain. The importance of the native pinewoods, in particular, has far outweighed their significance as a component of the Highland woodland resource, but the distinctive pattern of the pine-birch community and its associated flora and fauna, its recent history and its impact on the landscape of the Cairngorms are unique features of Britain's natural heritage. (Plates 21, 96 and Frontispiece)

The pine-birch woodlands in the Cairngorms have had a long history of continuity in this region, having been the climax vegetation type during post-glacial times and still occupying the dominant native woodland niche today. Although many changes have affected these woodlands over the centuries, there has been considerably less human and climatic influence and over a shorter period than in natural woodland anywhere else in Britain. Due, in part, to their remoteness and inaccessibility, these boreal woodlands remained relatively untouched by large-scale exploitation until much later, compared to the lowland woods, and still retain much of the character associated with the original natural forest.

Whether approaching the Cairngorms from Deeside or from Strathspey the mosaic of pine, birch and heather dominates the landscape of the extensive middle ground between the high tops and the agricultural land of the lower straths. This woodland mosaic, mainly of pine and birch but also containing additional tree and shrub species as well

as mires, open moor and other subsidiary habitats, represents a type of woodland which is quite different in ecological character from the natural climax forest found outside the Scottish Highlands.

The contemporary landscape and ecological values attached to the native woodlands of the Cairngorms are as great as their timber value was in previous centuries but, despite the many sectoral landuse interests which currently conflict with the future survival of these woods, there is optimism that their multi-purpose benefits will help to conserve this resource far more easily than any single purpose management.

POST-GLACIAL ORIGINS

About 7000 years ago over 50 per cent of the land area of the Cairngorms was clothed in the natural climax forest which became established after the end of the Pleistocene ice age. Paleoecological studies based on the analyses of pollen distribution in the peat deposits and loch sediments have suggested that birch, willow and juniper were the first tree species to colonize the Cairngorms area after the retreat of the ice sheets. They arrived about 9500 BP, having spread northwards from glacial refugia in continental Europe (Birks, 1989). Just under 9000 BP may have seen the arrival of hazel from the west although this species was probably restricted to locations where the edaphic conditions were most favourable. The early colonization by certain broadleaved species with soil-improving properties, such as birch, aspen

Table 9a   Trees and shrubs native to the Cairngorms

Alder	*Alnus glutinosa*
Ash	*Fraxinus excelsior*
Aspen	*Populus tremula*
Birch, Downy	*Betula pubescens*
Birch, Silver	*Betula pendula*
Blackthorn	*Prunus spinosa*
Cherry, Bird	*Prunus padus*
Cherry, Wild (Gean)	*Prunus avium*
Elder	*Sambucus nigra*
Elm, Wych	*Ulmus glabra*
Hawthorn	*Crataegus monogyna*
Hazel	*Corylus avellana*
Holly	*Ilex aquifolium*
Juniper	*Juniperus communis*
Oak, Pedunculate	*Quercus robur*
Oak, Sessile	*Quercus petraea*
Pine, Scots	*Pinus sylvestris*
Rose, Dog	*Rosa canina*
Rowan	*Sorbus aucuparia*
Whitebeam, Rock	*Sorbus rupicola*
Willow, Goat	*Salix caprea*
Willow, Grey	*Salix cinerea*
Willow, Eared	*Salix aurita*

Some of these species are rare or have a restricted natural distribution in the Cairngorms (e.g. elder and the rock whitebeam, *Sorbus rupicola*). Other small shrubs like gorse, broom, dwarf birch and additional montane willow species and their hybrids could also have been included in this list.

and willow, would have aided the conversion to mull humus in the developing soil profile. By 8800 BP pine had arrived in Strathspey and there was a rapid expansion of pine-dominant woodland throughout parts of the Cairngorms until about 7400 BP. Pine had first arrived in Britain from Europe some 10 500 years ago and had spread rapidly throughout Scotland. The source of the pine reaching the Cairngorms has been the subject of more than one hypothesis. Pine appeared independently and over a similar time period at several locations, including Wester Ross, the Cairngorms and south Scotland. Huntley and Birks (1983) and Bennet (1995) speculated that pine may have survived the Pleistocene ice sheets in refugia on the continental shelf to the west of Scotland or Ireland and then subsequently expanded from there. Alternatively, pine may have spread northwards from southern England but a more likely explanation is that there is more than one origin (Bennett, 1996).

The rates of spread varied for each species and in each locality, and depended as much on the methods of seed dispersal as on topographic features, soil type and local climate. Both birch and pine seed are wind dispersed and rapid colonization would be expected, but other trees, such as oak and alder, which reached the Central Highlands fairly soon after (about 6000 BP) and almost as rapidly, depended on a variety of animal or other long-distance disposal agencies. Chambers and Elliot (1989) have suggested that the expansion of alder

may have been assisted by disturbance created by beaver and human activities as well as by avian and water dispersal.

The extent of woodland distribution had probably reached its Holocene maximum between 7000 and 5000 BP, just prior to any significant human disturbance (Birks, 1988; Bennet, 1988). In the Cairngorms the maximum estimated tree line at that time was 880 m (Huntley *et al.*, 1997) which suggests that there were probably always sizeable areas of open habitat at the higher altitudes. The composition and distribution of the post-glacial boreal forest has been mapped for the main woodland types by McVean and Ratcliffe (1962) and by Bennet (1988). Both show substantial zones of unforested land across the montane parts of the Cairngorms with the remaining areas dominated by pine and birch woodland. The maps are not sufficiently detailed to highlight the location of other woodland types but 5000 years ago alder would probably have dominated the alluvial soils in the straths of the Dee, Don and Spey and oak would have been present on the more fertile low-ground sites.

Other components of the woodlands would have included all the species extant today (Table 9a). The forests of the Cairngorms were probably more diverse at this time although any assessment of the species composition in the main climax communities can only be speculative. The woodland composition at the upper tree line was probably pine with some birch, aspen, willow and juniper. The natural forests of pine, birch and alder at lower levels would most likely have reflected the pattern as described by McVean and Ratcliffe and, depending on site conditions, would have contained varying proportions of other subsidiary and understorey trees and shrubs. Even-aged stands of the shade-intolerant species might have been extensive, just as they are at present, but a selection of age classes would be represented over a given area – their distribution perhaps affected by external factors such as fire, windthrow, wild boar and beaver activity and the abandoned clearings occupied by the early Mesolithic peoples which could be considered as natural to the forest ecosystem as any other mammal. The popular conception of the 'Old Wood of Caledon' is of a landscape dominated by pine and this is the case in the east and central Highlands and in parts of the north-west. However, this is in contrast to the majority of the Highlands where birch and oak were, and still are, a major component of the native forests.

Around 4000 BP there occurred a significant climatic change in the Scottish Highlands with a sufficient increase in precipitation and oceanic conditions to cause a decline in the forest area and an increase in the formation of blanket bog. This was particularly extensive in the north and west and possibly caused some local extinction of the pine but there was no significant change in the vegetation of the Cairngorms. The reasons why more of the forest area disappeared in the north-west compared to the Cairngorms forests are not clear, but there may have been an element of the anthropogenic disturbance in the oceanic marginal zones of the north-west which tipped the balance (Birks, 1988). However, such climatic events in the Cairngorms would have increased periglacial processes in the montane zone and probably resulted in a lowering of the treeline.

EARLY FOREST CLEARANCE

The impact of the early Neolithic communities on the forests of the Highlands varied in different parts of the country and were probably temporary at some locations, allowing forest recovery, and masked by the greater effects of climate change in other areas. The Neolithic people were shifting cultivators, kept domestic animals and used fire and axes to clear forests. One of the earliest records of clearance in Strathspey is at Loch Garten over 3600 BP and O'Sullivan (1977) suggests that this is probably linked to the migration of people into the area. In lower Deeside Neolithic agriculture was well established by 5500 BP, as shown by the recent excavations at Balbridie which have confirmed the presence of breadwheat and flax from that period (Fairweather & Ralston, 1993). The large size of the Balbridie timber building also indicated the large quantity of oak timber that must have been required to construct a building with 27 × 14 metre dimensions, and the effect on the natural forest, though local, was probably significant. The associated grazing activities practised by these early stone age farmers may have helped to maintain heathland in the fertile straths and, over a period of perhaps many centuries, would have begun to encroach on the forests of the Cairngorms.

Despite the probable changes in the vegetation pattern of the lowland straths of the Spey, Don and Dee by the early settlements and pastoral activities of the Neolithic period onwards, there is evidence that the pine-birch forests survived relatively intact until about 300–400 years ago, much later than natural forests anywhere else in Britain. At Abernethy, for example, there is an unbroken pine pollen profile from post-glacial times to the present and, although parts of the forest were cleared for pastoral farming 3500 years ago, these areas regenerated after the farming ended (O'Sullivan, 1977). However, there was an increase in *Calluna* heath and a decrease in the amount of birch, which indicates the kind of changes these early pastoralists had inflicted on the woodland composition and extent. Nevertheless, the more acid mor soils of the pinewoods were much less hospitable to farming than the fertile alluvial soils of the river valleys. McVean and Ratcliffe's (1962) map of the reconstructed woodland distribution prior to human intervention shows oak in the Spey and Dee valleys, but early cultivation probably reduced this to scattered fragments or caused local extinctions. Increasing population pressure and the requirements for buildings constructed out of oak and other hardwoods would have diminished this resource still further (Carlisle, 1977).

Many of the earliest maps (Blaeu, 1654; Pont, *c.* sixteenth century) show extensive natural woodland in the Cairngorms area, particularly in the uplands where they still exist today (Plate 67). Few woods are shown in the lower straths, for example the Avon and lower Deeside, and it is probable that much of these large, possibly broadleaved, woods had been cleared gradually over the centuries and before the map-making expeditions of the 1500s. The Forest of Birse was destroyed long before the eighteenth century because it was accessible and perhaps also because it was a commonty (Callander, 2000). Some deterioration of the climate may also have caused a lowering of the tree line as indicated by the report in the Old Statistical Accounts (Sinclair, 1791–99) on the taking of fir roots from the mosses and hills of Glen Avon to be used as a fuel.

From the thirteenth century onwards came the first recorded attempts at managing the forest in order to safeguard the resource, or at least reserve it for a particular purpose. In 1226, Alexander II had granted the forest of Rothiemurchus to the Bishop of Moray who was then able to use the area for sport and grazing and who could also benefit from the tolls levied on tenants for foggage and herbage. In 1383, the then Bishop employed a head forester, since at that time there was a conflict of interest between the value of the forest as a hunting reserve and the grazing and wood-cutting activities of the tenants. Fines of £10 sterling were levied on illegal hunting and felling, and the pasture tolls were introduced in order to limit the degree of grazing. In the fifteenth century Mar and Abernethy were royal forests used by the king as hunting reserves. Such a designation meant that some measure of protection was conferred on these areas as both the habitat and the game were to be preserved (Gilbert, 1979).

During the middle ages there were widespread timber shortages in the Scottish Lowlands due to heavy demands for the building of churches, monasteries and castles and the increasing grazing pressure of domestic livestock. Forest Laws were enacted to prohibit burning, restrict grazing and encourage tree planting and, in 1535, the death penalty was introduced for a third wood-cutting offence (Gilbert, 1979). Timber was also imported from Lochaber and from Denmark, and it is now generally accepted that the timber reserves of the Lowlands of Scotland were virtually exhausted by the sixteenth century (Steven & Carlisle, 1959). Yet the forests in the Highlands remained more or less intact from major exploitation and in the Cairngorms were to remain so until well into the next century.

THE COMMERCIAL EXPLOITATION OF THE FOREST

The natural forests of the Highlands began to be exploited by outside interests from about 1600, when new timber sources were required for the production of iron ore and for the construction of ships for the navy. Woods on the west coast and other accessible locations were used initially as extraction to loch and sea was more feasible. One of the earliest records of the sale of woodland in Strathspey is from about 1631, when woods in the parishes of Abernethy, Kincardine and Duthil were leased for £1666 sterling. The trees were considered to have a low value at that time, contracts with the timber merchants were vague in their terms and tenants still retained rights of servitude. The extraction of the timber was, however, difficult as the early efforts to float timber down the Spey, using currachs (small hide-covered boats) which towed the rafts of wood, were not very successful (Nairne, 1891).

By the early eighteenth century the value of the great natural timber resources of the Cairngorms was much more appreciated and, in 1695, a sawmill was erected at the mouth of the River Quoich and annual fellings carried out in the accessible parts of the Mar woods, while in 1725 fir (pine) timber from Glentanar served the whole of the district around it (Steven & Carlisle, 1959). Around 1728, the York Buildings Company purchased, for £7000, a 15-year lease to cut 60 000 fir trees from Abernethy. This was an elaborate operation involving 120 horses and waggons etc., with sawmills erected and an iron foundry built near Nethybridge. The business was too extravagant and became insolvent a few years later but it did perfect a viable method of floating the timber down the Spey to the sea, which was to pave the way for all future timber harvesting on both sides of the Cairngorms. The system which was developed involved the construction of large rafts of 60–80 logs bound together with a platform of deals on top and guided downstream by two men with oars (Plate 66). Sunken rocks were removed when the river was low by building fires and throwing water on them to cause cracking (Nairne, 1891; Sinclair, 1791–99; Steven & Carlisle, 1959).

Other timber sales which followed included 'one million choice fir trees' from Abernethy and Dulnain in 1769, despite the record of a fire at Abernethy in 1746 which was said to have destroyed two and a half million trees. During the late 1700s, the River Dee was used to transport large numbers of logs from the pinewoods of Mar and, about the same time, the woods of Garmaddie at Balmoral were being felled. The floating of the logs to Aberdeen could only be carried out when the river was in spate and problems often arose when collisions occurred between the rafts and the bridges. The bridge at Potarch, for example, was destroyed about 1812 and *The Bridges (Scotland) Act,* 1813, was passed to prevent damage to certain bridges. This Act prohibited the floating of logs between November and March and during bridge maintenance, and restricted the passing rafts to one at a time (Anderson, 1967).

A map of the upper Spey which was compiled by the surveyor William Anderson (1770) shows extensive natural woods around Loch Morlich, and also highlights the large rocks and rapids in the River Luineag. Towards the end of that century the exploitation of Rothiemurchus had begun and the methods of extraction, using horses, water-powered sawmills and the building of dams and sluice gates at Loch Morlich and Loch Einich to assist the transport of the logs to the Spey are vividly described in Grant (1972). In the lower straths agricultural expansion was limiting the growth of birch and alder woods. Birch was felled for charcoal production,

leather tanning, local domestic use including the making of farm implements, roof beams, furniture, bowls, ropes, and as a fuel (Lines, 1984). Large areas of alder, which occupy the most fertile soil but which are regarded as 'useless for manufacture', were being converted to fields (Sinclair, 1791–99).

The forest of Glenmore was considered to be the most remote and inaccessible of all the pinewoods and may have been the last relatively untouched natural forest left in Britain at the beginning of the nineteenth century. In 1783 the timber was sold for £10 000 and the felling of the forest was completed by 1805. In order to facilitate transportation to the Spey, the River Luineag was deepened and straightened and large numbers of 'deals, spars, logs, masts' were sent down to the sea at Garmouth every year (Sinclair, 1791–99). The timber from Glenmore was particularly valuable to the shipbuilding industry as the native pine was considered the equal of oak and during this period 47 ships, the largest being 1056 tons, were built at Garmouth (Steven & Carlisle, 1959). About 1820, an attempt was made at Rothiemurchus to manage the woods sustainably, by enclosing the area just felled in order to protect regenerating seedlings. Had this plan of dividing the forest into compartments 'been pursued from the beginning there would never have been an end to the wood of Rothiemurchus' (Grant, 1972).

During the first half of the nineteenth century extensive felling was carried out in most of the main pinewood areas. The Napoleonic Wars placed a heavy demand on British timber supplies and prices were high. Mar, Glentanar, Rothiemurchus, Abernethy, Glen Feshie and Dulnain were all involved in commercial timber operations which largely serviced the shipbuilding industry. 1822 ha at Abernethy and 1215 ha at Dulnain were advertised for sale in 1805, and Mar and Glentanar woods were advertised in 1809 (Anderson, 1967). Ballochbuie escaped the large-scale felling, but a tramway was proposed to aid extraction, and the wood was only saved when Queen Victoria purchased Balmoral and timber extraction on the estate ceased.

At the end of the Napoleonic wars the price of timber fell and, in 1841, it was no longer economic to transport timber by road, for example from Glentanar to Aberdeen. The floating of logs down the Dee during winter floods was still feasible and some of the best remaining pine trees on Mar were extracted between 1811 and 1855. The exploitation of the pine after the wars still continued at Abernethy and in 1839 there were ninety men employed in the forest, although the timber trade declined in the second half of the century despite the arrival of the railway (Steven & Carlisle, 1959).

Between the end of the eighteenth and the middle of the nineteenth centuries the natural forests of the Cairngorms were severely depleted, at least of the best of the timber trees, and it was said that the incessant clearances made Strathspey look bleak (Nairne, 1891; Sinclair, 1791–99; Smout, 1999). However, a sufficient number of seed trees must have been left for the area to regenerate naturally, as the first edition of the Ordnance Survey map (surveyed *c.* 1870) shows extensive woodland over much of the main pinewood areas. There are also several accounts from contemporary observers which show that there was prolific regeneration of trees after felling (Grant, 1972; Nairne,1891; Sinclair, 1891–99). Lauder in 1830 claimed that the growth of pine seedlings at Rothiemurchus was 'as thick as a nurseryman's seedbed' and described the forest of Glenmore 'to be fast replenishing itself' (in Steven & Carlisle, 1959).

In addition to the natural regeneration which some owners, like Seafield at Abernethy and Grant at Rothiemurchus, actively promoted by enclosing young trees with dykes, planting on a fairly large scale had begun in the middle of the nineteenth century. The planting of local origin pine took place in various parts of the north section of Abernethy, some of it to fill gaps in areas of natural regeneration, and pine and larch were extensively planted at Mar, Invercauld and Balmoral (see also Chapter 10).

THE DECLINE OF THE FOREST

The main era of exploitation had now ended although native pine was felled on the lower slopes of Creag Mhigeachaidh in Glen Feshie in 1870, and some timber rafts continued to be floated down the Dee and the Spey at the beginning of this century (Cash, 1905). The landowners had by now embarked on new, more profitable ventures which included letting some of the forest areas for sheep grazing and developing the sport of open hill deer stalking.

Until the late eighteenth century red deer in the Highlands had declined in number and distribution, partly due to the loss of their natural woodland habitat. The extensive forests around the Cairngorms were among the few locations where deer survived (Callander & MacKenzie, 1991b). The huge rents paid for stalking meant that there was little incentive to expand the forest and every incentive to expand the deer population. One of the earliest of the modern deer forests was at Mar and, as a result of high deer numbers from at least the end of the eighteenth century, there has been very little natural regeneration since that time (Watson, 1983; Gordon, 1949). A similar situation has existed in most of the other pine forests with high browsing levels limiting successful regeneration to a few crags, gorges and steep slopes. Rothiemurchus and Glenmore became deer forests in 1859, Kinveachy (Dulnain) in 1864 and Abernethy in 1866 and, in 1869, ten tenants and 450 sheep were removed from Abernethy to make way for this new development (Orr, 1982). It was fortunate that the extensive regeneration, which followed the large-scale fellings of the late eighteenth and early nineteenth centuries became well established prior to the increase in browsing pressure, for it is these very trees that make up the mature fragments of pine that are extant today.

Another landuse practice which helped to prevent regeneration of the forest was muirburning, which was employed in the management of heather and pasture for sheep and grouse, but which restricted the natural succession of moorland to woodland by destroying the young tree seedlings. In the last century grouse shooting was almost as profitable as the deer and in some estates like Rothiemurchus resulted in the removal of sheep as early as 1827 to make way for grouse management (Orr, 1982).

There was a further resurgence in large-scale felling operations in the native pinewoods during the two world wars of the twentieth century. Very extensive areas of both planted and natural pine were extracted, for example by the Canadian Forestry Corps, from nearly all the main native pinewoods (Table 9b). The Forestry Commission census of 1947–49 records the areas felled during the first half of the century, although it did not distinguish between planted and self-sown trees or, in many cases, identify the species, but from the map locations most sites are known to have been of pine. Additional areas had been lost to fire, housing, sawmill yards, powerlines and a loch. Many of the felled sites are still bare ground today or have little more than a scattering of mature granny pine, due to the continuing presence of a large red deer population.

THE LAST FORTY YEARS

During the latter half of the twentieth century the area and condition of the native woodland continued to decline. The work of Steven and Carlisle (1959) in the early 1950s had highlighted the predicament of the native pinewoods and provided an accurate baseline for monitoring subsequent changes to these areas. Between 1957 and 1987, for example, 18 per cent of the area of native pine had been lost to felling or to underplanting (Bain, 1987). Considerable felling had occurred at Abernethy, some as recent as 1984, and many of the underplanted sites had been heavily thinned prior to ploughing and planting (Table 9c). Virtually all the felled areas have been planted with conifers, mainly local-origin Scots pine but also exotic conifers and non-local pine, particularly at Glenmore. Losses due to fire, windthrow and natural mortality have exacerbated the decline

Table 9b   Areas of wartime fellings (ha)

Forest	pre-Aug 1939	1939–1949
Abernethy	1057	494
Kinveachy	2151	1968
Rothiemurchus	1577	384
Glenmore	F	–
Glen Feshie	–	F
Glentanar	–	F
Mar	320	392
Ballochbuie	–	–

F = heavy felling occurred; (figures not available).
NB Most pre-1939 fellings took place during World War 1.
All area data include planted and self-sown crops, but at two locations (Mar & Glentanar) most of the felling was of planted trees.
Source: Forestry Commission, Census of Woodlands 1947–49. Field data books for Aberdeenshire & Inverness-shire. Scottish Record Office, Edinburgh.

Table 9c   Native pinewood losses in the Cairngorms 1957–1987 (areas in hectares)

Forest	Underplanting		Felling	Fire/wind
	local origin Scots pine	other origins and species		
Abernethy	232	169	226	27
Kinveachy	–	–	–	–
Rothiemurchus	–	277	–	–
Glenmore	–	94	–	–
Inshriach	–	–	155	–
Glen Feshie	11	2	–	–
Glentanar	–	90	–	25
Mar	–	25	–	–
Ballochbuie	–	–	25	–
TOTAL	443	657	406	52

[1957 total = 8,552 ha; total area lost = 1,558 ha or 18 per cent]
Source: Bain, 1987)

in the mature pinewoods when there was no natural regeneration to replace these losses. (Forest plantations are discussed in more detail in Chapter 10).

Changes have also occurred in the area and location of birchwoods during the past four decades. Many birchwoods have been converted to conifer plantations, cleared for agricultural use and housing or have diminished in area due to the mortality of the older trees and the pressure of overbrowsing (Plate 65). A survey of the birchwoods of Deeside established that, although the total area of birch had remained unchanged over the past forty years, considerable losses had occurred (over half the birchwoods present in 1947 had disappeared by 1987). These were partially compensated for by an increase in the area of birch, mainly at one location, the Muir of Dinnet (Brown & Wightman, 1988). The majority of birch in upper Deeside is now mature or in a moribund condition due to the lack of adequate regeneration. A similar situation may have developed in Strathspey where many of the upland birchwoods are also in a moribund condition. Yet birch has expanded in the lower straths (Plate 61), for example to the north-east of Grantown, and in the lower tributaries of Glentruim, Glenlivet and Strathavon. This recent regeneration is largely a consequence of changes in landuse practice. In Deeside in the 1960s there was a reduction in sheep numbers, a cessation of muirburning and voluntary deer control. In the northern Cairngorms, a rise in the number of hillwalkers and skiers has affected deer movements and contributed to the regeneration (Chapter 11).

Other localized areas of regeneration, particularly of pine, have developed in the Forest of Birse (Plate 61) and at Coilacreich on Deeside, and at Glenmore and Rothiemurchus in Strathspey, where the pine has recolonized open moorland. However, these localized areas of native woodland expansion do not compensate for the losses elsewhere and the overall pattern of woodland decline is apparent throughout the Cairngorm area. Some of the most recent regeneration remains vulnerable to muirburn and casual felling is still a common practice.

The majority of all native woodlands in the Highlands are unenclosed and, as these woods are often the only available shelter in upland areas, they are frequently exposed to a disproportionate density of browsing animals throughout the year (MacKenzie, 1987). In the Cairngorms, the main factor behind the lack of successful regeneration, to replace the losses sustained by natural mortality or expand the woodland cover, has been the dramatic rise in the red deer population. High deer densities have been common in the Cairngorms for a long time and have prevented regeneration in areas like Mar for over 200 years (Watson, 1983). In the past thirty years the number of wild deer in Scotland has doubled, while in the period 1967 to 1986, the Deer Commission for Scotland's counts for the Cairngorms-West Grampian and East Grampian areas indicated a 36 per cent increase in the population, although numbers have not risen further in the past decade (Callander & MacKenzie, 1991b, Youngson & Stewart, 1996) (see also Chapter 11).

It is the longevity of the Scots pine, at over 250 years, in places like Ballochbuie, Mar, Abernethy and Glen Feshie, that has ensured the survival of these forest remnants, despite the high browsing levels. Nevertheless, the ecology, composition and structure of these woods has probably altered considerably over the centuries as a consequence of these pressures (Gimingham, 1977). Most pine and birch woods possess an impoverished species composition and there tends to be an even-aged structure which is predominantly biased towards the mature size classes. In many Cairngorms pinewoods, for example, broadleaved species like birch, rowan, aspen and willow are rare or are restricted to gorges, rock ledges or steep slopes. Such trees are favoured browse species (Mitchell, Staines & Welch, 1977), have a shorter life cycle, and would therefore tend to disappear long before the pine when there was a consistently high level of browsing. Alternatively, they would be surviving only in the few locations inaccessible to deer.

Many woods have also experienced a reduction in stocking density due to fire, windthrow and old age. This effect, in a normal forest cycle, would have contributed to the natural diversification of the forest structure as regeneration filled the gaps with younger trees or other species. The regeneration which has taken place, however, has occurred in cycles whenever browsing became reduced, and much of the forest's development has been in a perpetual pioneer phase with little opportunity to progress to a stable boreal ecosytem. In addition, the creation of excessive gaps in the canopy has resulted in increased light levels and a change in the composition of the ground flora; many pinewoods are now little more than a scattering of trees over heather moorland, while the reduction in the broad-leaved component has caused a loss of soil fertility (Miles, 1985). The removal of tree cover is known to interrupt the hydrological cycle with a consequent increase in waterlogging and podzolization (Brady, 1984). Logging, burning, cultivation and prolonged grazing may have increased the spread of upland heaths, or contributed to retrogressive succession by the leaching of soil nutrients. The lack of broadleaved trees, such as birch and alder, with soil improving properties or the ability to fix nitrogen, meant that the fertility of the soil could not be replenished.

The contemporary protection afforded to native woodland in Scotland began with the notification of Sites of Special Scientific Interest, after the formation of the Nature Conservancy (now Scottish Natural Heritage) in 1949, but was limited to sites of conservation importance. However, the SSSI system was often ineffective in reducing browsing levels unless voluntary management agreements, to reduce sheep or deer numbers or to erect exclosures, were enacted. Concern over the decline in the native pinewoods led to the creation of the Native Pinewood Discussion Group (now the Native Wood-land Discussion Group) which initiated a conference at Aviemore in 1975 (Bunce & Jeffers, 1977). Then, in 1978, the Forestry Commission introduced a Native Pinewood Grant Scheme, but its success was limited and most of the management activities involved ploughing and planting rather than the promotion of natural regeneration (Bain, 1987). More recently, public concern about the loss of native woodland and the rapid expansion of huge conifer plantations resulted in a series of important legislative changes aimed at protecting the remaining woods and creating new native woods. The first of these was the Forestry Commission's Broadleaves Policy, introduced in 1985, which was to herald the end of any further conversion of native broadleaved woods to conifer plantation or other land use, and to provide enhanced grant aid for the creation of new broadleaved woods. In addition, the *Wildlife & Countryside (Amendment) Act*, 1985, charged the Forestry Commission to seek a reasonable balance between timber production and wildlife conservation. Later changes included a revised Woodland Grant Scheme with improved financial incentives for the regeneration of native broadleaved woods and the management of existing woods and new grants and guidelines for the management of the native pinewoods (Forestry Authority, 1993 & 1997; Forestry Commission, 1989).

The guidelines attached to the pinewoods scheme set strict criteria for management which promoted natural regeneration as the preferred method of establishment and, although utilizable timber production would be encouraged, the main objectives of the scheme are multi-purpose. The guidelines for the regeneration of other native wood-lands, however, are not as strict. The Forestry Practice Guides, produced recently by the Forestry Authority, also recommend natural regeneration as the preferred method of establishment but where planting of native broadleaves is employed it is only suggested that local origin stock be used (Forestry Authority, 1994).

In 1992 further positive changes took place when the Forestry Commission was reorganized. The Forestry Authority set up an Advisory Panel for the management of native woodlands in the Highlands, subsequently expanded to cover all of Scotland, and Forest Enterprise launched a major initiative to restore and expand native woodland on its land (Forest Enterprise, 1992 & 1993). At Glenmore, Forest Enterprise has removed large areas of non-native conifers in order to regenerate the scattered native pine remnants which had previously been underplanted.

While those statutory changes had been developing, other organizations, including various non-government agencies and the voluntary sector, had been conducting surveys and producing reports and policies relating to the conservation and sustainable management of native woodland in Scotland (e.g. Bain, 1987; Callander, 1987; House of Commons, 1990; MacKenzie, 1987; RSPB, 1993; Walker & Kirby, 1989; Wightman, 1992). Scottish Natural Heritage had completed its Ancient Woodland Inventory, although subsequent analyses have established that not all native woodland in Scotland is contained within the Inventory and total area data will therefore be an under-representation (Roberts *et al.*, 1993). Several initiatives to provide advice on the practical management of native woodlands were also started. The first of these was Scottish Native Woods, a company set up by the voluntary sector to promote the restoration and expansion of Scotland's native woodland. Within three years a partnership of four government agencies had established Highland Birchwoods to promote the same ideals within Highland Region.

Designations which relate to specific localities have emerged in recent years as a response to the need for a more co-ordinated approach in the management of land. Indicative Forestry Strategies and Environmentally Sensitive Area status will have an impact on the character of the native woodland resource in the Cairngorms, and Callander and MacKenzie (1991a) have introduced the concept of a collective identity to the 'Highland Deeside Forest' as well as the forests of Strathspey and Highland Perthshire. Then, in 1991, the Secretary of State for Scotland set up the Cairngorms Working Party to prepare recommendations for an integrated management programme for the Cairngorms area. Its Report (1993) and that of the successor to the

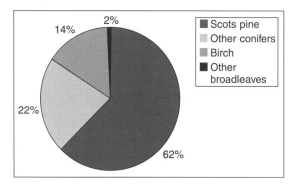

Figure 9.1 Main woodland types in the Cairngorms (includes all planted and self-sown woods)

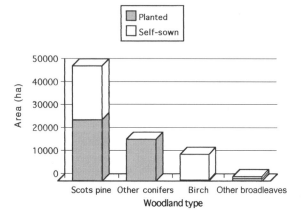

Figure 9.2 Main woodland types in the Cairngorms – proportions of planted and self-sown

Working Party, the Cairngorms Partnership (1997), have proposed the creation of two large forests, the Forest of Strathspey and the Forest of Mar, with the objective of conserving and extending the native forest in order both to protect it and provide multi-purpose benefits. The present extent of this native woodland, referred to by its old name of the Caledonian Forest in the Working Party's Report, is described in the next section.

Recent Scottish Natural Heritage policy has widened the scope of forests in the landscape by developing the concept of the Forest Habitat Network where core forest areas, such as the Cairngorms, would be linked to other areas by restoring the connections between wooded habitats. A particular rationale for such a network of different wooded habitats would be the prevention of ecological isolation. The Cairngorms already has the makings of such a forest network and has been proposed as a pilot project area to promote the concept (Peterken *et al.*, 1995).

While the past ten years have seen very significant developments in the policies affecting native woodlands, as well as a huge growth of public interest in the value of these woods, there is still a considerable amount of active progress required if the decline of native woodland in the Highlands is to be halted or reversed. In the Cairngorms, the Royal Society for the Protection of Birds purchased Abernethy Forest with the principal aim of restoring the pinewood, and a consortium of non-government conservation

organizations attempted to buy Mar Lodge estate for the same reason (Conservation Consortium, 1993) though it was eventually acquired in 1995 by the National Trust for Scotland. Major land purchases by conservation bodies are, in part, a reflection of the failure of statutory policies to safeguard some of the finest native woodland habitat in the Cairngorms.

However, during the last five years the Cairngorms area saw a significant rise in the planting and regeneration of native woodlands under Forestry Commission grant schemes (MacKenzie, 1999). Nationally, the Forestry Commission is now committed to the improvement and expansion of the native woodland resource (Scottish Executive, 2000), and locally in the wider Cairngorms, the statutory agencies provide guidance on the nature and location of new woodland and encourage the good management of existing native woodland (Cairngorms Partnership, 1999).

PRESENT EXTENT AND COMPOSITION

The catchment of the Cairngorms, which encompasses Strathspey and Highland Deeside, contains the most concentrated pattern of native forest cover in Scotland.* There are about 62 500 ha of native woodland, which is equivalent to 14 per cent of the land area or 19 per cent of the land area under 600 m Above Sea Level (ASL), the notional tree line for natural forest in this area. Several native woods exceed 1000 ha in size and are thus among the largest in Britain, while the region also contains over half the area of surviving native pinewood recorded by Steven and Carlisle (1959). The importance of this region for native woodlands attains further significance since out of a total forest area of 81 056 ha, 57 per cent is self-sown native woodland (Figures 9.1 and 9.2).

The self-sown pine and birch in Strathspey and Highland Deeside form a closely intermixed pattern with plantations dominated by Scots pine (Plate 61). This extends from the River Feshie to beyond Grantown in Strathspey and from Mar to Aboyne on Deeside, encircling the Cairngorms to the east, north and west. This forest-dominated landscape begins at about 150 m ASL and reaches 600 m ASL at several locations. At Creag Fhiaclach in the western Cairngorms, however, there is an upper tree line at about 650 m ASL (Plate 62) where there is a transition from mature pine forest through dwarf, semi-prostrate pine and juniper (krummholz condition) (Plate 63) to true sub-alpine scrub, possibly the only known location of a natural climate-related tree line in Britain (Chapter 3, p. 31). The pine on Creag Fhiaclach has succeeded because the terrain consists of steep slopes and boulder scree which may have offered some protection against browsing deer. Following a reduction in browsing levels across the northern

* Woodland statistics are based on the study areas described in Callander and MacKenzie, 1994; Dunlop, 1994; and MacKenzie, 1997. Data excludes woodland in the southern part of the Cairngorms (Highland Perthshire and the Angus Glens).

slopes of the Cairngorms there has been a slow but progressive colonization of shrubby pine and juniper between 600 and 700 m ASL. In time, it is likely that this area will also develop into another natural treeline and subalpine zone above the existing pinewood (French *et al.* 1997; MacKenzie, 1995). On Deeside, recent pine regeneration at Coilacreich has also spread to over 600 m ASL and further expansion is only being prevented by deer browsing and muirburn (Callander & MacKenzie, 1991a).

An important part of some of the pinewood communities in Strathspey is the wooded bog complex, where Scots pine trees constitute a more or less permanent component of ombrotrophic, or rain-fed, bogs. The somewhat drier climate and less oceanic conditions in the Cairngorms appear to favour its development and Abernethy forest contains the largest extent of relatively undisturbed wooded bog habitat in Scotland (McVean & Ratcliffe, 1962). Growth of the pine rarely exceeds a metre in height due to the high water table and poor nutrient base but in the drier bog margins taller trees merge into the mature pinewood. In some bogs the pines attain greater sizes and, although growth may produce unusual shapes, the trees can be well over 100 years old. The conditions necessary for bog pine to achieve these larger sizes are not immediately clear but are probably related to aspects of the topography or past disturbance. Valley bogs, for example, will receive mineral-rich seepage from the adjacent glacial ridges while the existence of drains, plough lines and old peat workings could reduce the level of the water table (Mackenzie & Worrell, 1995).

The general composition of the native woodlands of the Cairngorms has been described by several authors (McVean & Ratcliffe, 1962; Peterken, 1981; Steven & Carlisle, 1959) and classified more recently by the National Vegetation Classification (NVC) system (Rodwell, 1991). In the past few years a considerable amount of woodland survey work has been conducted to facilitate the development of an overall management strategy for the native woodland resource, as recommended by the Cairngorms Working Party. Surveys have focused on historical changes (Brown & Wightman, 1988), regeneration (Watson & Hinge, 1989), woodland extent and the genetic origin of the Scots pine (Callander & MacKenzie, 1994; Dunlop, 1994) and age structure, condition, and the National Vegetation Classification (NVC) communities present (Ader, 1996; McInroy, 1996; MacKenzie, 1997; Tidswell, 1988 & 1995). The woodland Special Areas of Conservation (SAC) have also been mapped by Scottish Natural Heritage in some detail, using the NVC system of classification. The data produced by all these surveys have been digitized to provide an integrated GIS database of all woodland in the Cairngorms area (see also Chapter 3).

These native forests are almost entirely dominated by the two species, pine and birch, which together make up over 95 per cent of the native woodland area. The Scottish Highlands are the only part of Britain where pine and birch form a natural

climax which is typical of the boreal forests of the northern hemisphere. This is not an 'ancient landscape', however, but has been much modified by anthropogenic means over the past few centuries. In Deeside, and in Strathspey, there are large areas of pure pine (Plate 64), pure birch and woods with a relatively heterogenous mixture of the two species. It is difficult to determine whether this present composition is a natural one, or whether it should be more diverse in its structure and in its component species. Pine and birch are shade-intolerant species and regenerate in even-aged stands, although in the longer term natural gaps, varying site conditions and selective browsing would create more of a mosaic.

The absence of many other species in pure birchwoods like Morrone and Craig Nordie on Deeside has generally been attributed to past management and overbrowsing. Both woods may once have contained pine. Similarly, many pinewoods may once have contained birch as well as other broadleaves (Rodwell, 1991). In Strathspey, birchwoods such as Craigellachie which are on neutral base-rich soils may have contained oak, ash and elm in the past (Peterken, 1981). At Ryvoan, where there is a variety of mineral-rich soil types, the tree species composition within the pinewood is more diverse than in the adjacent Rothiemurchus Forest. River gorges, such as the Tullich Burn on Deeside, contain virtually all the native tree species known to occur in the Highlands. Although gorge sites possess their own unique micro-habitats, capable of supporting a diverse range of species, these remnant woodlands do indicate some of the potential variation that could occur on appropriate sites within the main woodland zone.

Other native tree species found within the pine-birch woodland include rowan, juniper, willow (mainly *Salix caprea, S. cinerea & S. aurita*) and aspen. Alder is common along riverbanks, usually as a linear stand, and there are occasional small stands of bird cherry and holly in many birch and pine-woods. Ash, gean and most of the other species listed in Table 9a are rare in the region. Oak is limited to a small number of locations such as Craigendarroch on Deeside and Kincraig in Strathspey. Their status is unclear but most are likely to be of planted origin, although possibly growing on oak sites. Apart from the few oak stands, some small aspen stands and frequent alder along the riverbanks, pine and birch dominate the canopies of all the native woodland. In most of the upland locations the birch has been recorded as *Betula pubescens,* but elsewhere the two tree species of birch commonly co-exist in the same stand (Chapter 3, p. 26 and Fig. 3.2). The most abundant understorey shrub is juniper which is frequent in numerous pine and birchwoods and also exists as a seral scrub on open areas on the fringes of woods, although the latter situation may be a remnant following the loss of the tree canopy.

The native or semi-natural woodlands of the Cairngorms are generally recognized as composed of the self-sown descendants of those tree species which colonized the Highlands after the retreat of the ice sheets. However, not all the self-sown native woodlands are direct descendants as there are a number of sizeable areas of recent regeneration which have passed through a planted phase. With the possible exception of the oak and some recent plantings, virtually all the self-sown deciduous woodland is genuinely native in origin. Among the pine woodlands, the Steven and Carlisle sites plus a number of other pinewoods are all recognized as being genuine. These account for 53 per cent of the total area of self-sown pinewoods in the Cairngorms. A further 26 per cent consists of pine which may have originated partly from genuine sources and partly from planted pine: these include several large areas of pine on Deeside, notably Coilacreich, Muir of Dinnet and part of the Forest of Birse. As the original source for these trees has been identified as planted pine grown from local origin seed and, in most cases, only a single generation of planted trees has been involved, the genetic integrity of these self-sown woods has probably been maintained (Callander & MacKenzie, 1991a). The remaining proportion of self-sown pinewoods also originates from planted sources but their genetic identity may be in some doubt. The most extensive area is adjacent to, and within, the Forest Enterprise plantation at Glenmore. The pine regeneration there arises from a mixture of planted pine of unknown or non-local origin seed and from the few remnants of genuine Caledonian pine. However, the gene pool has probably been diluted by the overwhelming numbers of non-native Scots pine and the new self-sown woodland might not be considered a genuinely native one.

CURRENT STATUS AND MANAGEMENT

About 74 per cent of the pinewoods in Strathspey and 47 per cent of the pinewoods of Deeside are contained within Sites of Special Scientific Interest. Most of the native pinewoods are also designated under the European Habitats Directive as Special Areas of Conservation. Several birchwoods are also within SSSIs, for example, Creag Dhubh and Alvie, and there are a number of woodland National Nature Reserves of particular value to nature conservation, for example, Abernethy (Plate 64) and Craigellachie in Strathspey, and Morrone Birkwood and Glentanar on Deeside. Over half the area of native woodlands is contained within the boundaries of the Cairngorms and Deeside & Lochnagar National Scenic Areas. This designation reflects the outstanding qualities which the native pine and birchwoods confer on the landscape of the Cairngorms.

Although not a statutory form of protection, many native woodlands are listed in the Ancient Woodland Inventory which is available for consultation during the course of any planning investigation. The Inventory includes 60 per cent of the native woodland on Deeside but only about three-quarters of this is Ancient or Long-established in origin. These statistics affect the value of the Inventory in two important ways. First, the Inventory cannot be used as a register of all native woodland in the Cairngorms and, second, although ancient woods may have a higher nature

conservation value, they sometimes lack site continuity and there may be a shortage of historical map sources. This means that less reliance should be placed on the ancient category (Callander, 1986; Roberts *et al.*, 1993).

The Forestry Commission has compiled a register of all the native pinewoods, including the Steven and Carlisle sites, and also other pinewoods that have been proved to be genuinely native. This register (Forestry Authority, 1994), along with the Commission's guidelines, which favour a strong presumption on the use of natural regeneration to restock or rejuvenate pinewoods, will help to safeguard their genetic identity.

Management activities to promote rejuvenation or expansion of the native woodland area have been increasing in the past few years. Their main objective has been to increase biodiversity and restore semi-natural woodlands, and most involve the use of fencing to exclude deer, rabbits and livestock. Exclosures by themselves are not the ideal solution for woodland regeneration as they tend to create islands of thicket growth within an otherwise moribund wood. However, they are the most often used compromise because to fence an entire wood is prohibitvely expensive and would remove valuable grazing and shelter from the deer range. It would also be unnatural to the ecology of the woodland as browsing is a normal activity which aids the diversity of the ecosystem. Nevertheless, perimeter or ring fencing has been used with some success at Glentanar, Invereshie and Rothiemurchus and, more recently, at Ballochbuie.

The main objectives of most attempts at native woodland management have been to promote regeneration, because the woodland itself is in poor condition and because the resource, throughout the Highlands, has been severely depleted over the past decades. However, there have also been some attempts at positive native woodland management with the primary aim of producing timber. Sustainable management of the pine and birch woods of Glentanar has been successful for some years and there are now several birchwoods, for example, on Tulchan Estate in Strathspey and Dinnet Estate on Deeside, which have been brought into management under the Woodland Grant Scheme.

At Abernethy, where the RSPB is managing the pinewood in order to promote its regeneration, internal fencelines have been taken down (to reduce woodland grouse mortality as a result of collisions with fences) and a policy of reducing deer numbers to a level where regeneration becomes successful has been implemented. This attempt to restore the red deer as an animal of the forest and its margins, and ensure that the population reaches a balance with its woodland habitat, is true sustainable management of both the woodland and the deer. In the Cairngorms NNR, on land owned by Scottish Natural Heritage (Invereshie/Inshriach), deer numbers are being reduced to a more sustainable level and encouraging regeneration of the woodland is occurring (p. 134 and Plate 71). Similar policies are being introduced on the Mar Lodge Estate (National Trust for Scotland). At the Crannach on

Deeside, the aims of management are more multi-purpose. The restoration of pine and birch woodland is carried out with a mixture of natural regeneration and planting, but without ground preparation and with the minimum of fencing, in order to achieve woodland diversity and obtain a sustainable crop of timber.

Ironically, it is native woodlands like Coilacreich, where there is no statutory protection, no fencing and no positive woodland management, that have experienced some of the best regeneration and now possess some of the best diversity. The Forest of Birse is also developing into a structurally diverse woodland, after colonizing an area of former grouse moor which had been without tree cover for at least three centuries (Callander, 2000). In Strathspey, the regeneration at Glenmore will eventually attain a state where, despite the non-native trees and the reduction in genetic continuity, it becomes a valuable habitat for nature conservation, thus posing a dilemma for its long-term management.

Most native woodlands in the Cairngorms, however, including those within SSSIs, are unenclosed and unmanaged. Many of the remote and upland woods are severely degraded because the maintenance of high deer numbers is promoted, rather than the management of the deer and their habitat on a sustainable basis. Brown and Wightman's (1988) study on Deeside described over 50 per cent of the birchwoods as being moribund (Plate 65), while Callander and MacKenzie (1991a) and Watson and Hinge (1989) recorded few significant areas of pine or birch regeneration west of Crathie, and none at all west of Braemar. In Badenoch & Strathspey, a survey of the native broadleaved woods recorded over 80 per cent with insufficient young trees or saplings for woodland regeneration, particularly in the upper Spey (Tidswell, 1988).

The poor condition of so many woods, with their impoverished composition and structure and the lack of young trees to replace the demise of the older ones, mean that many will now have reduced vigour and, as the the habitat will continue to deteriorate, eventual regeneration will become much more difficult. Further losses of native woodland are a loss, not just of a relic of the original Forest of Caledon, but also of the many multi-purpose values which only these woods possess: nature conservation, soil improvement, timber production, shelter for deer and livestock and a major contribution to the landscape.

CONCLUSIONS

The Cairngorms, one of the most densely wooded areas in the country, contains over 25 per cent of its land area under 600 metres as forest, including over half the area of remaining pinewoods in Scotland. The overall character of the region is influenced by the two most common tree species, Scots pine and birch, which together account for over 76 per cent of the total woodland area of 81 056 ha. About 57 per cent of this woodland is self-sown while the plantation areas in Highland Deeside and Strathspey are dominated by Scots pine, thus maintaining the high degree of nativeness throughout this impressive landscape.

If the native woodland is to survive in the present climate of competing landuse interests, the threats which can still cause a decline in the area and condition of these woods need to be identified. High browsing levels are recognized as the main factor behind the lack of regeneration in many woods, yet the red deer problem still has to be satisfactorily addressed (Chapter 11).

The removal of non-native conifers is being attended to in some of the native pinewoods although there are still several areas of pine of non-local or unknown origin, for example at Glenmore and Glenlivet. In addition, there has been a major increase in the planting of native woodlands during the last few years but with no guarantees that the broadleaved trees are of local, or even Scottish, origin (MacKenzie & Callander, 1995). This threat to the genetic identity of the native Scots pine is potentially more serious than the proximity of the exotic species. The woodland habitat can be restored if lost or destroyed but the gene pool, once lost, is gone forever. The existing gene pool of the native species is considered the best adapted to local environmental conditions and thus more able to cope with the possibility of global climatic change (Souter & Spencer, 1991). Genetic conservation is already well recognized in the Forestry Commission's Native Pinewood Guidelines (Forestry Commission, 1989), and there are strict rules applied to the seed source for the Scots pine. With the native broadleaves, however, the situation is less clear as it is only a recommendation that the seed is of local or Scottish origin (Forestry Commission, 1999).

There is, however, another feature of the present native woodland resource which may require attention. Much of the extensive pine regeneration on Highland Deeside has passed through, in part at least, a single planted generation. Callander and MacKenzie (1991a) established that, as the planted trees were likely to be of local origin, genetic continuity has been maintained. Such woodland is thus indistinguishable in structure from the genuinely native pinewood and its habitat value therefore just as important. The Forestry Commission is not able to recognize these woods in their Pinewood Register as they are an anomaly in the present system of definitions. These self-sown pinewoods have no formal designation and could, in theory, be converted to a commercial plantation of non-native species.

The future of the native woodlands of the Cairngorms offers more promise for improvement in the coming years than at any other time during the past century, provided sufficient attention is given to the most vulnerable woods, at the earliest opportunity. The scope for merging five of the six major pinewoods in Strathspey is a very feasible option. Only 1 km separates Abernethy from the

Rothiemurchus pines via Ryvoan Pass and Glenmore, while Rothiemurchus is already continuous with Inshriach and the Glen Feshie remnants are less than 1 km away. This would create a native pinewood about 40 kilometres long. On Deeside, there is the potential for creating a natural upper tree line between Crathie wood and the Muir of Dinnet. This would restore an almost unbroken transition from the alder and mixed woodland of the River Dee and its tributaries to sub-alpine scrub at over 600m ASL.

The recent changes in forestry policy, new financial incentives and guidelines and a wider appreciation of the multi-purpose values of native woodland should encourage a more sustainable form of management. Indeed, there is now a commitment by the Government to develop a strategy for sustainable development as part of the UK Biodiversity Action Plan. Costed Habitat Action Plans have already been drawn up for the native pinewoods and these are currently at the stage of implementation (Scottish Biodiversity Group, 1997). The restoration of the Caledonian forest will be a gradual process which requires the co-operation of everyone if their characteristic flora and fauna are to thrive. The distinctive pine-birch resource of the Cairngorms is an attribute which is as much a part of the landscape as the mountains, lochs and rivers, and is an integral part of the economy of the region in terms of its tourism, wildlife and commercial forestry values. This balance of complex associations could easily be altered unless there is a co-ordinated approach to maintain the native character of the woodland resource.

REFERENCES

Anderson, M.L. (1967) *A history of Scottish forestry.* Nelson, London.

Anderson, W. (c. 1770) *Plan of lands from Cairn Gorm to River Spey.* RHP 2502. Scottish Record Office, Edinburgh.

Bain, C. (1987) *Native pinewoods in Scotland – a review 1957–87.* RSPB, Edinburgh.

Bennet, K.D. (1988) A provisional map of forest types for the British Isles 5000 years ago. *J. Quat. Sci.* **4**, 141–144.

Bennet, K.D. (1995) Post-glacial dynamics of pine (*Pinus sylvestris* L) and pinewoods in Scotland. In: Aldhous, J.R., ed., *Our pinewood heritage.* Conference proceedings. Forestry Commission/Royal Society for the Protection of Birds/Scottish Natural Heritage, Farnham. pp. 22–39.

Bennet, K.D. (1996) Late-Quaternary vegetation dynamics of the Cairngorms. *Bot. J. Scotl.* **48**, 51–64.

Birks, H.J.B. (1988) Long-term ecological change in the British uplands. In: Usher, M.B. & Thompson, D.B.A., eds, *Ecological change in the uplands.* Special publication number 7 of the British Ecological Society. Blackwell, Oxford. pp. 37–56.

Birks, H.J B. (1989) Holocene isochrone maps and patterns of tree-spreading in the British Isles. *J. Biogeogr.* **16**, 503–540.

Blaeu, J. (1654) *Atlas Scotiae.* Amsterdam.

Brady, N.C. (1984) *The nature and properties of soils.* Macmillan, New York.

Brown, I.R. & Wightman, A.D. (1988) The birchwoods of Deeside 1947–87 – a declining resource? *Scott. For.* **42**, 93-103.

Bunce, R.G.H. & Jeffers, J N.R., eds. (1977) *Native pinewoods of Scotland.* Proceedings of Aviemore symposium, 1975. Institute of Terrestrial Ecology, Cambridge.

Cairngorms Partnership (1997) *Managing the Cairngorms. The Cairngorms Partnership Management Strategy.* The Cairngorms Partnership, Grantown-on-Spey.

Cairngorms Partnership (1999) *Cairngorms forest and woodland* framework. The Cairngorms Partnership, Grantown-on-Spey.

Cairngorms Working Party (1993) *Common sense and sustainability: a partnership for the Cairngorms.* The Scottish Office, Edinburgh.

Callander, R.F. (1986) The history of native woodlands in the Scottish Highlands. In: Jenkins, D., ed., *Trees and wildlife in the Scottish uplands.* ITE symposium no. 17. Institute of Terrestrial Ecology, Huntingdon. pp. 40–45.

Callander, R.F. (1987) *The productive use of native woodlands in the Scottish Highlands.* Rural Forum Scotland, Perth.

Callander, R.F. (2000) *History in Birse.* Birse Community Trust, Finzean.

Callander, R.F. & MacKenzie, N.A. (1991a) *The native pine woodlands of Highland Deeside.* A report for the Nature Conservancy Council, North-East (Scotland) Region, Aberdeen.

Callander, R.F. & MacKenzie, N.A. (1991b) *The management of wild red deer in Scotland.* Rural Forum Scotland, Perth.

Callander, R.F. & MacKenzie, N.A. (1994) *The native woodlands of Highland Deeside.* A report for Scottish Natural Heritage, North-East Region, Aberdeen.

Carlisle, A. (1977) The impact of man on the native pinewoods of Scotland. In: Bunce, R.G.H., & Jeffers, J.N.R., eds, *Native pinewoods of Scotland.* Proceedings of Aviemore symposium, 1975, Institute of Terrestrial Ecology, Cambridge. pp. 70–77.

Cash, C.G. (1905) Timber floating at Rothiemurchus. *Cairngorm Club Journal* **4**, 301.

Chambers, F. M. & Elliot, L. (1989) Spread and expansion of *Alnus* Mill. in the British Isles: timing, agencies and possible vectors. *J. Biogeogr.* **16**, 541–550.

Conservation Consortium (1993) *Mar Lodge Estate: a new future.* Conservation Consortium (RSPB, WWF, JMT), East Kilbride.

Dunlop, B.M.S. (1994) *The native woodlands of Strathspey.* Scottish Natural Heritage research, survey & monitoring report no. 33. Scottish Natural Heritage, Edinburgh.

Fairweather, A.D. & Ralston, I. (1993) The neolithic timber hall at Balbridie, Grampian Region, Scotland. *Antiquity* **67**, 313-323.

Forest Enterprise (1992) *A future for Forest Enterprise native pinewoods.* Forest Enterprise, Inverness.

Forest Enterprise (1993) *A future for Forest Enterprise Highland broadleaves.* Forest Enterprise, Inverness.

Forestry Authority (1993) *Woodland Grant Scheme.* The Forestry Authority, Edinburgh.

Forestry Authority (1994) *The management of semi-natural woodlands.* Forestry Practice Guides 3–8. Forestry Authority, Edinburgh.

Forestry Authority (1997) *Woodland Grant Scheme.* The Forestry Authority, Edinburgh.

Forestry Commission (1989) *Native pinewood grants and guidelines.* Forestry Commission, Edinburgh.

Forestry Commision (1999) *Using local stock for planting native trees and shrubs.* Practice note. Forestry Commission, Edinburgh.

French, D.D., Miller, G.R. & Cummins, R.P. (1997) Recent development of high altitude *Pinus sylvestris* scrub in the northern Cairngorm mountains, Scotland. *Biological Conservation* **79**, 133–144

Gilbert, J.M. (1979) *Hunting and hunting reserves in medieval Scotland.* John Donald, Edinburgh.

Gimingham, C.H. (1977) Status of pinewoods in British ecosystems. In: Bunce, R.G.H., & Jeffers, J.N.R., eds, *Native pinewoods of Scotland.* Proceedings of Aviemore symposium, 1975. Institute of Terrestrial Ecology, Cambridge. pp. 1–4.

Gordon, S. (1949) *Highways and byways in the Central Highlands.* Macmillan, London.

Grant, E. (1972) *Memoirs of a Highland lady, 1797–1827.* John Murray, London.

House of Commons (1990) *Agriculture Committee, second report: land use and forestry, volume 1 (session 1989–90).* HMSO, London.

Huntley, B. & Birks, H.J.B. (1983) *An atlas of past and present pollen maps for Europe: 0-1300 BP.* Cambridge University Press, Cambridge.

Huntley, B., Daniell, R.G. & Allen, Judy R.M. (1997) Scottish vegetation history: The Highlands. *Bot. J. Scotl.* **49**, 163–175.

Lines, R. (1984) Man's use of birch – past and present. *Proc. Roy. Soc. Edinb.* 85B, 203–213.

McInroy, A. (1996) *Cairngorms native woodland survey – Tayside Region.* Scottish Natural Heritage, Battleby, Perth.

MacKenzie, N.A. (1987) *The native woodlands of Scotland.* Friends of the Earth (Scotland), Edinburgh.

MacKenzie, N.A. (1995) *A survey to evaluate the potential for the restoration of native woodland in Gleann Einich and the Lairig Ghru, Rothiemurchus Estate.* A report for Finlayson Hughes, Inverness.

MacKenzie, N.A. (1997) The native woodlands of Strathavon and Strathdon. *Scottish Natural Heritage research, survey and monitoring report* (in press). Scottish Natural Heritage, Edinburgh.

MacKenzie, N.A. (1999) *The native woodland resource of Scotland: a review 1993–1998.* FC Technical Paper 30. Forestry Commission, Edinburgh.

MacKenzie, N.A. & Callander, R.F. (1995) *The native woodland resource in the Scottish Highlands: a review of current statistics.* FC Technical Paper 12. Forestry Commission, Edinburgh.

MacKenzie, N.A. & Worrell, R. (1995) A preliminary assessment of the ecology and status of ombrotrophic wooded bogs in Scotland. *Scottish Natural Heritage research, survey and monitoring report,* no. 40. Scottish Natural Heritage, Edinburgh.

McVean, D.N. & Ratcliffe, D.A. (1962) *Plant communities of the Scottish Highlands.* HMSO, London.

Miles, H. (1985) The pedogenic effects of different species and vegetation types and the complications of succession. *J. Soil Sci.* **36**, 571–84.

Mitchell, B., Staines, B.W. & Welch, D. (1977) *The ecology of red deer.* Institute of Terrestrial Ecology, Cambridge.

Nairne, D. (1891) Notes on Highland woods, ancient and modern. *Trans. Gael. Soc. Inverness.* **17**, 170–221.

Orr, W. (1982) *Deer forests, crofters and landlords.* John Donald, Edinburgh.

O'Sullivan. P.E. (1977) Vegetation history and the native pinewoods. In: Bunce, R.G.H., & Jeffers, J.N.R., eds, *Native pinewoods of Scotland.* Proceedings of Aviemore symposium, 1975. Institute of Terrestrial Ecology, Cambridge. pp. 60–69.

Peterken, G.F. (1981) *Woodland conservation and management.* Chapman and Hall, London.

Peterken, G.F., Baldock, D. & Hampson, A. (1995) A forest habitat network for Scotland. *Scottish Natural Heritage research, survey & monitoring report.* no. 44. Scottish Natural Heritage, Edinburgh.

Pont, T. (*c.* 16th. century) *Manuscript maps.* National Library of Scotland, Edinburgh.

Roberts, A.J., Russell, C., Walker, G.J. & Kirby, K.J. (1993) Regional variation in the origin, extent and composition of Scottish woodland. *Bot. J. Scotl.* **46**, 167–189.

Rodwell, J.S., ed. (1991) *British plant communities, volume 1: Woodland and scrub.* Cambridge University Press, Cambridge.

Royal Society for the Protection of Birds (1993) *Time for pine: a future for Caledonian pinewoods.* RSPB, Edinburgh.

Scottish Biodiversity Group (1997) *Biodoversity in Scotland: the way forward.* The Scottish Office, Edinburgh.

Scottish Executive (2000) *Forest for Scotland: the Scottish forestry strategy.* Scottish Executive, Edinburgh.

Sinclair, Sir J. (1791–99) *The statistical account of Scotland.* Edinburgh.

Smout, T.C. (1999) The history of Rothiemurchus woodlands. In: Smout, T.C. & Lambert, R.A., eds, *Rothiemurchus: nature and people on a Highland estate, 1500–2000.* Scottish Cultural Press, Edinburgh.

Souter, R.G. & Spencer, J.W. (1991) The conservation of genetic variation in Britain's native trees. *Forestry* **64**, 1–12.

Steven, H.M. & Carlisle, A. (1959) *The native pinewoods of Scotland.* Oliver and Boyd, Edinburgh.

Tidswell, R.J. (1988) *A botanical survey of the semi-natural deciduous woods of Badenoch and Strathspey District.* SFSU report S 34. Nature Conservancy Council, Edinburgh.

Tidswell, R.J. (1995). *A botanical survey of the semi-natural deciduous woods of Highland Deeside.* A report for Scottish Natural Heritage, North-East Region, Aberdeen.

Walker, G.J. & Kirby, K.J. (1989) *Inventories of ancient, long-established and semi-natural woodland for Scotland.* (Research and survey in nature conservation no. 22). Nature Conservancy Council, Peterborough.

Watson, A. (1983) Eighteenth century deer numbers and pine regeneration near Braemar, Scotland. *Biol. Conserv.* **25**, 289–305.

Watson, A. & Hinge, M. (1989) *Natural tree regeneration on open upland in Deeside and Donside.* Nature Conservancy Council, North-East (Scotland) Region, Aberdeen.

Wightman, A.D., ed. (1992) *A forest for Scotland: a discussion paper on forest policy.* Scottish Wildlife and Countryside Link, Perth.

Youngson, R.W. & Stewart, L.K. (1996). Trends in red deer populations within the Cairngorms core area. *Bot. J. Scotl.* **48**, 111–116.

CHAPTER 10
Man and Woodlands

J. Atterson and I. Ross

THE DESTRUCTION AND EXPLOITATION OF THE NATURAL FOREST

After the last Ice Age which wiped out most, if not all, tree growth in Scotland, much of the Cairngorms area would have been recolonized by trees by about 6000 years ago except for the high plateaux that exceed 900 m above sea level (ASL) (Pears, 1975) and sites which were very wet or covered by rock screes. The wet sites were hollows or flat, poorly drained soils where peat would have been accumulating. Some flat valley floors would also have been flooded by beaver dams, creating very wet areas with sparse cover or no trees. This forest would have been dominated by Scots pine intermixed with birch on the higher and drier sites and giving way on the richer soils to the larger broadleaved trees such as elm and oak. However, ash did not reach this area until possibly 4000 years ago (Birks, 1989). Alder and willow would be found on the wetter sites in the major valleys and up the burn sides. Other species, such as aspen and juniper, were present in the pinewoods; cherry and hazel were among the components of the lower, broadleaved forest; while holly and rowan would have been present throughout, the rowan in any gap created by windthrow or disease. At that time, possibly 50–80 per cent of the land surface below the natural tree line would have been covered by trees. (A more detailed account of post-glacial history appears in Chapter 9.)

Extensive areas of even-aged pine would have been a feature following fires started by lightning in the drier, more continental climate of that time. As mature, seed-bearing pine can survive fires where other species perish, burnt areas regenerated only with pine would have resembled plantations of a single species. In fact, pollen analyses show that the forest on the western slopes of the Cairngorm plateau consisted mostly of Scots pine (Pears, 1975).

Wind would also have had a marked effect on the forest. Catastrophic gales have a return period of about 50 years in this country at the present time (Gloyne, 1968). If a similar return period existed in the past, swathes of trees windthrown at various times would not have been uncommon (Atterson, 1980) and regrowth of varying ages and height would have covered the fallen trunks. Fires and gales occurring at random intervals and in random places would have created a mosaic of woods varying greatly in area, tree size and age, and uniformity. Large trees of all species of excellent form would have occurred in all but the highest and wettest parts of the forest.

Man began clearing this forest about 5500 years ago (Cole, 1970) in Neolithic times for agricultural purposes, but seems to have had little effect around the Cairngorms, as few archaeological sites date from that period in the area. It would have been an inaccessible and inhospitable part of Scotland because of the continuous forest cover, the distance from the coast, the relatively high elevation and last, but not least, the severe winters.

The climate began deteriorating about 4000 years ago, becoming progressively wetter and cooler. This, combined with lightning fires that would have destroyed some of the existing forest, encouraged the growth of peat, even on sloping ground, which inhibited the regeneration of the forest (Plate 20). Charcoal from such fires can frequently be found under the blanket peat on many sites throughout the Highlands including the Cairngorms area, for example, below the Coire na Ciste car park above Glen More Forest. Fire was not uncommon at that time even on areas of blanket peat. In north Sutherland, careful examination of a peat profile (Gear & Huntley, 1991) showed that between 4000 and 3500 years ago charcoal over 2 mm in size appears every 20 years, and under 2 mm in size every 6 years on average. Whether this frequency of fire was caused by lightning or man will never be known.

The natural forest progressively declined in area over the intervening millennia (Darling, 1949), with man having a marked influence in the Cairngorms area only in relatively recent times when he cleared much of the forest for timber, subsequently using the land for grazing, and thereby preventing its regeneration (see Chapters 3 and 9). People would have migrated into the area in noticeable numbers by the Middle Ages, but only cleared the forest locally for agriculture and for the domestic use of timber for building and fuel. Extraction of logs from within the forest would have been by oxen, which have a much steadier pull than horses. Oxen break their tackle less frequently than horses which tend to lunge forward when a load becomes snagged. Exploitation for non-local use began after 1600 AD but did not have any significant effect in Strathspey or Upper Deeside until water transport was introduced in the 1700s.

The Rivers Spey and Dee and their tributaries were used to float large numbers of logs from the higher parts of these valleys to the coast where the timber was used for house and boat building. In the late 1700s, pine logs were hollowed out by boring at Rothiemurchus, floated down the Spey and then shipped to London where they were used as underground pipes for the public water supply (Fraser, 1956). The first Statistical Account of Scotland (Sinclair, 1797) records that in 1792 the hills of the Parish of Alvie were extremely barren, frequently rocky and covered with heath. It also notes that there was not one single Scots pine within some miles of the church in the Parish of Kingussie and Inch. The name 'Kingussie' is derived from the Gaelic meaning the 'head of the pinewood', which indicates that the pine forest extended up the Spey as far as the village but not beyond. The lack of good local hardwood in Strathspey at that time is also noted. A detailed account of the origins and history of the Strathspey forests has been written by Dunlop (1994).

Of the Parish of Blair Athole on the south side of the Cairngorms area, the Statistical Account says, 'The last century, and the beginning of the present, have destroyed much wood, by fire and otherwise. Places still bear the name of woods, where there is not a tree to be seen now'. It adds that there were no extensive woods, but many small ones when the Account was written in the early 1790s.

Upper Donside had been cleared of forest for agricultural use by the mid-seventeenth century. An old rhyme says, 'Ae mile o' Don's worth twa o' Dee, Except it be for fish and tree', and it was truly descriptive in its day. A map by Sir Robert Gordon of Straloch, dated 1654, shows the whole run of the River Don as treeless. On neighbouring Deeside extensive remnants of the native forest survived in Mar, Ballochbuie, Glen Tanar and the Forest of Birse. The first Statistical Account of Scotland (Sinclair, 1797) for the Parish of Birse lying just to the east of Aboyne records that 'a great part of the parish was, and is still, covered with natural woodland, such as fir (pine), birch, ash, alder, mountain ash (rowan), gean, holly, hazel, aspen and some oaks'. The name 'Birse' derives from the Gaelic 'Preas' meaning 'a wood or thicket'.

FOREST REGENERATION

Many of these woods were under active management even as early as the sixteenth century. There was evidently no lack of skill in forest management or understanding of the concept of sustained yield, as the following record shows. In 1694 five 'birelymen' were appointed by the Earl of Aboyne to 'appryse' (value) the birch woods between Kandakyle and Deecastle. This they did, 'Honestlie, faithfullie and impatialle according to their knowledge and declare the saids woods are not 10 merks worse at this time nor the same was at the last appretiatione in the year Nintie ane years, and the reason they alleage that the saids woods is valued above the last appryse is because of the growth of the wood . . . and finds that the forester has done his dutie in proportioni of the saids haill woods' (Aboyne Estate records). Evidently the rate of felling had been carefully controlled to match the growth increment of the wood.

Most of the areas felled to supply local needs were managed to regenerate naturally in the early years because grazing domestic animals were carefully herded. Deer were also fewer than today, probably because of a higher percentage cull for sport and the 'pot' and because of the more frequent hard winters during the 'Little Ice Age'. Timber prices were high, which encouraged owners to regenerate the forest naturally, by protecting it from grazing and to plant where natural regeneration did not occur.

Extensive plantations of Scots pine were established from the beginning of the eighteenth century in many parts of Scotland until the late 1700s when European larch began to be used, as it had been found to grow faster and produce a more valuable timber than pine (Selby, 1842). Some plantations were planted with mixtures of equal numbers of larch and pine while others had a mixture of two larch to one pine. Ten to twelve thousand trees were planted per hectare, producing dense stands which required thinning. Selby comments that naturally regenerated stands did not require thinning because of the range of tree sizes.

The first Statistical Account of Scotland (Sinclair, 1797) for the Parish of Aboyne states: 'Beside a considerable quantity of different kinds of woods *planted* in the parish of Aboyne there is a large forest of *natural* wood in Glentanar'. The precise location and extent of the planted woods are not given but the Earl had built 'eighteen miles of boundary to his farm and plantations. The whole stone fences, including subdivisions, must be at least 40 English miles in length.' (Sinclair, 1797).

About the same time (1790), Farquharson of Invercauld was writing, 'It is not my intention to dissuade from planting Scotch fir but to encourage those that have the proper soil and situation to do so, being of the opinion that where these circumstances agree, and there planting not in lines, but irregularly and thicker than common, the trees will come to be of equal size and value with the natural ones. In confidence of this I have planted several millions on the sides of hills out of reach of seed from natural firs' (Anderson, 1967). It is suspected that some of Farquharson's handiwork still survives but it is difficult to be certain.

The Statistical Account for the Parish of Birse records that 'Besides the natural wood, there are some thousand acres inclosed and planted with various forest trees; fir (pine), birch, ash, elm, beech, plane, horse chestnut, spruce, larch and willows of all sorts, all in a thriving state and many of them are already fit for use. The parish has always produced a deal of wood'. Few details are readily known of the locations of these early plantations, and many records remain to be studied.

LARGE-SCALE EXPLOITATION AND REGENERATION

In the mid-eighteenth century extensive areas of standing timber were sold in Strathspey and the technique of rafting logs downstream to the ship-yards at Speymouth was developed. On Deeside extensive felling began in Mar and Ballochbuie towards the end of that century. In 1808 a severe gale blew down large numbers of trees in Finzean and Glentanar that required clearance at a much faster rate than had been customary in these woods. The price of timber was at a high level due to the Napoleonic wars and the problem of transporting logs to the coast had been overcome. It was this event that triggered extensive felling programmes on both estates that were to continue for some 35 years. In the whole of upper Deeside not only were the native woods exploited during this period but the mature plantations created over the preceding century were also heavily depleted.

Buoyed up by the value of timber, the work of replanting, or at least enclosing areas of regenerating woods to protect them from livestock, was continued through this period. Land around Monaltrie near Ballater was planted for the first time in the early nineteenth century, as indicated by the fact that a 1790 map of this area shows none of the enclosed woodlands which appear on later maps. Land at Craig a' Chleirich, north of Braemar, was also planted around that time. This wood was felled about 60 years ago during the 1939–45 war; its remnants are still visible from the A93 straight ahead on the approach to Braemar from the south as a narrow strip of mature trees running along the mid-slope.

In 1842, Selby wrote that 'the indigenous forests of Scotland, which formerly occupied so large an extent of its territory, have, within the last sixty years, been greatly reduced, in consequence of the demand for Pine timber, occasioned by the difficulty of obtaining wood from the Baltic during the late wars; some, indeed, are nearly obliterated, such as that of Rannoch, which once occupied an extensive area . . . Such, also, has been the fate of the forest of Glenmore, once famous for the size and age of its timber . . .' During this period, Glenmore timber was used to build 41 sailing ships at the mouth of the Spey, totalling 19 000 tons including a frigate of 1050 tons called the *Glenmore*. He says that the size of the former trees in Glenmore could be judged from a plank presented to the Duke of Gordon by William Osbourne, a timber merchant from Hull, who purchased the forest in 1783. That plank was displayed in the entrance hall of Gordon Castle; it measured 5 ft 5 in wide and 6 ft 2 in long, had 'the texture of the finest Red-wood Pine' and 235 annual growth rings. It can still be seen in the Department of Forestry at the University of Aberdeen. In 1824, while walking through Glenmore, Selby described this area, previously occupied by a magnificent forest, as 'a scene of savage wildness and desolation . . . the surface of the ground in almost every direction was littered with the decaying tops and loppings of the felled trees'. He goes on to say, however, that Sir T.D. Lander found during a visit at a later time the forest regenerating quickly, 'the seedling firs starting in countless thousands'.

Selby describes the destruction of Rothiemurchus in a similar fashion pointing out that the timber had been of excellent quality but not of equal size to the pines of Glenmore. Of the ancient forest of Abernethy, he says that the timber was of superior quality, was very resinous and had little sapwood.

On the other side of the Cairngorms, he records that the forests of Braemar and Invercauld were very extensive with pines as large as any in Scotland and that he had 'frequently admired the beautiful forms and huge proportions of some of those near to Mar Lodge and the falls of the Dee'. 'But alas!', he writes, 'since we last visited that interesting district, we have learnt with regret that the axe has been let loose within the precincts of the forest of Mar'.

By around 1845 most of the merchantable trees had been cleared from Deeside. The end of the Napoleonic wars had caused a slump in the price of timber and the woodcutters' villages were abandoned. Extensive areas of young forest still existed because, where grazing animals were excluded by the stone dykes of the old plantations, natural regeneration managed to survive and grow. It is now possible in parts of Deeside to trace the third generation of naturally regenerated trees which originate from the eighteenth century plantations. The presence of larch in an old wood is often taken as evidence that the whole wood was planted rather than self-sown. However, the diary of the Finzean Estate Forester in the mid-nineteenth century reveals his practice of planting up gaps in naturally regenerated Scots pine with European larch. This technique, along with Farquharson's practice of planting 'not in rows', can now make it very difficult to distinguish genuinely native woods from those which have gone through a planted rotation.

That period also saw the replanting of oak at Dinnet and on Craigendarroch Hill at Ballater. These woods, which are still standing, were planted on what are believed to be sites with a long history of oak woodland cover. Extensive areas of Scots pine and European larch were also planted by the Earl of Aboyne and other Deeside landowners at this time but details of the extent of this planting, along with many other pieces of information, still lie in old estate records awaiting thorough research.

The Scots pine seed used for these plantings was probably obtained from local trees. Indeed, there was a thriving export trade in this seed. One Aboyne resident recorded his grandmother's recollection that in Glen Tanar from around 1809 to 1840, 'yearly, representatives of seed merchants came from England and collected the seed of the fir (Scots pine) trees, it being in great demand. Sheets were spread on the ground round some of the finest specimens and the seed collected in this way' (Glen Tanar Estate records). As a result of this practice of local seed collection, very few Scots pine of non-local origin were introduced to Deeside at this time and consequently the genetic strain of the native species remained largely unaltered.

In 1866, import duty on timber was removed and large quantities from America and the Colonies began to arrive, forcing down the price of home-grown timber and making the regeneration of felled forests economically unattractive (Matthews, 1976). Felling continued but the cleared land was then used for sheep farming which was particularly profitable from 1832 until 1875 and which prevented trees from regenerating.

Queen Victoria purchased Balmoral in 1848 and the fashion for highland sporting estates brought an influx of new landowners with new ideas and with priorities centred on shooting and fishing. Tree planting for them was confined to the creation of avenues and landscaping around the new shooting lodges. Existing areas of forest were preserved but not regenerated so that the creation of new plantations virtually ceased. In other words, no forest management was practised. This is typified by Glen Tanar Estate with its long history of forest management, where by 1895 the list of estate employees included 12 gamekeepers but no foresters! There were notable exceptions, for instance the Farquarsons of Invercauld, who still own the estate, maintained a steady programme of tree planting through the 1880s and into the early part of the twentieth century.

By the late 1800s, the dearth of woodland and consequently of home-grown timber was causing concern. Several Royal Commissions and government committees were set up between 1885 and 1916 to consider a forest policy for Great Britain that had the dubious distinction of being the largest timber importer in the world at that time (Shaw, 1956). Finally, after the war of 1914–18, when much of the remaining forest was felled, the decision was taken that forests would have to be re-created. As a result, the Forestry Commission was set up in 1919 charged with increasing the area of productive woodland throughout Great Britain.

The 1914–1918 war certainly caused wide-scale tree felling. Log floating was no longer needed for timber transport. By that time, it was common practice to set up mobile, steam-powered saw mills in or near the woods and, with the network of turnpike roads and the railways through Strathspey and up Deeside to Ballater, the transport of the sawn timber presented few problems. Records of exactly which areas were felled in this era are sketchy. Forests which had regenerated naturally or which were planted following the fellings early in the previous century, would have been almost one hundred years old and considered ready for clear cutting while forests dating from the middle part of the nineteenth century would have been immature and, therefore, spared until the next global conflict in 1939–45.

Across Scotland during the 1920s, tree planting was fashionable: landowners sponsored George Forest on his seed collecting expeditions to Asia, arboreta were established on several estates, specimen trees were planted and, what is more important, estate tree nurseries were re-established and foresters began to feature again in the ranks of estate employees. This wave of enthusiasm had only a minor impact, however, and with the notable exceptions of estates such as Seafield, Glen Tanar and Ballogie and also the Forestry Commission which acquired Alltcailleach, Glenmore and Inchriach, tree planting continued at a low ebb. Many areas felled in the Great War on Deeside were to remain devoid of tree cover for over half a century. For those who were planting, a whole range of exotic tree seeds was now available in quantity and new plantations of Douglas fir, Sitka spruce and the Noble and Grand firs appeared in Deeside and Strathspey for the first time. With Scots pine, there was still a strong tendency for estates to collect seed locally and many of the plantings were of local genetic origin.

As elsewhere, the 1939–45 war had a devastating impact on the forests of the Cairngorms. To aid the war effort, teams of Canadian woodcutters arrived to set up new logging camps and mobile sawmills. The Canadians also brought mechanization to timber harvesting for the first time. Although felling was still done with the axe and hand saw they were no longer dependent on the horse. The tracked tractors and winches of the Canadians removed timber from the woods at an unprecedented rate. Bulldozers created logging roads and new four-wheel-drive lorries made the journey to the sawmill more quickly. The foundations of the bridge they built across the Dee above Inverey can still be seen. The Canadian Timber Corps felled 160 000 m³ in Upper Deeside and 350 000 m³ in Strathspey (Wonders, 1987 & 1991). The slopes behind Mar Lodge still show the bleached stumps dating from these wartime fellings.

Some of the native forests of Abernethy, Rothiemurchus, Glen Tanar, Ballochbuie, upper Glen Derry (Plate 96) and Glen Quoich were saved.

Table 10a   Area (ha) of Forestry Commission land 1994 – woodland and open areas

	Woodland Area	Open Areas	Total
Strathspey	5056	1332	6388
Upper Deeside	644	99	743
Total	5700	1431	7131

Source: Forest District Managers

Table 10b   Forestry Commission land 1994 – area (ha) by species

Location	Scots pine	Other Conifers	Broadleaves	Total
Strathspey	3483	1508	65	5056
Upper Deeside	459	151	34	644
Total	3942	1659	99	5700

Source: Forest District Managers

The plantations dating from the 1920s also survived due to their immaturity. Much of what would have been 100-year-old stands of trees dating from the mid-nineteenth century was gone and the forest cover of the Cairngorms area reached its lowest level of all time. The Forestry Commission's 1947–9 census (Forestry Commission, 1950) recorded 7588 ha of felled woodland in mid and upper Deeside, 45 per cent of which had been felled before 1939. The total area of coniferous woodland left standing was only 6604 ha of which 93 per cent was Scots pine.

Returning servicemen were recruited by the private estates and the Forestry Commission in great numbers to begin the task of replacing the lost woodlands. Owners were encouraged firstly by the scenes of devastation on their land and secondly by the grant incentives delivered by the Forestry Commission's Dedication Scheme. Once again many estates began collecting seed, set up forest nurseries, and the work of replanting began in earnest.

By the end of the 1939–45 war in the Cairngorms area, the Forestry Commission had planted about 2200 hectares some of which was the restocking of old felled sites. The main species used was Scots pine with spruce being a major component in Glen More and European larch in Alltcailleach. Just after the war the Commission acquired further land in the Cairngorms area at Tornasheen in Strathdon, at Glenlivet in Morayshire and in Glen Doll in Angus. In all, almost 13 500 ha of plantable land were purchased, and by 1965 eighty-five per cent of this had been planted, mostly on bare land and mostly with Scots pine. In 1994 the Forestry Commission had less than 6000 ha of forestland in the Cairngorms area, which was only about half of the former total, mainly because Glenlivet and Alltcailleach have been sold. Tables 10a, b and c show the composition and area of the Forestry Commission woodlands on either side of the Cairngorms, which indicates that most of them consist of Scots pine with a good range of ages.

Less than a decade later the 'Great North Gale' of 1953 created even more havoc in what was left of the forests of north-east Scotland. Even for this recent period, accurate data are difficult to discover. Some estates in the Cairngorms area lost 30 000 m³ of timber, others double that amount. Temporary encampments and mobile steam-powered sawmills were again concentrated in the area. One of the largest was at the Bridge of Potarch, not far to the east of the Cairngorms area, where four sawmills operated. A working example of this type of sawmill can now be seen at the Landmark Centre at Carrbridge. Although the mills were still in the steam age, the work of clearing the windthrown timber was aided by the introduction of the handheld, petrol-engined powersaw to the area for the first time. This machine along with the construction of permanent electric-powered sawmills laid the foundation of the timber industry we know today.

The job of restocking the areas windthrown by the gale was added to the task already in hand, and replanting the forests of Deeside and Strathspey was pursued with vigour by the private estates and the Forestry Commission for four decades. Between 1947 and 1990 the area of coniferous woodland in mid and upper Deeside was increased from 6604 ha, which included the self-sown woods, to 12 147 ha of planted woodland and 8998 hectares of self-sown woodland, a total of 21 415 ha, more than a threefold increase. In some parts of the district it was only by the late 1980s that the extent of tree cover was restored to the levels of the late nineteenth century.

The first comprehensive survey of the woodlands of mid and upper Deeside was carried out in 1990 by Callander and MacKenzie. They covered the four parishes of Crathie & Braemar, Glen Muick, Tullich & Glen Gairn, Aboyne & Glen Tanar and Birse. This area they defined as 'Highland Deeside'. Some 8544 hectares of planted Scots pine woodland were recorded. More than 20 per cent of this area dates from the nineteenth century and less than 20 per cent from the first half of this century, while some 60 per cent of the total area is less than 40 years old (see Table 10d). The planting of non-native conifers

Table 10c   Forestry Commission land 1994 – area (ha) by age classes

Location	>75 yrs old	40–75 yrs old	0–40 yrs old	Total
Strathspey	302	1587	3167	5056
Upper Deeside	0	443	201	644
Total	302	2030	3368	5700

Source: Forest District Managers

Table 10d   Mid and upper Deeside planted woodland – area (ha) by age classes

Species	Pre-1861	1861–1910	1911–1930	1931–1950	1951–1970	1971–1990	Total
Scots pine	854	1008	320	926	3715	1614	8437
Non-native conifers	53	163	59	394	1896	661	3226

Source: Callander & MacKenzie, 1991

totals some 3226 hectares and shows a similar structure of age classes. Some of the non-native conifers are of a respectable age and are prominent features of the landscape around Braemar. The mature larch trees around Invercauld House and at Inverey are but two examples.

A growing tendency over the latter half of the twentiety century had been to plant an increasing proportion of non-native conifers for timber production. The proportions increased from 7 per cent in 1949 to almost 17 per cent of all coniferous woodland, but even for plantings in the decade to 1990 the area of planted pine still exceeded the area of non-native conifers, and Scots pine still accounts for 70 per cent of all planted coniferous woodland. Callander and MacKenzie concluded that a high proportion of the planted Scots pine was of local origin (Table 10e).

The area of planted Scots pine in 'Highland Deeside' is more than equalled by the area of self-sown Scots pine at 9000 ha. While some of this self-sown area is genuinely natural forest, it is difficult to determine exactly which woods have descended from 'an unbroken line of naturally regenerated trees' and which might be descended at some stage from a planted generation. Some woods are probably a combination of both. Certainly the mosaic of planted and self-sown Scots pine woods has become so complex over the last half century that it has become increasingly difficult in some places to distinguish between the two.

On the other side of the Cairngorms in Badenoch and Strathspey, the area of high forest is over 20 000 ha, 65 per cent of which is Scots pine and 10 per cent is broadleaved species (Williamson, 1991a). Over 70 per cent is less than 35 years old and has not reached its potential for timber production and consequently for forest employment. The Indicative Forestry Strategy prepared by the Highland Region (Highland Regional Council, 1993) indicates that

the Districts of Badenoch and Strathspey and of Nairn had 81 people employed in forestry in 1990 and that this number would rise to over 200 by the year 2020 AD, after which it would fall if the current very low rate of forest expansion does not rise markedly. Williamson (1991b) estimated that employment could increase in Badenoch and Strathspey to over 290 and that up and downstream multipliers could increase this number by a factor of five. If these figures are applied to the area of the Forest of Spey, the number employed in forestry would be over 750 and a similar number would apply to the Deeside Forest. (For details of the Forest of Spey and Deeside Forest, see p.127 and Fig. 17.1.) These calculations do not allow for any change in productivity, but if these proposed forests are worked in ways to enhance amenity, recreation and conservation, this would mean a higher level of employment would be required, offsetting any likely productivity gain.

Some of the up and downstream jobs associated with timber production will be outwith the area, but two of the most modern sawmills in Britain are located within the Cairngorms area, one near Aboyne on Deeside and the other at Boat of Garten on the Spey. Many other jobs would be created by the larger forest area, in sporting and in tourism, the latter including ranger services and accommodation.

FOREST RESEARCH

During most of the twentieth century, when the main aim was to establish productive woodland, the Forestry Commission research effort was geared to find the most cost-effective methods of establishing and maintaining the most productive species yielding good saw timber. Experiments on cultivation, fertilizing, species choice, seed origin and tree breeding were done on a variety of sites throughout Britain. In addition, plots were established at the higher altitudes to determine the upper limit of productive tree growth.

Some experiments were done in the Cairngorms area, including high elevation plots. In 1930 one such plot was established just above the upper limit of the forest in Glen More at 480 m ASL. A range of species, including Scots pine and spruces, was planted. Lodgepole pine was a notable success in this plot. In 1969–70 another experiment was established well above the forest at 620 m ASL. This second plot is a prominent feature on the slope to the north of the Coire na Ciste car park (Plate 70). This altitude was thought to be about the present natural tree line in this part of the Cairngorms and the tree growth does fall off markedly in the top half

Table 10e   Seed origins of planted pine woodland in mid and upper Deeside

Locality	% Area
Highland Deeside (local)	57
Morayshire	5
NE Scotland – unspecified	26
Upper Strathspey	1
Finland	<1
Norway	<1
Unknown origin	10

Source: after Callander & MacKenzie, 1991

of the plot which goes up to about 640 m ASL. In the lower half, the tree growth is remarkably good and is similar to the average rate of growth for Scotland. Plate 68 shows a naturally sown birch of excellent form growing among lodgepole pine within this plot at an elevation of 610 m ASL. Today, naturally sown Scots pine can be found growing up to an elevation of about 800 m ASL above Glen More Forest.

The natural (potential) tree line around the Cairngorms in the present climate is probably between 600 and 700 m ASL (Pears, 1968) (Plates 62, 63) and would be lower on the western slopes exposed to the prevailing wind but higher on the eastern slopes and on slopes where the land rises much higher than 700 m ASL. The elevation up to which trees would produce usable timber is likely to be 100 to 150 m below the natural tree line and again will vary with the severity of the local exposure.

DISCUSSION

The exploitation and partial regeneration of the natural forests around the Cairngorms, combined with the more recent planting of non-native species, such as Norway spruce and larch from Europe and Sitka spruce and lodgepole pine from the north-west of North America, has resulted in a very mixed forest ranging from remnants of the natural forest to plantations of a single, non-native species. The natural remnants vary from small scattered groups of old pine or young birch to much larger areas of older birch woodland on steep valley sides or uniform older pine stands dating from large fires one or two centuries ago.

The soils vary from relatively rich alluvium that is mainly used for agriculture, to nutrient-poor ironpan soils and acid peats. The ironpan soils have developed under the heather-dominated moorland created by man through repeated burning with consequent loss of nutrients in smoke and by leaching of the ash. Gimingham (1956) described how this habitat is affected by repeated burning. Some nutrients are replenished by rainfall except for phosphorus which is present in rain in very minimal amounts. Such soils also suffer from winter waterlogging and summer drought because of the impervious ironpan. As phosphorus is an essential element for plant growth and as rooting is restricted on these soils, the rate of tree growth is much slower than it would have been on the natural woodland soils.

The average growth rate of trees in Britain is 10 m^3 ha^{-1} yr^{-1} which is faster than the rates in Scandinavia (Johnston, 1975), Canada and Russia, and in tropical forest, and faster than in most of Europe (Christie & Lines, 1979). However, because of the generally poorer geology, the higher than average elevation and the higher ratio of pine to spruce in the Cairngorms area, the average growth rate will be slower than the British average and would become even slower if the spruce plantations were to be replaced by pine or broadleaved species, especially if such woodlands had a higher proportion of open space. The rate could fall from a value of say 9 m^3 ha^{-1} yr^{-1} at present to about 5. Despite this possible reduction, the total potential timber production from the area will increase if the total forest area increases as proposed.

Fire has always been a major cause of forest destruction and the practice of muirburning over the past century or two has destroyed and prevented forest regeneration. Many of the remaining natural pinewoods have no regeneration among or adjacent to the old trees because of such burning either for deer or grouse. The subsequent heavy grazing by deer or the repeated strip burning to maintain continuous red grouse habitat has continued to kill any regenerating trees.

The plantations are generally of a uniform age and relative tree size. In upper Deeside they are mostly Scots pine, in Strathspey they consist of Scots pine, spruce and some lodgepole pine, while to the north, for example in Glenlivet, they have a significant amount of larch in addition to the pines and spruces.

Despite the removal of the best trees over several centuries, present-day woods are unlikely to be markedly poorer genetically than their predecessors. The wide range of rate of growth and of form of individual trees within a wood is determined mostly by the growing conditions and not by the genetic quality of the trees that probably does not vary greatly from individual to individual. Trees which appear poor in quality may owe this to growing conditions – climate and soil – which vary from microsite to microsite, or to damage caused by weather, animals, insects or disease, all of which vary from tree to tree. The apparently poorer individuals, however, can generally produce good offspring.

The two main tree species that dominate this area, Scots pine and birch, can both produce excellent timber (Plate 69). Scots pine timber is strong but light, does not warp easily, holds nails well and its sapwood readily absorbs preservatives (Riddoch, 1967; Harding, 1988). It is, therefore, used extensively for fencing, joinery and construction. However, it can suffer from blue stain if left too long after felling during the summer months. Blue stain does not affect the strength of the timber, but looks unsightly. It can also contain black knots if branches do not drop off. Birch timber is one of the strongest timbers commonly grown in Britain (Petty, 1991) and is comparable in strength to beech, with the toughness of ash (Elliott, 1991). This, together with a very even grain makes it very suitable for turning (spindles, brush backs, handles), furniture making and high class joinery, and also for making plywood and particleboard. Also, because of its lack of flaking, it makes a very uniform, hardwearing floor (Wall, 1994). Unfortunately birch timber has not been available in quantity and of sufficient size and quality to create a market in this country (Seaman, 1994). A charitable trust, known as Highland Birchwoods, has been set up by a partnership of the Forestry Commission, Scottish Natural Heritage, the Highland Regional Council and Highlands and Islands Enterprise to encourage the management and extension of birchwoods and the marketing of birch timber throughout the Highlands (Kennedy, 1993).

Very little timber is produced from the semi-natural pine/birch woods at the present time. The almost total absence of young trees in many woods has led to a concern that the felling of older trees equates to further loss of a scarce resource. Preservation without regeneration, however, will result in eventual loss of the woodland. Where there is available land on the flanks of the forest to allow expansion, or where the mature trees are widely spaced, regeneration should be encouraged in the available space (Plate 71). In well-stocked woods, however, regeneration with light-demanding species such as pine and birch, is only possible once gaps have been created by felling some of the existing trees. Many of these trees produce excellent timber which should be extracted and used while the poorer stems can be left to rot for conservation reasons. The guides to the Management of semi-natural woodlands (Forestry Authority, 1994b & c) lay down guidelines on how these woodlands can be managed to combine timber production with the maintenance of conservation and amenity interest. The priority that is given to each objective will obviously differ within and between various types of woodland. A recently published booklet (Forestry Commission, 1998) briefly explains what native woodlands are, what they are used for and why they are special.

The more recent plantations around the Cairngorms have been producing small roundwood from thinnings for some time, and clear felling of the earliest plantings, together with some premature felling for restructuring, have started. Restructuring is being done to regenerate remnants of natural woodland within the plantations or to improve the age class structure to give a more even annual production of timber whilst creating more biodiversity (Ratcliffe, 1993), conserving water and wildlife and improving the appearance and amenity of the forests as suggested in the Forestry Commission's Guidelines (Forestry Commission, 1989, 1990, 1991, 1992, 1993, 1995).

THE FUTURE

The future development of forestry around the Cairngorms should concentrate on sustainability as outlined in the Report of the Cairngorms Working Party (Cairngorms Working Party, 1993). Following recommendations in this report, the Secretary of State for Scotland established the Cairngorms Partnership Board in 1994 to produce a management strategy which was published in 1997 (Cairngorms Partnership, 1997). The strategy views forestry as part of an integrated land management programme with a sustainable base. Its first objective is to encourage the management of the woodland throughout the Cairngorms area for:

- timber production and other woodland produce;
- the enhancement of nature conservation and biodiversity;
- the protection of water quality and quantity;

- the furtherance of outdoor recreation opportunities;
- a range of other uses with an emphasis on local employment and job creation.

To support this principal objective, a number of other objectives were declared, including:

- the consolidation and encouragement of regeneration of existing native woodland, including the growth of high altitude scrub and the formation of a natural tree line;
- the development of the Deeside Forest and the Forest of Spey as models of integrated and sustainable land use, and the promotion of the distinctive identity of these two Forests for maximum local benefit.

This set of objectives displays considerable changes in the attitudes of the Government, the woodland owners and their managers and the local communities from the not-too-distant past when the main objective was to plant as much land as possible to re-create a forest reserve following the significant reduction in productive forest during the two world wars. The woodlands created then still dominate the scenery today and their composition and appearance reflect the simpler objectives of their era. It will take some considerable time to attain the more complex objectives now in place and it will be an equally long time before the landscape of the Cairngorms fully reflects the bold new vision of the future.

The creation of the Deeside Forest and the Forest of Spey is part of that vision and the Deeside Forest initiative was launched in 1996 and the Forest of Spey initiative in 1998. These forests will build on, and extend, the native woodland and the plantations of native pine of local origin throughout the area. The term 'Forest' may be misleading as the area will include a mosaic of land uses, including moorland, farmland, wetlands and also towns and villages. However, woodland cover will become extensive and visually dominant in the landscape.

The main tree species should be Scots pine and birch, with aspen, willow, alder, oak, ash, elm and cherry with the shrub species rowan and juniper in varying proportions depending on altitude, aspect, soil and exposure. The preferred method of regeneration should be by natural seeding without soil disturbance, but where a species is not present on a suitable site, planting of stock grown from seed collected from trees of local origin could be done. Ground preparation by scarifying and/or tining should only be used on seriously degraded sites, for example where a thick litter layer had built up, dense vegetation has become established or a strong ironpan has developed under heather. Rodwell and Patterson (1994) give detailed advice on the creation of new native (natural-type) woodlands while the Forestry Practice Guides on native pinewoods (Forestry Authority, 1994c) and upland birchwoods (Forestry Authority, 1994b) explain how to manage these existing native woods. In addition to encouraging native woodland, the current proportion of non-native tree species should be maintained to produce a higher yield of utilizable timber on the more fertile sites to provide more employment both in the forest and with local processors.

A wide variation in age and tree density should be encouraged to ensure the continuity of the forest and diversity of habitat with a consequent wide range of animals and plants, a pleasing landscape and considerable amenity and recreational benefits. Such forests would have the potential to supply timber and other products, such as game and edible fungi and to provide continued employment, in perpetuity. Most of the woods within these forests could sustain some level of timber production; some would be managed primarily for timber production while, at the other end of the spectrum, others would be reserved as undisturbed, natural ecosystems. In yet other areas management would be chiefly for public recreation while sport shooting could be carried out over most of the forest area except where public recreation was very high or wildlife conservation was the primary aim. The emphasis on any particular form of management will vary with site conditions and the owner's aspirations. In other words, these forests would produce a variety of benefits: to the landowner, to the people working on the land and to the public who would enjoy the amenity, the facilities and the produce.

Eventually, if deer numbers were reduced to less than five per hectare, all the land below 800 ± 100m ASL could carry trees from low scrub at the highest levels to very large trees in the lower valleys. However, other forms of land use will prevent such extensive forest cover. On some of the higher slopes, particularly in the north-east and south-west sectors, repeated burning of the vegetation to encourage red grouse populations would prevent tree regeneration. On some of the better soils on the lowest slopes and in the valleys, soil cultivation to grow agricultural crops and intensive grazing by domestic animals will prevent trees becoming established. These open areas together with areas of deep peat, marshland, open water, screes, the montane plateaux and windthrown forest will create a matrix of forest and open land which will provide a wide variety of habitats, a pleasing, forest-dominated landscape, recreation opportunities of many kinds and a higher level of employment than at present. The Cairngorms Forest and Woodland Framework (Cairngorms Partnership, 1999) describes how the future development of the forests and woodlands in the Cairngorms area could proceed.

The United Kingdom imports 84.5 per cent of its current requirement for timber and timber products (Forestry Commission, 2000) and, despite a continuing increase in home-produced timber until the third decade of this century, 75 per cent will still have to be imported. The Jaakko Poyry report (1998) points out that there is presently substantial over-capacity in most sectors of an increasingly globalized timber products industry. However, because of the country's high dependency on imported timber, the domestic sawmilling industry has the opportunity to expand by replacing imported products, and increase the consumption of British grown timber at a cumulative average growth rate of 3.5 per cent per annum until 2018.

Because of the continuing demand for timber, a desire for more native forest and the incentives offered by the Forestry Commission's revised Woodland Grant Scheme (Forestry Authority, 1994a, Forestry Commission, 2001) to manage and extend such forest, the Cairngorms area should in future be a part of Scotland that has a very high percentage of woodland cover, much of which will be of native species. These woods will produce a sustainable supply of good quality timber as well as being an attractive habitat for wildlife, the local human population and a large number of tourists and sportsmen and women.

REFERENCES

Atterson, J. (1980) *Gambling with gales.* British Association for the Advancement of Science, Section K★ (Forestry), Salford.

Anderson, M.L. (1967) *A History of Scottish Forestry.* Volumes I & II. Nelson, London.

Birks, H.J.B. (1989) Holocene isochrone maps and patterns of tree-spreading in the British Isles. *Journal of Biogeography* **16**, 503–540.

Cairngorms Partnership (1997). *Managing the Cairngorms. The Cairngorms Partnership Management Strategy.* Cairngorms Partnership, Grantown-on-Spey.

Cairngorms Partnership (1999) *Cairngorms Forest and Woodland Framework.* Cairngorms Partnership, Grantown-on-Spey.

Cairngorms Working Party (1993) *Common sense and sustainability: a partnership for the Cairngorms.* The Scottish Office, Edinburgh.

Callander, R.F. & Mackenzie, N.A. (1991) *The Native Pine Woodlands of Highland Deeside.* Report for The Nature Conservancy Council, Aberdeen.

Calder A.M. & Gill, J.G.S. (1988) Forestry on Speyside: its evolution and production. In: Jenkins, D., ed., *Land Use in the River Spey Catchment,* ACLU Symposium No. 1.

Christie, J.M. & Lines, R. (1979) A comparison of forest productivity in Britain and Europe in relation to climatic factors. *Forest Ecology and Management* **2**, 75–102.

Cole, S. (1970) *The Neolithic Revolution.* British Museum (Natural History), London.

Cumming, Sir William Gordon, Bt. (1994) Scotland's uplands – the future. *Scot. For.* **48**, 2.

Darling, Sir Frank Fraser (1949) *History of Scottish Forests.* British Association for the Advancement of Science. Reprinted in *The Tree Planter's Guide to the Galaxy* 7 (1992). pp. 25–6.

Dunlop, B.M.S. (1994) Strathspey Forests – Origin and History. In: *The Native Woodlands of Strathspey.* Scottish Natural Heritage Research, Survey & Monitoring Report No. 33. SNH, Edinburgh.

Elliott, G.K. (1991) The uses of birch in industry. In: Lorrain-Smith, R. & Worrell, R., eds, *The Commercial Potential of Birch in Scotland.* FICGB, London.

Forestry Authority (1994a) *Woodland Grant Scheme.* Forestry Authority, Edinburgh.

Forestry Authority (1994b) *Upland Birchwoods.* Forestry Practice Guide 6. Forestry Authority, Edinbugh.

Forestry Authority (1994c) *Native Pinewoods.* Forestry Practice Guide 7. Forestry Authority, Edinburgh.

Forestry Commission (1950) *Census of Woodlands.* Forestry Commission. HMSO, London.

Forestry Commission (1990) *Forest Nature Conservation.* Forestry Commission Guidelines. HMSO, London.

Forestry Commission (1991) *Community Woodlands. Forestry Commission Guidelines.* HMSO, London.

Forestry Commission (1992) *Forest Recreation.* Forestry Commission Guidelines. HMSO, London.

Forestry Commission (1993) *Forests & Water.* Forestry Commission Guidelines. HMSO, London.

Forestry Commission (1994) *Forest Landscape Design.* Forestry Commission Guidelinds. HMSO, London.

128

Forestry Commission (1995) *Archaeology. Forestry Commission Guidelines.* HMSO, London.

Forestry Commission (1998) *Native Woodlands of Scotland.* Forestry Commission, Edinburgh.

Forestry Commission (2000) *Forestry Facts and Figures 1999–2001.* Forestry Commission, Edinburgh.

Forestry Commission (2001) *Woodland Grant Scheme. Applicants' Pack.* Forestry Commission, Edinburgh.

Fraser, J. (1956) Forests and Plantations. In: Walton, J., ed., *Glenmore, Cairngorms. National Park Guide.* HMSO, London.

Gear, A.J. & Huntley, B. (1991) Rapid changes in the range limits of Scots Pine 4000 years ago. *Science* **251**, 544–7.

Gimingham, C.H. (1956) Fire on the hills. *J. For. Comm.* **25**, 148–150. (First published in *Arbor*, Aberdeen University Forestry Society Magazine).

Gloyne, R.W. (1968) The structure of wind and its relevance to forestry. Supplement to *Forestry*, 7–19.

Harding, T. (1988) British Softwoods: properties and uses. *Forestry Commission Bulletin.* 77. HMSO, London.

Highland Regional Council (1993) *Indicative Forestry Strategy.* Highland Regional Council, Inverness.

Jaakko Poyry (1998) *Future Development Prospects for British Grown Softwood.* Jaako Poyry Consulting, London.

Johnston, D.R. (1975) Tree growth and wood production in Britain. *Phil. Trans. R. Soc., Lond.* B271.

Kennedy, D. (1993) Major Birch Project. *Forestry and British Timber.* **8/93**, 22–29.

Matthews, J.D. (1976) The evolution of the forests. In: Edlin, H.L., ed., *Forests of NE Scotland.* Forestry Commission Guide. HMSO, London.

Pears, N.V. 1968. Post-glacial tree lines of the Cairngorm Mountains, Scotland. *Trans. Bot. Soc. of Edinb.* **131**, 361–394.

Pears, N.V. (1975) Tree stumps in the Scottish hill peats. *Scot. For.* **29**, 4, 255–9.

Petty, J.A. (1991) The properties of birch timber. In: Lorrain-Smith, R.E., & Worrell, R., eds, *The Commercial Potential of Birch in Scotland.* FICGB, London.

Ratcliffe, P.R. (1993) *Biodiversity: Britain's Forests.* Forestry Commission, Edinburgh.

Radcliffe, P.R., Peterken, G.F. & Hampson, A. (1998) *A Forest Habitat Network for the Cairngorms.* Scottish Natural Heritage Research Survey and Monitoring Report 114. Scottish Natural Heritage, Edinburgh.

Riddoch, W.J. (1967) The utilization of Scots pine. *J. For. Comm.* **35**, 27–8.

Rodwell, J. & Patterson, G. (1994) Creating new native woodlands. *Forestry Commission Bulletin.* 112. HMSO, London.

Seaman, A. (1994) Birch – the full story. *Forestry & British Timber,* **4/94**, 24–30.

Selby, P.J. (1842) *A History of British Forest-Trees, indigenous and introduced.* Voorst, London.

Shaw, D.L. (1956) British forestry development in the early twentieth century. *J. For. Comm.* **25**, 177–180.

Sinclair, Sir John (1797) *The Statistical Account of Scotland, 1791–7.* Edinburgh.

Wall, E. & Co. (1994) *Native Hardwood Flooring – a Pilot Study.* Report by Eamonn Wall & Co. *Forestry & British Timber* **4/94**, 22–3.

Williamson, J.D.A. (1991a) *Forestry Statistics.* Unpublished paper presented to the Cairngorms Working Party.

Williamson, J.D.A. (1991b) *Benefits of Commercial Forests.* Unpublished paper presented to the Cairngorms Working Party.

Williamson, J.D.A. (1991a) *Forestry Statistics.* Unpublished paper presented to the Cairngorm Working Party.

Williamson, J.D.A. (1991b) *Benefits of Commercial Forests.* Unpublished paper presented to the Cairngorms Working Party.

Wonders, W.C. (1987) The Canadian Forestry Corps in Scotland during World War II. *Scottish Geographical Magazine* **103**, 1, 21–31.

Wonders, W.C. (1991) *The 'Sawdust Fusiliers'.* Canadian Pulp & Paper Association, Québec.

CHAPTER 11

Red Deer and Their Management in the Cairngorms

B.W. STAINES AND R. BALHARRY

In this chapter we discuss the role of red deer and their management in the Cairngorms and the conflicts that arise with other land users. These problems relate especially to overgrazing and the regeneration of native woodlands, but also to damage on other aspects of the natural heritage, agricultural crops and to the increasing number of conflicts between deer managers and people using the hills for outdoor recreation. To do this, we first set the scene with a brief history of red deer *Cervus elaphus* (Plate 72) in the Highlands, and in the Cairngorms in particular. We then describe relevant aspects of the biology of red deer, and finally debate the issues. We concentrate our attention on the problems in the core area of the Cairngorms drawing on evidence from outside this area where it is appropriate.

BACKGROUND

Red deer are an integral part of the ecology, folk lore and history of the Scottish uplands. In the Cairngorms, especially in the core area dominated by five large estates, the open landscape owes much to the long tradition of maintaining high numbers of red deer for sport. The history of the red deer population here in many ways mirrors that in Scotland as a whole.

Hunting deer in the Cairngorms goes back at least to the twelfth century. By the mid-sixteenth century, red deer were almost extinct in the Scottish Lowlands but they survived in the Highlands where they were jealously guarded. Only 'properly qualified

persons' were allowed to kill deer then. The fine for unlawfully killing 'deare or raes' (red or roe deer) was 'ten pundies' for the first offence, 'twentie pundies' for the second and 'fortie pundies' for the third. However, if the perpetrators were 'not responsall in guddes', they were put in the stocks or in prison for '8 days on bread and water'. If they committed a third offence, they were to suffer 'hanging to the death' (Ritchie, 1920)!

The traditional method of hunting was by driving deer with men and hounds. Some of these drives, or tainchels, were massive, using up to 2000 men. They were prepared several weeks or even months in advance with the beaters driving the deer towards the predetermined 'trap', or eileirg (Gordon, 1925). In 1529 there was a great drive for King James V on Atholl where 'threttie scoir [600] of hart and hynd, with other small beasties, sick as roe and roe-buck were slain'. Again, in 1563, the Earl of Atholl organized a hunt for Queen Mary when, after two months of tainchel-driving on the lands of Atholl, Badenoch, Mar and Moray, 2000 Highlanders are reputed to have driven more than 2000 deer to the eileirg; 360 were subsequently killed (Ritchie, 1920).

Whilst hunting remained a popular sport for a few, red deer conflicted with other interests, especially agriculture. The adverse impact of man on the Highland red deer population probably reached its peak in the late seventeenth and eighteenth centuries. More woodlands were cleared to provide timber, charcoal for smelting, and especially to create grazings for large-scale sheep farming

(Mitchell *et al.*, 1977). Since sheep became more profitable, many estates, especially in the west and north-west Highlands, let their forests as sheep-walk and red deer were regarded as competitors. By 1811, only six deer forests remained with substantial numbers of red deer. Interestingly, three of these were in the Cairngorms area at Mar, Atholl and Invercauld (Clutton-Brock & Albon, 1989); hence the core area of the Cairngorms has probably had more continuous impact from red deer than elsewhere in the country. In addition, because of the continued interest in deer in the Cairngorms area, sheep numbers would likely have been lower there than in other parts. For example, Scrope (1839) reports how sheep-clearing started as early as 1790 on Mar forest.

In the middle years of the nineteenth century, deer hunting once more became fashionable, especially amongst the *nouveaux riches* of industrial Britain, and the number of deer forests increased. In the absence of natural predators, and a deliberate underculling of hinds, the deer population steadily rose. The advent of the breech-loading rifle meant a change in the whole tradition of deer hunting, with the more individual sport of stalking replacing the large deer drives (Scrope, 1839; Whitehead, 1960). This said, some driving of deer to rifles still occurred in the Cairngorms up to the First World War.

The increase in the deer population, however, led to more conflicts with agriculture and with forestry. These conflicts, the so-called 'red deer problem', resulted in seven government inquiries between 1872 and 1954. The early problems were largely concerned with crofting and agriculture, red deer being perceived as competitors for valuable grazings and damaging root crops and cereals. Following the formation of the Forestry Commission in 1919 and the concomitant expansion of commercial forestry, there were increasing reports of damage to trees, although this was not really recognized as a major problem until the late 1960s.

Conflicts with nature conservation did not feature prominently in the early debates, although it had been recognized for decades that high numbers of deer were damaging habitats and inhibiting the regeneration of many native woodlands (e.g. Ritchie, 1920; Gordon, 1925; Darling, 1937; Mitchell *et al.*, 1977). It was only in the late 1980s that wildlife conservation interests began to be debated as an important issue more generally (Staines, 1991).

RED DEER HABITATS

Although originally an animal of open woodland or the woodland edge, red deer were forced to occupy the open moorlands of Scotland following the destruction of the native forests. They were able to adapt to the harsh conditions of the Scottish uplands whereas other deer such as reindeer *Rangifer tarandus* and moose *Alces alces* became extinct and roe deer *Capreolus capreolus* were confined to the relict woodlands in a few parts of Highland Scotland (Ritchie, 1920). Concomitant with this change in habitat occupation by red deer was a decline in body size and reproductive performance, a subtle adaptation to their impoverished and exposed habitats (Ritchie, 1920; Lowe, 1961; Mitchell *et al.*, 1977).

In the Cairngorms, red deer are still primarily open-hill dwellers, although they use the sparse remnants of the native pinewoods, especially in winter. In recent years, however, previously-fenced commercial woodlands have been opened to them for winter shelter and to relieve grazing pressure on other parts of their winter range, for example, at Glen Feshie, Glen Quoich, Glen Lui.

In addition to using native woods in winter (Plate 73), red deer are now resident in most large commercial plantations, such as at Inshriach on the western flank of the Cairngorms. These deer are hefted to the woods and use them year-round, not merely in winter. From here, they may venture on to adjacent open ground where they can damage the regeneration of native woodlands or agricultural crops.

RED DEER BIOLOGY

Two aspects of red deer biology are particularly important when trying to understand the conflicts between landuse interests and their solutions: the segregation of the sexes and hefting behaviour.

Sexual segregation. For most of the year red deer stags and hinds segregate, and their winter ranges are often discrete and traditional. Watson and Staines (1978) studied sexual segregation in red deer in Glen Clunie and on Mar Lodge. The home ranges of the hind and stag groups in Glen Clunie in winter overlapped very little and range size was correlated with the number of deer in the group. Hind groups (mean, 124) were significantly larger than stag groups (mean, 47), but this may not be the case everywhere in the Cairngorms, especially where stags are concentrated at supplementary feeding sites in winter.

It is commonly believed that stags occupy lower parts of the glens in winter, and certainly this is the case in some areas such as Glen Lui, Glen Quoich and Glen Feshie. However, elsewhere, as in Glen Clunie, both stag and hind ranges are found throughout the glen and the minimum altitudes in both are similar (Watson & Staines, 1978). Clutton-Brock and Albon (1989) found a comparable situation on Rum. Hind ranges, however, had higher maximum altitudes.

The interesting point is that hinds occupied ranges that overlie greater areas of base-rich rocks, on average having more than five times as much per deer as did stag ranges (Watson & Staines, 1978). Likewise, Staines and Crisp (1978) found that 90 per cent of hind ranges in Glen Feshie overlie the relatively more fertile Moine schists, whereas half of the stag ranges overlie granite. Compared to stags, hinds had ranges with more than three times as much ground over the fertile brown earths and alluvial soils and more than seven times as much over 'flushed' areas. Analyses of stomach contents showed that hinds ate significantly more grasses and

Table 11a   Counts of Red Deer in the East and West Grampian counting blocks by the Deer Survey and the Red Deer Commission

	Year	Stags	Hinds	Calves	Total	Source
West Grampians	1953–5	2550	-5960-		8510	FFD
	1967	8480	11 360	4010	23 851	RDC
	1983	10 650	17 030	5400	33 080	RDC
	1995	12 405	15 216	4457	32 078	RDC
East Grampians	1953–5	2650	-5300-		7950	FFD
	1966	3100	5050	1900	10 050	RDC
	1975	6590	9720	3000	19 310	RDC
	1986	7400	13 760	4360	25 520	RDC
	1994	8560	12 440*	4360	25 360	RDC

* Some 2–300 hinds and calves were known to have moved into plantations before the count, and it is estimated that the decrease in hind numbers was probably less than 1000 (Deer Commission for Scotland, pers commun.). FFD = Darling, 1958; RDC = Red Deer Commission.

less heather in winter than did stags, and that the nitrogen levels in their stomachs (an indicator of food quality) were also significantly higher.

So, under high hind densities plant biomass on the preferred grasslands is low and stags are obliged to feed on less palatable, but more abundant forage such as heather (Staines & Crisp, 1978; Clutton-Brock et al., 1987). In other words stags and hinds compete for food in winter, with the hinds winning.

Hefting.   Deer are strongly hefted to an area. This is particularly so in hinds, but also stags when they are mature (Lowe, 1967; Staines, 1974, 1977; Mitchell et al., 1977; Clutton-Brock & Albon, 1989; Red Deer Commission, 1991). The Red Deer Commission (RDC, now the Deer Commission for Scotland. DCS) ear-tagged more than 1700 calves in the West Grampians between 1967 and 1985 (RDC, 1988). From its return, it showed that 92 per cent of hinds and 60 per cent of stags were recovered within 2 km of the area where they were marked.

In their classic study of red deer on Rum, Clutton-Brock and his colleagues (see Clutton-Brock & Albon, 1989) allowed a local sub-population to increase by 2.5 to 3 times. Throughout the period very few hinds emigrated from the area despite the very high density, but the stag population dropped with more emigration of young stags and little immigration of stags from other areas. Again, high densities of hinds adversely affected the stag population.

THE CAIRNGORMS DEER POPULATION

Numbers on Mar Forest were probably at their lowest in the late eighteenth century until the Earl of Fife actively encouraged the deer stock for stalking. In an analysis of the Earl's diaries (1784–92), Watson (1983) shows how the Earl's perception of the 'scarcity of deer seen' changed over the period, seeing the equivalent of 10 deer per day in 1784 but over 100 per day in 1791. Numbers presumably rose still further, for in 1839 Scrope stated that, on Mar, there was 'a regular stock of about 3000'; an estimated 3000 were seen in Glen Quoich alone in around 1850 (McConnochie, 1923). From the numbers of deer shot since then to the present day, the population must have remained high throughout (Whitehead, 1960).

The key parts of the Cairngorms area were surveyed by Fraser Darling's small team in 1953–1955 (Darling, 1958), and after the formation of the RDC in 1959 systematic and more reliable counts of the deer population in Scotland were made. The RDC (DCS) uses larger teams of stalkers and they count large areas more or less simultaneously, keeping in contact with mobile radios thus avoiding double-counting of groups. The counts are considered to be underestimates (see Stewart, 1976, for methodology).

The DCS has classified the red deer range into blocks that have fairly discrete populations of deer. The core area of the Cairngorms falls into the West Grampian Count Area (224 600 ha). The West Grampians were completely counted in 1967, 1983 and 1995 with a part-count in 1991/2; the East Grampians (118 600 ha) were counted in 1966, 1975, 1986 and 1994 (Table 11a). Although the core area is only part of the West Grampians area, the figures for both count areas give an indication of recent trends in the local deer populations.

In 1991/2, bad weather meant a complete count in the West Grampians was impossible. Nevertheless, the Strathspey section was completed in March 1992 and the results indicated an increase there of 1300 stags (+53%) and 100 hinds (+63%) since 1983. These figures must be interpreted with some caution as the whole Count Area was not covered. However, the subsequent 1995 count confirmed the increase in stags with little change in the total population. Nevertheless, the fact that there has been an increase in overwintering stocks from 1983 is surely undeniable (Cairngorms Working Party, Report by the Technical Sub-Group on Woodland, June 1992).

The important features are that not only is there a marked increase in hind numbers since 1966/7 in both the East and West Grampians (146% and 34% respectively), but also that stags have increased (176% and 46%). This latter point is very relevant because many estates will argue that there are fewer stags on the ground and locating stags for stalking is more difficult.

The relative densities of deer, based on the 1983 winter count, were estimated by the Technical Sub-Group (Woodlands) of the Cairngorm Working Party in 1992. These are reproduced in Fig. 11.1. They show the marked difference in pressure from deer on various areas of the Cairngorms in summer

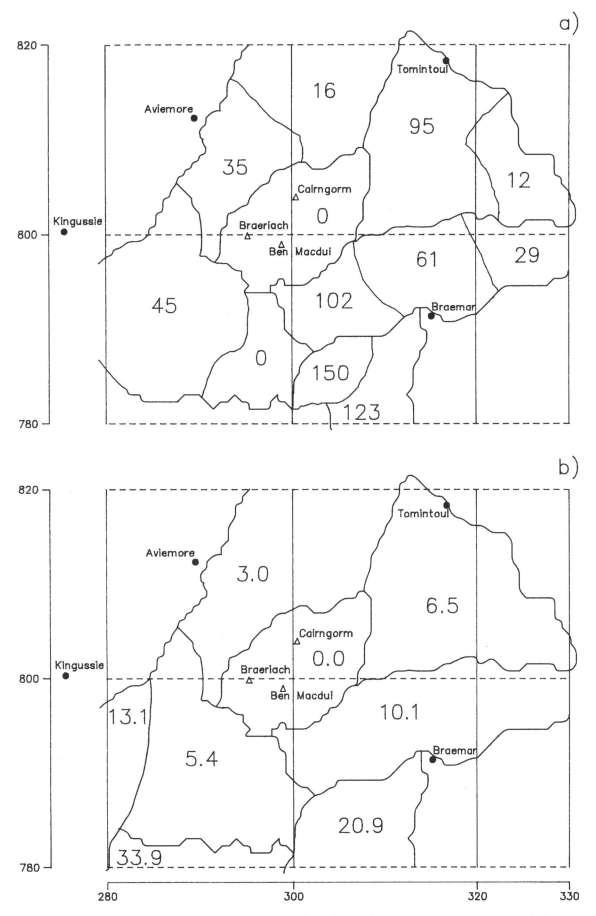

Figure 11.1 Estimated stocking densities (number/100 ha) of red deer on (a) winter and (b) summer ranges in the Cairngorms (based on the RDC 1983 winter count. Source: Cairngorms Working Party Technical Sub-group (Woodlands), 1992).

and winter. Of particular note are the very high densities in the areas of the remnant Caledonian woodland west of Braemar.

THE ISSUES

The main ecological issues are:
- The lack of regeneration of native woodland;
- The grazing impacts of red deer on other plant and animal communities.

The main land-use issues are:
- The conflict between woodland and vegetation recovery and deer stalking;
- Loss of heather moorland, and its effect on the 'grouse moor economy';
- Loss of revenue and employment to the estates;
- Loss of capital values;
- Conflicts between stalking and outdoor recreation.

Woodland regeneration. The lack of woodland regeneration in the Cairngorms, particularly of the precious native Caledonian pinewood, is probably the main concern to conservationists. The main agent preventing regeneration here is thought to be red deer although other grazers, such as hill sheep, rabbits *Oryctolagus cuniculus* and mountain hares *Lepus timidus* may be important locally. The impact of red deer has been recognized by ecologists for decades (e.g. Ritchie, 1920; Darling, 1958). In 1925, Seton Gordon pointed out that the failure of the native pinewoods to regenerate in upper Deeside was due to the large numbers of red deer wintering there. Watson's (1983) analysis of the Earl of Fife's diaries (1783–92) showed that the lack of regeneration could be attributed to the deliberate increase in deer numbers around that time. Subsequent analyses of the age-structure of the pinewoods in part confirms this (Nixon & Cameron, 1994).

Many factors affect the regeneration of woodlands such as seed availability, soil conditions, seed bed, altitude, tree density and the surrounding vegetation (Miles & Kinnaird, 1971a, b; Hester & Miller, 1995). Nevertheless, from the numerous exclosures in the Cairngorms such as at Glen Derry, Glen Feshie, Invereshie and Ballochbuie, it is clear that once red deer are denied access to potential woodland areas, regeneration will take place (Plate 72).

Yet regeneration can occur without fencing. Following the developing of skiing at Cairn Gorm in 1960, together with a high cull of red deer in the Forestry Commission plantations around there, regeneration of Scots pine occurred away from the forest edge up to about 500 m (Hester & Miller, 1995). There was an initial surge of regeneration which started to tail off after 1980, possibly because the available niches had been filled; but it also co-incided with a rise in the local deer population. At Inshriach (3085 ha), the deer density was decreased from around 1/10 ha to 1/39 ha. This allowed small saplings of Scots pine, previously held in check by grazing, to get away (Staines *et al.*, 1995) (Plate 71). A reduction of deer from 1/4 ha to 1/19 ha and the removal of the sheep stock at Creag Meagaidh NNR

(3940 ha) has allowed the regeneration of birch *Betula* spp., rowan *Sorbus aucuparia* and other hardwoods.

In Glen Feshie, different treatments (burning and scarifying) were given in an exclosure adjacent to the Badan Mosach wood. Although not properly assessed, superficially it appears that there are no significant differences in the rates of regeneration between the two treatments and the control. However, it could be that there were many niches at this site because of the previously high deer density; under other circumstances, interference to create a seedbed might be necessary. Nevertheless, from all these examples, if red deer are kept out or reduced, regeneration will occur.

The obvious answer is, of course, to reduce grazing pressure. Traditionally this has been done by fencing deer out of areas. However there is a large body of opinion against fencing, arguing that stock reduction is the best solution (Watson, 1993).

Fencing is costly. Currently a deer-proof fence costs *c.* £5-£7 per metre to erect. The life of a fence in the Cairngorms would be 20 years at the most, so at least two generations of fencing would be required to allow regenerating trees to reach a height safe from browsing. Secondly, in many parts of the Cairngorms within the woodland zone it is impractical to fence because of the steepness and nature of the ground.

Fences are obtrusive on the landscape. They hinder outdoor recreation and are instrumental in causing significant deaths of many woodland grouse (Catt *et al.*, 1994). Finally, the absence of natural grazers within a fenced area may allow the development of different types and structures of vegetation from those that would occur when grazers are present (Kirby, Mitchell & Hester, 1994); low levels of grazing can promote greater botanical diversity (Mitchell & Kirby, 1990).

In some areas, where stalking is the primary objective, fencing may be the only practical answer – *in the short term.* However, where exclosures are put up, there must be a reduction in deer numbers to reflect the amount of wintering ground lost (Staines *et al.*, 1995). Fencing should not be automatically accepted as the first option, and reducing deer numbers locally has been shown to be effective in promoting regeneration. However, we recognize that reducing deer numbers to a level compatible with tree regeneration could have deleterious effects on the economy of sporting estates.

Other vegetation. Whilst there is good evidence for red deer being the primary agent in preventing tree regeneration in many areas, their effect on other vegetation communities is less clear. It is difficult to separate the effects of deer from those of sheep and other herbivores. But, certainly there is great concern among some landowners that increased numbers of red deer have caused a loss of heather moorland, especially in the Angus glens, but also in Deeside and Donside. In fact, some estates previously managed solely as grouse moors are capitalizing on the increase in range and numbers of red deer by letting stalking to counteract the loss of revenue from low red grouse numbers over recent years. They are encouraging deer which, of course, will browse the heather on which the grouse depend, making conditions for a recovery of the grouse population even more unlikely.

In Grampian Region, 25 per cent of heather moorland was lost between the 1940s and 1970s (Sydes, 1988), 25 per cent of this loss being attributed to deer and sheep grazing coupled with poor burning practice. Watson (1989) observed a change from heather to grass-dominated swards in Glen Clunie, where sheep numbers had remained the same but where deer numbers had increased considerably. More quantitative evidence for red deer affecting heather moorland comes from Mar Lodge and Glen Feshie. At Glen Feshie, there have been marked changes in the botanical composition of the main glen from 1967–72. Around 30 cattle were summered there from 1967–72 but sheep were absent; grazing from rabbits and hares was light. However, there was a large overwintering stock of red deer (*c.* 45/100 ha, Fig. 11.1). From analyses of aerial photographs and ground survey, it was found that stands of pure heather declined (38%–22% cover) and grassland increased considerably (22%–29+%) (Staines *et al.*, 1995). However, this decline was most marked in the north and west of the main glen where deer received supplementary feeding in winter (Plate 75) and where neighbouring grassland had been limed and fertilized. Away from these sites heather cover increased slightly.

Likewise, at Glen Lui on Mar Lodge estate, heather cover declined from 65 per cent in 1946 to 40 per cent in 1989 in areas where several hundred deer received supplementary winter food and the ground had been fertilized. A little higher up the glen, in the contiguous Glen Derry where there was no feeding or fertilizing, heather declined only from 66 per cent in 1946 to 62 per cent in 1989 (Staines *et al.*, 1995). Concentrating animals in areas for supplementary food can, therefore, have a deleterious effect on heather as well as on those sites where tree regeneration is wanted. Nevertheless, we must remember that all feeding sites in the Cairngorms core area are in the woodland zone rather than the open moor. In a small survey of supplementary feeding on the five main estates in the core area plus four contiguous estates, we found that over 3000 stags and nearly 2000 hinds were receiving supplementary food. On at least four estates, some fertilizing of the grazings had taken place. The reasons for giving additional food in winter were equally to keep stags from marauding on neighbouring ground, to reduce mortality, to improve deer quality and to reduce pressure on other ground.

There have been no objective studies of the economics of winter feeding, nor of its effectiveness or deleterious effects. Certainly winter feeding has increased considerably over recent years. In one small study at Glen Feshie in 1974, Wiersema (1974) found that only a few, dominant stags actually got winter feed (cobs), getting as much as 17 per cent of their daily energy requirements. Other,

young and sub-dominants were 'held' in the area but did not benefit from the feed. This concentration of animals is likely to have consequences for increased parasitism and, as noted above, adversely affects surrounding vegetation. Used wisely, supplementary feeding can be a useful management tool to aid control and the distribution of deer. Currently it seems to be in part responsible for maintaining high deer densities, above the carrying capacity of the habitat.

Apart from heather moorland, heavy grazing restricts or damages important montane species such as alpine sowthistle *Cicerbita alpina* and purple coltsfoot *Homogyne alpina* (Francis *et al.*, 1991). Perceived changes in deer distribution, with large groups being seen on the mountain plateaux in summer (Francis *et al.*, 1991), are causing concern that rare montane species may be lost to overgrazing and that excessive trampling may lead to soil erosion.

Other conflicts. Although we have concentrated our discussion on the interactions between red deer and the natural heritage, conflicts also occur with forestry and agriculture. High densities of red deer damage commercially grown trees by browsing the leaders and side shoots of young trees and eating the bark of older ones (Staines & Welch, 1989; Gill, 1992). Over Scotland as a whole, the Forestry Authority estimates a net annual cost of £5.31 million attributable to deer, based on the costs of fencing (£2.44 million), rangers' salaries, etc. (£1.22 million), and loss of timber due to deer damage (£2.4 million), minus the income from let-stalking and venison (£1.26 million) (information based on the early 1990s, Gill, pers. comm., 1994).

In addition, deer in winter maraud on to agricultural land, especially where this abuts forestry plantations, as in parts of the northern and western Cairngorms. The problems of red deer in winter are clearly seen in Braemar, where even private gardens have to be protected by deer-fences.

CONCERNS

To allow woodland regeneration without fencing, deer numbers will have to be reduced. There is little objective evidence to suggest what densities of deer will allow regeneration, although there have been guesstimates of around 5/100 ha (Staines *et al.*, 1995; SNH, 1994). However, the necessary reductions in deer numbers to achieve woodland regeneration alarm many managers of sporting estates who fear that lower numbers will result in a loss of sport, income and employment. They also fear that low numbers on other ground, such as on adjacent NNRs, could lead to an emigration of 'their' deer to areas of low density – the so-called 'vacuum effect'.

While lower numbers could mean that fewer deer can be shot, this may be compensated by the effects of density on population and individual performance. It has been long recognized that, where a population is not resource limited, low density leads to faster growth rates, earlier puberty, higher fertility and enhanced survival (Staines,

1970, 1978; Mitchell *et al.*, 1977). The converse was elegantly shown by Clutton-Brock and his colleagues on Rum. They allowed a sub-population to rise by 2.5 to 3 times over a period of 16 years (1971–87). During that period, the fertility of adult hinds decreased with puberty being up to 2 years later than expected, and there was increased overwinter mortality of calves, especially stag calves, and lower recruitment. In addition, fewer stags used the area and they showed poorer performance, their antlers being significantly lighter at high densities (Clutton-Brock & Albon, 1989). The authors showed that yield, in terms of either the potential numbers killed or of venison, was at its optimum when the population was roughly half its final total. Thus, not only do high numbers, especially of hinds, adversely affect stag numbers and quality but also it is clear that similar yields could probably be attained with much lower densities than at present.

In a subsequent study, Clutton-Brock and Albon (1992) showed that, where hinds were lightly culled (6 per cent or less of the population), the cull of stags could be increased by 30 per cent by simply increasing the hind cull to 16–18 per cent. Mere adjustments to the cull and to sex ratios could, therefore, also increase yields.

Another important point is that the number of stags stalked is not necessarily related to the density of stags on an estate. This is because the number that can be shot is dependent on external factors such as the number of stalkers, the number of beats and days available, conflicts with other estate interests over grouse shooting, or fishing, weather and, frequently, tradition. Some estates (i.e. the 'hind forests') rely on stags moving on to their land during the stalking season. There is some evidence in the Cairngorms area that these movements have been later on some estates in recent years, thus making the available 'season' shorter. Deer managers clearly need to know the minimum number of hinds that are required to provide stalking for a given number of stags. Alternatively, if numbers are reduced to a certain level, given that performance will increase, what then will be the sustainable cull of stags?

A modification of current stalking could greatly ease the conflicts. That is, if the market expectation of shooting mature stags could be changed to that of selling stalking *per se*. If estates shoot only mature animals, they need a much higher population of both stags and hinds to support their cull. In a relatively simple model, Stewart (1990) showed that for a cull of around 650, a stock of 6250 stags was required if stalking concentrated on mature deer (his 'Traditional' model). If, however, the cull were spread over all age-classes (his 'High culling' model) then only 3800 deer were required. In addition, this would provide better quality venison from the younger deer. Such models are invaluable to guide management, but there is a hesitancy in adopting them and a long-established fear of over-culling. Demonstrations of the effects of lower deer densities on sport and income and habitats are badly needed.

Another concern is loss of employment (some 20 full-time stalkers in the core area, with 10–15 part-time employees). In the Cairngorms, given the difficulty of the terrain, we cannot see that there will be a loss of employment since the stalkers will always be necessary to maintain a cull which will become more difficult with lower densities. At Abernethy and Creag Meagaidh NNR, increased culling has in fact led to an increase in manpower. It could be that, in areas of conservation interest, some stalkers will take on other estate duties such as range management. This is not a new concept; in many parts of the north and west of Scotland stalkers became stalker/shepherds as a response to the fluctuating fashions of stalking and sheep farming.

The capital values of estates are based on the number of stags stalked and naturally would be affected if the number shot was reduced. These values rose considerably in the late 1980s reaching a peak of £20 000 – 40 000 per stag stalked in 1990 (Callander & MacKenzie, 1991). This declined again to £10 000 – 20 000 in 1993 reflecting not only a surplus of sporting estates on the market, but also the economic recession (SNH, 1994) and the volatility of the market. Until a different system of valuation is in place, there will always be the likelihood of estates losing value if the number of stags stalked decreases. Nevertheless, as we have already argued, many estates could shoot the same number of stags with a much lower population. The numbers of stags shot in the Cairngorms area has varied little over the last twenty years yet the population has doubled (SNH, 1994). In fact, despite the fears of estate managers that stag populations are declining, all evidence suggests that, in the Cairngorms, they are increasing (p. 132).

A further fear expressed by deer managers is that there will be a 'loss' of deer from high density to low density areas, thus affecting estates over a wider area than that on which the reductions are made. While no specific research has addressed the problem, there is some evidence to suggest that it is unlikely to occur, at least in the short or medium term. This is because hinds are strongly hefted to their home range. In any case, should it occur, it could be counteracted simply by changes in the management of the estates' culls. Given that most deer managers agree that there are too many deer, if they concentrated their cull on that part of their estate next to the area of low density, such as on an NNR, this would in turn create another low-density area, in effect, a buffer zone (Figure 11.2). Any movement of deer from high density areas would then be drawn initially into their own area of low density and would, therefore, still be under the estate's control.

The final issue is that of access, and of disturbance to deer by the increasing use of the hills for outdoor recreation. This increase is quite considerable, the number of clubs having increased from around 30 in 1970 to around 80 in 1990, mountain rescues increasing from *c*.70 to 290 over the same period (Scottish Mountaineering Club records). The issues were reviewed by Staines and Scott (1994) for the Countryside Commission for Scotland. The arguments being made were that disturbance by recreationists adversely affected the cull, and that deer were so disturbed that mortality

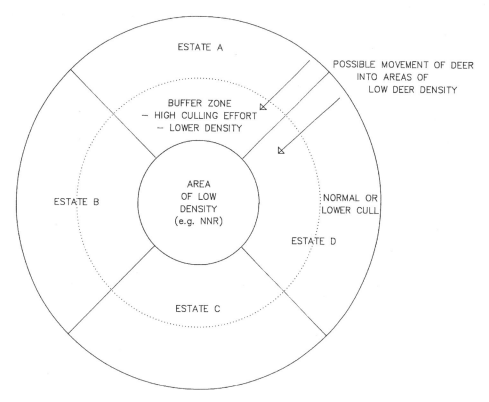

Figure 11.2 Schematic representation of a culling strategy to counteract any possible movement of deer from high to low density areas.

increased at calving time and also in late winter. Staines and Scott emphasized that any disturbance to deer had welfare considerations, especially when deer were stressed for other reasons such as inclement weather or shortage of food. But they found that there was no good evidence for increased winter mortality amongst deer, nor of desertion by mothers during the calving season, that could be attributed to disturbance. Areas with high visitor pressure had similar recruitment and mortality rates to those with little or no disturbance. In fact, the greatest disturbance to deer was clearly from shooting.

Staines and Scott concluded that the main problem was disruption to stalking. All the estates interviewed, including those in the Cairngorms, recognized that there was considerable disruption with some stalks lost, often on a daily basis. Yet all estates eventually achieved their target cull, albeit with increased effort. The problem was, therefore, largely one of frustration, rather than of economics or of animal welfare. However, if the number of visitors increased still further, it is possible that achieving satisfactory culls could be hindered. Nevertheless, at sites where visitors have been encouraged, such as at Creag Meagaidh NNR and the RSPB reserve at Abernethy, large culls have been achieved despite an increase in recreational activity.

CONCLUSIONS

Red deer management clearly affects many natural heritage interests, especially the regeneration of native woodlands. Where woodland regeneration is the primary aim, we advocate that a reduction in deer numbers to levels compatible with regeneration is the preferred method. We believe that the estates would not necessarily lose much income if there were subtle changes in management such as promoting stalking *per se* rather than the trophy value of stags, and an adjustment of the sex ratio. There would be increases in performance and, therefore, revenue also, due to lower deer density.

The conflicts that occur are between people and their different objectives for land management. Special consideration should be given to parcels of land where these conflicts occur, especially those of national and international importance such as the Cairngorms. Partnership between land users, as proposed by the Cairngorms Working Party (1993), is a way forward. It remains to be seen if it will work.

REFERENCES

Cairngorms Working Party (1993) Common sense and sustainability: A partnership for the Cairngorms. HMSO, Edinburgh.

Callander, R.F. & MacKenzie, N.A. (1991) The management of wild red deer in Scotland. Rural Forum, Scotland.

Catt, D.C., Dugan, D., Green, R.E., Moncrieff, R., Moss, R., Picozzi, N., Summers, R.W. & Tyler, G.A. (1994) Collisions against Fences by Woodland Grouse in Scotland. *Forestry* **67**, 105–118.

Clutton-Brock, T.H. & Albon, S.D. (1989) *Red deer in the Highlands.* Blackwell Science, Oxford.

Clutton-Brock, T.H. & Albon, S.D. (1992) Trial and error in the Highlands. *Nature* **358**, 11–12.

Clutton-Brock, T.H., Iason, G.R. & Guinness, F.E. (1987) Sexual segregation and density related changes in habitat use in male and female red deer (*Cervus elaphus*). *J. Zool. Lond.* **211**, 275–289.

Darling, F. Fraser (1937) *A herd of red deer.* Oxford University Press, London.

Darling, F. Fraser (1958) *West Highland Survey.* Oxford University Press, London.

Francis, J.M., Balharry, R. & Thompson, D.B.A. (1991) The implications for upland management: a summary paper. In: Rose, H., ed., *Deer, Mountains and Man.* British Deer Society & Red Deer Commission.

Gill, R.M.A. (1992) A review of damage by mammals in north temperate forests. 1. Deer. *Forestry* 65, 145–169.

Gordon, S. (1925) *The Cairngorm hills of Scotland.* Cassell, London.

Hester, A.J. & Miller, G.R. (1995) Scrub and woodland regeneration: prospects for the future. In: Thompson, D.P., Hester, A.J. & Usher, M.B., eds, *Heaths and Moorlands: Cultural Landscapes.* HMSO, Edinburgh.

Kirby, K.J., Mitchell, F.J. & Hester, A.J. (1994) A role for large herbivores (deer and domestic stock) in vegetation management in British semi-natural woods. *Arboricultural Journal* 18, 381–399.

Lowe, V.P.W. (1961) A discussion on the history, present status and future conservation of red deer (*Cervus elaphus* L.) in Scotland. *Terre et la vie* 1, 9–40.

Lowe, V.P.W. (1967) Observations on the dispersal of red deer on Rhum. In: Jewell, P.A. & Loizos, C., eds, *Play, territory and exploration in mammals.* Symp. Zool. Soc. Lond. 18. pp. 211–228.

McConnochie, A.I. (1923) *The deer and deer forests of Scotland.* Witherby, London.

Miles, J. & Kinnaird, J.W. (1971a) The establishment and regeneration of birch, juniper and Scots pine in the Scottish Highlands. *Scott. For.* 33, 102–119.

Miles, J. & Kinnaird, J.W. (1971b) Grazing with particular reference to birch, juniper and Scots pine in the Scottish Highlands. *Scott. For.* 33, 280–289.

Mitchell, B., Staines, B.W. & Welch, D. (1977) *Ecology of red deer: a research review relevant to their management in Scotland.* Institute of Terrestrial Ecology, Cambridge.

Mitchell, F.J.G. & Kirby, K.J. (1990) The impact of large herbivores on the conservation of semi-natural woods in the British uplands. *Forestry* 63(4), 333–353.

Nixon, C. & Cameron, E. (1994) A pilot study of the age structure and viability of the Mar Lodge pinewoods. *Scott. For.* 48, 22–27.

Red Deer Commission (1988) Annual Report. Appendix B. HMSO, Edinburgh. pp. 35–39.

Red Deer Commission (1991) Movements and distribution of red deer in the Cairngorms. Unpublished submission to the Cairngorms Working Party.

Ritchie, J. (1920) *The influence of man on animal life in Scotland.* Cambridge University Press.

Scottish Natural Heritage (1994) *Red deer and the natural heritage: SNH Policy Paper.* SNH, Edinburgh.

Scrope, W. (1839) *The art of deer stalking.* John Murray, London.

Staines, B.W. (1970) *The management and dispersion of a red deer population in Glen Dye, Kincardineshire.* Unpublished Ph.D. thesis, University of Aberdeen.

Staines, B.W. (1974) A review of factors affecting deer dispersion and their relevance to management. *Mammal Rev.* 4, 79–91.

Staines, B.W. (1977) Factors affecting the seasonal distribution of red deer (*Cervus elaphus*) at Glen Dye, north-east Scotland. *Ann. appl. Biol.* 87, 495–512.

Staines, B.W. (1978) The dynamics and performance of a declining populations of red deer (*Cervus elaphus*). *J. Zool. Lond.* 184, 403–419.

Staines, B.W. (1991) Factors affecting the distribution and abundance of red and roe deer in Great Britain. *Richerche di Biologia della Selvagginoi, Supplemento* 19, 237–251.

Staines, B.W. & Crisp, J.M. (1978) Observations on food quality in Scottish red deer (*Cervus elaphus*) as determined by chemical analyses of the rumen contents. *J. Zool. Lond.* 185, 253–259.

Staines, B.W. & Scott, D. (1994) *Recreation and red deer: a preliminary review of the issues.* Scottish Natural Heritage Review, no. 31. SNH. Edinburgh.

Staines, B.W. & Welch, D. (1989) An appraisal of deer damage in conifer plantations. In: McIntosh, R., ed., *Deer and forestry.* Institute of Chartered Foresters. Edinburgh. pp.61–76.

Staines, B.W., Balharry, R. & Welch, D. (1995) The impacts of red deer and their management on the natural heritage in the uplands. In: Thompson, D.B., Hester, A.J. & Usher, M.B., eds, *Heaths and Moorlands: Cultural Landscapes.* HMSO, Edinburgh.

Stewart, L.K. (1976) The Scottish red deer census. *Deer* 3, 529–532.

Stewart, L.K. (1990) Why? In: McCulloch, N.H., ed., *Deer Management Conference.* Red Deer Commission, Inverness. pp. 4–10.

Sydes, C. (1988) Recent assessments of moorland losses in Scotland. *CSD notes* 43. SNH, Edinburgh.

Watson, A. (1983) Eighteenth century deer numbers and pine regeneration near Braemar, Scotland. *Biol. Conserv.* 25, 289–305.

Watson, A. (1989) Land use, reduction of heather and natural tree regeneration on open upland. *ITE Annual Report 1988.* HMSO, London.

Watson, A. (1993) Defects of fencing for native woodlands. *Native Woodlands Discussion Group Newsletter Nov. 18,* 53–55.

Watson, A. & Staines, B.W. (1978) Differences in the quality of wintering areas used by male and female red deer (*Cervus elaphus*) in Aberdeenshire. *J. Zool. Lond.* 186, 544–550.

Whitehead, G.K. (1960) *The deer stalking grounds of Great Britain and Ireland.* Hollis & Carter, London.

Wiersema, G. (1974) *Observations on the supplementary winter feeding of red deer on an estate in the Central Highlands of Scotland.* Unpublished M.Sc. thesis, Agricultural University, Wageningen.

CHAPTER 12

Grouse and Moorland Management

P.J. HUDSON

INTRODUCTION

The Cairngorm high plateau is surrounded by large extensive areas of heather-dominant moorland, principally owned by private individuals with a major interest in the management and production of grouse shooting and deer stalking. Historically, interest in grouse shooting increased during the middle of the nineteenth century when Queen Victoria bought Balmoral Castle, making it fashionable to own and manage an upland sporting estate. The Cairngorms area in particular has been renowned for its sporting value, partly because of the experience of spending a day in the foothills of the Cairngorms, and partly because of the diversity of sporting opportunities available in the area provided by red grouse *Lagopus lagopus scoticus* (Plate 76), ptarmigan *Lagopus mutus*, black grouse *Tetrao tetrix*, capercaillie *Tetrao urogallus*, red deer *Cervus elaphus*, roe deer *Capreolus capreolus*, salmon *Salmo salar* and brown trout *Salmo trutta*.

There can be no doubt that the interest in the sporting aspects of the Cairngorms has influenced both the extent and nature of the vegetation and had consequences for the landscape. On the positive side, there has been sensitive management of the heather moorland resource, through burning coupled with grazing, to benefit moorland species. Estates have cared for large tracts of land and maintained the wilderness nature of the area while employing local people, attracting income and making a significant contribution to the economy (Hudson 1992, 1994). On the negative side, heather management has not encouraged woodland regeneration, some estates have built unsightly hill roads to assist management and there has been persecution of protected raptors.

This chapter examines aspects of the sporting interest in game birds, in particular the red grouse. Pheasants, partridges, ptarmigan, black grouse and capercaillie are also harvested and management of several of these species is of conservation interest, but the number harvested and revenue generated is relatively insignificant compared with red grouse.

METHODS AND DESCRIPTION OF SPORTING ESTATES IN THE CAIRNGORMS

The sporting estates referred to in this chapter all lie within the area identified by The Cairngorms Working Party. Generally, estate boundaries coincide with watersheds and rivers and most of these also correspond with the outlines of the Cairngorms area but with exceptions, notably on the south-eastern part of the area. As a rule, all those estates with a significant expanse of moorland within the Cairngorms area have been included, even if this was only a small proportion of a large estate.

Information on numbers of birds harvested and estate management policy regarding sheep stocking density, keeper employment and responsibility was obtained from postal surveys undertaken in 1983

139

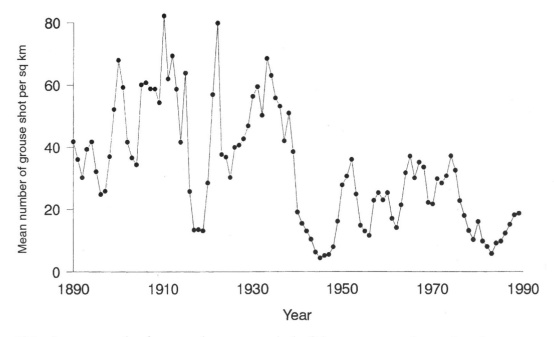

Figure 12.1   Average grouse bag for managed grouse moors in the Cairngorms expressed as numbers shot per square kilometre.

and again in 1989. Further environmental data such as underlying rock quality, temperature and weather conditions, along with environmental data such as heather production, heather mosaic and the presence of ticks and louping ill, were obtained during visits to the estates or from government offices as outlined by Hudson (1992).

A total of 74 sporting estates were identified and 63 responded with details although the amount of information varied between estates. A total of 46 estates provided details on many aspects and these represented a total of 2080 km² of managed sporting estate and averaged 45 km² in area.

HISTORICAL CHANGES IN RED GROUSE NUMBERS

The numbers of grouse shot each year from 1890 to 1990 have been obtained from 43 estates and expressed as mean numbers shot per square kilometre (Figure 12.1). The 100 years can be divided into three periods. Initially numbers of grouse shot between 1900 and 1940 were variable but ranged from 35 to 80 birds shot per square kilometre. In the second period, few birds were shot during both of the World Wars but following the second war, numbers failed to recover to former levels and remained between 15 and 40 birds per square kilometre. The third period covers the 1980s when numbers fluctuated, falling to a low density and then showing some recovery. These bag records are similar in many ways to the average grouse bags for the whole of Scotland (Hudson, 1992), but this is perhaps not surprising since the Cairngorms area includes a significant proportion of Scotland's grouse moors.

The pattern of grouse distribution between estates is far from uniform and there has been a tendency for a small proportion of the estates to shoot eight to ten times the number shot on other moors. Nevertheless, as numbers of grouse have fallen the pattern of grouse density, exhibited by bag records, has changed during the last 50 years with relatively few estates now shooting the large bags recorded during the 1930s (Figure 12.2).

HISTORICAL REVIEW OF GROUSE RESEARCH

The red grouse is probably one of the most studied birds in Britain and with a significant area of moorland around the Cairngorms it is hardly surprising that a large amount of work has been undertaken in this part of Scotland. While several authors have referred to changes in grouse numbers, the first scientific study was conducted by Edward Wilson and others under the chairmanship of Lord Lovat and The Committee of Inquiry on Grouse Disease, and produced one of the first detailed monographs on grouse; *The Grouse in Health and Disease* (Leslie, 1911).

Low numbers after the Second World War stimulated the Scottish Landowners Federation to initiate studies of red grouse. Research was started in 1956 under the direction of Professor Wynne Edwards of Aberdeen University, with David Jenkins, Adam Watson and Gordon Millar as the first field workers in what became in 1960 the Nature Conservancy's Unit of Grouse and Moorland Ecology. Later the Unit was incorporated into the Banchory Research Station which, in 1972, was transferred to the Natural Environment Research Council's Institute of Terrestrial Ecology. The work of the 'Grouse Unit' concentrated at first on two study areas in Glen Esk, moving from 1961 to Kerloch and later to

Plate 72
Red deer stag outside a deer fence. Note the dramatic difference in the grazed and protected areas.
Photo: Dick Balharry.

Plate 73
Red deer hinds and calves in open birchwood. Creag Meagaidh.
Photo: Dick Balharry.

Plate 74 *(below left)*
Ponies still provide cost-effective means of extracting deer carcasses.
Photo: Dick Balharry.

Plate 75 *(below right)*
Stags at winter feed – Luibeg.
Photo: Brian Staines.

Plate 76
Red grouse *(Lagopus lagopus scoticus)*.
Photo: Neil Cook.

Plate 77
Heather burning – recently burnt patches picked out by light snow. 1986.
Photo: Charles Gimingham.

Plate 78
Heather burning.
Photo: J. Parkin, Scottish Natural Heritage.

Plate 79
Fish traps on the Girnock Burn on upper Deeside in winter. The trap in the foreground catches adult salmon swimming upstream to spawn in the autumn. Beyond that is the smolt trap which catches juvenile salmon on their downstream migration to the sea. These traps are operated throughout the year by the Freshwater Laboratory of Fisheries Research Services.

Photo: David Hay.

Plate 80
Fish traps on the Baddoch Burn, a tributary of the Clunie Water, have also been operated by the Freshwater Laboratory, Fisheries Research Services, since 1989. The Baddoch Burn produces similar numbers of salmon smolts to the Girnock but they are older due to colder water temperatures that slow growth.

Photo: David Hay.

Plate 81
Adult salmon in the River Avon.

Photo: Ross Gardiner.

Plate 82
A sea trout in the River Avon.
Photo: Ross Gardiner.

Plate 83 *(centre left)*
A small pike in the River Spey.
Photo: Ross Gardiner.

Plate 84 *(centre right)*
A pair of adult sea lampreys
constructing a nest in the River Spey.
Photo: Ross Gardiner.

Plate 85
Arctic charr from Loch an
t' Seilich in Glen Tromie.

Photo: Peter Maitland.

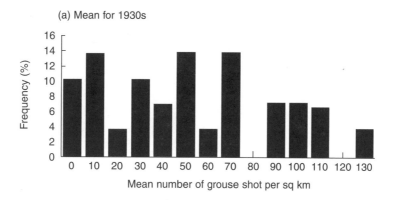

(a) Mean for 1930s

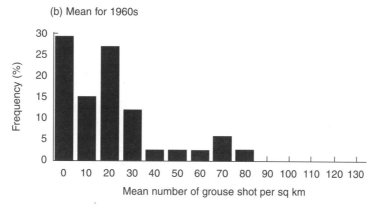

(b) Mean for 1960s

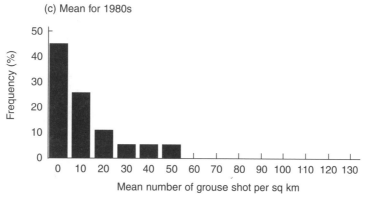

(c) Mean for 1980s

Figure 12.2   Frequency distribution of mean grouse bags for grouse moors in the Cairngorms during three decades. Note that the proportion of grouse moors shooting large numbers per square kilometre has decreased. Each bar represents range, i.e. 0 = 0–9; 10 = 10–19, etc.

Rickarton, both on the eastern fringe of the Grampian Mountains.

Correlations were demonstrated between heather management by burning (Plates 77, 78) and the number of grouse territories on a moor. This was interpreted on the basis that a territory normally has to include both young, short heather for feeding and taller, mature heather for shelter and nesting. This requirement is best met by a patchwork of small fires producing a fine-grained mosaic of heather of differing heights.

Population data collected by the Unit led its members to suggest that year to year changes in numbers (giving rise to cycles or longer-term trends) might be caused by spacing behaviour, while predation and parasitism had little significant effect (Jenkins, Watson & Miller, 1963). Adam Watson and Robert Moss investigated mechanisms that could generate changes in spacing behaviour,

in particular the levels of aggressiveness of males when establishing and maintaining territories. Following detailed studies, theories that maternal nutrition might have a role in determining the aggressiveness of the offspring, or that genetic changes might drive the changes in aggressiveness, were rejected (Moss & Watson, 1985). More recently, however, investigations have begun to examine the possible effects of kin selection (natural selection working on close relatives) leading to reduced aggression between related birds and changes in tolerance which could drive changes in aggression (Moss & Watson, 1991).

Intensive and extensive studies of the population biology of red grouse were also started in northern England by Peter Hudson of the Game Conservancy Trust in 1979. These indicated that parasites have a significant role to play in causing population cycles. Subsequent experiments and modelling demonstrated that parasites reduced the breeding production of grouse (Hudson, 1986a & b) and that the effects were sufficient to generate population cycles (Hudson, *et al.*, 1992; Dobson & Hudson, 1992; Hudson *et al.*, 1998). In 1986 Peter Hudson moved to Scotland and initiated similar studies centred on Strathspey, finding that unlike the earlier research in Glen Esk, territorial grouse were dying from predation. This predation was operating in an inverse density dependent manner, with high losses of grouse to predators at low densities (Hudson, 1992). More recently, Simon Thirgood and Steve Redpath have been investigating the interaction between raptors, grouse and other moorland prey in a detailed study based in the Scottish Borders, but with comparative study areas in the Cairngorms. Lawton (1990) provides an independent review of our understanding of grouse populations and their management.

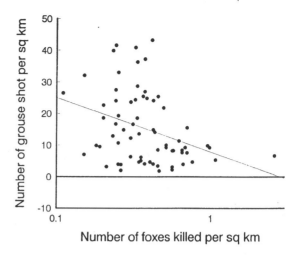

Figure 12.3 Relationship between numbers of grouse shot and number of foxes killed on a large estate within the Cairngorms area.

SPATIAL VARIATIONS IN NUMBERS OF RED GROUSE SHOT BETWEEN ESTATES

The size of the average grouse harvest will be influenced by a number of environmental and ecological factors including food quality, predation pressure and the prevalence and abundance of parasites. A study by Picozzi (1966) examined the variation in bag records of grouse between 26 estates in north-east Scotland and found 67 per cent of the variation in grouse bags could be accounted for through variation in the nutrient richness of underlying rock and heather management. While multiple regression techniques will never demonstrate a cause and effect relationship, these results implied that high grouse bags were associated with good habitat management on base-rich soils, and carried the implication that on any particular moor the primary aspect of grouse management should be to burn many small areas of heather moorland in a mosaic pattern.

A similar analysis was undertaken to determine if this kind of relationship also occurred within the Cairngorms during the 1980s. It used average numbers of grouse shot during that period and included a larger number of dependent variables, as summarized in Table 12a. The results from step-up multiple regression analysis showed that the only variable significantly associated with average bag records was the density of keepers on an estate: where more keepers were employed larger numbers of grouse were shot per square kilometre. Even so, this association accounted for only 20 per cent of the variation (F = 7.2235, degrees of freedom = 29, P = 0.0113). Surprisingly, neither underlying geological conditions nor heather mosaic ranking showed any association with average bag, as had been found in Picozzi's study. Moreover, keeper density did not appear to offer an alternative way of indicating heather burning pattern, since there was no correlation between keeper density and heather mosaic ranking (r = 0.020, P > 0.1). This may appear surprising since keepers have two principal tasks for grouse moor management, the control of

predators and the burning of heather (Plate 78). It might be expected that where there are more keepers there should be better burning practice, but this does not appear to follow. Perhaps the reason is to be found in the fact that the best burning practice is often achieved where temporary labour is employed specifically to assist keepers in burning. Well burnt moors are those where keepers are keen to produce a good mosaic of different aged heather stands (Plate 77) and are prepared to employ additional labour for this purpose. Hence there may be little relationship between density of keepers and heather mosaic.

Other than heather burning, keepers are employed to control foxes and crows. The fox in particular is a principal predator of grouse, that can be legally controlled. The implication is that a high density of keepers on an estate results in better fox control and consequently more grouse. Further evidence to support this comes from a positive association between keeper density and number of foxes killed per square kilometre between estates

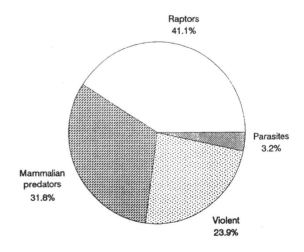

Figure 12.4 Causes of death of red grouse determined from corpses collected on study areas in the Cairngorms.

Table 12a **List of dependent variables used in the multiple regression for examining factors associated with variations in average grouse bag**

Variable	Description
Base richness	Estimated base richness of underlying rocks determined from maps of solid geology (see Picozzi, 1966, Hudson, 1992)
Altitude	Average height of moor above sea level
Area of moor	Area of heather moorland
June Temperature	Average daily June temperature from Met. Office
Days of snow cover	Average number of days of snow cover from Met. Office
Wetness	Average number of wet days (> 1 mm rain)
Heather productivity	Estimated from temperature and rainfall between April and August (see Hudson, 1992, for more details)
Heather mosaic ranking	Subjective assessment of heather burning pattern
Keeper density	Density of keepers on estate
Louping ill	Presence or absence
Sheep management	Sheep density and presence or absence of sheep in winter

(Hudson, 1992). However, there may be differences between estates since year to year variations in grouse bags on the southern part of the Cairngorms area showed an inverse relationship between foxes and grouse (Figure 12.3).

Radio tracking studies and the examination of corpses confirm that the ultimate cause of mortality in grouse within the region was predation (Figure 12.4). Other factors may predispose grouse to predation, such as territorial status (Watson, 1985) and parasites (Hudson, Dobson & Newborn, 1992), although these were found not to be important within the Cairngorm area (Hudson, 1992).

Given the information available, the current limiting factor on grouse within the Cairngorms region may well be predation and the control of predation by keepers. However it should be stressed again that this analysis does not show that employing more keepers would necessarily result in more grouse. Some other factor indirectly related to keeper density may be influencing grouse numbers. For example there is a weak positive correlation between keeper density and heather productivity ($r = 0.353$, $P < 0.1$), implying that more keepers are employed on estates where heather productivity is high. While heather productivity was not a significant variable included within the multiple regression, only a coarse measure of heather production was used, estimated indirectly from mean temperature and rainfall. Indeed more direct measurements of both heather production and predation could explain a greater proportion of the variation in the bag records.

A similar analysis undertaken by Hudson (1992) for mean bag records during the 1980s for the whole of Britain explained 70 per cent of the variation in numbers shot and included, in order of importance, June temperature, keeper density, heather mosaic ranking, heather productivity, altitude and base richness. Picozzi (1966) did not include a measure of predation within his early analyses, and if we exclude keeper density from the multiple regression in the 1980s analyses it is interesting to note that soil quality becomes the sole variable in the multiple regression even though it accounts for only 15 per cent of the variation in bag records ($F = 6.49$, $P = 0.015$).

TEMPORAL CHANGES AND POPULATION BIOLOGY OF RED GROUSE

Investigations of changes in numbers of red grouse and their breeding production have been undertaken in various parts of the Cairngorms area. A total of 11 study areas have been monitored for the past eight years, all based on managed grouse moors, with three in the north, two in the south, three in the west and three in the east of the Cairngorms. Each of these study areas consists of one square kilometre of heather moorland in which the total number of grouse are counted twice each year, once in spring to determine breeding density and again in July to determine breeding production, usually shown as the number of young grouse reared per hen. On three of these sites (all in the west) nests were sampled each spring to determine clutch size and hatching success, and to estimate (using the other population data) the ability of grouse to lay a full clutch of eggs, as well as egg mortality and chick losses.

Key factor analyses of these 11 study areas show that breeding losses were the demographic factor causing year to year changes in numbers of grouse on eight of the sites and winter losses on the remaining three. At the three sites where breeding production was monitored intensively, chick losses were identified as the key factor influencing the year to year changes in breeding production. Taken as a whole, these data imply that annual changes in numbers of grouse in the Cairngorms area are determined by variations in breeding production, and the demographic factor influencing variations in breeding production is chick survival.

INIMICAL FACTORS INFLUENCING CHICK PRODUCTION AND THEIR MANAGEMENT

In general, the analysis of available data indicates that differences in average grouse bags between estates are related to density of keepers, and such effects could operate through the control of predators. Within Cairngorm study areas, the year to year variations in grouse abundance are influenced by grouse breeding production and in particular chick losses. The inimical factors that could influence this chick mortality are considered here.

Louping ill. Louping ill is a disease of the central nervous system caused by a flavivirus and transmitted between hosts, principally grouse and sheep, by the sheep tick *Ixodes ricinus.* Mortality in red grouse is high, with 80 per cent of infected birds dying, but mortality of sheep is variable depending on breed and previous exposure to the virus. The virus requires the presence of the tick vector but not all tick populations are associated with Louping ill (further details in Hudson 1992). Within the Cairngorms area there are a few pockets of ticks and some Louping ill, particularly on the moorland areas along stretches of the Spey, especially around Grantown. On these moors the prevalence of antibody in young grouse can exceed 60 per cent in some years, representing a mortality amongst young grouse exceeding 90 per cent.

Active control of the disease can be tackled through three approaches. The first is to reduce the population of susceptible hosts available for the virus. Since mortality in grouse is high and sheep appear to be the only alternative reservoir, the size of the susceptible sheep population should be reduced and this could effectively be achieved through vaccination. Adult sheep should carry natural immunity reinforced by an annual challenge, and young lambs an immunity obtained through the ewes colostrum. Hence only the yearling sheep (hogs) appear susceptible and vaccination of them should lead to a reduction if not local extermination of the disease. Such actions have worked in some parts of Britain, notably parts of northern England, but have failed in parts of the Cairngorms. Current research is investigating the persistence of this disease and the routes through which the disease is maintained (Hudson *et al.,* 1995).

A second approach to controlling the disease is to eliminate the vector and prevent transmission between hosts, an approach similar to that used in the control of malaria. Adult ticks require a mammalian host to sustain the life cycle and only rarely are adult females seen on birds, so the tick population can be removed either by treating the mammals or removing them. Ticks can be killed on domestic stock through dipping and the application of pour-on treatments. The abundance of other large mammalian herbivores which may act as significant tick hosts, including red deer and mountain hares *Lepus timidus,* can be reduced or eliminated through shooting or fencing.

The third approach is to remove the coarse grass and bracken vegetation which produces a thick mat layer and a good overwintering habitat for the ticks. In northern England studies have shown that the removal of bracken can reduce the size of the tick population and the level of infection in red grouse (Hudson, 1985). Control of coarse grasses, such as purple moor-grass *Molinia caerulea,* may also be beneficial but large-scale control may be impossible and prove prohibitively expensive.

Caecal nematodes. A large proportion of red grouse is infected with the caecal nematode *Trichostrongylus tenuis.* When burdens are high, usually in excess of 3000 worms per bird, the condition of the hen grouse is reduced and breeding production impaired (Hudson, 1986b). The important point to note is that, unlike Louping ill, the parasitic worm does not cause direct damage to the chicks but reduces the ability of the female grouse to care for the chicks. Extensive monitoring and experimental studies have demonstrated the significance of this parasite to the population dynamics of grouse, causing dramatic decreases in the size of some grouse populations following heavy infections (Hudson *et al,* 1992, 1998). Rates of infection are greater following years of high grouse density, particularly in grouse populations on wet heaths where the damp conditions favour parasite transmission.

In most parts of the Cairngorms, grouse densities are relatively low and worm burdens tend not to increase to high levels. Nevertheless, several of the grouse moors on wet heath have experienced high worm burdens which have reduced chick survival. The impact of the parasitic worm can be reduced through two techniques, either direct dosing of adult grouse or the application of medicated grit. Direct dosing involves the capture of grouse during the winter months and the oral application of an anthelmintic to reduce worm burdens. Techniques for catching and treating grouse have been remarkably successful and at least 2 grouse moors close to the Cairngorms area regularly catch and treat in excess of 3000 grouse each winter. The second method is to apply medicated grit; grouse take natural quartz grit to store within their gizzards as an aid to digestion. Medicated grit is similar to the grit that is traditionally placed on the hill by keepers but coated with a fine layer of kernel fat incorporating an anthelmintic which, when taken as a split dose over several days, is highly effective against parasites. Field trials have confirmed the efficacy of both techniques (Hudson, 1992; Newborn *et al.,* 1994).

Predation. A number of predators are known to take young grouse chicks and can severely impair grouse breeding production. Crows *Corvus corone,* red foxes *Vulpes vulpes,* stoats *Mustella erminea* and hen harriers *Circus cyaneus* are all recorded as regular predators.

Comparative studies on Lewis where foxes and stoats are absent found a dramatic increase in the size of the grouse bag on estates that undertook rigorous crow control compared with estates that did not, suggesting that the removal of crows as egg and chick predators improved breeding production and bag size (Hudson, 1992). Observations have recorded foxes regularly returning to their dens with a 'ball of grouse chicks in their mouth' although foxes also take adult grouse throughout the year. Evidence suggests that foxes may well have a significant impact on grouse populations (Hudson, 1992). Numbers of foxes killed by keepers in Scotland have increased steadily and this together with other evidence suggests the fox population has increased. The cause of this is not clear although the increase has been in line with the recovery of the rabbit population after myxomatosis (Hudson, 1995).

Detailed radio tracking studies on broods of grouse in parts of Angus have recorded high losses with 45 per cent of broods being totally lost within the first five days of life, principally through stoat predation (Hudson, *et al.,* 1994). Much of this heavy predation was in areas with a large rabbit population, implying that the rabbits were sustaining a stoat population which was also having an impact on the survival of grouse. The role of rabbits as a food source supporting a population of generalist predators, both stoats and foxes, can have some important consequences for the grouse population, since the number of grouse taken seems to be relatively constant but the proportion of grouse lost from the population is greater when grouse densities are low. In such circumstances this can lead to a 'predation trap' with low grouse densities being suppressed further by the predation. The solution to this problem is first to control the predator population and secondly to reduce the alternative food source which appears to be rabbits.

Hen harriers regularly take grouse as part of their diet. Studies within the Scottish Highlands, including the Cairngorms area, have shown that young grouse constitute 32 per cent of the harriers' diet and managed grouse moors with breeding harriers produced on average 17 per cent fewer young grouse (Redpath, 1991). At the present time studies are being extended to investigate in a more extensive manner the numerical and functional response of harriers to moorland prey species and evaluate more accurately the effects of raptors on grouse populations (Redpath & Thirgood, 1997). While it is illegal to persecute birds of prey, there is evidence in the Scottish Highlands that persecution still occurs on managed grouse moors (Etheridge, 1993).

Chick food. Red grouse chicks eat invertebrates, mostly insects, during the first two to three weeks of life, providing a rich digestible protein diet that assists their growth to a point where they can live exclusively on heather. Experimental laboratory studies have demonstrated that grouse reared with abundant invertebrates grow faster and survive better than chicks reared on a diet of heather alone (Hudson, 1986a). Studies in the west of the Cairngorms area have found low chick growth and survival on some of the drier moors and this is associated with low abundance of invertebrates and few signs of invertebrate remains in the droppings of the broods (Hudson *et al.*, 1994). The evidence indicates that a lack of invertebrate food can be an important factor influencing the survival of grouse chicks but raises the question why invertebrate abundance appears to be low. Annual changes in invertebrate abundance in the uplands are associated with wetness but regular burning practices may reduce the organic content of the

peaty soil and reduce the suitability of the habitat for invertebrates.

Heavy grazing pressure reduces the biomass of vegetation so it seems likely that herbivores will have a direct impact on the herbivorous arthropods associated with the vegetation and thus may reduce the availability of food for grouse chicks. Extensive sampling of blaeberry *Vaccinium myrtillus* has shown that heavily grazed plots had only 28 per cent of the number of lepidopteran larvae that were found on ungrazed sites, although the biomass of the blaeberry was reduced only to 43 per cent by the heavy grazing (Baines, *et al.*, 1994). In other words, the grazing animals appear to have had a greater than expected impact on the lepidopteran larvae, which may have consequences for the availability of food for grouse. Such effects are also seen in heather-dominant moorland although the significance to the insect population requires further work.

Grouse broods frequently utilize wet bog flushes to obtain their invertebrate food (Hudson, 1986a), and in an attempt to provide additional invertebrates Hudson (1988) created an artificial bog flush which produced nearly four times the number of invertebrates. Whether such flushes are attractive to grouse and increase chick production is not known.

VARIATION IN NUMBERS OF OTHER GAME BIRDS

Other game birds occur within the Cairngorms area and while they are not as significant to estates in terms of income the area does carry a significant proportion of the British populations.

Capercaillie. Capercaillie were common and widespread throughout Scotland in the seventeenth century but numbers were greatly reduced at the end of the twentieth century. The last Scottish capercaillie was shot probably in 1785 in Deeside. Capercaillie were generally considered to be extinct in Scotland until Lord Breadalbane imported a number of birds in 1837 from Sweden and started a captive breeding programme to reintroduce them. Following a series of reintroductions, capercaillie became established throughout a large part of the remaining Scots pine forest which has an open canopy and a reasonable carpet of blaeberry. With increased afforestation by the Forestry Commission, populations were thought to have increased and spread, and indeed capercaillie were considered a pest species of young plantations. Numbers subsequently fell during the 1970s and the birds are now restricted to three principal areas along the Spey, the Dee and the Tay with smaller isolated populations in the central and southern Highlands.

The cause of the recent fall in capercaillie numbers is not fully understood, but a number of factors including wetter June periods, predation, loss of blaeberry through overgrazing, general habitat destruction and collisions with deer fences have all been highlighted. Management practices have included increased predator control, particularly foxes and crows, removal of deer fences and reduced grazing pressure by deer and sheep to encourage the regeneration of a suitable habitat. Nevertheless concern about the Scottish population will continue as the larger continental population continues to decline and the Scottish population is restricted to a few fragmented areas of forestry, with probably fewer than 2000 individuals.

Black grouse. As with the capercaillie, the population of black grouse has fallen, with a dramatic range reduction and a fall in numbers such that some of the best remaining populations of black grouse are now in Tayside (Baines & Hudson, 1995). The major factors influencing the decline of black grouse are probably similar to those affecting capercaillie, although loss of habitat has probably come about through agricultural intensification and the loss of habitat diversity on the edge of the moorland area where grazing pressures and burning practices have replaced the scrub with heather and bracken. Numbers of black grouse can increase locally when ground is planted for forestry but they vacate such areas when the forest trees form a canopy. Management priorities usually involve the reduction in grazing pressure and control of predatory foxes and crows.

Ptarmigan. Restricted to the Scottish Highlands, ptarmigan inhabit the mountain plateau and alpine habitats, with a large proportion of the British populations centred in the Cairngorms area. Originally numbers of ptarmigan were found further south in Wales, the Lake District, northern England and the Scottish borders, but the population has become restricted to the Scottish Highlands probably as a consequence of habitat destruction through heavy sheep grazing.

Annual changes in ptarmigan numbers are probably influenced by chick survival, which can be very low following periods of harsh summer weather or when invertebrate food is not available during the first two weeks of life. Mortality of adults is often caused by predation, principally by foxes but also by golden eagles. Clear management advice is not available but good fox control, the removal of litter, which may attract scavenging foxes and crows, and reduced grazing pressure can be considered beneficial.

CONCLUSIONS

Red grouse management is a significant form of land use in the Cairngorms area which has influenced the structure of the vegetation and its associated animal communities. Variations in numbers of red grouse between estates are associated with the level of keepering, such that apparently there are more grouse on areas where control of foxes and crows is better. Within estates, annual variations in red grouse numbers are influenced by chick survival, and the factors that influence this survival together with management prescriptions are discussed above. The Cairngorms present a diversity

of sporting interests and carry significant populations of the other British grouse species including capercaillie, black grouse and ptarmigan. All these species appear to have suffered from the direct loss of habitat, principally through overgrazing, but may also have suffered reduced breeding as a consequence of predation.

REFERENCES

Baines, D., Baines, M. M. & Sage, R. (1994) The importance of large herbivore management to woodland grouse and their habitats. In: Jenkins, D., ed., *Proceedings of the Sixth International Grouse Symposium*, Udine, Italy. pp. 93–100.

Baines, D. & Hudson, P.J. (1995) Changes in numbers of Black Grouse in Scotland. *Bird Study* **42**, 122–131.

Dobson, A.P. & Hudson, P.J. (1992) Regulation and stability of a free-living host-parasite system: *Trichostrongylus tenuis* in red grouse. II Population models. *J. Anim. Ecol.* **61**, 487–500.

Duncan, J. S., Reid, H. W., Moss, R., Phillips, J. D. & Watson, A. (1979) Ticks, louping ill and red grouse on moors in Speyside, Scotland (*Lagopus lagopus scoticus*). *J. Wild. Manag.* **43**, 500–505.

Etheridge, B. (1993) The Hen Harrier. In: Gibbons, D. W., Reid, J. B. & Chapman, R. A., *The new atlas of breeding birds in Britain and Ireland: 1988–1991*. Poyser, London.

Hudson, P. J. (1985) Bracken and ticks on grouse moors in northern England. In: Smith, R.T. & Taylor, J.A., eds, *Bracken: Ecology, land use and control technology*. Parthenon Publishing, Carnforth. pp. 161–170.

Hudson, P.J. (1986a) *The Red Grouse. The Biology and Management of a Wild Gamebird*. The Game Conservancy Trust, Fordingbridge.

Hudson, P.J. (1986b) The effects of a parasitic nematode on the breeding production of Red Grouse. *J. Anim. Ecol.* **55**, 85–92.

Hudson, P.J. (1988) Spatial variations, patterns and management options in upland bird communitites. In: Usher, M.B. & Thompson, D.B., eds, *Ecological change in the uplands*. Blackwell Science, Oxford. pp. 381–397.

Hudson, P. J. (1992) *Grouse in Space and Time*. Game Conservancy Trust, Fordingbridge.

Hudson, P.J. (1995) The future for grouse management in Scotland. In: Thompson, D.B.A., Hester, A.J. & Usher, M.B., eds, *Heaths and Moorlands: Cultural landscapes*. HMSO, Edinburgh. pp. 282–293.

Hudson, P.J., Booth, F., Hurley, M.M. & Howarth, D. (1994) Problems with red grouse chick survival. *Game Conservancy Annual Review* **25**, 120–122.

Hudson, P.J., Dobson A.P. & Newborn, D. (1992) Do parasites make prey vulnerable to predation? Red Grouse and parasites. *J.Anim.Ecol.* **61**, 681–692.

Hudson, P.J., Dobson, A.P. & Newborn, D. (1998) Prevention of population cycles by parasite removal. *Science* **282**, 2256–2258.

Hudson, P.J., Newborn D. & Dobson, A.P. (1992) Regulation and stability of a free-living host-parasite system: *Trichostrongylus tenuis* in Red Grouse. I. Monitoring and parasite reduction experiments. *J .Anim.Ecol.* **61**, 477–486.

Hudson, P.J., Norman, R., Laurenson, M.K., Newborn, D., Gaunt, M., Jones, L., Reid, H., Gould, E., Bowers, R. & Dobson, A. (1995) Resistance and transmission of tick-borne viruses: *Ixodes ricinus* and louping-ill virus in red grouse populations. *Parasitology* **111**, supplement, 49–59.

Jenkins, D., Watson, A. & Miller, G. R. (1963) Population studies on red grouse (*Lagopus lagopus scoticus*) in north-east Scotland. *J. Anim. Ecol.* **32**, 317–376.

Lawton, J. H. (1990) *Red grouse populations and moorland management*. British Ecological Society, Ecological issues No. 2. Field Studies Council.

Leslie, A.S., ed. (1911) *The Grouse in Health and Disease*. Committee of Enquiry on Grouse Disease, London.

Moss, R. & Watson, A. (1985) Adaptive value of spacing behaviour in population cycles of red grouse and other animals. In: Sibley, R.M. & Smith, R.H, eds, *Behavioural*

Ecology – Ecological Consequences of Adaptive Behaviour. pp. 275–294. Blackwell Science, Oxford.

Moss, R. & Watson, A. (1991) Population cycles and kin selection in red grouse *Lagopus lagopus scoticus. Ibis* **133,** Supplement I, 113–120.

Newborn, D., Hudson, P.J., Booth, F. & Howarth, D. (1994) Parasite control during 1993. *Game Conservancy Annual Review* **25,** 117–199.

Picozzi, N. (1966) Grouse management in relation to the management and geology of heather moors. *J. Appl. Ecol.* **5,** 483–488.

Redpath, S.M. (1991) The impact of hen harriers on red grouse breeding success. *J. Appl. Ecol.* **28,** 659–671.

Redpath, S.M. & Thirgood, S.J. (1997) *Birds of prey and red grouse.* HMSO, London.

Watson, A. (1985) Social class, socially induced loss, recruitment and breeding of red grouse. *Oecologia* **67,** 493–498.

147

CHAPTER 13
Fish Populations

R. Gardiner and D.W. Mackay

INTRODUCTION

The Cairngorms area (Cairngorms Working Party, 1993) has a complex radial drainage pattern which comprises headwaters of eight important Scottish east coast river systems, the Tay, Spey, Findhorn, Deveron, Don, Dee and North and South Esks (Figure 13.1). There is a substantial extent of high mountain which results in the area including many of the highest fresh waters in the UK. The sources and substantial lengths of the upper main rivers of the Spey and Dee systems are included, and these main rivers reach relatively large sizes within the area (Spey, 55 m width and Dee, 40 m width). There is a substantial network of tributaries (Figure 13.2) and many small lochs of which the largest is Loch Muick (220 ha in extent). Much of the area has slow-weathering rocks and well-leached shallow soils, and streams and lochs which are acid, nutrient-poor and sensitive to acid deposition. This is particularly true of the central granitic mountain core. There are also areas which overlie richer rocks, such as limestone and graphitic schist.

In British fresh waters there are 55 species of fish (Maitland & Campbell, 1992). These are mainly native species, but the total includes some which have been introduced from other countries. Of these, only 13 are present in the Cairngorms area (Table 13a). The low number reflects both the history of colonization and spread of species within Britain and the suitability of the habitat for particular species.

Some of the fish found in the Cairngorms area, namely the sea lamprey *Petromyzon marinus* L., the river lamprey *Lampetra fluviatilis* (L.)/brook lam-

prey *Lampetra planeri* (Bloch) pair, Atlantic salmon *Salmo salar* L., brown/sea trout *Salmo trutta* L., arctic charr *Salvelinus alpinus* (L.), eel *Anguilla anguilla* (L.) and three-spined stickleback *Gasterosteus aculeatus* L., were able to colonize Scottish fresh waters from the sea at the end of the last glacial. However, unlike the east coast of England, there were no suitable freshwater connections to allow colonization of Scottish fresh waters with wholly freshwater fish from the continent as the ice retreated. As a result there were initially species of fish in English fresh waters which were not present in Scotland (Wheeler, 1977). Since then, mainly because of deliberate or inadvertent transfers by man, there has been a steady and continuing spread of many of these purely freshwater species into Scotland (Maitland and Campbell, 1992), including pike *Esox lucius* L., minnow *Phoxinus phoxinus* (L.), stone loach *Barbatula barbatula* (L.) and perch *Perca fluviatilis* L. which are present in the Cairngorms area.

The rainbow trout *Onchorhynchus mykiss* (Walbaum) has also been introduced to a number of waters in the Cairngorms area, although it has not established any self-maintaining populations. This fish is a native of the Pacific coast of North America.

A number of general papers and articles on fish in the Cairngorms area, or the main rivers originating there, are already available, and these provided information useful in the preparation of the present chapter (Nethersole-Thompson & Watson, 1974; Jenkins & Bell, 1985; Maitland, 1987a; Shearer, 1988).

148

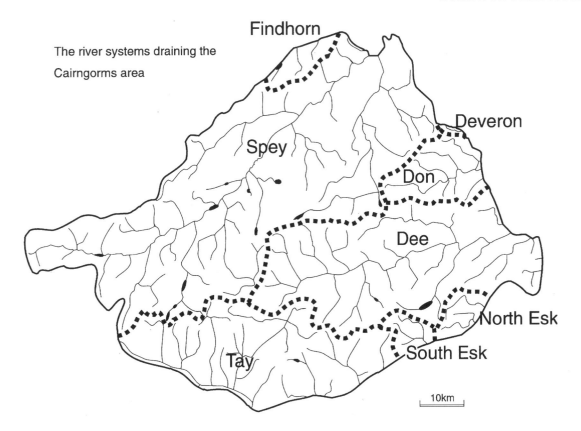

The river systems draining the
Cairngorms area

Figure 13.1

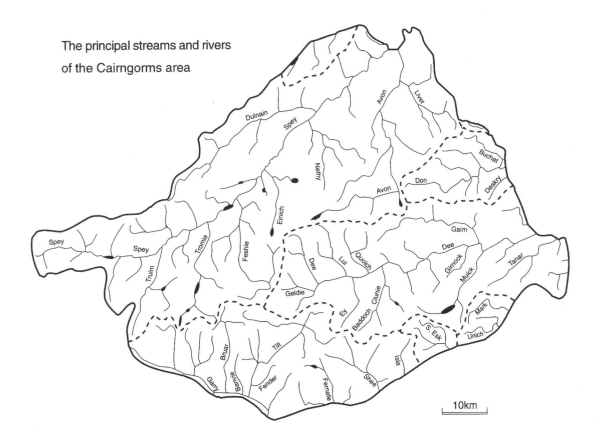

The principal streams and rivers
of the Cairngorms area

Figure 13.2

Table 13a   List of fish species found in the Cairngorms area

LAMPREYS Family Petromyzonidae

Sea lamprey *Petromyzon marinus* L.
River lamprey *Lampetra fluviatilis* (L.)
Brook lamprey *Lampetra planeri* (Bloch)

SALMON, TROUT and CHARR Family Salmonidae

Atlantic salmon *Salmo salar* L.
Brown/sea trout *Salmo trutta* L.
Rainbow trout *Onchorhynchus mykiss* (Walbaum)
Arctic charr *Salvelinus alpinus* (L.)

PIKE Family Esocidae

Pike *Esox lucius* L.

CARPS Family Cyprinidae

Minnow *Phoxinus phoxinus* (L.)

LOACHES Family Cobitidae

Stone loach *Barbatula barbatula* (L.)

EELS Family Anguillidae

Eel *Anguilla anguilla* (L.)

STICKLEBACKS Family Gasterosteidae

Three-spined stickleback *Gasterosteus aculeatus* L.

PERCH Family Percidae

Perch *Perca fluviatilis* L.

THE VARIOUS SPECIES

Sea lamprey. (Plate 84). This is the largest species of British lamprey with some adults reaching about 2 kg in weight and 1 m in length. It is fairly widespread in the mainstems of the larger rivers of the Scottish east coast, and in June and July there are runs of mature adults from the sea which spawn in the reaches of the Spey as far upstream as around Kingussie and the middle Dee between Ballater and Dinnet. At this time of year they are also sometimes seen in the lower pools of the fish ladder at Pitlochry Dam on the River Tummel. Spawning takes place in shallow pebbly or stony runs, often at the tail end of pools, in warm sunny weather when pairs of lampreys may be seen constructing large spawning pits by moving stones with the aid of their suckers. As with other lamprey species there is a larval stage of several years spent burrowed in areas with mud, silt or sand beds where the larvae feed on algae and detritus. The young sea lampreys then metamorphose into adult form and migrate to the sea where they use their sucking mouths to parasitize fish. Adult salmon entering rivers sometimes bear the distinctive scars of sea lamprey attacks.

The River Spey has been nominated as a candidate Special Area of Conservation for sea lampreys under the European Habitats and Species Directive.

River lamprey. This has a similar life history to the sea lamprey and is again fairly widespread in the rivers of the Scottish east coast, particularly in their lower reaches. The mature adults are smaller than those of the sea lamprey and commonly about 30 cm in length. Within the Cairngorms area it may occur in the River Spey.

Brook lamprey. This is a closely related species to the river lamprey but spends its entire life in fresh water. The adults are small, commonly about 12 to 16 cm in length, and do not feed. It may be a non-anadromous form of the river lamprey rather than a truly separate species, and it can be found in stretches of stream above waterfalls which would not be accessible to the river lamprey. It is common and widespread in the rivers and lower reaches of tributary streams in the Cairngorms area.

Atlantic salmon. (Plate 81). Salmon are common and widespread in all eight river systems draining the Cairngorms area, and adult salmon ascending from the sea reach the Cairngorms on each of these systems (Gardiner & Egglishaw, 1986). Spawning of salmon generally takes place in November and December and adult salmon can enter river systems either immediately before spawning or many months earlier, although they do not feed in fresh water. As is also often true of the upper catchments of large rivers, the rivers of the Cairngorms area are important spawning areas for the spring and early summer runs of salmon which mainly enter river systems in January to May. These are generally 2 sea winter salmon, 3 to 6 kg in weight, with some 3 sea winter salmon, 6 to over 12 kg in weight. There is also a run of 1 sea winter fish, 2 to 3 kg in weight, apparently destined for the same spawning areas, which enter the river systems in May to July. Electronic counters on some of the rivers give information on the number of salmon ascending.

Given suitable conditions, after entry to the Rivers Spey and Dee from the sea, salmon can press quickly upstream and enter certain tributaries (including the Rivers Avon, Feshie, Tromie and Truim, the Water of Tanar and the Clunie Burn) in late spring and early summer. However, more commonly salmon remain in the main stem until immediately before spawning. Radio-tracking studies on the Dee, Spey and Tay systems have elucidated many of the details of the upstream movement of adult fish. The radio-transmitters are small, and are inserted into the stomachs of the fish where they remain for many months. The fish are tracked from the bankside, and can also be followed from the air. Remote receiving stations can also be placed along the bank to time the passage of individual fish. By these techniques, salmon on the

150

Main spawning streams for Atlantic
salmon in the Cairngorms area

10km

Figure 13.3

River Dee, for example, were tracked for periods of up to nine months, from their time of entry, through spawning and their return downstream. Spring fish were tracked to spawning grounds in the Cairngorms area including the River Dee at Balmoral and Invercauld and the Rivers Gairn and Muick, while grilse which entered the River Dee in the autumn used spawning sites much lower on the river (Hawkins & Smith, 1986; Laughton, 1989, 1991; Webb, 1989, 1990; Webb & Hawkins, 1989).

Spawning of salmon takes place both in the main rivers and in the tributary streams. Satisfactory spawning areas for salmon are stable areas of pebbles and cobbles, relatively free from silt and fine sand, and in fast-flowing shallow water. In many small upland streams the availability of satisfactory spawning areas is not a factor which would be likely to limit the size of the populations. However, wash-out of eggs in flood events or mortalities during acid episodes may result in numbers of young fish below that which a stream would be expected to be able to accommodate, even where an otherwise sufficient number of adults has spawned.

The juvenile fish, or 'parr', spend several years in fresh water before migrating to sea, at which stage they are known as 'smolts'. In fresh water the young fish become imprinted with the scent of the water and this allows them to home relatively accurately as returning adults. In the Cairngorms area the main-stems and larger tributaries are often free from

major obstructions to the upstream movement of adult salmon but the side tributaries are steeper and frequently blocked by waterfalls. Even where smaller streams are not obstructed by waterfalls their shallowness often limits upstream movement, particularly in low flow conditions, with streams of less than two metres in width being rarely used by salmon. The main spawning streams for salmon are shown in Figure 13.3. In many of the streams juvenile salmon dominate the fish communities. In the Cairngorms altitudes of 450 to 500 m are commonly attained by adult salmon; less commonly they reach over 550 m, for example on the Rivers Avon and Feshie. These are among the highest altitudes reached by salmon in the UK although experimental stockings at altitudes of up to 900 m, carried out in the 1970s in the Cairngorms area by the Fisheries Research Services (FRS) Freshwater Laboratory (previously known as Freshwater Fisheries Laboratory), showed survival to be possible at higher altitudes.

The extent of stream accessible to spawning adult salmon and the streams' ability to provide food and shelter for the young fish often set the upper limit on the stock of salmon which a river can support. Since 1966, the FRS Freshwater Laboratory has carried out year-round trapping on the Girnock Burn (Plate 79), a tributary of the River Dee within the Cairngorms area, to investigate the relationship between the number of adult salmon spawning in the stream and the number of young salmon produced (Buck & Hay, 1984). This work showed that around 40 female salmon with evenly distributed spawning sites would produce close to the maximum number of smolts which the stream is capable of producing. A number of other studies have been carried out at this important field site. These have included investigations into the territoriality and physiology of the juveniles, the spawning behaviour of adults and the contribution to spawning made by mature male parr and the role of genetics in the growth and survival of the juveniles (Buck & Youngson, 1982; Huntingford *et al.*, 1992; Jordan & Youngson, 1991; Youngson *et al.*, 1983; Armstrong & West, 1994). Since 1989 experimental traps have also been operated by the Freshwater Fisheries Laboratory on another upper Dee tributary within the Cairngorms area, the Baddoch Burn (Plate 80).

In recent years electrofishing survey work to investigate distribution and densities of juveniles has been carried out within the Cairngorms area on the Rivers Spey, Don, Dee and Tay by the biologists of the District Salmon Fishery Boards and FRS Freshwater Laboratory. These surveys have concentrated on smaller streams and confirmed that those which support the highest densities of young salmon have good accessibility to spawning adult salmon, fairly fast to fast current speeds (0.5 to 0.8 ms^{-1}) and many riffles with a varied bed of pebbles, cobbles and boulders.

Because of difficulties of sampling, less is known about the juvenile populations of larger rivers which constitute much of the potential nursery area. Efforts to fill this gap in our knowledge are currently being made by FRS Freshwater Laboratory and these are confirming the major importance of the large rivers as smolt producers.

The growth rate of young salmon has been shown to depend on water temperature during the growing season, their density and the food supply. The food supply is closely related to surface geological conditions and land use. In the Dee catchment Shackley and Donaghy (1992) found that 80 per cent of the variation in growth rates of juvenile salmon between sites can be accounted for by altitude and stream alkalinity. The growth rate is important in determining how many years the young fish need to spend in fresh water before they migrate to sea as smolts. Within the Cairngorms area this ranges from two to four years with the young fish typically spending three or four years in the highest streams and two to three years elsewhere.

As has already been noted there is a considerable extent of stream which, because of waterfalls, is inaccessible to adult salmon, or accessible only with difficulty. Efforts have been made to increase stocks by bringing these areas into use by improving accessibility, or by stocking. On the River Ericht (Tay) the improvements to adult accessibility have been particularly successful and the river now supports a large run of salmon. As the Cairngorms area is a stronghold for stocks of valued runs of spring salmon, which are presently at a low level as a result mainly of high levels of natural marine mortality, it

seems likely that efforts will continue to be made to maintain or increase stocks there. The tendency for spring-running in these upper catchment stocks is likely to have a strong genetic component and there is a growing awareness that any stocking aimed at enhancing spring runs will require appropriate material.

The River Spey has been nominated as a candidate Special Area of Conservation for Atlantic salmon under the European Habitats and Species Directive, and consideration is also being given to nominating the Rivers Tay and Dee.

Brown/sea trout (Plate 82). There is a wide variety of forms of trout differing in appearance, average size and migratory tendencies. Some trout spend their entire life in one short stretch of stream and may only reach 20 cm in length in a life span of 6 or 7 years. At the other extreme are sea trout with a life history similar to that of the salmon in that much of the adult phase takes place at sea where rapid growth is possible and fish of about 45 cm in length are typical. Intermediate in migratory tendency are the river and loch trout which migrate to tributary streams to spawn.

The trout is the most widespread fish species in the Cairngorms area, found more or less in every stream and loch up to an altitude of about 450 m and commonly above this. In Scotland brown trout populations are frequently found in streams and lochs which lie above high waterfalls and are now isolated. Introductions by man to some of these waters seem likely. In addition, genetics work based on protein analysis indicates that some trout populations isolated above waterfalls may be based on an ancestral stock which was able to colonize waters immediately following the last glacial but later displaced by a new stock except in waters which were no longer accessible (Hamilton *et al.*, 1989; Stephen, 1984; Stephen & McAndrew, 1990).

Trout were previously reported to be present in Loch Etchachan (935 m altitude) and Loch nan Stuirteag (865 m) (Gordon, 1925) but no trout was found in either loch in a survey of 12 headwater lochs in the Cairngorms area carried out in 1983–1985 (Morrison & Harriman, 1992). It is not known whether the trout reported by Gordon were self-maintaining populations or the result of recent stockings. A dense population of small trout was found in the Dubh Lochainn of Beinn a' Bhuird, at 843 m, by Campbell (1970) and this may well be the highest altitude in the British Isles where there is currently an established population of fish. In these high lochs complete ice cover regularly lasts from January to April and the climatic conditions are the harshest experienced by any lochs in the British Isles. In Morrison and Harriman's survey the feeding by trout in some of the lochs was investigated. They found terrestrial insects to be important, which they attributed to the limited availability of aquatic food.

In lochs, where there is little in the way of stream to provide spawning and early nursery areas, the population frequently consists of small numbers of

Table 13b   Lochs containing Arctic charr in the Cairngorms area

Loch Insh (Spey)	Loch an t-Seilich (Spey)
Loch Cuaich (Spey)	Loch Einich (Spey)
Loch an Duin (Spey)	Loch Builg (Spey)
Loch Bhrodainn (Spey)	Loch Loch (Tay)

Information provided by Dr Peter Maitland
There may also be a charr population in Loch Avon (Spey)

relatively fast growing fish (Campbell, 1970). Some successful spawning is also possible on the stony littoral zones of high, cold lochs as has been reported by Morrison and Harriman (1992) in the case of Loch a' Bhanain, and this may allow larger populations to be present than would be expected. Conversely, where abundant suitable stream is available, dense populations of relatively slow-growing fish arise. In larger lochs some individuals ('Ferox' trout) may switch to a diet of charr and small troutwhich results in faster growth and a much larger size being attained.

Trout on spawning runs can penetrate very small tributary streams and these are frequently the preferred spawning and early rearing areas for river, loch and sea trout. Indeed many of the larger streams and rivers favoured by salmon have beds consisting mainly of large cobbles and boulders where smaller trout cannot satisfactorily spawn.

Trout show a preference for pools and runs of moderate depth, and cover provided by undercut banks, tree roots and overhanging vegetation is important. Numbers of larger trout are generally low where there is little water with these favourable characteristics.

Rainbow trout.   This easily reared fish has been introduced as a sport-fish to a number of lochs in the Cairngorms area, mainly in Strathspey, but has not established any self-maintaining populations, and their presence depends on continued introductions of reared fish and escapes from fish farms.

Arctic charr (Plate 85).   In the British Isles this attractive fish is mainly found in large, deep oligotrophic lakes. Although these waters would have been originally colonized from the sea there are no anadromous populations in Britain. The charr has been lost from a number of British waters and is

nationally and internationally considered threatened and in need of conservation (Maitland & Lyle, 1991). Dr Peter Maitland of the Fish Conservation Centre maintains an inventory of British waters containing charr. This shows the Scottish Highlands to be a stronghold for the species. Of about 200 recorded populations in the British Isles, 167 are in Scotland, mainly in the Scottish Highlands, with eight in the Cairngorms area (details in Table 13b). There are several others on the periphery of the Cairngorms area, including Lochs Roy and Laggan (Lochy); Loch Lee (North Esk); and Lochs Garry, Ericht, Rannoch and Tummel (Tay). The population in Loch Tummel has only recently been discovered (Dr Andy Walker, pers comm).

Arctic charr are characterized by a high degree of variability in body form and feeding ecology. Often more than one form (or 'morph') occurs in the same loch. Recent work on the charr of Loch Rannoch, which lies a little outwith the Cairngorms area, indicates that both genetic and environmental controls are involved in the development of morphs. Charr commonly feed in mid-water on zooplankton but there are morphs with heavier jaws and larger heads specializing on bottom-living animals.

Frequently there are abundant populations of small charr which grow only to about 150 g, but in Loch Insh they grow faster and individuals over 1 kg in weight are not uncommon. Unlike trout and salmon, spawning generally takes place along the loch shores. However, at least some of the charr of Loch Insh spawn in inflowing streams.

Pike (Plate 83).   The pike is a large, fast-growing predatory fish which is found in many lochs and sluggish reaches of some rivers in the Cairngorms area (Table 13c). Capable of short attacking bursts of speed, they are well camouflaged underwater to allow them to wait for other fish to pass close by. The pike of Lochs Davan, Kinord and Callater have been studied in some detail, including investigations into their feeding, growth rate and population sizes (Treasurer, 1990; Treasurer *et al.*, 1992; Treasurer, 1998) and foraging behaviour (Lucas *et al.*, 1991). Laughton (pers comm) has recently been carrying out some investigations on Speyside pike, partly in connection with a wider survey of Insh Marshes lochans (Breslin, 1993). The food items taken by Loch Insh pike included invertebrates, trout, charr

Table 13c   Waters containing pike in the Cairngorms area

Lochs Garten and Mallachie (Spey)	Loch Crunachdan (Spey)
Loch Pityoulish (Spey)	Loch Coaldair (Spey)
Loch Morlich (Spey)	River Spey, from Spey Dam downstream (Spey)
Loch Alvie (Spey)	Loch Callater (Dee)
Loch an Eilean (Spey)	Loch Davan (Dee)
Loch Insh and the Insh Marshes Lochans (Spey)	Loch Kinord (Dee)
Loch Gynach (Spey)	River Dee, from Mar Lodge downstream (Dee)
Loch Etteridge (Spey)	River Garry, from Killiecrankie downstream (Tay)
Lochan Uvie (Spey)	
Spey Dam Reservoir (Spey)	

Information for pike distribution on Speyside provided by Bob Laughton, Spey District Salmon Fishery Board.

and salmon smolts. The invertebrates were mainly in the smaller pike. A small sample of pike from Lochan Dubh Mor indicated that many of the pike there were cannibalistic with a diet of smaller pike, although small birds had also been taken.

Minnow. Minnows are found in a number of streams and rivers in the area including the mainstems of the Dee and Spey and the River Garry. In summer large shoals may often be seen. Minnnows also occur in some of the lochs.

Stone loach. This is present in the River Garry and the lower reaches of some of its tributaries.

Eel. This easily recognized fish is one of the most widespread fish species in the Cairngorms area, but only in the mainstems and in easily accessible tributaries and lochs of the Dee and Spey are they present in large numbers.

Spawning of eels takes place on the other side of the Atlantic in the Sargasso Sea. On their arrival in fresh water the youngest eels, 6 to 7 cm in length, known as elvers, are generally limited to the lower reaches of rivers. Progressive upstream movement of many of the eels takes place as they grow and this results in the eels found inland being older and larger than those further downstream. Eels require warm water to grow quickly. They are therefore generally slow-growing in Scotland and can be long-lived. Williamson (1977) showed that eels in Loch Insh took approximately 25 years to reach a length of 50 cm and 28 years in Loch Pityoulish. There was one exceptionally old eel (48 years, length 87 cm) in the Pityoulish sample. However, the return of eels to the sea as 'silver eels' generally takes place at an earlier age.

Throughout the British Isles, and elsewhere in Europe, elver runs into rivers have declined over the last few decades. It is not known what effect this has had on population sizes of larger eels. Some eels penetrate remarkably far into catchments and Nethersole-Thompson and Watson (1974) mention eels having been caught in the Lochnagar loch at 785 m above sea level and in July 2001 an eel was caught in the same loch during work by FRS Freshwater Laboratory (Peter Collen, pers comm). However, where eels moving upstream find access difficult the numbers found are low. In extensive survey work by FRS Freshwater Laboratory, few eels were found in the River Garry and its tributaries, although they were abundant downstream in the River Tummel. This difference may be the result of the fish pass at Pitlochry Dam being difficult for eels, particularly small ones, to negotiate.

Three-spined stickleback. Within the Cairngorms area sticklebacks are widespread in the Rivers Dee, Garry, Spey and Don and in the lower reaches of tributary streams and in associated lochs.

Perch. This distinctive fish is found at Lochs Kinord and Davan on Deeside and at the Castle Loch at Blair Atholl. It is also found in the deeper pools in the River Garry at Killiecrankie. Just outwith the Cairngorms area, there are perch, populations in Lochs Tummel and Faskally, and in the river connecting these lochs.

All stages of the life cycle of perch (eggs, larvae, juveniles, adults) have been examined closely in Lochs Kinord and Davan. Mortality of the young stages was high owing to cannibalism by adults on larvae, and predation by pike and adult perch on juveniles. However, the mortality rate of perch older than three years was low and perch of up to 17 years old were found. Growth rates were relatively high as a consequence of low stock abundance (Treasurer, 1983, 1989; Treasurer *et al.*, 1992). Recently, Carss (1993) has reported a drop in the numbers of large perch in the lochs, apparently as a result of predation by ospreys.

Grayling (*Thymallus thymallus* (L.)). Although not included in Table 13a, the grayling occurs just outwith the Cairngorms area in the River Tummel, downstream of Pitlochry Dam, having been introduced to the Tay system in the nineteenth century (Gardiner 1992). Since 1996, a few grayling have been caught by anglers fishing above Pitlochry Dam in Loch Faskally and the lower reaches of the River Garry at Killiecrankie. It is not known whether these fish have resulted from grayling managing to ascend the fish pass at the dam, or whether they are the result of an unauthorized stocking. Nor is it known whether a population will establish itself successfully above Pitlochry Dam.

FISHERIES

Within the Cairngorms area there are important sport fisheries for salmon and trout. The rights to fish for salmon on a water are heritable rights, which originally belonged to the Crown, but are now generally in other hands. They may be bought or sold or leased to a tenant. Generally the salmon fishings are divided into short 'beats', sometimes with a 'ghillie' to attend the fishermen. All river systems draining the Cairngorms area have District Salmon Fishery Boards which are responsible for ensuring adherence to statutory requirements and for local management (see Williamson, 1991).

Salmon fishing is carried out on all eight river systems which drain the Cairngorms area, although not necessarily within the area itself. The homing of salmon to the locality they had left as juveniles means that while the lower beats benefit from runs of salmon destined for upper catchments, the converse is not true. The spring runs of salmon destined for the upper catchment complement the summer and autumn runs destined for the middle and lower catchments and often result in the lower beats having productive fishing over a greater part of the season. The River Dee is particularly noted as a spring salmon river, and is a major contributor to the total Scottish spring salmon catch. In recent years catches have provided evidence of a general decline in numbers of spring salmon in the rivers of the

Scottish east coast (see, for example, Spey District Fishery Board, 1991; Laughton & Smith, 1993).

Within the Cairngorms area there are productive salmon beats on a long stretch of the River Dee and on the River Spey, notably from Grantown-on-Spey downstream. There is also salmon fishing on the Rivers Avon, Feshie and other Spey tributaries; on the Rivers Garry and Tilt and Shee Water; and on the River Don. Mills and Graesser (1992) give a detailed description of many of these waters.

The sea trout fishing rights are tied to the salmon rights. The River Avon and the stretches of the River Spey at Grantown-on-Spey and the River Dee at Dinnet are noted for their sea trout fishing.

Fishing for brown trout takes place both on the lochs containing trout and on some stretches of the rivers. The reaches of the River Spey around Kingussie, the upper reaches of the River Don and, on the periphery of the Cairngorms area, the River Tummel, are noted for their good trout fishing. The brown trout fishing rights belong to the owner of the adjoining land but are often leased to local angling associations or other tenants. Much of the Cairngorms area is included in the areas covered by the River Tummel Catchment Area, Upper Spey and Associated Waters and River Don Catchment Area (Part) Protection Orders which make fishing for brown trout or other freshwater fish without permission a criminal offence.

Some rod and line fishing for pike, perch and eels takes place and there is also fishing on waters stocked with rainbow trout. Charr are also taken, generally as a by-catch by trout fishermen. In the River Tummel downstream of Pitlochry Dam rod-and-line fishing for grayling is popular in the winter.

There was some commercial fishing for eels on Loch Insh using fyke-net in the 1980s and, in the more distant past, on Lochs Davan and Kinord, but the authors know of no commercial eel fishing being carried out at present within the Cairngorms area. In the past, there has also been gill-netting of pike on some lochs in Speyside in an effort to benefit the trout populations. There may be some potential for increased exploitation of some of these species (see, for example, Greer, 1984).

IMPORTANCE IN THE FOOD WEB

The populations of fish provide food for various species of predators present in the area, including otters, mergansers, goosanders, herons and ospreys, some of which are considered of national and international conservation value. Detailed studies on the feeding and ecology of these predators are being carried out on mid-Deeside and on the River Don by the Institute of Terrestrial Ecology (Jenkins, 1980; Jenkins & Harper, 1980; Jenkins & Burrows, 1980; Carss et al., 1990; Kruuk, 1990; Marquiss, 1988; Marquiss & Feltham, 1991; Kruuk et al., 1992; Carss, 1993). The studies on the predation of adult salmon by otters around spawning time on some tributaries of the River Dee are of particular interest. It was found that most of the fish taken were males, perhaps because their extensive excursions up and down stream made them vulnerable. As such the predation would be less likely to have an impact on breeding success than if more of the fish taken had been females.

THREATS TO THE POPULATIONS

The many threats to freshwater fish populations include damage to spawning or rearing habitat by acidification, forestry, land use, industrial and domestic pollution and hydro-electric developments; loss of access to spawning or rearing habitat; competitor or predator species; and overfishing. With migratory fish, stock levels within the Cairngorms area may, of course, also be affected by impacts outwith the area itself, either downstream, or in the sea, but these are not considered in detail in the present chapter.

Acidification. The poorly buffered catchments of parts of the Cairngorms area have a limited capacity to cope with acid deposition arising from major air pollution sources far from the area, which produce acid sulphur and nitrogen compounds from the burning of fossil fuels. The areas most at risk are those with thin base-poor soils on granitic geology. Jones et al. (1993) have obtained palaeolimnological evidence of acidification over the last century of several Cairngorms lochs. However, these lochs were less affected than those overlying similar geology in south-west Scotland.

In base-poor catchments high rainfall, particularly when combined with snow-melt, can result in low pH episodes in streams and rivers draining the catchments. These episodes can cause mortalities of young salmon and trout with salmon being slightly more sensitive than trout. These can kill salmon and trout at hatching and at smolting, which are particularly sensitive stages. The episodes may also be associated with mobilization of toxic aluminium compounds.

In streams with acid episodes, losses of fish may be sufficiently large to keep numbers habitually low or result in extinction. However, a detailed study on the Allt a' Mharcaidh, a tributary of the River Feshie, has shown that streams which are less severely affected may still produce sufficient older juveniles to populate a stream satisfactorily, even though losses at hatching and in the first summer due to acid episodes can be demonstrated (Harriman et al., 1990).

In those parts of the Cairngorms area which are at risk, a lack of historical information on the state of the populations makes it difficult to say how much damage has occurred. Morrison and Harriman (1992) found trout to be absent from lochs at very high altitude (900 to 1000 m) where conditions for spawning and feeding were very poor, but this was not necessarily connected with acidification. Trout were present in lochs at lower altitude even where no spawning streams were available and the pH of the water was sometimes below 5. However, they suggested, on the basis of the water chemistry, that the fish populations in poorly buffered waters in the Cairngorms area would be at risk if acidification progressed further.

It is reported that very few adult salmon now penetrate the upper reaches of the River Dee above the mouth of the Geldie Burn at 405 m above sea level, and this was borne out in survey work by Shackley and Donaghy (1992) when only two salmon parr were found at a site 1 km upstream of the junction with the Geldie Burn. There is evidence of these upper reaches of the Dee being much more heavily used in the past. Gordon (1925) mentioned the many salmon which congregated during summer months in a deep pool (Pol Iasg, the Fish Pool) where the Geusachan Burn meets the River Dee 8 km above the mouth of the Geldie at 495 m above sea level, and noted the Geusachan's importance as a spawning area for salmon, with large hauls made by poachers in past years. Similarly, on the upper River Avon few, if any, salmon now reach Faindouran at 585 m above sea level, although in the past they penetrated as far as the Fords of Avon, 6 km further upstream at 685 m above sea level (John Macdonald, pers comm). The upper stretches of both the Rivers Dee and Avon are very poorly buffered and acidification may well be one factor involved, although physical deterioration of habitat (see p. 155) and a decline in strength of the spring runs which use these upper catchments are also possible factors.

Forestry. The effects of forestry on water quality, habitat and fish stocks are complex and therefore difficult to predict. Acidification of streams is likely to be increased by afforestation to a greater or lesser extent depending on the species of trees planted. Drainage and road building operations, unless carried out precisely in accordance with the Forest and Water Guidelines (Forestry Authority, 1993) can result in large quantities of sediment being carried into streams by erosion. In the past dense planting of conifers right up to the edge of streams frequently caused dense shading which prevents the growth of bankside vegetation and again results in erosion and sedimentation. Sediment, especially at times of low flow, can blanket the stream bed and destroy the benthic fauna and young stages of salmonid fish. On the positive side, more modest numbers of bankside trees (especially deciduous trees) can encourage and promote healthy fish stocks. They give some shade and contribute to the food supply for fish, both directly in the form of insects dropping into the water and indirectly through shed leaves providing nourishment for benthic fauna. Bankside trees also provide refuge from predators among their exposed roots and contain the streams within their channels in the form of pools and runs, ideal for a mixed salmonid community.

The use of fertilizers and pesticides on forests inevitably leads to some loss to the aquatic environment. While the amounts involved may be quite small the impact on highly sensitive waters may be severe. Extraction of mature timber can also lead to substantial damage to stream habitats and fisheries if logs are dragged or transported across river channels.

Land use. Particularly at higher altitudes, the vegetation cover protecting the shallow, easily eroded soils of much of the central core of the area is readily damaged and slow to re-establish as a result of low nutrient levels, low temperatures, high exposure to wind and well-leached shallow soils. Pressures include over-grazing by deer and sheep, badly controlled heather burning, damage from walkers and skiers and the construction of hill tracks (Curry-Lindahl *et al.*, 1982). Once the vegetation cover is broken the exposed surface can act as a centre for subsequent erosional activity. Ballentyne (1991) reported abundant evidence in the Scottish Highlands for accelerated erosion over the past few centuries which he suggested might reflect climatic deterioration or human interference through burning or overgrazing of vegetation. Such damage results in coarse granitic sand accumulating in streams and rivers, infilling the spaces between larger bed material. This reduces cover for fish and the areas affected may be prone to egg washout. With finer material, clogging and compaction of the bed may occur, again with deleterious effects on spawning areas. Although many rivers in the central core of the Cairngorms area are apparently affected it is not known to what extent this is a recent phenomenon.

Some of the more low-lying streams in the area have been straightened as part of land drainage works and these activities frequently result in damage to salmonid spawning and rearing areas from which recovery is slow, although there may be the possibility of restoration work to aid recovery.

Industrial and domestic pollution. The sources of domestic and industrial wastes discharged to the rivers within the Cairngorms area are relatively few with none of them making a major impact on the quality of the receiving waters. The North of Scotland Water Authority operates waste water treatment plants at Dalwhinnie, Newtonmore and Kingussie which discharge to the River Spey prior to it flowing through the Insh Marshes Site of Special Scientific Interest and Royal Society for the Protection of Birds reserve.

Low nutrient concentrations in the River Spey are important in maintaining the Insh marshes as one of the few oligotrophic marsh systems in Britain. The Scottish Environment Protection Agency is currently evaluating the results of a major research project to determine whether nutrients released from waste treatment plants should be reduced to preserve the sensitive aquatic environment.

New or upgraded sewage treatment plants have been or are under construction at Aviemore, Kincraig and Cromdale (River Spey), and Carrbridge and Dulnain Bridge on the River Dulnain. Privately operated sewage treatment plants serve the skiing and outdoor pursuit areas of Cairn Gorm and Glenmore. Generally speaking these package plants produce satisfactory effluents. Industry in the form of distilleries, fish farms, forestry and farming causes minor pollution

Plate 86
The wild landscape of the northern corries of the
Cairngorms.
Photo: Roy Dennis.

Plate 87 *(centre right)*
The summit of Lochnagar, Christmas 1991 – a popular
good-weather destination even in winter.
Photo: Charles Gimingham.

Plate 88 *(below)*
Snow fences and tows at the Glenn Shee ski development,
as seen from the Cairnwell, August 1982.
Photo: Charles Gimingham.

Plate 93 *(above left)*
Tackling a snow slope - the
Black Spout, Lochnagar,
26 March 1910.

Photo: the Cairngorm Club.

Plate 94 *(above right)*
Members of the Cairngorm
Club on skis, Loch Avon,
15 March 1908.

Photo: the Cairngorm Club.

Plate 95 *(centre)*
Pine-clad lake, forest, moor
and hills - the essence of
Cairngorm conservation.
October 1993.

Photo: Neil MacKenzie.

Plate 96
A remnant of native Scots
pinewood - Derry Wood and
Luibeg Wood, Mar Lodge
Estate, July 1982.

Photo: Mike Matthew.

Plate 97
The northern slopes of the Cairngorm massif - zonation through forest to moorland and high plateau with Loch Morlich in the foreground, September 1982.

Photo: Mike Matthew.

Plate 98
The bed of the Luibeg Burn draining the high ground - left, Ben Macdui; right, Derry Cairngorm - July 1966.

Photo: Mike Matthew.

Plate 99
Open birchwood, heather and bracken - Muir of Dinnet National Nature Reserve, September 1983.

Photo: Charles Gimingham.

problems from time to time but has had no major long-term effect on the generally high quality of the waters in the area. Constant vigilance is required because the very purity of the waters in the area makes them sensitive to what in other areas might be considered trivial increases or changes in polluting pressure from organic wastes, nutrients, pesticides and eroded soils.

Hydro-electric developments. British Alcan abstracts water for hydro-electric purposes from the upper River Spey at Spey Dam, and Scottish and Southern Energy's Tummel-Garry scheme involves the whole Tummel catchment from Pitlochry Dam, and several Spey tributaries, the Rivers Truim and Tromie, Tromie and Allt Cuaich. Although there is extensive provision of fish passes and screens at dams and take-offs, there are a number of effects on the fish populations. For example, salmon are prevented from reaching previously available spawning areas on the upper River Garry and the Allt Cuaich, and there was flooding out of some of the spawning areas on the Rivers Tummel and Spey by Pitlochry and Spey Dams. On the River Tummel, spring salmon reaching Pitlochry Dam in the early months of the year are not able to ascend the ladder until the water temperature reaches about 6°C. On the other hand the flooded out areas have created new habitat for trout, perch and pike, although of concern is the damage caused by varying water levels to littoral zones of lochs used as impoundments.

To compensate for possible damage to salmon stocks caused by hydro-electric development in the Tummel-Garry area, efforts were made to improve the accessibility to adult salmon on certain rivers (which were believed not to be fully used by salmon as a result of waterfalls) and a hatchery was provided at Pitlochry Dam.

Obstruction of migration routes. The need to maintain access for salmon and sea trout to spawning areas has long been recognized. However, the sometimes different requirements for other fish such as brown trout, eels, lampreys and burn-spawning charr have not always been borne in mind when considering work which may affect free movement of fish in streams and rivers.

New introductions and spread of existing species. The appearance of new species in waters may have a dramatic effect through competition or predation. Cases are known of pike gaining access to waters containing populations of brown trout and completely eliminating them (Maitland, 1987b). The presence of perch and pike in Loch Davan and Kinord seems likely to be the reason for the rarity of trout in Loch Davan, and its absence from Loch Kinord.

Even within a species such as salmon or trout, local populations are generally genetically distinct as a result of natural selection. Introductions of fish from elsewhere can dilute the local gene pool and there is also the risk of introducing disease or parasites.

Levels of predator species. One question of particular concern to the District Salmon Fishery Boards with rivers in the area is the possible impact of predation by goosanders and mergansers on salmon populations. Recently, FRS Freshwater Laboratory has started a number of experiments in streams and rivers in the Cairngorms area to establish the capacity of the trout and salmon populations to accommodate losses by increased survival of those fish remaining.

Overfishing. The main target species for anglers in the area are salmon and trout. In the case of trout many of the small high lochs would be able to support only a light level of fishing pressure; remoteness alone may not in the future provide sufficient protection. Even apparently productive waters have only a limited capacity to continue to provide good fishing as angling effort increases. Work by the River Don Brown Trout Improvement Association has demonstrated a lack of older trout in the heavily fished lower reaches of the River Don in comparison with the more lightly fished upper reaches (Brian Shields, pers comm).

As already noted the area is a stronghold for the runs of spring salmon which are presently at a low level. Spring salmon are considered a particularly desirable target by anglers and effort levels can continue to be high even when the available number of fish is low. This may lead locally to high exploitation rates with a risk of leaving insufficient spawning fish to stock the waters fully with juvenile salmon. Because of this risk, fishery interests throughout the area are reducing the numbers of spring salmon that are kept by promoting 'catch-and-release' and, in the case of the Dee, by starting fishing later in the year.

REFERENCES

Adams, C.E., Huntingford, F.A., Greer, R.B. & Walker, A.F. (1992) The ontogeny of sympatric morphs of Arctic charr, *Salvelinus alpinus* (L.) from Loch Rannoch, Scotland. *Journal of Fish Biology* **41** (Supplement B), 180.

Armstrong, J.D & West, C.L. (1994) Relative ventricular weight of wild Atlantic salmon parr in relation to sex, gonad maturity and migratory activity. *Journal of Fish Biology* **44**, 453–457.

Ballentyne, C.K. (1991) Holocene geomorphic activity in the Scottish Highlands. *Scottish Geographical Magazine* **107**, 84–98.

Breslin, J.J. (1993) *Survey of the aquatic invertebrates and fish communities in the Insh Marshes lochans*. Scottish Natural Heritage Contract Report 07/93/F2B/227. Edinburgh.

Buck, R.J.G. & Hay, D.W. (1984) The relation between stock size and progeny of Atlantic salmon, *Salmo salar* L., in a Scottish stream. *Journal of Fish Biology* **24**, 1–11.

Buck, R.J.G & Youngson, A.F. (1982) The downstream migration of precociously mature Atlantic salmon, *Salmo salar* L., in autumn: its relation to the spawning of mature adult fish. *Journal of Fish Biology* **20**, 279–288.

Cairngorms Working Party (1993) *Common sense and sustainability: a partnership for the Cairngorms*. Report to the Secretary of State for Scotland. The Scottish Office, Edinburgh.

Campbell, R.N. (1970) The growth of brown trout *Salmo trutta* L. in northern Scottish lochs with special reference to the improvement of fisheries. *Journal of Fish Biology* **3**, 1–28.

157

Carss, D.N. (1993) Osprey predation in a simple fish community. In: *Report of the Institute of Terrestrial Ecology 1992–93*. National Environmental Research Council. pp 76–78.

Carss, D.N., Kruuk, H. & Conroy, J.W.H. (1990) Predation on adult Atlantic salmon, *Salmo salar* L., by otters, *Lutra lutra* (L.), within the River Dee system, Aberdeenshire, Scotland. *Journal of Fish Biology* 37, 935–944.

Curry-Lindahl, K., Watson, A. & Watson, R.Drennan (1982) *The Future of the Cairngorms*. The North East Mountain Trust, Aberdeen.

Forestry Authority (1993) *Forests and Waters Guidelines*. 3rd Edition. HMSO, London.

Gardiner, R. (1992) Scottish grayling: history and biology of their populations. In Lucas, M.C., Diack, I. & Laird, L., eds, *Proceedings of the Institute of Fisheries Management 22nd Annual Study Course*. pp. 171–178.

Gardiner, R. & Egglishaw, H. (1986). A map of the distribution in Scottish rivers of the Atlantic salmon, *Salmo salar* L. Department of Agriculture and Fisheries for Scotland, Pitlochry.

Gordon, S. (1925). *The Cairngorm Hills of Scotland*. Cassell, London.

Greer, R.B. (1984) Charr exploitation in Scotland. In: A. Holden, ed., *Proceedings of the Institute of Fisheries Management 15th Annual Study Course*, pp 128–137. Institute of Fisheries Management, West Bridgford, Nottingham.

Hamilton, K.E., Ferguson, A., Taggart, J.B., Tomasson, T., Walker, A. & Fahy, E. (1989) Post-glacial colonisation of brown trout, *Salmo trutta* L.: Ldh-5 as a phylogeographic marker locus. *Journal of Fish Biology* 35, 651–664.

Harriman, R., Gillespie, E. and Morrison, B.R.S. (1990) Factors affecting fish survival in Scottish catchments. In: Mason, B.J., ed., *The Surface Waters Acidification Programme*. Cambridge University Press, Cambridge. pp. 343–355.

Hawkins, A.D. & Smith, G.W. (1986) *Radiotracking observations on Atlantic salmon ascending the Aberdeenshire Dee*. Scottish Fisheries Research Report No. 36.

Huntingford, F.A., Thorpe, J.E., Garcia de Leaniz, C. & Hay, D.W. (1992) Patterns of growth and smolting in autumn migrants from a Scottish population of Atlantic salmon, *Salmo salar* L. *Journal of Fish Biology* 41 (Supplement B), 43–51.

Jenkins, D. (1980) Ecology of otters in northern Scotland. I. Otter (*Lutra lutra*) breeding and dispersion in mid-Deeside, Aberdeenshire in 1974–79. *Journal of Animal Ecology* 49, 713–735.

Jenkins, D. & Bell, M.V. (1985) Vertebrates, except salmon and trout, associated with the River Dee. In: Jenkins, D., ed., *The Biology and Management of the River Dee*. Institute of Terrestrial Ecology, Huntingdon. pp 83–93.

Jenkins, D. & Burrows, G.O. (1980) Ecology of otters in Northern Scotland. III. The use of faeces as indicators of otter (*Lutra lutra*) density and distribution. *Journal of Animal Ecology* 49, 755–774.

Jenkins, D. & Harper, R.J. (1980) Ecology of otters in Northern Scotland. II. Analyses of otter (*Lutra lutra*) and mink (*Mustela vision*) faeces from Deeside, N.E. Scotland in 1977–78. *Journal of Animal Ecology* 49, 737–754.

Jones, V.J., Flower, R.J., Appleby, P.G., Natkanski, J., Richardson, N., Rippey, B., Stevenson, A.C & Battarbee, R.W. (1993) Palaeolimnological evidence for the acidification and atmospheric contamination of lochs in the Cairngorm and Lochnagar areas of Scotland. *Journal of Ecology* 81, 3–24.

Jordon, W.C. & Youngson, A.F. (1991) Genetic protein variation and natural selection in Atlantic salmon (*Salmo salar*, L.) parr. *Journal of Fish Biology* 39 (Supplement A), 185–192.

Kruuk, H. (1990) Predator/prey relationships and species conservation of the otter. In: *Report of the Institute of Terrestrial Ecology 1989–90*. National Environmental Research Council. pp. 50–53.

Kruuk, H., Carss, D.N. & Conroy, J.W.H. (1992) Otter predation on salmonid fishes. In: *Report of the Institute of Terrestrial Ecology 1991–92*. National Environmental Research Council. pp. 59–61.

Laughton, R. (1989) *The movements of adult salmon within the River Spey*. Scottish Fisheries Research Report No. 41.

Laughton, R. (1991) *The movements of adult Atlantic salmon (Salmo salar L.) within the River Spey as determined by radiotelemetry during 1988 and 1989*. Scottish Fisheries Research Report No. 50.

Laughton, R. & Smith, G.W. (1993) Recent trends in the rod catches of Atlantic salmon, *Salmo salar* L., from four sites on the River Spey. *Aquaculture and Fisheries Management* 24, 671–679.

Lucas, M.C., Priede, I.G., Armstrong, J.D., Gindy, A.N.Z. & Vera, L. (1991) Direct measurements of metabolism, activity and feeding behaviour of pike, *Esox lucius* L., in the wild, by the use of heart rate telemetry. *Journal of Fish Biology* 39, 325–345.

Maitland, P.S. (1987a) Freshwater fish. In: Ormond, D,. ed., *Grampian Book*. Northern Times. pp. 113–115.

Maitland, P.S. (1987b) Fish introductions and translocations – their impact in the British Isles. In: Maitland, P.S. & Turner, A.K., eds, *Angling and Wildlife in Fresh Waters*. Institute of Terrestrial Ecology, Grange-over-Sands. pp 57–65.

Maitland, P.S. & Campbell, R.N. (1992) *Freshwater Fishes*. HarperCollins, London.

Maitland, P.S. & Lyle, A.A. (1991) Conservation of freshwater fish in the British Isles: the current status and biology of threatened species. *Aquatic Conservation: Marine and Freshwater Ecosystems* 1, 25–54.

Marquiss, M. (1988) Research on the Balmoral Estate: Goosander predation on juvenile salmon. In: *Environmental Research on the Lochnagar massif of the Balmoral Estate*. Aberdeen Centre for Land Use, Aberdeen. pp. 31–32.

Marquiss, M. & Feltham, M.J. (1991) Predation of juvenile salmon by red-breasted mergansers. In: *Report of the Institute of Terrestrial Ecology 1990–91*. National Environmental Research Council. pp. 44–46.

Mills, D. & Graesser, N. (1992) *The Salmon Rivers of Scotland*. 2nd Edition. Ward Lock, London.

Morrison, B.R.S. & Harriman, R. (1992) *Fish populations and invertebrates in some headwaters of the Rivers Dee and Spey*. Scottish Fisheries Research Report No. 53.

Nethersole-Thompson, D. & Watson A. (1974). *The Cairngorms: Their Natural History and Scenery*. Fish. Collins, London. pp. 77–80.

Shackley, P.E. & Donaghy, M.J. (1992) *The distribution and growth of juvenile salmon in the major tributaries of the River Dee catchment (Grampian Region)*. Scottish Fisheries Research Report No. 51.

Shearer, W.M. (1988) Fisheries in the Spey catchment. In: Jenkins, D., ed., *Land Use in the Spey Catchment*. (ALCU Symposium No.1) Aberdeen Centre for Land Use, Aberdeen. pp. 197–212.

Spey District Fishery Board (1991) *Annual Report and Research Summary 1987–1991*. Spey District Fishery Board, Forres.

Stephen, A.B. (1984) Electrophoretic evidence for population variation in brown trout (*Salmo trutta* L.) and the implications for management. In: Holden, A., ed., *Proceedings of the Institute of Fisheries Management 15th Annual Study Course*. Institute of Fisheries Management, West Bridgford, Nottingham. pp. 119–127.

Stephen, A.B & McAndrew, B.J. (1990) Distribution of genetic variation in brown trout, *Salmo trutta* L., in Scotland. *Aquaculture and Fisheries Management* 21, 47–66.

Treasurer, J.W. (1983) Estimates of egg and viable embryo production in a lacustrine perch, *Perca fluviatilis*. *Environmental Biology of Fishes* 8, 3–16.

Treasurer, J.W. (1989) Mortality and production of 0+ perch, *Perca fluviatilis* L., in two Scottish lakes. *Journal of Fish Biology* 34, 913–928.

Treasurer, J.W. (1990) The annual reproductive cycle, *Esox lucius* L., in two Scottish lakes. *Journal of Fish Biology* 36, 29–46.

Treasurer, J. (1998) Life-history strategies of pike in a high-altitude loch in Scotland. *Freshwater Forum* 11, 59–68.

Treasurer, J.W., Owen, R. & Bowers, E. (1992) The population dynamics of pike, *Esox lucius*, and perch, *Perca fluviatilis*, in a simple predator-prey system. *Environmental Biology of Fishes* **34**, 65–78.

Webb, J. (1989) *The movements of adult Atlantic salmon in the River Tay.* Scottish Fisheries Research Report No. 44.

Webb, J. (1990) *The behaviour of adult Atlantic salmon ascending the Rivers Tay and Tummel to Pitlochry Dam.* Scottish Fisheries Research Report No. 48.

Webb, J. & Hawkins, A.D. (1989) *The movements and spawning behaviour of adult Atlantic salmon in the Girnock Burn, a tributary of the Aberdeenshire Dee, 1986.* Scottish Fisheries Research Report No. 40.

Wheeler, A. (1977) The origin and distribution of the freshwater fishes of the British Isles. *Journal of Biogeography* **4**, 1–24.

Williamson, G.R. (1977) *Eels in the Scottish Highlands.* Highlands and Islands Development Board, Inverness.

Williamson, R. (1991) *Salmon Fisheries of Scotland.* Atlantic Salmon Trust, Pitlochry.

Youngson, A.F., Buck, R.G.J., Simpson, T.H. & Hay, D.W. (1983) The autumn and spring emigrations of juvenile Atlantic salmon (*Salmo salar* L.) from the Girnock Burn, Aberdeenshire: environmental release of migration. *Journal of Fish Biology* **23**, 625–639.

CHAPTER 14
Open Air Recreation in the Cairngorms

J.W. MACKAY

ORIGINS

On the morning of 23 June 1887, six Aberdeen hill climbers resolved to form the Cairngorm Club, now Scotland's oldest climbing club. Appropriately they made this resolution at the head of Loch Avon in the very heart of the Cairngorms, after over-nighting at the Shelter Stone and releasing fireworks on the summit of Ben Macdui as a contribution to celebrations of Queen Victoria's Golden Jubilee. While a modest event in itself, we can trace a line from this small gathering onwards to today's popular interest in enjoying open-air recreation in the hills.

The story of growing interest in open-air recreation in the Cairngorms begins with increased accessibility, initially through the coming of the railway to Ballater on the south side and the Highland Line to the north. These railways allowed the early climbers (Plates 92, 93, 94) easier access to the hills, although rail has now largely been superseded by the motor car. Growth in open-air recreation also reflects increasing wealth and free time in society, so that more people from a wider social spectrum are able to enjoy the outdoors – the early climbers were mainly from the business and professional classes. Perhaps the most important link with the past is a continuing appreciation of wild and challenging places. What moved the early climbers still moves us today.

The early members of the Cairngorm Club were by no means first to venture into these hills. As 'barren waste' the high ground has never attracted settlement, but people would have gone there for various reasons before deer forest ownership attempted to impose its own exclusivity in the nineteenth century. The first authenticated ascent of Cairn Gorm was by the botanist James Robertson in 1771, although there are references to earlier ascents. The hills at this time would not have been empty. The Cairngorms form the largest block of remote hill country in Britain, a major barrier to travel, but they are crossed by traditional pedestrian routes, and encounters could have been likely here with drovers, vagrants and other travellers. Herdsmen and residents from the lower glens would have been met, likewise hunters, deer watchers, poachers, gem collectors and, latterly, scientists and tourists.

It is the last two groups of visitors who have left written impressions of the area, and their accounts place much emphasis on the wildness of the scenery. John Hill Burton's short memoir of 1864, *The Cairngorm Mountains*, is rooted in the sublime and wild, and makes comparison with scenes from Alpine tours. He describes Loch Avon as . . . 'particularly wild and magnificent . . . like a fragment of the Alps uplifted and set down in Scotland'.

The rugged inner core of Loch Avon and also the upper part of Glen Dee command most attention in the early descriptions. Consider John Dunn's description of upper Glen Dee in 1847 from *A Day in the Wilderness*:

> . . . who shall portray the character of the Glen itself, its solemn gloom, its stern grandeur, its savage wildness? There is something almost incredible in the statement that in the heart of the land resounding like a great workshop with all its appliances of art, there should be found a spot existing in its primeval solitude.

160

Continuing through to today, the Cairngorms have been well served by many authors who have been moved by its landscapes, perhaps to create a greater volume of literature than exists for any other area of upland Scotland.

RECREATIONAL VALUE

This literary spotlight most often highlights the roughness and wildness of the high Cairngorms (Plate 86). While this is the largest block of hill country in Britain distant from public roads, it is not the most remote from human influence or the wildest part of the Highlands. It is penetrated by an extensive network of private estate roads, many of which date back to the Victorian deer forests as they are shown on the first (*c.* 1870) Ordnance Survey maps of the area. While these older estate roads are mainly on low ground in the glens, many ugly additions to them have been bulldozed in recent decades to allow vehicular access to high ground. The addition of other artefacts, buildings, bridges, cairns and so on, has contributed to the Cairngorms being less wild today than they once were.

Nevertheless there is still a strong sense of naturalness in the mountain zone, and there is a strong unity to the landscape. This unity comes from the simple structure and uniform rock type of the major granite masses which form the main mountain core, and also the Lochnagar massif. Most of the surrounding metamorphic rocks have little variety and the same acid infertility of the granite, except to the far south of the area. Hence, this is a landscape expressed in extensive and simple land forms, in bold patterns of rock outcrop, and in the predominantly granitic colours of rock and soils, and the detritus eroded from them.

From a distance, views of the Cairngorms do not signal dramatic mountain landscapes, indeed the far view is often of a bulky and brooding massif. Yet when viewed close to and internal to the mountain core, the rugged terrain is seen to be of outstanding quality, especially in the roughness of the massive boulder-fields, the rock falls and the great expanses of bare rock at the head-walls of the main glaciated basins – a strong impression of land left almost in the condition it was when the ice retreated. This roughness and bareness create an aura of barrenness and a sense of the dynamics of the geo-morphological processes which acted so powerfully in glacial times.

Other parts of Scotland have these qualities but not combined with such scale and remoteness. While there is unity in the overall landscape, there is strong contrast between the verticality of the steep ground and the expansive outward vistas from the high plateau. This contrast is always impressive, as the most dramatic landscapes are often hidden until the last moment of approach, whether they be corrie edge or the deep rock basins like Glen Avon or Glen Geusachan. Away from the mountain core of the Cairngorms and Lochnagar, the scenery is softer and has much less

drama but it is often remote, spacious and evocative, at its best perhaps in lonely, austere places like Gaick.

Compared with the topographic descriptions of the authors of the last century we have today a less sharply developed sense of wonder at these wild landscapes. That is perhaps part of evolving taste, probably influenced by more international travel and a wider range of experience of wild places against which people can make their judgements. Yet appreciation of wild places is strong and growing. While the aesthetics of the wild landscape are important to this trend, there are strong links with the physical elements in outdoor recreation, especially through increased participation in activities which thrive on physical effort and personal challenge. The Cairngorms provide ample scope to experience these challenges and to do so in settings of grandeur (Plates 86, 93, 94).

The pioneer climbers and walkers had a strong interest in the study of the natural history of the area. Today's recreational values are based more on the wider natural environment and the opportunity for the individual to engage in venturesome activities. The recreation value of the mountainous parts of the area might be summarized as follows:

- *Par excellence* the Cairngorms – especially in the winter – offer the climber and walker a wild mountain experience not replicated elsewhere in Britain. In winter the sense of challenge is heightened by harsh weather, short days and by distance. There are other remote places in Scotland which are less visited and with a higher quality of remoteness, but nowhere else has quite the same scale, or has anything like the same amount of high ground.
- There is opportunity for extensive walks on high ground which are of superb quality. The long-distance routes through the main hill passes are valued for their length, roughness and remoteness.
- The Cairngorms hold Britain's most reliable snow cover. The area is then of prime attraction for a range of winter sports – such as winter climbing and walking (Plate 93), off-piste ski touring and ski mountaineering (Plate 94), as well as downhill skiing on the developed ski fields.
- There is high quality rock for climbing, with the finest crags around the Loch Avon basin offering long and serious routes, although climbing is also to be found in most of the rock-bound corries in the inner Cairngorms and at Lochnagar.
- The quality of these hills, the post-war emphasis on introducing people to the outdoors and ease of access via the ski facilities, have all led to more training of people in outdoor skills, and also the training of trainers. Not all of this need take place in the Cairngorms but the area is pre-eminent for training in winter mountain-craft.

Interest in the natural history of the area is still strong. Montane birds command most attention but other features of the natural environment attract visitors with specialist interests. Above all, it is the quality of the setting within which these recreations are practised which is the over-riding attraction, as an inspiring setting for the challenge and endeavour required of the individual, and as an attraction in its own right.

The foreground to the mountains of moorland, glen and forest also has high recreational value, especially the remnants of Caledonian pinewood. While these ancient woods are impoverished in their extent and structure, they often have strong visual character, which comes from their open-ness and from the rough and venerable aspect of the older trees. The rich palette of earth colours on lower ground is distinctive: the browns and yellows of moorland, the dusky pinks of rocks and river gravels and the accent of blue-green of pine foliage. These glens, and their adjacent moors and straths, provide important transition ground for people going in to the high hills, but they also provide important recreation space for the enjoyment of less energetic pursuits, and serve more visitors today than the high ground. Importantly, they are the main venue of private use for the field sports of shooting and stalking, and game fishing.

CHANGING PATTERNS OF RECREATION

The early excursions of the Cairngorm Club were characteristic of their era (Plates 91, 92). At first only three outings per year were held, on the Spring, Summer and Autumn Holidays. They involved reserved coaches on the train, transfer onwards to the hills by carriage, with access facilitated by the proprietors. The hills were hardly crowded at this time, and this more leisurely pattern of enjoyment of the outdoors continued until the Second World War, with the Cairngorms being well appreciated for walking, climbing and natural history – a place for quiet family holidays, co-existing alongside the established private, recreational use of the land for field sports.

The use of the hills for war-time training contributed to today's emphasis on outdoor activities. Troops were trained for mountain warfare, with the prospect that the invasion of Europe might involve fighting in Alpine terrain, the commandos being trained at Braemar, and the Highland Division on the north of the massif where Norwegian troops were also billeted. The outcome was a residue of experience and commitment to outdoor training, and local enthusiasm to develop winter sports at Cairn Gorm, which had pre-war roots in early ventures in Scottish skiing. All this combined with a general desire to improve opportunities for recreation as part of a better post-war society.

Development to this end began on the Glen More side of the Cairngorms. One crucial early development was the outdoor centre at Glenmore Lodge. This was adopted later by the Scottish Sports Council and transferred to a new building close to the original shooting lodge, but still taking the name of Glenmore Lodge, a place of continuing influence in the development of outdoor pursuits in the Cairngorms. The old lodge continues in recreational use as a busy Youth Hostel.

As part of the movement for the enjoyment of the outdoors, there was considerable debate during and after the War about establishing National Parks. In Scotland, two reports of a 'Ramsay Committee' had made recommendations in 1945 and 1947 on the choice of national park areas and how such parks might be run. The intention of the second Ramsay Report was for strong public intervention, including some land ownership, and with an emphasis on opening up access and making provision for enjoyment of the outdoors. The proposed National Parks were seen by some people as important development tools, with potential to contribute to resolving the continuing 'Highland Problem' of economic decline and depopulation. In the event, the Ramsay proposals were not implemented and the Cairngorms, and the four other contenders for national park status were designated as National Park Development Areas, which allowed for some oversight by the Scottish Office of development control under Town and Country Planning legislation.

One tailpiece to this early story is that a sketch national park plan was prepared for the Cairngorms by one of the committees that lingered over this issue into the early 1950s. This sketch plan included proposals for a ski-tow on Cairn Gorm and for new road access into Glen More and through Glen Feshie, and for other improvements to access such as bridges and mountain huts.

Expansion of tourism in the area was led in the 1960s by the development of the Aviemore Centre as a joint public and private demonstration that leisure could be a potent force for investment and job creation in rural areas. This was paralleled by a study group on the Cairngorms, run by the Scottish Development Department (Technical Group on the Cairngorm Area, 1967) and involving the local authorities, which prepared a plan for a wider Cairngorms area, extending well beyond the mountain core over land southwards beyond Deeside to Atholl.

The prospectus in this plan was expansive, with proposals for new roads through the middle of the area, much improved access for open-air recreation and the search for other locations for new ski development, the aim being to spread the evident economic benefits of tourism over a wider area. This plan revived one of the visions in the 1940s debate about national parks, namely that outdoor recreation and tourism could be major forces in revitalizing Highland communities.

Many of the proposals of this report were not implemented; indeed it has subsequently been criticized for its lack of commitment to conservation. It could be said, however, that its spirit has been achieved in the continued growth of tourism investment, albeit that this is still largely concentrated in the Aviemore area, and that the emphasis has been more on commerce and provision for tourists on the low ground.

THE EXPANSION OF SKIING

Skiing has a long history in Scotland, initially connected with mountaineering and ski-touring. After the war more people were attracted to piste skiing, assisted by primitive mechanical uplift, initially at locations more accessible to the central belt of Scotland than Cairn Gorm, such as Ben Lawers, Glen Shee and Glencoe. Skiing was then part of the early outdoor training at Glen More, along with climbing, walking, sailing on Loch Morlich and canoeing on the main rivers.

The enthusiasm of individuals and their vision of a ski resort on the Cairngorms led to the formation in 1956 of the Strathspey Winter Sports Development Association. This group, soon reconstituted as the Cairngorm Winter Sports Development Board, obtained the support of local authorities, central government, the Forestry Commission and other local landowners to adopt the Glen More road as a public highway and to extend it up into Coire Cas. This new road opened in 1960 and the first major mechanical uplift, the White Lady Chairlift, came into use in 1961 (Plate 89).

Since that date, the ski development has expanded greatly although with some controversy. The original ski road soon had to be rebuilt to a much higher standard and this replacement road was itself upgraded in 1981. The development has depended heavily on public funds for its improved road access, for new uplift and also to carry the venture over lean snow years. The Highlands and Islands Development Board (now Highlands and Islands Enterprise) played an important role in supporting ski development at Cairn Gorm and, in 1972, it took over ownership from the Forestry Commission of that part of Glenmore Forest Park above the planted ground, which included the leased ski area and the Northern Corries.

Skiing has grown at two other sites on the edge of the wider Cairngorms area. First, at Glen Shee astride the high point of the A93 road, which has a stronger day-visit market from the central belt than Cairn Gorm and, second, at the Lecht, at the summit of the Cockbridge to Tomintoul road, which has created its own niche market, drawing mainly on families from the north-east of Scotland. Both Glen Shee and the Lecht depend on existing high level public roads. Like Cairn Gorm, they also depend on public investment in road improvements and snow clearing to secure operation throughout the winter. Planning consent for ski development has, in the past, been given on the far west of the area at Drumochter and adjacent to the high sections of the A9 trunk road, but no development has followed and downhill skiing there is now most unlikely.

Although Glen Shee has more uplift and Aonoch Mor in the west is expanding, Cairn Gorm is still Scotland's main ski resort in terms of all round facilities. At the busiest times it has had around half of the total volume of skiing in Scotland, with most of the participants (*c.* 80%) being on weekend or longer trips. However, the recent snow-poor years and development elsewhere have shifted the balance of use between the ski fields. Progressively the ski area expanded, at first within Coire Cas and then eastwards into the steeper Coire na Ciste. These two areas are linked together, mainly on the high part of the hill. There is car parking (Plate 89) for around 1200 cars so that, along with the clientele brought there by coach, there can be a population of skiers on the hill on the busiest days of the size of a small town of around 5–6000 people.

Skiing in Scotland is largely dependent on wind-blown snow, trapped naturally in sheltered terrain and, artificially, by extensive fencing (Plates 88, 89) and, in the early days at Cairn Gorm, by bulldozing to create hollows to gather snow. Thaw and frost can bring icy conditions on the pistes, and high winds can add to the difficulties of management requiring, for example, closure of chair-lifts.

All of these factors can cause congestion on the slopes at busy times. There can also be congestion on the access road, and a need to close it at Glen More on the busiest days for reasons of public safety. The road can be closed on 4–6 days each season because of snow drifts.

Growth in the ski market, crowding on the ski area and a need to open up more terrain suitable for less skilled skiers, have all led to previous bids to expand downhill skiing westwards from the present leased area, across the Northern Corries towards Lurcher's Gully. A major and contentious public inquiry held in 1981 blocked this ambition. On its renewal in a revised plan in 1988–9, westward expansion was stopped again. In this case, there was no inquiry as the proposal emerged in Highland Regional Council's draft Structure Plan, but there was much campaigning by both the skiing interests, on behalf of the scheme, and by those concerned that the conservation and recreational values of the Cairngorms were at risk (see also Chapter 15).

There has been confrontation and polarized debate between the proposals for expansion and the opposing arguments for conservation. Expansion has been promoted by local commercial interests, the skiing organizations, the local authorities and the development and tourism agencies. The opposition has been a consortium of voluntary conservation and other recreation bodies, aligned with the public conservation agencies.

Each side has seen the issue as being about principle – simplistically about jobs versus conservation – and the polarization has led to arguments being overstated. Although styled as a classic conservation versus development debate, in practice the argument has been as much between different recreation interests and different aspirations or ethos for enjoyment of the outdoors.

At centre to the argument against westward expansion was a view that it would cause serious impact on the wildness and natural heritage qualities of inner parts of the mountain core. While some of this would come in the winter, from easier access for off-piste skiing, climbing and walking, there is the prospect of more summer use, which could also have effects on the character of the plateau.

However, poor snow conditions in recent years have diverted attention away from any expansion. Decisions to bring in new European conservation designations also imply that, for the foreseeable future, any further growth of skiing facilities will have to be undertaken within the existing ski area.

Yet as the years pass, the older uplift needs replacement. Following another phase of controversy, a modern funicular railway has recently been constructed to replace the existing chairlifts and some of the older tows in Coire Cas. This new facility will open for the 2002 season and will provide uplift for skiing which is more secure against the problems of wind. More problematically, it is hoped that the funicular will attract more summer visitors to help finance its costs and to act as a new stimulus to local tourism. However, to meet concerns about more impact on the high plateau (a European designated site under the Natura 2000 programme) the public will not be allowed to exit in summer from the top station.

ACTIVE PURSUITS IN THE HILLS

The above sketch of the history of development of the Cairngorms ski field has run ahead of the story of how open-air recreation generally has developed in the area. But the ski development, and its road, have been crucial to the pattern of use of the northern side of the massif for tourism and for the growth of active pursuits and outdoor training in the mountains.

Other hill recreations have expanded through use of the ski road. Access has been eased for climbing and walking on the high ground, both in summer and winter. The Shelter Stone venue of the Cairngorm Club's genesis is now but a short step from the top of the chairlift, and access to the fine summer and winter climbing in the Loch Avon basin has been made much easier. The 1960s and 70s saw great expansion in winter climbing here and elsewhere in the area, especially at Lochnagar (Plate 87). Some of this was led by Aberdeen and Edinburgh climbers and some of it was led by improved ice-climbing techniques, developed by climbers based on the north side of the massif, particularly at Glenmore Lodge.

There has been increased use of the massif for other winter activities, notably winter walking, off-piste skiing, nordic skiing (mainly in spring) and ski mountaineering. There is a trend towards enhanced performance in many of these activities: people climb to higher standards and ski on steeper ground.

The numbers of accidents on the hill have grown, with the main causes being slips on hard snow, exhaustion and navigation errors. Three mountain rescue teams cover the Cairngorms: volunteer teams are based at Aviemore and at Braemar, while

Glenmore Lodge offers a third team, all backed by the close-at-hand RAF helicopter service, based at Lossiemouth. A notorious tragedy in 1965 caused deaths amongst a group of young schoolchildren on the plateau, lost in a storm while seeking one of the high refuges. This led to much more prudence about the safety of groups of young people using remote country. The venturesome character of mountain sports and the sometimes extreme hostility of winter conditions on high ground have led to continuing care and promotion of safety through publicity and training.

The easy access for outdoor training has caused growth in the numbers of centres operating in the area. Training groups can have a relatively short journey via the ski road and uplift to their study or training area. Excluding the youth hostels, there are centres operating on the north flank of the massif with bed space of over 300, and the armed services maintain their traditional links with the area, using the Cairngorms as a place to promote skills in skiing and mountain craft.

The leader in training is Glenmore Lodge, which places emphasis on specialist courses and on training other trainers, thus acting as a centre of leadership in skills. For winter training, Glenmore Lodge – and hence the Cairngorms – is the national centre. Field studies also attract organized parties from colleges or schools. These groups may visit the area from outside without having any permanent base within it, and the volume of these trips is difficult to estimate.

Deeside, and other parts of the wider Cairngorm area, have not been affected to the same extent by the commercial drive of tourism, but the upper Deeside economy is also dependent on visitors, and it draws in part on the Glen Shee ski development to the south and also on summer tourist traffic on the A93. An effort was made in the 1960s to introduce skiing at Mar Lodge, but at too low an altitude for any success. Deeside retains much of its original character; the vernacular tradition in buildings has largely been maintained, and the landuse pattern is still dominated by the large sporting estates. Here there is still a long walk in to the hills, but one which has increasing levels of use.

RECREATION ON LAND ADJACENT TO THE MASSIF

The Cairngorms attract visitors off the busy A9 tourist artery and to a lesser extent off the A93 on the south. The Glen More and ski road axis is a draw to the visitor who is not there to participate in active pursuits, but very few of them go further than the summit of Cairn Gorm. Many visitors do not go very far from the main car park at Coire Cas or stay long there, certainly because the weather is often inclement at this altitude for those wearing light summer clothing. Yet estimates of numbers of visitors at Coire Cas over the summer three months period total over 100 000, which implies that, over the whole year, this location is in the top bracket of busy visitor sites in Scotland.

Within Glen More, the Forest Enterprise provides a visitor centre and a busy camp site. It manages the confined recreation strip along the shore of Loch Morlich, where existing car parks often cannot cope with demand, and provides access throughout the Forest Park for walking and a wide range of other recreations. Rothiemurchus Estate offers attractive walking in the native pinewood by promoting walks and other attractions and by providing a ranger service.

The forests around the Cairngorms play an important role in open-air recreation. The native pinewoods have marvellous ambience, mentioned earlier, and the managed woods also provide space for recreation – mainly informal but in some cases unusual or special to its location. For instance – snow-lie permitting – Glenmore Forest is a national venue for Nordic skiing, as the sheltered forest roads can hold snow and have tracks cut for low level *langlauf* skiing. There is now much more off-road cycling in the area, especially on the forest and estate road network, sometimes by walkers and climbers seeking to shorten the long walk in to the hills. Except at Glen More, recreation provision for the general public on land peripheral to the mountain core is mainly low key and without active promotion.

The main provisions for the touring visitor have been led by commercial and other managed facilities, some with only limited connection to the outdoor resources of the Cairngorms. There are accessible historic sites such as Ruthven Barracks or Braemar Castle, and good interpretation of past cultural life at the Highland Folk Museum. There are several visitor centres, such as Landmark at Carrbridge which sets high standards of reception and provision. RSPB's show-case for the osprey at Loch Garten has played a key role in raising awareness and understanding of this fine bird, returned to our avifauna.

THE VISITORS

There are few good surveys of open-air recreation in Scotland's uplands. The Cairngorms are much better served than elsewhere, as government agencies have perceived the need to collect data to support management or their advocacy at public inquiries. The earliest full study was a week-long cordon survey of the main mountain massif undertaken by the Nature Conservancy Council (NCC) in 1974. This approach of interviewing visitors as they leave the mountain core was repeated by agencies preparing for the second proposal for expansion of skiing westwards to Lurcher's Gully. That survey was run in the summer of 1987 and it was extended through the following winter and spring. These data have been reviewed in a short, unpublished report to the former Countryside Commission for Scotland (ASH, 1992).

Growing public-body involvement in the management of the area has led to a series of new recreation surveys, led by SNH on behalf of a consortium of interests. A major survey of the use of the Eastern Grampians was undertaken in 1995

(SNH, 1998) and this was followed in 1997–8 by a repeat of the survey for the main Cairngorms massif, but extending the area of survey eastwards as far as Tomintoul (SNH, 1999). This has been followed by a Glen More visitor survey, including use of the ski-field (SNH, 1999). These surveys provide the best data available on the use of any major part of the Scottish hills for open-air recreation. Locally to the Cairngorms, only to the west of Glen Feshie and in Atholl is there a lack of data on the use of the hills and their surrounds.

Even with these new data, it is difficult to arrive at an overall estimate of the numbers of visitors to the mountain zone, as not all the hills have survey data, not all the low ground is covered, and the surveys cover different years. But with an estimate of around 150 000 for the 1995 East Grampians survey (high and low ground), an estimate of 123 000 for the Cairngorms survey in 1997–98 and around 500 000 in Glen More, including the ski-field, in 1998–99, it is not unreasonable to project that overall visits to the mountains of the wider Cairngorms area and their immediate surrounds will exceed one million, depending on the levels of use at the three ski-fields.

Major surveys of this kind give much detailed market research information about activities and about those who participate but they provide only a short-term picture without any indication of trends. Apart from use of the ski area in winter, trend data on use of the hills are very weak, except that the use of the chairlift in summer declined significantly over the past two decades.

One interesting data set comes from Adam Watson (1991) who has been counting visitors on the Cairn Gorm-Ben Macdui plateau over a long run of years. Although his observations are *ad hoc*, being made when he was visiting high ground for other purposes, their cumulative value is considerable. They show clearly the sharp growth in use of high ground following opening of the chairlift, but then the pattern stabilizes with no real growth (although variable between the years) since the mid-1970s.

THE IMPACT OF RECREATION

There should be some concern about the extent of ground damage from open-air recreation on the high and heavily visited parts of the Cairngorms. So severe is climate on the highest ground that vegetation recovery is very limited because of infertility, slow growth and the lack of viable seed. Montane vegetation communities are inherently sensitive, sometimes with a high proportion of mosses and lichens which are easily destroyed by trampling (p. 39). Baring of the ground leads quickly to the thin and rudimentary soil being blown away. While grass can be grown as a substitute, although artificial, vegetation cover at lower altitudes (given sufficient input of nutrients), recovery is poor on the highest ground, and introduction of non-native species would not be acceptable outside the ski area. There is little experience of how to re-establish a more natural and acceptable vegetation cover in the montane zone (see Chapter 3).

Trampling has been the main cause of damage. On and around the ski area, the number of paths has grown considerably and the popular routes have all become wider (Plate 90). But other human activities have interfered with natural processes, for example construction work, or new patterns of snow-lie along fence lines, which modify local drainage patterns and lead to increased small-scale water erosion. Simple activities such as moving boulders for path construction can contribute very locally to increased patterns of wind erosion on high ground. Yet it is difficult to assess the seriousness of the current damage. There is only a limited monitoring of past change and the overall extent of serious damage caused by recreation is small in comparison to the total area of high ground, some of which is subject to extensive natural erosion not connected with recreation by the public.

The low gradients on the plateau and the permeability of coarse granitic soils both contribute to minimizing surface water damage to paths, but low gradients and relatively smooth terrain encourage visitors to wander and add to the difficulty of path management. It is not wholly clear whether critical damage has been done to any valuable habitats or to fauna. But there is a longer-term concern here, even if the main effects are at present aesthetic, in that the most visited areas are bruised and have lost their former pristine qualities. Outwith the estate and forest road network, the lower-level paths are in mixed condition, generally being wide and damaged through long use and having had little investment in repair. However, most of these paths do not show a high level of dynamic change. Given resources, they are manageable, the principal difficulties lying in the extent of boulder fields, block screes and deep peat, all of which provide difficult terrain for path repair if sensitive results are to be achieved.

Higher levels of dynamic change (and challenge to management) could lie on the steep mid-hill paths, for example the steep route from Coire Raibeirt or Coire Domhain down to Loch Avon, or the ascent from Corrour on to the Cairn Toul plateau. All these routes are direct ascent, often at gradients well in excess of what is realistic for path stability, but even here the dynamic is not as serious as it might be, if located in wetter parts of the country. Yet this quasi-stability is illusory, as paths of this kind are always at risk of major damage by cloud-burst rainfall events.

There are some broad ascent paths up ridges that are difficult to evaluate. An example might be the Fiacaill of Coire Cas which carries heavy all-the-year-round traffic, often being bare of snow in winter. The condition of this ridge on its final steep slope is of a broad damaged zone, mainly bruised on the surface through disturbance of gravels, the scuffing and turning-over of small stones and the removal of lichens from the surface of larger blocks of rock. This becomes less problematic higher up as more solid rock emerges to armour the surface. The impact is mainly visual, as the form of this ridge and its robustness preclude any serious damage by running water. Yet here, as on the high plateau, the pristine nature of the ground has been impaired and something lost to the qualities of the place.

In recent years there has been a growing concern about the condition of hill paths and programmes of work have been sponsored on the HIE Cairn Gorm Estate, at Lochnagar, on the Mar Lodge Estate by NTS, and elsewhere. A major survey of the condition of these hill paths has been completed by SNH, with a view to a substantial programme of repair work. Nonetheless much remains to be done.

Impacts on ground-nesting montane birds are also difficult to evaluate. Dotterel appear to thrive on the plateau at present levels of public use and other rare birds nest periodically. Nonetheless there are some impacts on fauna arising from the presence of more people on high ground. There have been several recent habitat surveys to provide a base-line for monitoring future change. All this needs careful review as even the most confiding of upland birds will eventually be displaced by increased disturbance from the public.

Other effects of recreation include localized impacts such as those caused by high-level camping and overnighting in snow-holes by winter training groups, which cause concentrations of pollution and litter. But there is now much less of this winter activity, as the main outdoor training groups have reduced overnight stays on high ground.

As well as the physical limits to use of the high plateau implied by the sensitivity of the vegetation, there are limits to perceptual capacity – that is, the point at which visitors begin to feel that the experience which they seek in these places has become diminished, either by the presence of too many people, or by constant reminder of them by virtue of visible impacts on the ground. Little is known about such limits.

MANAGEMENT AND PLANNING FOR RECREATION

The Glen More road provides arrow-like access to the ski field. Either on foot or by mechanical uplift the visitor can quickly be on Cairn Gorm at the edge of the plateau. This pertains in both summer and winter and it has been potent in opening up the central part of the massif east of the Lairig Ghru for climbing, walking and outdoor training, as described above. Glen More itself is no longer a place of solitude and naturalness. It was converted into a commercial forest mainly planted with exotics, although Forest Enterprise has begun a major restructuring of the forest to reclaim the lost qualities of the native pinewood in the Forest Park.

There is still no coherent management of open-air recreation for the public. In 1969, the former Countryside Commission for Scotland responded to a letter of complaint in *The Scotsman* newspaper from Colonel Grant of Rothiemurchus that matters had got out of control in the public use and abuse of private land, and it initiated a ranger service to help co-ordinate management for open-air recreation. However, this effort did not have any longer-term impact on co-operation between different organizations and the Commission eventually withdrew its direct presence, although grants for ranger services and recreation facilities were continued.

Later (1989), in its response to the second proposal for westward expansion of skiing, the Commission called for a major new management initiative in Glen More. Then, in its Mountain Areas of Scotland review of 1991, the Commission called for a National Park solution (Chapter 17). The eventual outcome of the Mountain Areas report was a phase of government review through the Cairngorms Working Party, which proposed an ambitious agenda of action, to be achieved through a voluntary but co-ordinated approach to management for the area and, in turn, this led to the establishment of the Cairngorms Partnership (see Chapter 16).

While each of the bodies with responsibility for recreation management in the area has done something for its own interests, there has been little collective effort over the years to reflect the quality and national importance of the area. The strategy prepared by the Cairngorms Working Party, and the subsequent lead by the Partnership has helped greatly in preparing the ground for a more coherent approach to sustainable management of the area. The new legislation to create National Parks in Scotland (Scottish Parliament, 2000) and the Scottish Executive's proposal and recent consultation, reported on by SNH (SNH, 2001), provides a new opportunity to address the long-standing and as yet unresolved need for more investment in the management of open-air recreation. It is also an opportunity to tackle the past climate of contention between the local economic, and the conservation and recreation interests.

PROSPECT

Open-air recreation is now a dominant use of much of the land in the core of the area, both on the low ground and on the tops, including land designated for conservation and also some land in use for the traditional estate activities. The values that underpin enjoyment by the general public have had little recognition, nor are they upheld by adequate investment in management although there has been more expenditure in recent years. Yet, most of the commercial interests in the area depend on its natural qualities, but do so at one remove from the need to contribute to the care and maintenance of their resource base.

Of the recreation values discussed earlier, wildness and naturalness have constantly been under attrition from development, from land management and from increased use of the area, and these values deserve more protection. What

would Alexander Copland, first Chairman of the Cairngorm Club, and his five colleagues think if they were to travel today through Glen More, exiting from Aviemore along an urbanized thoroughfare? They would follow a highway which allows for driving speeds which are too high for sensible recreational travel, passing much new development and through a much changed forest and ski-field. On eventually reaching the summit of Cairn Gorm, they would meet a clutter of meteorological, radio and other scientific equipment, each with its own special interest justification.

Yet recreation, as practised by individuals, still has a weak place in debate about the future of the area. The conservation interests claim World Heritage status for the Cairngorms and there is an economic development argument which rests a good deal of its case on the promotion of open-air recreation. The commercial claim, however, is not coincident with all the recreation interest. Nor can recreation claim its own high moral ground, because it carries its own threat through the effects of over-use of the more sensitive areas.

It is evident that the recreation value of the Cairngorms depends highly on the environmental values. In special places like the Cairngorms the visitors should form a huge club of 'friends' for conserving its qualities. In turn, that makes the link back to 1887, when that small gathering of six hill climbers from Aberdeen was concerned to promote access to and enjoyment of the natural qualities of these hills. Those who today enjoy the Cairngorms environment face a greater challenge in acting both to guard these same qualities for their own and future use, and to recognize also their role in addressing the effects that more use of the area causes.

REFERENCES

The ASH Partnership (1992) *Cairngorm Visitor Survey 1987–88 – A Report on Supplementary Analysis of the Data.* Unpublished report to the Countryside Commission for Scotland. 56 pp.

Countryside Commission for Scotland (1989) *Skiing at Cairngorm – A Policy Paper.* CCS, Perth. 16 pp.

Countryside Commission for Scotland (1991) *The Mountain Areas of Scotland.* CCS, Perth. 64 pp.

Department of Health for Scotland (1945) *National Parks – A Scottish Survey.* Report by the Scottish National Parks Survey Committee – Chairman Sir J.D. Ramsay. Cmd 6631. HMSO, Edinburgh. 27 pp.

Department of Health for Scotland (1947) *National Parks and the Conservation of Nature in Scotland.* Report by the Scottish National Parks Committee – Chairman Sir J.D. Ramsay. Cmd 7235. HMSO, Edinburgh. 71 pp.

Dunn, J. (1847) *A Day in the Wilderness.* Aberdeen.

Hill Burton, J. (1864) *The Cairngorm Mountains.* Blackwood, Edinburgh.

Mackay Consultants (1988) *Cairngorm Visitor Survey – Summer 1987.* Inverness.

Mather, A.S. (1998) *East Grampians & Lochnagar Visitor Survey 1995: overview.* Scottish Natural Heritage Research Survey & Monitoring Report No. 104. SNH, Edinburgh.

Mather, A.S. (2000). *Rothiemurchus & Glenmore Recreation Survey 1998–9: final report.* Scottish Natural Heritage Research Survey and Monitoring Report No. 166. SNH, Edinburgh.

Morris, D., Hammond, E. & Kessler, C. (1974) *Cairngorm National Nature Reserve – a report on the characteristics of visitor use.* Unpublished report to the Nature Conservancy Council.

Murray, S. (1987) *The Cairngorm Club 1887–1987*. Cairngorm Club, Aberdeen. 136 pp.

Scottish Natural Heritage (2001) *The Report of a Proposal for a Cairngorms National Park: A new way of caring for a special place*. SNH on behalf of the Scottish Executive, Edinburgh.

Scottish Parliament (2000) *National Parks (Scotland) Act 2000*. HMSO, Edinburgh.

Taylor, J. & MacGregor, C. (1999) *Cairngorms Mountain Recreation Survey 1997–8*. Scottish National Heritage Research Survey & Monitoring Report No. 162. SNH, Edinburgh.

Technical Group on the Cairngorm Area of the Eastern Highlands of Scotland (1967) *Cairngorm Area*. HMSO, Edinburgh.

Watson, A. (1991) Increase of people on Cairn Gorm plateau following easier access. *Scottish Geographical Magazine* **107**, 99–105.

CHAPTER 15

Conservation of Nature and Landscape

E.M. MATTHEW

INTRODUCTION

The Cairngorms are the most important mountain area in Britain for nature conservation values (Ratcliffe, 1977), and arguably one of the foremost conservation areas of any sort in Britain. The high ground forms the southernmost large outpost of near-arctic habitat in Europe. It contains the most extensive mountain environment and the largest remnants of native forest in the British Isles. The Cairngorms are of national importance for their mountain, moorland and forest landscapes (Countryside Commission for Scotland, 1978) (Plate 95). They are also generally regarded as nationally important for mountain recreation pursuits. (Summaries of the main features of conservation importance follow; for fuller accounts see Chapters 2–6.)

LANDFORMS AND FEATURES*

The Cairngorms area is internationally important for the assemblage of pre-glacial, glacial and post-glacial landforms and features. Many are excellent examples in their own right but the total assemblage of features in a small area is unrivalled in the British Isles, and has few parallels in the world. The complex of landforms here provides excellent opportunities for the study of landscape evolution from the Tertiary period to the present day.

The landforms and features of the Cairngorms fall into five groups. The first is a group of pre-glacial features on the high ground. It includes the rolling surfaces of the plateaux with their shallow water-carved valleys, areas of weathered granite and granite tors. These features date from the Tertiary period when the climate was warmer than it is now. Some of them are found on other mountains in Britain but the range, scale and quality of all the pre-glacial features in the Cairngorms are unsurpassed elsewhere in the British Isles. In this respect the Cairngorms closely resemble areas in northern Finland and the Canadian arctic (Gordon & Sutherland, 1993).

The second group comprises features of glacial erosion and includes deeply eroded glacial troughs such as Glen Einich and Strath Nethy, glacial watershed breaches represented by the Lairig Ghru, the Cairn Gorm corries and probably the finest examples in Britain of glacial diversions of drainage. These features are internationally recognized as fine type examples. There are few areas in Britain that can equal the range of glacial erosion features here, and nowhere can demonstrate the close juxtaposition of a pre-glacial landscape with these features. The Cairngorms constitute a classic landscape of selective glacial erosion, and in this respect rank with examples from East Greenland, Labrador and Baffin Island.

---

* The landforms of the Cairngorms and their importance are fully described in Gordon, 1993, from which the material in this section is derived.

The third group, the landforms created by glacial meltwaters, is particularly well represented in the Cairngorms. It includes meltwater erosion channels, the hollows (kettle-holes) left by decaying blocks of ice and a range of meltwater deposits including eskers, kame terraces and dead ice hummocks and hollows. Some of these features are good examples of their type although they are not as distinctive as other examples from elsewhere in Scotland. However, taken together they provide clear evidence of the sequence of deglaciation. In this respect these features of the mountain core are comparable only with the meltwater features at Muir of Dinnet in the east of the Cairngorms area.

The fourth group consists of peri-glacial features formed in a cold climate. Particular peri-glacial features are as well or better represented elsewhere in the Highlands but it is the combination and range of features that distinguish the Cairngorms. The plateau surfaces provide the closest equivalent in Britain to the sub-arctic or fell-field landscapes containing blockfields, deflation surfaces and large-scale patterned ground. The slopes support a variety of mass-movement features including excellent examples of relict boulder-fringed solifluction lobes, protalus ramparts and rock glaciers. The Cairngorms contain more rock glaciers than any other mountain area in Britain. Small-scale peri-glacial features are still active in the Cairngorms. The whole assemblage of peri-glacial features in the Cairngorms is of national importance.

Finally, the fifth group of features includes peat deposits and bogs that provide a detailed record of the colonization of the area by plants since the end of the ice age and the subsequent development of the vegetation.

PATTERN OF LIFE IN THE CORE MOUNTAIN AREA

Vegetation (see Chapter 3)
The Cairngorm mountains contain the largest area of high ground in the British Isles. The soils are mainly derived from granite and are mostly acidic and infertile. Dwarf-shrub heaths dominated by heather *Calluna vulgaris* or blaeberry and other *Vaccinium* species are more extensive than grassland except locally on small outcrops of base-rich rocks around the flanks of the Cairngorms.

Prostrate lichen-rich heather and lichen-rich *Vaccinium* heaths are more extensive on the Cairngorms than anywhere else in Britain. The plateaux and summits support plant communities of the low to middle alpine zone including montane heaths dominated respectively by *Racomitrium*, three-leaved rush *Juncus trifidus* and stiff sedge *Carex bigelowii* together with moor mat-grass *Nardus stricta* snow-bed communities, moss and fern-dominated late snowbeds and alpine springs. The low alpine moss zone and the middle alpine zones together constitute the largest area of vegetation on high ground in Britain. Other nationally rare communities in the Cairngorms are alpine willow scrub, mountain bog-sedge *Carex rariflora* mires, heather-bearberry *Calluna-Arctostaphylos uva-ursi* heath and high altitude blanket bog.

The Cairngorm corries provide the most important range of habitats in Britain for calcifuge arctic-alpine vascular plants and many rare bryophytes associated with late snow. The diversity of montane plant communities and species in the Cairngorms is enhanced by outcrops of base-rich schists on the periphery of the granite which support a wide range of montane calcicole species. There are 77 montane vascular plant species out of 118 such plants found on British mountains. This puts the Cairngorms mountain core second only to Caenlochan and ahead of Ben Lawers in terms of the total number of these plants recorded.

Some 40 per cent of all plant communities found in the British uplands are unique to Britain, and about 30 per cent of these unique types are found in the Cairngorms.

The Cairngorms contain some of the largest native woodland remnants in Britain (Plate 96). Dominated by Scots pine, they are the most localized native woodland type in Britain, being confined to the Scottish Highlands. They support a specialized northern boreal fauna and flora. The only authentic fragment of a natural, altitudinal tree line in Britain is found on a spur on Creag Fhiaclach in Rothiemurchus (Plates 62, 63). Because of the steeply sloping nature of the ground the zonation is compressed, but in the northern Corries native woodland is recolonizing a wider extent of ground.

The altitudinal zonation of the vegetation extending from forest to the alpine zone (Plate 97) and characteristic of base-poor soils in the more continental eastern Highlands is best developed in the Cairngorms. The vegetation is diversified across the zones by stream gullies draining the plateaux (Plate 98). The topography governs the degree of exposure and there are marked transitions between snow-bed vegetation and windswept montane heaths.

Lochs and burns
The highest corrie lochs in the Cairngorms are arctic-alpine in character, low in nutrients and with a very impoverished fauna and flora, numbering only some 15 species, none of which has been recorded from other deep water lakes in Britain. The aquatic moss and liverwort communities seem to be unique in Britain. The scanty invertebrate fauna has a few adaptable or high altitude species. The larger glacial lakes of Loch Einich and Loch Avon at lower altitudes are also extremely poor in nutrients but they have a more diverse fauna and flora. The corrie lochs are unique British examples of arctic-alpine lakes, and together with Loch Einich and Loch Avon, are regarded as of international importance. The headwaters of the River Dee and the River Avon are the highest streams in Britain and are rated of national importance for their alpine characteristics.

Animal life
The fauna of the Cairngorms is characteristic of northern, montane areas of Britain. The main invertebrate interest is in the rare beetles, flies and moths of the high ground, and the rare spiders,

bugs, beetles and sawflies of the pinewoods and the low ground (Chapter 5). The Cairngorms has the second highest number of Red Data Book* species of any Scottish site recorded in the Invertebrate Site Register.

The Cairngorms are of exceptional importance within Britain and the European Union for a range of bird species associated with mountain plateaux, open moorland and native pine forest (Chapter 4). The altitudinal gradation over a relatively short distance between these habitats is of outstanding interest and results in the area supporting a unique assemblage of Annex One and other rare migratory birds.† There is a total of 11 Annex One bird species, of which 10 breed on the National Nature Reserve and eight occur in nationally or internationally important numbers. This is the most important site in Britain, and probably also in the European Union, for its assemblage of specialist mountain plateau bird species, which includes dotterel, ptarmigan and snow bunting. The Cairngorms are of special importance for raptors and other species associated with open moorland habitats. These include hen harrier *Circus cyaneus*, merlin *Falco columbarius*, golden eagle *Aquila chrysaetos*, peregrine *Falco peregrinus* and short-eared owl *Asio flammeus*. The native pinewoods of the Cairngorms support a highly distinctive bird community comprising capercaillie *Tetrao urogallus*, Scottish crossbill *Loxia scotica* and crested tit *Parus cristatus*.

These superlatives were recognized by the Cairngorms Working Party who were . . . 'of the unanimous conviction that the Cairngorms Area is a very special place which deserves and requires special treatment and the highest level of care and attention' (Cairngorms Working Party, 1993).

THE WIDER AREA

The wider area of the Cairngorms contains many features which are highly regarded for their nature conservation values. The granite mountain of Lochnagar (Plate 87) reflects many of the important features of the Cairngorms but on a smaller scale. Caenlochan, at the eastern end of the Dalradian mica schists and limestone outcrops, has great vegetation diversity and floristic richness. The Perthshire hills of Beinn a' Ghlo and Ben Vrackie are part of the same group of nationally important upland sites situated on the same outcrops. The Drumochter Hills have one of the biggest areas of species-poor *Racomitrium* – stiff sedge heath in Britain. Blanket bog, heath and *Vaccinium* snow-beds are also well developed. The extensive area of the Monadhliath is largely covered by blanket bog but there is also a range of montane heath and acid grassland communities here. The Ladder Hills in the north-east of the area contain a range of lichen-rich blanket bog and heath communities. Coyles of Muick is rated of national importance for its serpentine outcrops with their distinctive flora. Taken together these hills make up some of the most important mountain environments in Britain.

The moorlands of the eastern Highlands are prime examples of a habitat which is globally rare but widely represented in the Cairngorms area. Below about 600 m most of the moorland has been derived from woodland, and although it supports a relatively low diversity of species, it has special importance for the plants and animals that are characteristic of it. The best moors occur on the less acid soils in the east of the area. The Muir of Dinnet is the largest area of a species-rich type of heath dominated by heather and bearberry, which is restricted to north-east Scotland. The adjacent hills of Morven and Mullach Dubh are predominantly covered by species-poor heather heath but the herb-rich type with bearberry occurs in patches. A feature of this site is the preponderance of juniper *Juniperus communis* and abundance of lichens in the summit heath.

Both Strathspey and Highland Deeside are well wooded. Recent studies by Callander and MacKenzie (1991) and Dunlop (1994) have shown that woodland occupies 15 per cent of Strathspey and 18 per cent of Highland Deeside. The woodlands are composed predominantly of native species, principally Scots pine and birch, which account for 84 per cent of the total woodland in both areas. Some 20 per cent of the total woodland in Strathspey and 25 per cent in Deeside comprise the living descendants of the pioneers that colonized the area after the ice age, without any intervening planted generations. Other self-sown woodlands of pine and birch account for 48 per cent of total woodland in Strathspey and 54 per cent in Highland Deeside. The genuinely native and other self-sown woodlands, which may be derived from planted pine, cannot be distinguished on habitat grounds. A marked characteristic of the planted pines is that they have been derived mainly from local parents. Dunlop calculated that 56 per cent of planted pines on Strathspey are of Strathspey provenance. On Deeside Callander and MacKenzie calculated that 57 per cent of planted pines were of Highland Deeside origin. No other areas in Britain contain such a large proportion of woodland of native species and local origin.

The authentic native pinewood remnants on Deeside include Glen Tanar, Ballochbuie and the Cairngorms pinewoods of Mar described by Steven and Carlisle (1959). A number of additional woods have been accepted on to the Forestry Commission's Register of genuine native pinewoods. In Strathspey, Abernethy Forest is the largest native pinewood in Scotland. Abernethy also contains nationally important forest bogs, a rare habitat type in Britain. Other native pinewoods are Kinveachy Forest and the contiguous forests of Glenmore, Rothiemurchus, Inshriach, Invereshie and Glen Feshie. Birch woodland (Plate 99) is widespread throughout the Cairngorms area but other native broadleaf woods are scarce and small.

* Red Data Book for Invertebrates lists species which occur in fewer than 16 ten km squares in Britain.

† Annex One of the EEC Wild Birds Directive 79/409 lists species which are rare or vulnerable in the European Union.

Lochs are poorly represented in the Cairngorms area but two rivers, the Spey and the Dee, are considered to be of national importance. Few wetlands have survived reclamation but a remnant of the formerly extensive fen and swamp communities of the River Spey floodplain has survived at the Insh Marshes and is rated of international importance.

Three sites deserve special mention for their landform assemblages. Lochnagar has one of the best examples in Scotland of a suite of peri-glacial boulder lobes and terraces, and contains a fine example of a corrie with corrie moraines. At Muir of Dinnet the assemblage of meltwater features is one of the best in Scotland. The assemblage of outwash and river landforms along the length of the River Feshie is also of national importance.

HISTORY OF CONSERVATION

Prelude. The first signs of official interest in the conservation of the Cairngorms came from the Addison Committee in the early 1930s. The Committee called for new measures to protect the countryside and singled out the Cairngorms for possible National Park status. The Committee's proposals were never implemented and the debate about the need for protection of the countryside continued throughout the 1930s.

Foundations. The Second World War heightened interest in the future of the countryside in Britain. The Labour Government appointed the Scottish National Parks Committee in 1946. In its report (1947), the Committee confirmed that five areas, including the Cairngorms, should be established as National Parks. The Committee also recommended a Biological Service and the establishment of nature reserves. A further report published in 1949, listed 51 areas which the Committee recommended for conservation. It proposed that the high ground above 2500 ft in the central Cairngorms should be a National Park Reserve. The Committee advised that if National Parks were not established National Park Reserves should become National Nature Reserves (NNRs). The purpose of NNRs was to provide protection to habitats, species and geological features and the opportunity for scientific monitoring. It envisaged that knowledge of the factors producing changes in plant and animal communities would be of economic value to agriculture, forestry and fisheries. The Committee proposed that NNRs would normally be owned by the State but could remain in private ownership if the proprietor was willing to collaborate in the conservation of wildlife. Public access would be controlled by the Biological Service.

The Committee proposed that Nature Conservation Areas (NCAs) should be established to preserve their existing landscape or scientific value or both. They would not be acquired by the state, nor would public funds normally be used for management, although in certain cases limited grants might be made available to help maintain wildlife. There would be no interference with sporting rights. The Committee considered that it was essential that the Biological Service should be consulted on all planning matters affecting the NCAs. An NCA was to be essentially a monitoring and research area, subject to landowners' consent.

The Committee recommended four sites in the Cairngorms area as NCAs. These were the Valley of the Quoich, the Muir of Dinnet, Dinnet Oakwood and Glen Doll and Coire Fee including Canness and Caenlochan.

When the *National Parks and Access to the Countryside Act* reached the statute book in 1949 there was no provision for National Parks in Scotland. The NCA concept was embodied in a modified form in the Site of Special Scientific Interest (SSSI) provisions of the Act. The Act set up a government wildlife service on a Great Britain basis in the form of the Nature Conservancy with authority to establish NNRs and notify SSSIs.

The Nature Conservancy. In 1951 the five areas that had been proposed as Scottish National Parks were designated National Park Development Areas, giving the Secretary of State for Scotland oversight of all planning decisions.

In 1954 the Nature Conservancy declared the Cairngorms NNR. At 16 068 hectares this was by far the largest NNR in Britain, and one of the largest in Western Europe. Most of the reserve was established by Nature Reserve Agreements (NRAs) with the private owners of Rothiemurchus, Mar and Inshriach estates, although the Nature Conservancy purchased 2157 ha at Inveresie from the Forestry Commission. These were the first NRAs to be negotiated by the Nature Conservancy. They were secured for modest sums, gave the Conservancy limited rights, mainly control over research activities and the ability to appoint wardens, and relied on the co-operation and goodwill of the proprietors. The NRAs did not alter conditions for public access. The Nature Conservancy responded to the fears of the local authorities that there would be restrictions on public access to the new reserve by convening a meeting with open-air interests and local authorities in December 1953 and set up a Cairngorms Consultative Panel. The panel met only once.

The Nature Conservancy completed the first Management Plan for the Cairngorms NNR in 1959. The main objectives of management have changed little since then. They were to:

(a) allow the reserve with its plants and animals to persist naturally as far as possible under the NRA and access conditions, and

(b) rehabilitate any parts severely disturbed, e.g. all felled woodlands.

In addition research was to be encouraged, particularly research directed to conservation and improved land management. The mountain pastures would be allowed to develop naturally to supply food for the red deer, cattle and sheep. The effects of concentrated grazing in deer wintering areas were to be watched with a view to preventing pasture deterioration. The deer cull in Invereshie was to be conducted by the warden to maintain a well-balanced deer stock. Elsewhere stalking remained under the control of the proprietors. Problems of Scots pine regeneration were being researched, including spot-sowing experiments. The principal objectives of management identified in 1958 have stood the test of time. There was an awareness then of some of the issues which would become major problems in later years.

Decade of developments. During the 1960s the Nature Conservancy established NNRs at Caenlochan, Craigellachie and Dinnet Oakwood and large extensions to the Cairngorms NNR by NRAs in Glen Feshie and Glen Avon. The Conservancy tried to buy Glen Feshie in 1962 but the estate was acquired by Lord Dulverton, a man who had a reputation as an active promoter of nature conservation.

This was the decade of major developments in the Cairngorms area. The ski road was built giving access to a large car park in Coire Cas, and a chairlift ascending to over 1100 metres. Cafés, restaurants and ski tows quickly followed. At the same time the Scottish Office encouraged the development of a large holiday resort and leisure centre in Aviemore. Meantime the Glen Shee Chairlift Company built tows, lifts and cafés on the slopes between Meall Odhar and Cairnwell. Construction techniques in these early days were not sensitive to the special needs of fragile mountain environments, and serious mistakes were made, creating problems that have persisted for many years.

In 1967 the Scottish Development Department published a report on the Cairngorms area (Technical Group on the Cairngorms Area of the Eastern Highlands of Scotland, 1967). This was in essence a development report based on the tourism and recreation potential of the area. The group proposed ski development in the northern Corries of Cairn Gorm, on Sgoran Dubh Mor and Carn Ban Mor, Drumochter, Beinn a' Bhuird and Ben Avon with new road access, and new public roads through Glen Feshie and Glen Tilt and linking Tomintoul with Crathie and Nethybridge with Glen More.

The Countryside Commission for Scotland was established in 1968 with responsibility for the conservation and enhancement of the natural beauty and amenity of the Scottish countryside and for promoting its enjoyment. One of the early initiatives of CCS was to appoint a Cairngorms project officer to co-ordinate the work of outdoor interests in the area and to assess and try to resolve recreation problems.

Meanwhile the Nature Conservancy had produced a rehabilitation plan for Glen Feshie. The Conservancy encouraged Glen Feshie Estate to establish blocks of woodland, mainly of Scots pine, but including non-native conifers, whose purpose was to provide food and shelter for red deer. The plan also included provision for fertilizing the riverside flats to improve the quality of grazing. This

was considered necessary to compensate in part for the loss of former deer wintering ground by the extensive afforestation in the lower glen. With Lord Dulverton's agreement the Conservancy also began a study of the ecology and management of the red deer herd. This research soon ran into difficulties over conflicts of aims between the direction of the research programme, the economic imperatives as seen by the estate and the conservation needs of the nature reserve. The study was eventually terminated when the Nature Conservancy was split and the research branch became the Institute of Terrestrial Ecology (ITE) in 1973.

Decade of audit. The split of the Nature Conservancy came about as part of the Conservative Government's policy of separating the customer from the contractor. The conservation branch of NC (the customer) was taken out of the Natural Environment Research Council (NERC) and put under the wing of the Department of the Environment (DoE), with a new title, the Nature Conservancy Council (NCC). The research branch of NC (the contractor) stayed with NERC and became ITE. This separation damaged the coherence of NCC, but the larger budget of DoE was soon reflected in a rapid expansion of manpower and resources in NCC.

Throughout the 1970s the NC/NCC carried out a major review of conservation needs by means of site safeguard in Britain. This involved for the first time systematic survey and an evaluation of the sites needed to safeguard the full range of geographical variation of the communities of plants and animals across Britain. The results of this work were published in the two volumes of the Nature Conservation Review (NCR) (Ratcliffe, 1977). In the NCR the Cairngorms were shown to be of international importance for nature conservation. A further 21 sites in the Cairngorms area were considered to be of national or international importance.

A second revision of the Cairngorms NNR Management Plan was drafted, which identified the need for a major reduction of deer, but this was not endorsed by the proprietors. A period of tension began as the conflict between the interests of the private estates and the conservation needs of the Cairngorms NNR were more explicitly stated in internal NCC reports. One of the casualties of this tension was the Cairngorms Consultative Panel (p. 174).

On the international scene, the Ramsar Conference on the conservation of wetlands of international importance was held in 1971. The Convention was ratified by the British Government in 1976. Five of the Cairngorms lochs were designated Ramsar sites in 1981. Of greater significance was the *European Wild Birds Directive* which came into effect in 1979. This Directive places an obligation on a government to safeguard the habitats of certain scarce or endangered species of birds. Among the measures to be taken is the designation of a network of Special Protection Areas (SPAs) for birds of European importance. There are already some SPAs in the Cairngorms area, and others will probably follow (p. 204).

During the 1970s NCC declared new NNRs at Muir of Dinnet, Morrone and Glen Tanar. The Royal Society for the Protection of Birds (RSPB) acquired land at Loch Insh and Loch Garten. The North East Mountain Trust (NEMT), a new consortium of climbing and hill walking clubs in the North East, was formed and began to produce well researched and argued reports on environmental issues.

The 1970s ended with a clear demonstration of the deficiencies of the SSSI provisions of the 1949 Act. In 1979 Seafield Estate sold 607 ha of predominantly native pinewood in Abernethy Forest SSSI to a new commercial forestry company, Thomson Scottish Forestry (TSF). Following discussions with NCC, TSF undertook to plant only local provenance Scots pine and to lease 100 ha of forest bog to NCC. However it was not prepared to abandon its plan to plough, drain and plant up other boggy areas, and to supplant naturally regenerating pine on the drier moraines by planting up the gaps. The construction of forest roads throughout the property added to development of what was formerly a near natural part of the site. This work was undertaken against NCC advice on an NCR site notified as an SSSI, but nevertheless with grant aid and support from the Forestry Commission. Ironically TSF sold this property to the Royal Society for the Protection of Birds (RSPB) in 1990, which has since blocked the drains to try to restore forest bog conditions to part of the site. Other damage is less easily rectified. This case demonstrated how powerless NCC was to prevent damage even on NCR sites before the *Wildlife & Countryside Act* brought in mandatory consultations measures in 1981 involving delays for negotiation.

Decade of conflict. NCC declared Abernethy Forest a National Nature Reserve by Nature Reserve Agreement in 1982, and purchased Dell Wood at Abernethy in 1986. NCC also declared Creag Meagaidh NNR on the south-west border of the Cairngorms area in 1986. The land had earlier been purchased by Fountain Forestry a few years after removal of the sheep stock. NCC opposed the company's application to afforest 1400 ha on this NCR site, using a mixture of predominantly non-native conifers. However, after the Secretary of State had approved the offer of planting grant for 800 ha, NCC met Fountain Forestry's sale price which was based on the land's value for commercial timber. Because it had secured the sporting rights with the land at Creag Meagaidh NCC was able to put into practice the policy it had advocated in the Cairngorms and elsewhere of reducing the deer herd to a level where natural regeneration could occur without fencing. Neighbouring estates, the Red Deer Commission, other deer interests and the local community were kept fully informed by NCC. Some were concerned that NCC would create a deer vacuum on Creag Meagaidh that would attract deer on to the reserve from adjacent ground, creating a deer sink. So far there has been no sign of

this effect and regeneration and spread of the birch woodland on the reserve has been dramatic.

NCC has been able to encourage similar natural regeneration at Invereshie and Inshriach (purchased by NC in 1966). The NRA with Glen Feshie Estate was renegotiated in 1987 and the protection of this sector improved by an extension of the reserve and additional constraints on management. NCC was not able to secure a commitment to reduce red deer by a significant amount, however, and settled for a programme of rotational fencing to encourage tree regeneration within a succession of enclosures. A similar programme was agreed with Mar Lodge Estate. Here also the then proprietor was not willing to agree to the big reduction in the numbers of deer needed to secure the unfenced regeneration of the forest. NCC was able to protect the standing remnants of native pine in Glen Derry and Glen Quoich by extending the agreements. Negotiations to renew the NRA with Rothiemurchus Estate began in 1984. These proved to be complex and protracted and were not concluded until 1992. Here also standing trees were protected for the lifetime of the agreement. There is a better balance between the numbers of trees and deer on Rothiemurchus than on Mar or Glen Feshie, and the agreement is designed to achieve an appropriate reduction in deer numbers if monitoring studies by Scottish Natural Heritage (SNH, the successor to NCC) show that unfenced regeneration is not getting established.

A key event in the 1980s was the passing of the *Wildlife & Countryside Act* (WCA) in 1981. Part One of the Act consolidated most of the previous species protection legislation. Part 2 was designed to improve the protection given to habitats and species, mainly through the SSSI mechanism. The *National Parks and Access to the Countryside Act 1949* had merely obliged planning authorities to consult the NC before giving planning consent within an SSSI. While the WCA did not change the procedures for developments that needed planning permission, it introduced a new set of procedures to protect SSSIs from damage caused mainly by farm and forestry operations, which are not regulated by the planning Acts. NCC had to inform owners and occupiers of the reasons for notifying an SSSI, the extent of the area involved, and the operations that might damage the features of special interest. In turn owners and occupiers were obliged to give four months notice to NCC if they intended to carry out a listed operation. Government believed that most landowners and farmers were sympathetic to nature conservation and only needed to be made aware of the necessary management for the SSSI to co-operate in its safeguard. In the minority of cases where NCC was not able to persuade the owner or occupier to modify their plans it was envisaged that NCC would get their co-operation by offering compensation for profits they would forgo.

NCC had to undertake the massive task of renotifying all SSSIs under the new terms of the WCA and this job occupied much of its energy throughout the 1980s. The programme was not handled with as much sensitivity as it should have been in some areas, partly because NCC was pressed by government to complete the renotification programme as quickly as possible, and partly because the implications of the procedures were not entirely clear to NCC at the start. The programme generated hostility in some areas from owners and occupiers who objected to the bureaucracy, the delay and the absence of appeal to an independent arbiter, and from some local authorities who saw SSSIs as a constraint on development opportunities.

Meanwhile unhindered by statutory responsibilities the Voluntary Conservation Bodies (VCBs) were acquiring land, building their membership and exerting an increasingly effective influence on environmental affairs. The RSPB extended the Insh Marshes and Abernethy reserves and bought the Glen Avon sector of the Cairngorms NNR. The Scottish Wildlife Trust (SWT) acquired an interest from the Forestry Commission to manage the Ryvoan Pass sector of Glen More Forest as a native pinewood reserve.

The downhill ski industry was thriving in Scotland in the 1970s. A new ski area was opened at the Lecht and major expansion took place at Glen Shee.

At Cairn Gorm the Chairlift Company submitted an application for expansion on to the slopes west of Coire Cas. This new ground offered extensive nursery slopes, often restricted elsewhere on Cairn Gorm by limited snow cover or difficulties of access. With the support of the Highlands and Islands Development Board (HIDB), which owned the land, the company submitted a planning application for a road from Coire Cas into Lurcher's Gully with lifts, tows and snow fences on the slopes between. Objections to the application came from the two statutory conservation agencies, NCC and CCS, and a wide range of other bodies. The Scottish Secretary 'called in' the application and ordered a public inquiry. The Company and the landowners were supported by Highland Regional Council (HRC), the Scottish Sports Council and the Scottish National Ski Council. Prominent objectors at the public inquiry included NCC, CCS, Grampian Regional Council, the International Union for Nature Conservation, the RSPB, the NEMT, SWT and local conservationists, the Badenoch and Strathspey Conservation Group.

The objectors planned for the inquiry with great care. Their own evidence was prepared and rehearsed, and the developer's case was carefully researched. Conservation witnesses spoke at the inquiry with conviction and authority. The Secretary of State agreed with the Inquiry Reporter's recommendation that the application be refused because of the area's outstanding scientific, scenic and recreational importance. However, he did not rule out the possibility of a more limited scheme which required no new road access.

The second attempt to extend ski developments into Lurcher's Gully was more carefully planned. The Cairngorm Chairlift Company prepared a development plan and the HIDB drafted a

management plan for its Cairn Gorm estate. Meantime NCC notified the Northern Corries as an SSSI against stiff opposition. Shortly after this the NEMT drew the attention of the Scottish Affairs Committee members, who were investigating the HIDB, to the management of the Cairn Gorm estate. The Committee's report, published in 1985, recommended that there should be no ski development within the Northern Corries SSSI. This recommendation was not accepted by the Government which pointed out that the National Planning Guidelines for ski developments (Scottish Development Department, 1984) recognized that further ski developments on Cairn Gorm should be possible subject to considerations of access and consultation with interested parties. The consultation was undertaken by Highland Regional Council which convened a working group to review the future of downhill skiing on Cairn Gorm and the options for development. With the exception of NCC, the working group concluded that expansion westward to Lurcher's Gully was feasible without significant damage to visual amenity or nature conservation. It had become clear to NCC that while the new proposal was likely to be less harmful than the earlier plan it was also unacceptable.

The same conclusion was reached by most of the voluntary groups that had opposed the original Lurcher's Gully development. They formed the Save the Cairngorms Campaign and set about energetically to raise public awareness. Both sides used campaign literature, videos, parliamentary lobbying and a variety of media techniques to gain public support. No planning application was made but a policy supporting the ski development was included in Highland Region's draft Structure Plan. After wide consultation the Secretary of State deleted the policy from the Structure Plan in 1991, and for the second time in 10 years ski developments proposals at Lurcher's Gully were rejected. The inquiry and the conflict over the second attempt to develop Lurcher's Gully was a key issue in the debate over the future of the Cairngorms.

Without doubt the Lurcher's Gully developments were the most bitterly contested proposals in the Cairngorms Area since the war. Few would disagree that the resolution of such conflicts could be better managed.

The World Conservation Strategy (WCS), published in 1980, identified the Scottish Highlands as a priority biogeographic area in need of improved measures of protection. In response NCC and Grampian Regional Council convened a conference at Braemar on the theme of the WCS in Grampian. Seventy delegates attended, participating in four workshops on farming, forestry, the wildlife resource and landscape, recreation and tourism. Amongst its conclusions, the conference recommended that the Cairngorms required high levels of unified conservation management and should be under the sole ownership of a new and specially created body. The wildlife syndicate recommended that red deer numbers in the Cairngorms NNR should be reduced considerably to a level that is compatible with the natural environment (Grampian Regional Council/Nature Conservancy Council, 1984).

In 1981 the IUCN General Assembly called on the British Government to 'take all practical steps to secure for the Cairngorm Mountains protection appropriate to their international significance'. The World Wilderness Conference twice, in 1983 and 1987, called on the British Government to propose the Cairngorms to IUCN as a World Heritage Area. Professor Kai Curry-Lindahl, a noted world authority on conservation, commented in 1990 that it was an absurd paradox that neither the British Government nor the NCC had tried to remedy the (deteriorating) situation by acquiring the whole area as a strict nature reserve. It is now high time to do so, he said, before the Cairngorms becomes irreversibly destroyed (Curry-Lindahl, 1990).

The decisive decade. The 1990s saw some signs of a wider acceptance of the claims of conservation. Traditional attitudes persisted in some places, however, as the conflict over the Insh Marshes shows. Extensive floods in Badenoch in the late 1980s, which widely affected property, aroused local concerns and persuaded HRC to commission an engineering study. The engineering solution for the relief of floods above Kincraig was to dredge the bed of the River Spey below Loch Insh. NCC was concerned that this study did not assess the ecological consequences for the Insh Marshes and the physical features of the alluvial fan of the River Feshie, and therefore commissioned the Institute of Hydrology (IH) to study these consequences. The riparian proprietors saw the engineers' scheme as an opportunity to reclaim the Insh marshes or Insh Meadows, which in the nineteenth century grew crops of hay and flax. They gave notice to NCC of their intention to carry out a dredging operation in the bed of the Spey at its confluence with the Feshie but agreed to await the results of the IH study. The study showed that the dredging scheme would lower flood waters but would also reduce water levels on the lower Insh Marshes by up to one metre. The impact would not extend above the River Tromie confluence, and would therefore make no difference to the flooding of property at Kingussie and further upstream. The proprietors then gave NCC notice of a less ambitious dredging scheme but before IH could assess its effect on water levels the contractors began to remove trees on the islands in the River Spey where the relief channel was to be dug. At the request of SNH the Secretary of State served a Nature Conservation Order to halt the work. The IH study forecast that the new dredging scheme would have little impact on water levels upstream so SNH consented to this new scheme.

The Order remained in place as the proprietors had not withdrawn their original notice for a bigger dredging scheme. Objections to the Order were heard at a public inquiry in 1993. The Secretary of State accepted the Inquiry Reporter's recommendation that the order should stay in place but be modified to allow maintenance of the smaller channel.

It was clear that the limited extent of the benefits of flood control in this scheme was not considered sufficient by the Secretary of State to outweigh the considerable damage that would be done to national and international conservation values had it gone ahead.

In 1989 the Government announced its intention to break up NCC and to merge NCC in Scotland with CCS. The *Natural Heritage (Scotland) Act* 1991 brought the concept of sustainability into legislation for the first time. SNH was required to 'have regard to the desirability of ensuring that anything done, whether by SNH or any other in relation to the natural heritage of Scotland is undertaken in a manner which is sustainable'. SNH was also expected to develop partnerships to pursue its aims. In all other respects the new agency inherited the functions of its predecessors.

As one of its last major initiatives the CCS published a report on the Management of the Mountain Areas of Scotland (Countryside Commission for Scotland, 1990). The Commission recommended that four areas of special importance, including the Cairngorms, should become National Parks. Secondly, it made general recommendations for the better management of upland areas throughout Scotland. The Scottish Secretary rejected the Commission's proposal for National Parks but set up the Cairngorms Working Party (CWP) in March 1991.

The Members of the CWP represented a cross section of interests in the Cairngorms area. Their remit from the Scottish Secretary was to consider what changes are necessary in land use to achieve an integrated management strategy, taking into account the conservation and enhancement of natural resources, social and economic benefits and access for recreation. The Scottish Secretary emphasized that any future management structure should be firmly based on the voluntary principle.

The CWP concluded that the Cairngorms area is outstanding in natural heritage terms and deserves and requires special treatment and the highest level of care and attention to revitalize the quality of the natural environment (Cairngorms Working Party, 1993). The natural heritage features must be protected and enhanced and damaged habitats restored. The Caledonian forest should be extended and distinctive open ground such as the heather moors of the Eastern Cairngorms should be maintained. Environmentally friendly farming practices should be promoted. Adequate monitoring systems to give warning when limits of acceptable changes are reached must be provided, and remedial action must then be taken. The precautionary principle should be applied whenever there is reasonable doubt about the precise impact of potentially damaging developments. Finally, the Working Party concluded that the people of the area need to be committed to the success of an integrated strategy to revitalize the quality of the natural environment.

These conclusions were generally welcomed by conservation spokesmen. Criticism was, however, directed at the CWP's recommendations for developing and implementing the management strategy. Its solution was a formal partnership of local authorities and public agencies with a Partnership Board, advisory committee and partnership staff. The CWP report argued that the voluntary principle should be tested in the context of a management strategy, supported by advisory services and adequate incentives. However, the report saw regulation as necessary to safeguard limits of acceptable change, especially through the planning process, and as a last resort measure to protect environmental features of national or international importance. For instance the CWP suggested that government might legislate to give last resort powers to the Red Deer Commission to control deer numbers on grounds of significant damage to the natural heritage, and that the European Directives are likely to provide powers to prevent damage to Natura 2000 sites, which are Special Protection Areas (SPAs) designated under the *Wild Birds Directive* and Special Areas of Conservation (SACs) designated under the *Habitats and Species Directive*. The report proposed that the voluntary principle be assessed over five years while assistance and advice is concentrated on key sites of environmental importance currently under threat, such as the native pinewoods.

The Government accepted most of the recommendations of the CWP and set up the Cairngorms Partnership (CP) in 1994. The CP was tasked to produce a Management Strategy through consensus based on the principle of sustainable development. The Strategy was published after extensive consultation in 1997. It gives overriding priority to the protection and conservation of the high hills by minimizing human impacts and repairing or reinstating damage. It seeks to encourage the regeneration of native woodlands, including high altitude scrub, and to develop the Deeside Forest and the Forest of Spey. It looks to manage deer populations at levels which would allow for the conservation and enhancement of native woodland and moorland and to reduce the amount of deer fencing in the area.

The Partnership has no independent power. The Government gave no direction to the agencies represented on the Partnership to co-operate and no suitable funding arrangments have been made to give incentives to local managers to manage the estates and land in ways that are sympathetic to the aims of the Management Strategy. The Partnership's views have been ignored by government: the Scottish Office ignored its request to call in the planning application for the funicular railway on Cairn Gorm. Its days may be numbered in any case, as plans for a National Park in the Cairngorms are implemented.

Selection of the Natura 2000 sites in the Cairngorms area proceeded during the 1990s. A number of areas have now been submitted for designation, although the protective powers of the European Directives, which CWP saw as providing an important regulatory function, are limited. Protection of Natura 2000 sites is based on tightened SSSI procedures. For developments requiring planning permission, planning authorities must show that where no alternative sites are available the development is of overriding national importance in the public interest. If the site contains priority habitat types the overriding interest must relate to issues of human health or public safety. Priority habitats in the Cairngorms area include Caledonian forest, active blanket bog and alluvial forests.

The influence of the VCBs continued to grow in the 1980s. Three opportunities to acquire land in the Cairngorms arose in the 1990s. A consortium of the RSPB, the World-wide Fund for Nature (WWF) and the John Muir Trust, made an unsuccessful bid in 1992 to buy Mar Lodge Estate. Subsequently in 1995 this important estate was acquired by the National Trust for Scotland (NTS). This estate promises to be a model of conservation management. Red deer have been heavily culled and the beneficial effects on the natural establishment of native trees and shrubs are already becoming evident. Plantations of exotic conifers are being felled and estate roads on high ground have been closed and the ground reinstated.

In 1994 Glen Feshie estate was put on the market. A bid by the RSPB and the John Muir Trust to secure backing from the National Heritage Memorial Fund to purchase was unsuccessful, mainly because the rival bidder, the Will Woodlands Charitabale Trust, claimed to be a conservation organization. This newcomer stated that a major objective was to regenerate the native woodland. Will Woodlands turned out to be a group of London-based bankers and solicitors with little knowledge of the Cairngorms or Highland estate management. Sensibly, they appointed a group of experts to advise them but so neglected to act on the advice given that one of the group felt obliged to resign. Will Woodlands then demonstrated its sensitivity by erecting a large industrial clad shed in the glen for storing equipment and feed for deer. After several years' silence the Trust announced a plan for 17 km of fencing for woodland regeneration purposes but made no mention of how the deer would be reduced to sustainable levels. Shortly after, in 1997, Will Woodlands announced its intention to sell Glen Feshie to the highest bidder. For the third time in ten years a key part of the Cairngorms was to change hands to a private buyer. Although a consortium of public bodies (SNH, FC, Highland Council and HIE) and non-government organizations (John Muir Trust and NTS) was organized to buy the estate, it was sold to a Danish businessman, Mr Klaus Helversen, in November 1997. The estate's initial proposals are thought to include plans for substantial reductions of deer to allow natural regeneration, supplemented by some fencing.

Deer management policy came under review during the 1990s. The revised *Deer (Scotland) Act 1996* makes provision for landowners and the Deer Commission for Scotland to control deer to prevent damage to the natural heritage. SNH supported the Commission's proposal that the deer population should be reduced by 100 000 animals as a first step, and backed the Deer Management Groups as the key to integrated management of red deer and their habitat.

On Deeside landowners, the Forestry Commission and SNH completed a report showing how the special character of the woodland on Highland Deeside could be perpetuated and enhanced. In Strathspey the Forestry Commission announced a new management plan for Glenmore Forest, which was approved in 1995. As part of its management strategy for the native pinewoods, the plan would involve restoring two-thirds of the forest to native Scots pine by gradually removing non-native species. A similar policy would be adopted elsewhere on the Commission's estate.

The Scottish Office Agricultural and Fisheries Department (SOAFD) designated the Cairngorms Straths as an Environmentally Sensitive Area (ESA) in 1993. This is a voluntary scheme. Entrants receive payments for adopting a range of environmentally friendly, traditional farming operations, such as protecting hay meadows and improved pastures, moorland and native woodland, and restoring stone dykes, ponds and landscape features.

The 1990s saw the beginning of a change of attitude towards environmental conservation. Conservation was becoming recognized as a legitimate land use and it was more widely accepted that key wildlife sites should be managed for their conservation interest. European and British government policies were making adjustments to reduce food surpluses. The Forestry Commission no longer had to pursue unrealistic planting targets. Fiscal policies were adjusted to slow down the engines of environmental destruction. However one area where conflict between development and environmental interests continued at the end of the 1990s was in the old battleground of downhill skiing on Cairn Gorm. In 1994 the Cairngorm Chairlift Company submitted a planning application for a funicular railway to run for 2 km from the Coire Cas car park to an enlarged Ptarmigan restaurant. The railway would run on 93 concrete pillars 2 metres thick, 18 m apart and up to 6 m high. At the upper end the railway would enter a 250 m long tunnel cut into the granite bedrock and gravel. The Ptarmigan restaurant would be replaced by a highly visible visitor centre and 250-seat restaurant. Some 18 000 tons of rock and rubble high on the mountain would need to be excavated and disposed of. The total cost of the project is estimated at £17 million.

SNH initially objected to the funicular plans, mainly on the grounds that it would lead to increased numbers of visitors to the Cairngorms Natura 2000 site, and cause aggravated damage to the rare and sensitive mountain habitats and disturbance to rare breeding birds. After complex negotiations the developer modified the design of the new Ptarmigan building and revised the Visitor Management Plan. A key part of this is a programme monitoring the numbers of visitors and their behaviour along with the features of special conservation interest. In addition the developer undertook to seal non-skiing visitors inside the Ptarmigan building. These provisions were confirmed by a legally binding agreement under Section 50 of the planning Acts, and consequently SNH withdrew its objection.

In 1996 Scottish Wildlife and Countryside Link presented an alternative, involving closure of the ski road to all but service vehicles, removal of the Coire Cas and Coire na Ciste car parks with reinstatement of the ground, and a gondola link between Glen More and Coire Cas. This proposal was not welcomed by the planning authority and planning permission for the funicular application was granted in May 1997.

The Scottish Office then approved a £9 million grant to the project from HIE and supported its bid for £2.9 million of European Union funds. The European funding application was temporarily suspended as the European Commission objected, partly to allow investigation into the environmental impact of the scheme. Subsequently, funding was confirmed subject to a number of conditions, and construction, due to be completed by the end of 2001, has commenced.

Concern has been widely expressed that the Section 50 Agreement will not stand the test of time. It has been calculated that the funicular will need to attract 200 000 to 250 000 summer visitors to be viable, that is 100 000 more than any other local visitor attraction and four or five times current chairlift ticket sales in summer. The big investment to support the funicular at Cairn Gorm will likely be at the expense of the other ski centres in Scotland.

Meanwhile the planning approval was challenged by the NGOs in court. The RSPB and the WWF jointly lodged a petition for judicial review at the Court of Session in Edinburgh. The grounds for the review were whether the boundaries of the Cairngorms SPA and SAC are consistent with the terms of the Directives and secondly whether the Section 50 Agreement protects the Natura 2000 site. The petition was rejected.

Many regard the funicular project as a throwback to the worst type of planning and development mistakes on Cairn Gorm of earlier decades. Professor Christopher Smout, the Deputy Chairman of SNH, wrote to *The Scotsman* in May 1996:

> A thoroughly unsatisfactory proposal of this sort, rushed through in an atmosphere of controversy, is the last thing that should be foisted on one of the most important mountain areas in Northern Europe . . . we are likely to be faced with another economic, political and planning disaster in the Highlands.

WHERE WE ARE TODAY

Without question the most serious problem in the Cairngorms is the high number of red deer which prevent natural regeneration of woodland, scrub and tall herb communities (see Chapter 11).

Red deer numbers in the Cairngorms Area have doubled since the 1960s and deer have spread eastward. They have also lost traditional wintering grounds which have been fenced for forestry. The most obvious effect of this has been the widespread repression of tree regeneration, the destruction of the altitudinal scrub zone and the confinement of tall herb communities to cliff ledges inaccessible to deer. In some places deer have destroyed the heather sward and caused soil erosion. Management of deer for sporting purposes has also had some undesirable side effects. All-terrain vehicles, which have replaced ponies as a means to extract carcasses on most estates, have damaged vegetation, and poorly constructed hill roads have caused soil erosion and damaged visual amenity and wild land values.

Deer themselves would benefit from a reduction in their numbers. In a smaller population deer would achieve greater body weight, antler size and better reproduction. Other wildlife would also benefit from the spread of native woodland, scrub and other vegetation communities of the deer range.

Sporting estates, however, are valued on the size of their stag cull and proprietors are anxious to maintain a good stock of stags to meet their obligations to their stalking clients. Owners are also keen to keep professional stalkers employed and maintain the prop to the rural economy that stalking and venison sales provide. In order to meet these concerns, compromises to reverse the decline of the native woodland remnants have been reached by using fences. Fencing, however, has many drawbacks. These include the high cost of deer fences, breaching caused by snowdrifts, avalanches, and windblown trees, loss of birds killed by striking the fences, failure of native broadleaf trees to survive when the enclosure is opened up to deer, increased grazing and browsing pressure on unfenced land, blockage of public access and the damage to visual amenity caused by rectangular blocks of woodland.

Reduction of the deer population has to be planned and executed over the whole of a natural deer range. This needs co-operation, commitment and resources. The Red Deer Commission (now the Deer Commission for Scotland) has called for a reduction for many years. Action needs to be sustained over a long period. Reform of the *Deer (Scotland) Act* may have provided the necessary mechanisms for regulation to protect natural heritage interests. A large reduction of deer numbers in the core area has begun, but a prolonged effort will be needed.

Commercial forestry has had a smaller impact in the Cairngorms area than in many other parts of Scotland but Callander and MacKenzie in Deeside and Dunlop in Strathspey have shown that even in these areas recent plantings have included more non-native conifers. The ending of tax benefits in 1988, and new Woodland Grant Schemes, which have increased the incentives to plant native broadleaf trees and local Scots pine and encourage natural regeneration, have not entirely halted this trend.

Even where native tree species predominate in commercial forestry there are some adverse effects on wildlife. Fencing has excluded red deer from traditional wintering grounds, putting greater pressure on unfenced native woods. Ploughing and drainage destroy naturally developed soil profiles. Timber extraction routes can be visually harmful

within areas of high landscape value. Clear felling is disruptive to visual amenity and wildlife. Selective and coup felling would be more environmentally acceptable in forests in sensitive areas. On the other hand even commercial forests composed of non-native species bring some benefits to wildlife. They provide shelter to wildlife and comparative freedom from disturbance between thinnings and final felling.

Grouse moors are a highly valued habitat of great European importance (Chapter 12). The desirable balance between woodland and moorland in the Cairngorms area is being addressed. There is general agreement that most of the native pine woodland remnants should be encouraged to spread naturally to their altitudinal limits.

SNH is conducting research into the grouse moors of north-east Scotland to identify the moors that are most important for wildlife and to record their management. This should provide a database that will be useful in the debate about the balance between woodland and moorland.

Traditional grouse moor management provides many benefits for the wildlife adapted to this environment, but it has some drawbacks. Grouse moor managers have bulldozed new hill roads to improve access for shooting guests. Muirburn regimes are rarely ideal for wildlife other than grouse. Predator control may involve the illegal persecution of protected species. Nevertheless there is concern that the poorer moors where grouse stocks are very low may be forced to convert to commercial forestry. However, so long as there is a strong demand for grouse shooting this unique habitat will be maintained at no cost to the taxpayer. It would be a serious loss to conservation if all the grouse moors were planted up, but there is scope for a new type of forestry on these moorlands, involving native species established in a mosaic pattern with open spaces and glades providing a wide variety of game, including red and black grouse, capercaillie, mountain hare and red and roe deer.

Farming, together with forestry, has been responsible for creating much of the character of the present Cairngorms landscape. Domestic grazing animals on the moors and hills have modified the natural vegetation, helping to prevent regeneration of the native woodlands and scrub. Cattle were an important part of the Highland economy until the nineteenth century, but sheep replaced them as the principal livestock on the hill. There are now few sheep in the mountain core area although they continue to be an important part of the economy of the wider area.

Cultivation is confined to the straths and glens. This is a low-key type of farming. It has greatly modified the landscape but has created habitats not without benefit for the wildlife which is adapted to the meadows, marshes, shelter belts, farm woodland and farm buildings and the rhythms of the farming year.

Until recently British agricultural policy was to maximize food production. Land reclamation was subsidized and intensive farming methods were encouraged. Reclamation was widespread in the

Cairngorms area with marginal hill land being brought back into cultivation for the first time since the mid-nineteenth century when the rural population was at its maximum. In the post-war years many wetlands, bogs and marshes were also drained for the first time. Species adapted to traditional farming methods have declined, the most notable recent example perhaps being the corncrake, but the Cairngorms area has suffered less than the more intensively farmed parts of Britain. The Common Agricultural Policy of the European Community generated large food surpluses and so policies to reduce excess food production were introduced recently. Land reclamation is no longer supported and measures to protect and enhance the natural heritage are being introduced.

Much of the low ground in the Cairngorms area was included in the Cairngorm Straths Environmentally Sensitive Area (p. 178), and the lessons learned are being applied more widely through the Rural Stewardship Scheme.

There are few industries in the Cairngorms area apart from widely scattered whisky distilleries and sawmills. However, more distant industries have a significant impact in the area. The acid soils of the Cairngorms are sensitive to pollution from nitrous oxides and sulphur dioxide in the atmosphere since they are poorly buffered. High altitude aggravates aerial pollution as concentrations of pollution are greatest in the mists and low cloud which persist longest on high ground. The pulses of concentrated, extremely acid runoff that occur in thaws flush through the drainage system and create high degrees of stress in freshwater organisms. The need for systematic monitoring of atmospheric pollution and its ecological impact on freshwater systems and snow-bed communities in particular should be addressed now that the Cairngorms area is included in the international Environmental Change Network. This network will support and supplement the work that is being done already to monitor pollution levels in the Cairngorms.

The development of Aviemore, the ski road and ski developments on Cairn Gorm since the early 1960s has had a significant local impact. Small areas of the River Spey-Insh Marshes SSSI and the Craigellachie NNR were taken to construct the new A9 trunk road. New housing developments, caravan sites and roads have also brought about minor losses of wildlife habitat. There is some concern at the loss of native and amenity woodland habitat to housing developments but the total area lost so far has been small. All the same if this trend continues the loss to local communities may become significant because the amenities worst affected are in places close to where most people live.

The second major problem in the Cairngorms is the selective pressure on wildlife caused by the rise in visitor numbers. This is where there has been the most public conflict between land uses, and yet wildlife and landscape conservation, recreation and tourist interests share many values and ought to be in alliance to safeguard a common resource.

Cairn Gorm has been the focus of conflict. The plateau between Cairn Gorm and Ben Macdui supports a wider range of montane species than any other plateau area. It is also, through the ski road and chairlift, the most accessible area of high ground. Montane vegetation thrives in the severe climate but it is vulnerable to the pressure of human trampling. The post-war increase of visitor numbers to the high ground has had a visible effect. Where footpaths have been widened, the gravelly soil has been eroded, vegetation has been destroyed and disturbance has increased. However, even now the damage is localized, and the adverse impact on amenity and wild land values has been more significant than on wildlife.

SNH has been measuring the impact of visitors on the wildlife of the mountain plateau for several years. Management measures to direct visitors away from the most vulnerable areas are needed. This could be achieved through the joint efforts of agencies involved in the Cairngorms Partnership to provide appropriate literature, displays and exhibits in public places and visitor centres, through ranger services providing guided walks and talks, through the provision of alternative attractions on robust sites following, for example, the model of Landmark at Carrbridge, and the provision of more mountain bike routes on challenging but robust terrain on the lower ground.

The impact of visitors is more readily contained on low ground, especially in woodland. There is a need for more access to be provided and advertised on lower ground, both near to where people live and most visitors stay.

A more controversial issue is the question of restoring the 'long walk in' on the north side of the Cairngorms. The need for this radical measure has been debated. Now that the funicular railway is being built on Cairn Gorm, control over the number of people gaining easy access to the plateau is promised. It would then be possible to manage recreational use of the plateau on a more sustainable basis that at present.

Statutory conservation in Britain is based on the voluntary principle and enshrined in the *National Parks and Access to the Countryside Act* 1949 and the *Wildlife & Countryside Act* 1981. The principal measures used to protect sites of importance to nature conservation are the declaration of NNRs and the notification of SSSIs. SNH inherited criteria for the selection of biological and earth science SSSIs from NCC (Nature Conservancy Council, 1989, 1990). Until 1981 the only statutory requirement attached to an SSSI was that the planning authority had to consult NCC before granting planning permission for developments on SSSIs. In Scotland NCC could ask the Secretary of State to call in a planning application on an NCR site. NCC could not prevent harmful developments that did not need planning permission and a few sites in Scotland were damaged by agricultural and forestry developments before 1981. The WCA obliged owners and occupiers to consult SNH before carrying out any operation listed as having the potential to damage the interest of the site. This gives SNH the opportunity to offer a management agreement to prevent the damage if persuasion is not successful. Notification of an SSSI can be a catalyst for complaints that SNH is damaging local employment opportunities, though these have seldom been substantiated. Notification has also been thought to stimulate proposals for developments that would not otherwise have been contemplated.

NNR status has been reserved for sites of national importance to nature conservation. But not every site of such importance has been declared a NNR. NCC policy was to reserve this status for cases where there was a threat or an opportunity. Some exceptions involving purchase of land by NCC have been mentioned earlier. NCC and now SNH have last resort powers of compulsory purchase but they have never been used in Scotland.

To what extent have NNRs and SSSIs been an important tool of conservation in the Cairngorms area? It is difficult to judge the protection that has been afforded by the statutory conservation sites. How often have potential developers been diverted from these sites? This can never be known, but the authors of the 1967 Cairngorms report ruled out any ski development on Braeriach although they asserted that it had more potential than any ski area in Scotland. One objector at the public inquiry into the new A9 trunk route proposed an alternative eastern route, but this was rejected partly because it would have entered the Cairngorms NNR. Local authority strategic plans now contain stronger protective policies for NNRs and SSSIs. There is a general presumption against harmful developments on statutory conservation sites.

The voluntary NRAs have safeguarded some wildlife interests in the Cairngorms, preventing exploitation of the native pinewood remnants and controlling muirburn, grazing by domestic stock and some sporting activities. Although protection has been increased by recent renewals of the NRAs, they mostly fall short of addressing the deer problem. Few positive measures have been possible under the NRAs; research projects, sign-posting, fencing and until the mid-1970s some tree planting, have been possible although it has to be said that lack of positive action has been partly due to NCC's policy of minimal interference and lack of resources for reserve management.

NCC was criticized for being too passive in the Cairngorms and for not tackling the problem of high deer numbers. Partly this has been because the deterioration in the environment is slow and unspectacular. NCC's policy was to work with the landowners on the basis that their co-operation and goodwill was the only firm basis that there was for conservation. This approach was conditioned by the government policy of reliance on the voluntary principle in conservation. Compulsory purchase was an option of last resort but had to be approved by the Secretary of State, and was reserved to prevent the complete destruction of the interest of a site. In the Cairngorms NCC saw regeneration within fenced enclosures, which could be achieved with the co-operation of the proprietors, as a viable alternative to a general reduction of deer numbers. It was recognized that a general reduction in deer

numbers could only be achieved it if was applied throughout a natural deer range.

The European Directives on Wild Birds and Habitats and Species are likely to exert a new imperative within those sites which the Government designates as Natura 2000 sites. Harmful planning developments within these sites which are opposed by SNH will proceed only if they are of overriding national importance and no alternative site is available. Appeals to the European Commission are likely to ensure that the protective mechanisms are strictly applied. It will be important to ensure that NNRs and SSSIs which do not qualify as Natura 2000 sites do not suffer from lack of resources or a relaxation of protection as a consequence.

The growing influence of the VCBs has been demonstrated in several ways; by the effective campaigns fought against ski developments in Lurcher's Gully and the evidence given to the Scottish Affairs Committee examination of the Highlands and Islands Development Board. The link up of the VCBs in Scotland in Scottish Wildlife and Countryside Link (SWCL) in the 1980s was an important step by the voluntary movement towards achieving a coherent voice and therefore a more powerful influence on events. The Cairngorms Campaign, which originally brought the voluntary bodies together as a task force which fought to remove the policy supporting the Lurcher's Gully development from Highland Region's Structure Plan, continues as a pressure group. Although unsuccessful in acquiring Mar Lodge or Glen Feshie estates, the RSPB remains an important landowner in the Cairngorms area. It is now a highly professional conservation body which retains a campaigning zeal and a talent for publicity.

Despite the growth in the influence of the VCBs during the last 20 years, local support for conservation is still patchy. Highland Regional Council has given support to potentially harmful economic developments, notably in the ski industry, in the past. Badenoch and Strathspey District Council supported flood prevention schemes on the Spey which would have had damaging ecological consequences for the Insh Marshes. This Council also opposed the renotification of nearly all the SSSIs in the District as a matter of principle. In contrast Grampian Regional Council supported the objectors at the Lurcher's Gully public inquiry, supported the principles of the World Conservation Strategy and took the lead in setting down management guidelines for the eastern Cairngorms (Grampian Regional Council, 1990).

Government agencies have been criticized in the past for their poor performance in environmental conservation. The Forestry Commission's new policy for the native pinewoods is an example of a change in attitude. The Commission also provides special incentives for the maintenance and enhancement of privately owned native pinewoods and the creation of new native pinewoods. Forest Enterprise also manages its commercial plantations in a more sympathetic way, providing more space for native broadleaves, leaving more unplanted areas and diversifying the age structure to enhance visual amenity. Similar management in private forests is encouraged by the Forestry Authority grant schemes. The Scottish Office Agriculture and Fisheries Department introduced the ESA scheme in the Cairngorms area. Agricultural policy no longer encourages maximum food production and grant schemes for land reclamation have been closed. The development policies of Highlands and Islands Enterprise have been modified and the periodic strident criticisms of NCC indulged by its predecessor, the Highlands and Islands Development Board, have been absent.

Key actors in the rural scene are the landowners. The VCBs are acquiring large estates in the Cairngorms area. It seems likely that other important areas in the mountain core will come into conservation hands soon. Private owners are moving away from traditional attitudes to land management. Most owners in the Cairngorms area have joined the Deer Management Groups, which are now giving serious attention to the problem of the excessive deer population. On Deeside it was the landowners that took the initiative to tackle the threat to the natural qualities of the forest there.

Not least among the general influences for good in the Cairngorms area is the development of environmental education at all learning levels. Important new initiatives are being launched which should provide great benefits in the long run in the Cairngorms area, as elsewhere, by conditioning public perceptions and raising awareness.

The principal lesson learned from the history of the past 40 years in the Cairngorms is that the statutory conservation measures based on the voluntary principle are unlikely alone to reverse the damage being done to the natural heritage without the support of a balanced package of incentives and penalties. Furthermore statutory conservation measures are mainly about the safeguard of sites and fail to make a connection with wider conservation problems, such as the management of red deer throughout their range.

The development of an articulate, politically astute voluntary conservation sector acting together and deploying soundly based scientific arguments is proving to be increasingly effective in the Cairngorms.

THE FUTURE

In recent years commentators have often claimed that the Cairngorms are at a crossroads. Britain's premier conservation area has suffered serious neglect and attrition for too long. Efforts to arrest the decline have lacked resources, will and conviction. The solutions to the problems are not simple and will not be painless, but there is some cause for optimism. The Scottish Parliament passed the *National Parks (Scotland) Act* in 2000, and shortly afterwards Ministers formally proposed the establishment of a National Park in the Cairngorms area. There is a wide spectrum of interests that has the energy and commitment to achieve conservation goals in the Cairngorms. Included in this spectrum are the more perceptive landowners, who see the

opportunities and challenges that will arise under the new regime, and are willing to meet them. There is also a new generation of local authority councillors who see the sort of future that an ecologically sustainable policy for the Cairngorms area would have for stable long-term employment and local prosperity.

In the long run the core area of the Cairngorms should support a forest of pine and birch with an abundant understory of juniper. Associated trees would be alder, willow, rowan, aspen and gean (wild cherry), while on the better soils of the straths there would be oak, ash, wych elm and hazel. This forest would extend up to the natural treeline with glades, rocky outcrops and forest bogs breaking up the canopy. It would have a varied structure, with some thick, dense stands, while elsewhere it would be more open (Plate 99). There would be an abundance of young trees and natural regeneration, and in time old, over-mature trees and dead standing and lying timber, providing homes for forest invertebrates and birds and shelter for a variety of mammals. Above the natural treeline there would be a zone of alpine scrub of stunted birch and pine with mountain willows, prostrate juniper and dwarf birch. Above this would be open heather moorland with a variety of heaths, blanket bog and locally tall herb communities. Further uphill again the zone of mountain heaths and snow-beds, alpine springs and flushes and boulder fields would show only minor changes from today due to freedom from stress caused by pollution and the erosion caused by trampling pressure.

Around the mountain core there would be a thriving commercial forest composed of local provenance Scots pine and birch, much of it having regenerated naturally, managed by selective and group felling, with some compartments left to grow on to become over mature and some groups left indefinitely.

Deer numbers would be adjusted to be in balance with their habitat, with an annual cull minimizing natural deaths. Income from stalking and venison would be maintained by the higher premiums paid for size of carcass and antler, and supplemented by sporting income from a range of forest game.

Elsewhere, and particularly in the east of the area, the better moors would continue to be managed for red grouse. The muirburn cycle would be adjusted to achieve the optimum range of heather and associated plant communities for grouse and other moorland fauna. This would mean that patches of willow, birch and pine would be left to provide cover and diversity, flushes would be protected to provide insect food for young birds, and steep slopes, scree and rocky outcrops would not be burnt.

The farmland in the glens and straths would be managed to optimize wildlife habitats. The incentives in the current ESA scheme would provide the basis for this regime. Permanent set aside would be used to grow native oak, ash, elm and willow. The effects of floods would be dissipated by allowing floodwaters to disperse on river flood plains.

Comparison with western Norway is instructive. Here small farms prosper in a mixed forest and farm landscape under a regime that subsidizes farmers with a living wage, efficient public transport and good public services. There would, as in Norway, be freedom for responsible public access to uncultivated land. In the mountain core zone access would be restricted to activities which do not involve built facilities such as roads, car parks, buildings and bridges, and which do not need mechanical aids such as ski lifts or vehicles. An exception would have to be made for the existing ski area on Cairn Gorm, but the long walk in to the mountains on the Glen More side of the hills would be restored outwith the skiing season.

Employment opportunities would be greatly increased in labour-intensive activities: sensitive forest management involving selective felling and extraction; crafts using timber; the supply of venison and other game products. An expanded and integrated ranger service and a permanent footpath repair and maintenance workforce would service visitors and climbers. Keepers, stalkers, ghillies and game managers would provide quality sporting experience to clients. Retail outlets would serve the needs of outdoor recreation activities including climbing, skiing, biking, water sports and so on. Nature study, formal and informal environmental education and research into the diverse natural environments of the Cairngorms would provide more employment. Essential environmental monitoring and repair work could provide additional opportunities for local employment. It is to be expected that proprietors would see the value of integrating estate economics to the new agenda for sustainable development, and that local authorities would recognize the advantages for job creation in developing and maintaining a high quality environment in the Cairngorms.

In the long term it is hoped that the need for statutory site safeguard in the form of NNR, SSSI and NSA might disappear. The European Directives would still impose certain monitoring and reporting protocols for the key areas designated as Natura 2000 sites. World Heritage and Natura 2000 status could create additional income from the European Commission and IUCN to assist with the maintenance of approved management standards, bringing more income and benefits to the area.

The vision described here may seem Utopian but there is a moment of opportunity now and mounting evidence of a new spirit of co-operation to manage this special area in an appropriate way. There is certainly potential for a new approach in the statutory aims of National Parks in Scotland with the integration of conservation of natural and cultural heritage, sustainable use of natural resources, promotion of understanding and enjoyment and the sustainable economic and social

development of communities. It is imperative that the opportunity is not squandered and that the outstanding environmental quality of this area, on which so much depends, is not only protected but improved in the long term.

REFERENCES

Cairngorms Working Party (1993) *Common Sense and Sustainability: A Partnership for the Cairngorms.* Report to the Secretary of State for Scotland. HMSO, Edinburgh.

Callander, R.F. & MacKenzie, N.A. (1991) *The Native Pine Woodlands of Highland Deeside.* Report to the Nature Conservancy Council. NCC N.E. (Scotland) Region, Aberdeen.

Countryside Commission for Scotland (1978) *Scotland's Scenic Heritage.* CCS, Perth.

Countryside Commission for Scotland (1990) *The Mountain Areas of Scotland. Conservation and Management.* CCS, Perth.

Curry-Lindahl, K. (1990) The Cairngorms National Nature Reserve (NNR), the foremost British Conservation Area of International Significance. In: Conroy, J.W.H., Watson, A. & Gunson, A.R., eds, *Caring for the High Mountains: Conservation of the Cairngorms.* NERC Institute of Terrestrial Ecology and Aberdeen University Centre for Scottish Studies, Aberdeen. pp. 108–119.

Dunlop, B.M.S. (1994) *The Native Woodlands of Strathspey.* Draft report to Scottish Natural Heritage, Edinburgh.

Gordon, J.E. (1993) The Cairngorms. In: Gordon, J.E. & Sutherland D.G., eds, *Quarternary of Scotland.* Chapman and Hall, London. pp. 259–276.

Gordon, J.E. & Sutherland, D.G., eds, (1993) *Quarternary of Scotland.* Chapman and Hall, London.

Grampian Regional Council (1990) *Managing the Cairngorms. The Issues.* Grampian Regional Council, Aberdeen.

Grampian Regional Council/Nature Conservancy Council (1984) *The World Conservation Strategy and Grampian Region. Report of the Braemar workshop.* Grampian Regional Council, Aberdeen.

Nature Conservancy (1959) *Cairngorms National Nature Reserve. Management Plan.* NC, Edinburgh.

Nature Conservancy Council (1989) *Guidelines for the Selection of Biological SSSIs.* NCC, Peterborough.

Nature Conservancy Council (1990) *Earth Science Conservation in Great Britian.* NCC, Peterborough.

Ratcliffe, D.A. (1977) *A Nature Conservation Review* Cambridge University Press, Cambridge.

Scottish Affairs Committee (1985) *The Highlands and Islands Development Board.* HMSO, London.

Scottish Development Department (1984) *National Planning Guidelines for Skiing Developments.* Unpublished document circulated by SDD, Edinburgh.

Scottish National Parks Committee/Scottish Wildlife Conservation Committee (1947) *National Parks and the Conservation of Nature in Scotland.* Cmd. 7235. HMSO, Edinburgh.

Scottish National Parks Committee/Scottish Wildlife Conservation Committee (1949) *Nature Reserves in Scotland.* Cmd. 7814. HMSO, Edinburgh.

Scottish Natural Heritage (1994) *Red Deer and the natural heritage.* SNH, Edinburgh.

Steven, H.M. & Carlisle, A. (1959) *The Native Pinewoods of Scotland.* Oliver & Boyd, Edinburgh.

Technical Group on the Cairngorm Area of the Eastern Highlands of Scotland (1967) *Cairngorm Area.* HMSO, Edinburgh.

PART 3

The Future of The Cairngorms

Towards an Integrated Management Strategy

C.H. GIMINGHAM

Throughhout this book there have been several recurrent themes: first, that the biodiversity, ecology, history, landscape and land use of the Cairngorms area are of prime importance; second, that at present it is inadequately protected and is subject to damaging influences; and third, that integrated, sustainable management based on the best available ecological knowledge and understanding is vital if deterioration is to be arrested and future generations are to inherit a place no less fine than it is today. While there is still much to be found out, our present fund of knowledge should be enough to establish a sound set of objectives for future management and planning. To begin with, however, there are lessons to be learned from a brief review of some of the errors and failures of the past and present, and from the recent history of efforts to promote integrated management. Many of these matters have already been touched on or discussed in earlier chapters, but they are drawn together here and their significance assessed.

WHAT IS GOING WRONG?

Despite the best efforts of numerous individual and corporate landowners and managers, there are many signs that all is not well and that significant damage and deterioration has occurred. Some of this has been ongoing for almost as long as there has been human occupation of the area, but much of it is of quite recent origin. Attention to this was drawn by Curry-Lindahl (1974, 1990) who described the Cairngorms as 'Britain's foremost conservation area' and claimed that it was being 'damaged and gravely threatened by unwise developments'. He was surprised by 'the weak protection given to this outstanding area' and the lack of appropriate planning.

The causes of ecological damage and deterioration fall into two main groups: 1) aspects of land management which have led to the loss of habitat diversity or potential, and 2) pressures inflicted by the rapid increase in popularity of the area to visitors, tourists and participants in various forms of outdoor recreation.

Land use and management

The progress of deforestation over most of the land below the potential tree limit has been described in Chapters 9 and 10. On the one hand, the timber resource was exploited for use as fuel or in construction, while on the other there was an ever-present demand for land as range for grazing animals.

The effects of deforestation have been varied and far-reaching. Diversity of vegetation, and hence of both flora and fauna, has been greatly reduced. On the hill slopes the former mixture of rather open pine-birch woodland, interspersed with glades and clearings occupied by heath or bog and patches of juniper or birch scrub (p. 108), has been replaced by extensive, relatively uniform heather *Calluna vulgaris*

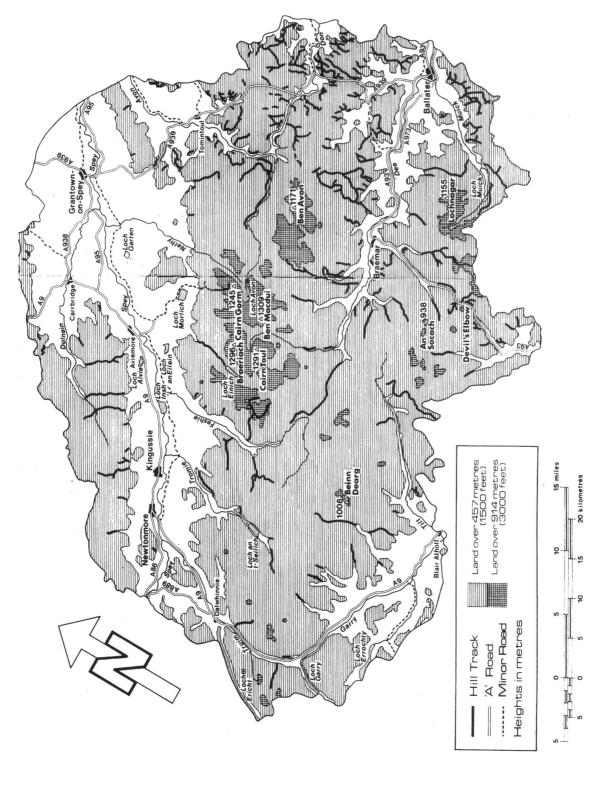

Figure 16.1 Proliferation of hill tracks in the Cairngorms (from Countryside Commission for Scotland *Vehicular Tracks in Upland Scotland* (1978); reproduced with permission).

moorland, or areas of species-poor acidic grassland with sedges and rushes in the wetter places. The dominance of heather has accelerated podsolization and acidification of the upper layers of soil. In places an impermeable iron pan has formed in the illuvial (B) soil horizon, leading to surface waterlogging, increasing depths of peaty humus and eventually to replacement of the heather by acid bog vegetation. Loss of the forest in the western part of the area where rainfall is high has also led to increased soil wetness and peat formation. The sub-alpine scrub zone in the region of the treeline has almost completely disappeared (p. 31), while in the valleys much of the broadleaved woodland has been destroyed and replaced either by crops or grazing land.

A general feature of these changes is the replacement of mixed vegetation by wide expanses of uniform, rather species-poor communities. The effects of grazing, at first by cattle and sheep but more recently by sheep alone or together with red deer, have been to reinforce the kinds of change initiated by deforestation. Often the heather has been damaged by intensive grazing and has given place to coarse grasses on drier sites or to cotton-grass *Eriophorum* spp. and deer-grass *Trichophorum cespitosum* in peaty areas. Such trends represent ecological deterioration since they have led to great reductions in the populations of plants and animals typical of the original vegetation and fauna and to lack of diversity in the resulting heaths and grasslands. The soils have often become wetter, more acid, with poorer nutrient cycling and hence reduced potential productivity. In some cases where the vegetation cover has been disrupted by intensive deer grazing, erosion has been initiated.

These are relatively long-term ecological changes, brought about in the first place by traditional forms of land use. However, recent instances of excessive concentration on sheep or deer, or a combination of the two, have profoundly influenced the landscape, producing the familiar 'open' terrain of heather-covered or grassy hills instead of lower slopes well clothed with trees. While the resulting landscapes are often admired, the systems which produced them may not be indefinitely sustainable and perhaps are not ecologically desirable on such a large scale.

Where the hills are heather-covered, especially in the drier eastern part of the area, another form of land use, the grouse moor, has emerged (Chapter 12). This has involved management by periodic burning of the vegetation in order to maintain uniform stands of young vigorous heather and to promote rapid regeneration following the fires. Although this practice led to controversy amongst ecologists and conservationists in the decades around the middle of the twentieth century, research indicated that the effects of any one fire-event on the nutrient status of the ecosystem were small (McVean & Lockie, 1969). Nevertheless the periodic burning has led over the years to a reduction in the number of species on regularly managed moors, restricting the flora to plants capable of withstanding this treatment. It has also

promoted the reassertion of heather dominance on each occasion.

On the positive side, however, the wide expanses of heath and moorland are desired by sportsmen and have great landscape value, as well as some importance to conservation in view of the presence of certain characteristic birds, insects and other fauna. Where carefully controlled and well managed, this form of land use is generally regarded as acceptable even if it does not meet all aspects of current definitions of sustainability. It is when the principles of good muirburning are not observed that serious damage may occur. For example, if heather is allowed to become too old and woody before burning, regeneration may be slow, because in the older stands fires are more intense and the plants less able to sprout. Too frequent burning may also be damaging to heather. Slow regeneration can lead to surface erosion or replacement of heather by unwanted species such as wavy hair-grass *Deschampsia flexuosa* or bracken *Pteridium aquilinum*. Other examples of bad practice include fires on steep slopes or at high altitudes, whether deliberate or accidental, which may initiate processes of surface erosion and loss of vegetation. While many grouse moors in the Cairngorms area are well managed, instances of all these types of failure to observe good practice may be found.

A further consequence of the predominant use of land for sporting purposes has been the proliferation of bulldozed hill tracks in many parts of the Cairngorms (Watson, 1984). With the replacement of ponies by four-wheel drive vehicles for removal of deer carcasses, estates have felt the need for more substantial tracks, and the result has been a network of unsightly gashes across the hills which has been much criticized by walkers, visitors and indeed residents in the area (Fig. 16.1). Such gashes are extremely slow to heal and sometimes if carelessly sited start processes of erosion. A degree of control was introduced in 1981 in those parts of the area designated as National Scenic Areas, where permission from the Local Authority was required for creation of tracks at altitudes above 300 m. More recently this provision has been extended to tracks at any altitude in NSAs. However, a great deal of damage was done to the landscape before the restriction was in place, and even since then in a few instances where the rules have been disregarded. This is not to deny that, if estates are to achieve the desired levels of cull of red deer to reduce damage by overgrazing, rapid removal of carcasses from the hill is necessary to ensure good condition of the venison. Some tracks are essential, but these must be kept to a minimum and carefully planned and built to reduce their visual and ecological impact.

While the extent of past destruction of native forests is universally deplored, some aspects of more recent reafforestation have also been cited as instances of what has been going wrong. In an area of supreme nature conservation importance it is held that large, uniform plantations of exotic tree species are inappropriate and do little to restore lost biodiversity or improve the soil. Taken as a whole, the Cairngorms area has been less subject to this kind of forestry than other places, but examples are not difficult to find both on Forestry Commission land and private estates. Even where Scots pine *Pinus sylvestris* has been planted, the seed source has in the past sometimes been foreign to the area, putting at risk the genetic integrity of the native stands of pine. The economics of estate management may require the revenue from the faster-growing and more valuable tree species, and there is a place for them in some of the more peripheral parts of the area, where forest restructuring and other measures may in time improve their appearance and increase diversity. In the region of the mountain core and its surrounding slopes and valleys, however, there are strong arguments for promoting a closer approximation to the native woodland composition and structure (Chapter 9). The Forestry Commission has in recent years moved towards this position (Chapter 10) and with appropriate incentives now in place private landowners are in a position to do likewise, but it is not yet clear whether, in the absence of a comprehensive landuse strategy, there is sufficiently universal agreement on objectives.

Agricultural land use in the Cairngorms area consists mainly in the pastoral activities of hill farms and crofts. However, there are also substantial areas of mixed and arable farming in the straths and other lowland parts (Chapter 8). Apart from the relatively limited areas of richer soils, much of the land is not highly productive and has been subject to less intensive agricultural pressure than in more fertile districts. The traditional low-intensity farming systems are, however, under increasing economic pressure and yet they are of considerable importance to wildlife, especially plants and birds. Trends towards intensification and specialization of farming methods, on the one hand, or abandonment of farms on the other, are evident in some places and in general do not serve the wider interests of conservation. It is to be hoped that the recent introduction of the Environmentally Sensitive Areas (ESA) designation in the Cairngorm Straths (p. 204) will help to restore a balanced system of land management here.

Consequences of increased visitor and recreational pressures. Mention has already been made of the continuing increase in popularity of the Cairngorms and use of the area by walkers, mountain bikers, mountaineers, skiers and devotees of other sports such as hang-gliding. While their impact is largely confined to limited areas and most of the high ground is little disturbed, considerable problems are being created in the form of footpath erosion on popular routes, such as the path up Lochnagar, the Northern Corries footpath and the Lairig Ghru, or vegetation destruction and disturbance to wildlife as around the summit of Cairn Gorm. Perhaps the greatest conflict has arisen over the provision of skiing facilities at Cairn Gorm, in Glen Shee and at The Lecht. This is discussed in detail in Chapter 14; here it is relevant to point out that inevitably the construction of pistes, ski-lifts, tows and buildings destroys vegetation, disturbs

wildlife and damages the landscape, but that efforts are now made to keep these impacts to a minimum and to avoid the mistakes of the past. Many conservationists recognize that there is a legitimate demand for recreational opportunities and that despite the intrusion caused by the three main ski areas they are here to stay. What has been a highly contentious issue is the extent to which they should be permitted to expand in areas of high nature conservation value or parts of National Nature Reserves such as the Northern Corries or Glas Maol near Glen Shee.

In summary, it is evident that there is a wide range of examples of what has been going wrong, extending from the original deforestation to the demands of an increasingly mobile array of visitors. Decision-making on land use lacks quality and suffers from being largely in the hands of specialist interests. This results in failure to relate policy in forestry, agriculture and deer management (to name just a few of the issues) to the objectives of conservation and sustainable development. The inevitable outcome has been conflict between rival claims for the use of land. The lack of any general management strategy or planning guidelines has permitted poor standards of design of new developments and buildings and of provision for visitors as well as a proliferation of undesirable features such as hill tracks. In general land management has, until recently, paid scant attention to ecological principles and values, and incentives for good practice have been inadequate. The unsatisfactory nature of the current provision for protecting the quality of remoteness of the mountains and their unique scenic and wildlife features, and resolving conflicts, is evident and testifies to the lack of a coherent policy and accepted priorities for the area as a whole. There is also need for a more comprehensive strategy for the provision of information and interpretation relating to the whole area, and perhaps also for orientation centres at key tourist points such as Aviemore.

Inadequacies in the administrative framework. Instances of ecological deterioration, conflicts between opposing interests and cumbersome procedures for resolving them, all demonstrate inadequacies in the present administrative arrangements. Decisions on rural land use, whether made by private landowners or organizations, are dictated by economic factors, often controlled by European politics. In the absence of any agreed set of objectives and the means to promote them, owners and occupiers of land can hardly be blamed for this, and some are to be praised for maintaining high standards of responsibility and a broadly conservationist approach in the face of economic constraints. Unfortunately, however, the agencies which had interests or activities in the area, including the Forestry Commission, the (former) Scottish Office Agriculture and Fisheries Department, the Highlands and Islands Enterprise and the Tourist Boards were not sufficiently co-ordinated. In justifiably seeking first the advancement of the type of land use they existed to serve, they sometimes pulled in different directions, while in the past nature conservation has seldom been treated as a land use in its own right, with the potential for generating an economic benefit to the area. In so far as planning legislation affects the issue mainly as regards buildings, roads, other infrastructure and the development of settlements, problems were created by the fact that for Structure Plan purposes three Regional Councils were involved, and five District Councils responsible for Local Plans covering parts of the territory. After local government reorganization in 1996 the area was split between five Authorities (Aberdeenshire, Angus, Highland, Moray, and Perth and Kinross). A degree of co-operation has been achieved but comprehensive planning is virtually impossible, and the design and location of new developments have often proved less than ideal. The planning process itself has been the subject of criticism because, when objections are raised to significant development proposals, it may lead to expensive and protracted public inquiries with consequent polarization of opinion.

There is also an understandable feeling that those who live and work in the area have too little influence over decisions which directly affect them, and that there is too little democratic control over the powers of the 'public' bodies that make them. Others hold the view that national and international interests have too little say on the future of an area recognized as of universal importance. Both sides to that argument would probably agree that there is as yet no adequate framework of strategic guidance at a national level. This lack has underlain a number of past conflicts between those whose major concerns are for nature and countryside conservation and those whose interests lie on the one hand in provision for recreation and tourism or, on the other, estate management – both, to varying degrees, contributing much-needed employment. It would be accepted on all sides that some aspects of conservation-orientated management involve economic sacrifice, but that this could be offset by incentives directed towards positive action rather than compensation for refraining from damaging practices.

In general, it is widely held that this magnificent region, much of it in a near-natural condition, is subject to various threats and lacks sufficient protection. At the same time the local communities feel that their needs are given insufficient attention, landowners claim that the sacrifices they are called on to make in the interests of conservation or public access are inadequately compensated, while tourists and visitors sometimes complain about the quality and availability of provision for their legitimate aims or about interference with their cherished freedom to enjoy open country. It is difficult to reconcile all these conflicting demands, and perhaps we are expecting too much of an area of such prime importance and should be prepared to submit to more restrictions. At all events, the conclusion has been inescapable that an agreed, comprehensive and integrated management strategy for the Cairngorms has been badly needed.

STAGES IN THE EVOLUTION OF A MANAGEMENT STRATEGY

Hitherto the resolution of conflict between rival landuse interests in the Cairngorms has had to be achieved on an *ad hoc* basis, in the absence of any established set of overall objectives. Inevitably this is unsatisfactory to at least some of the parties concerned. There is also growing concern over the evidence of continued damage. This has been due to a large extent to the lack of any comprehensive overview of the needs of the entire area, with the result that its several parts are managed as independent units serving different 'sectoral' interests without integration.

The Cairngorms National Nature Reserve. A start towards rectifying this situation was made by the (then) Nature Conservancy (NC, later the Nature Conservancy Council, NCC) in 1954, when some 16 000 ha were designated a National Nature Reserve (NNR) (Chapter 15). At the time, only about one-seventh of this area was owned by the NC, the rest being incorporated on the basis of management agreements with the landowners. Further declarations in 1962 and 1966 expanded the NNR to its present size of 25 950 ha, of which 12 per cent is owned by Scottish Natural Heritage (SNH) (Fig. 16.2). Establishment of the Nature Reserve provided the opportunity to draw up a Management Plan for the Reserve, first produced in 1959 and revised in 1968, 1978, 1987 and 1991. For the first time a number of aspects of management of a substantial portion of the core of the Cairngorms were related to specific objectives framed for the main purpose of nature protection. In a Statement of Policies in 1978, the NCC adopted a zonation of the Reserve: 1) a strict Natural Zone, 2) a Managed Natural Zone, and 3) a Natural Environment Recreation Zone, thus foreshadowing the approach of the Countryside Commission for Scotland and the Cairngorms Working Party when developing their ideas for a management strategy. Over the years the NCC's objectives for the Reserve were broadened to encompass conservation in a wider sense than that of nature protection, specifically to include habitat management. At altitudes above 800 m the main aim was to allow ecosystems to evolve with the minimum of interference, while below 800 m it was to restore native woodland, scrub and tall herb communities (NCC 1991a). It was also its policy to encourage the appreciation and study of the Reserve 'for activities which depend on its natural qualities' (NCC, 1987).

The system adopted for the establishment of the NNR, however, failed to break the mould of management directed towards special, often incompatible ends. On those areas actually owned by the NCC management was succesfully orientated towards nature conservation aims, but on the privately owned estates, although NCC staff had an extremely valuable influence, the Agreements had to respect the estates' demands to manage their own land for their own interests, particularly sporting interests. While sometimes these could be reconciled

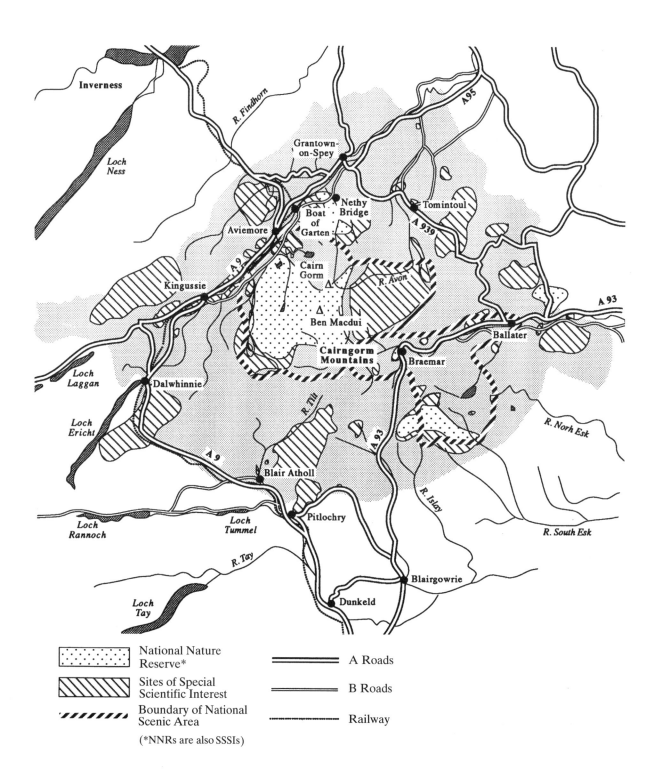

Figure 16.2   Distribution and approximate extent of conservation designations in the Caingorms area.

with the needs of conservation, in others they could not. One obvious example has been the failure to achieve the aim of 'permitting the extension of native forest and sub-alpine vegetation, mainly by the management of red deer at levels which will allow a progressive change in the vegetation towards desired goals'.

The NNR agreements, valuable as they have been, have suffered from three main limitations: 1) they cover only a part of the total area – even if it is accepted that the NNR contains some of the most valuable territory, there are sites of high quality outside it, and it is the integrity of the whole area that is at stake; 2) they do not achieve an integrated approach, agreed by all parties, to the management of the area as a whole; and 3) they are vulnerable to change following renegotiation when agreements lapse or ownership changes.

The first of these problems has been addressed, to some extent, by designation of a considerable area to the east of the NNR and several additional smaller areas as Sites of Special Scientific Interest (SSSI, Fig. 16.2). This designation confers a degree of protection, in that notice must be given of intention to undertake any of a number of 'potentially damaging operations' so that SNH has an opportunity to object. However, the introduction of SSSIs has contributed only marginally to the achievement of an overall management strategy.

In these ways NCC and its successor bodies the Nature Conservancy Council for Scotland (NCCS) and Scottish Natural Heritage (SNH) have played a vital role in promoting conservation principles in some of the most sensitive habitats, but it fell to other bodies to influence management on a still wider canvas.

Report of the Technical Group on the Cairngorms area of the Eastern Highlands of Scotland.

One of the first attempts to take a broad overview of the issues relating to land use in the the Cairngorms arose from recognition of the increasing potential of the area for recreation and the mounting pressures this creates. In 1962 a Technical Group was set up by the Secretary of State for Scotland, consisting of representatives of the Scottish Development Department and the Local Authorities concerned, the then County Councils of Aberdeen, Banff, Inverness, Moray and Nairn, Perth and Kinross). Their Report (Technical Group on the Cairngorm Area, 1967) accepted the importance of landscape quality, remoteness and wildlife, to the extent that it said: – 'of importance therefore will be the steps taken to achieve the greatest possible richness and diversification which natural circumstances permit'. However, it is perhaps significant that the chapter on 'Landscape, Conservation and Preservation' came at the end of a report which was largely devoted to recognizing the potential of the area for the promotion of existing land uses – agriculture, forestry, deer forests and grouse moors – and especially the scope for development of tourism and recreational activities (Chapter 14). It made little attempt to initiate progress towards integrated management, beyond suggesting the setting up of an independent Warden Service, and concluding with the following paragraph:

> This Report demonstrates the need for the various interests in the Area to join together with mutual benefit to achieve fulfilment in the many aspects of future development and to preserve the more intangible assets such as remoteness which are so easily destroyed. With the continued goodwill of all the persons and bodies vitally concerned much can be achieved, particularly in the spirit of the initiative already shown by the people living within the Area and whose livelihood is bound up with its viability. It may not be over-stressing the position to say that without their participation in the future, as in the past, the full potential will not be achieved.

This statement of principle is directly parallel to the approach adopted some 25 years later by the Cairngorms Working Party (1993), with the difference that the latter has made detailed proposals outlining a possible integrated management strategy and a mechanism intended to achieve the kind of co-operation which, even after a quarter of a century, was still lacking (p. 192 and Chapter 17).

The statutory planning process.

Local government reorganization in 1974 resulted in a division of the Cairngorms area between three Regional Councils. The greater part of the area came within the jurisdiction of two of these: the Grampian Region took in the eastern sector while the north and west fell within the Highland Region. A smaller, southern portion belonged to Tayside Region. It was a statutory requirement for each Council to prepare a Structure Plan for its Region, and in meeting this obligation the Councils and their Planning staffs made substantial contributions to the formulation of proposals and policies for the management of the Cairngorms area, despite the fact that they were unable to take a comprehensive overview or prepare plans for the area as a whole.

A Structure Plan for Highland Region appeared in 1980 and Grampian Region produced a Rural Area Structure Plan in 1985. However, both of these were subsequently revised and considerable progress made in addressing current problems of management in the Cairngorms area. A new Structure Plan for Highland Region was approved in 1990, while a draft Written Statement for a new Grampian Region Structure Plan appeared in 1992. These documents, although differing in emphasis, adopt broadly similar aims, including conserving natural features and resources, securing social and economic benefits for local communities, and providing facilities for tourism and recreation. Both plans recognize the 'high conservation and heritage importance' of the Cairngorms. In the course of preparing its Structure Plan, Grampian Regional Council published in 1990 a useful statement on *Managing the Cairngorms – the Issues*, in order to foster wider discussion. Although dealing only with the east Cairngorms, this document raised most of the important questions concerning the area as a whole. It clearly recognized the increasing pressures and accepted that the primary aim of management should be to 'conserve and enhance the natural features of international, national or local importance', and that policies to secure social, economic and recreational benefits should be developed within that framework.

None the less, because the planning process remained in the hands of more than one Local Authority there was potential for disagreement and lack of integration. For example, during the preparation of its Structure Plan, Highland Regional Council issued a consultative draft of its Written Statement in which support was expressed for a proposal to provide additional downhill skiing facilities located in Lurchers Gully to the west of the existing provision at Coire Cas. It was argued that 'because of the relatively small scale and limited distribution of skiing developments in relation to the extensive areas of conservation designations in the Region, wildlife and landscape interests will not be significantly affected', and that 'the special ambiance of the Northern Corries SSSI can be maintained'. This position was challenged by Grampian Regional Council, which was disposed to adopt a more protective stance. It regarded the Highland Region's policy in respect of Lurchers Gully as 'unacceptable insofar as it could be interpreted to permit development of ski access facilities in such a way as to offer a second easy summer route to the high Cairngorms plateau', thus creating a potential threat of damage to Grampian Region's sector of the area. In the event, following much public debate, the Secretary of State for Scotland withheld approval of this particular provision, which accordingly was omitted from the final version of the Highland Region Structure Plan, published in 1990. (For a fuller discussion of this controversial issue see Chapter 14.)

In many other respects the attitudes of the two Councils were more convergent, and Highland Region was ready to agree to a proposal by Grampian that the two bodies should collaborate to form an advisory group to 'monitor developments and advise on future management of the skiing area'. It was also agreed that they should discuss with other interested parties the preparation of a Cairngorm Management Plan. This would no doubt have been a valuable move had it not been overtaken by the establishment of the Cairngorms Working Party (p. 194).

Encouraged by the Scottish Office, both Highland and Grampian Regional Councils were active in preparing Regional Indicative Forestry Strategies. Although developed independently of the Structure Plans, the latter incorporate the policies and recommmendations of the Indicative Forestry Strategies. To give guidance and facilitate proposals for forestry development, land with potential for forestry is divided into the following categories: Preferred areas, Prospective areas and Sensitive areas. Much of the land in the Cairngorms is unplantable because of altitude and exposure, while of the rest, mainly the straths and surrounding countryside, a considerable proportion is regarded as 'sensitive'. This indicates that scientific, landscape or archaeological concerns might render approval for plantation forestry unlikely. However, the scope for expansion of native pine forest, as discussed in Chapters 9 and 10, is not constrained by this classification. Where 'prospective' areas are indicated on the maps (Fig. 16.3) there may be some feature which could be adversely affected by planting but forestry proposals here would be viewed favourably if they can be integrated with other interests.

In these ways Indicative Forestry Strategies, while not attempting to take on the role of management plans, represent a step in the direction of integrating one particular type of land use into the future pattern of the area as a whole.

A National Scenic Area. Following recommendation in 1978 by the Countryside Commission for Scotland (CCS) in its publication *Scotland's Scenic Heritage,* the designation 'National Scenic Area' (NSA) was applied by the Secretary of State for Scotland to parts of the Cairngorms in 1981 (Fig. 16.1). This is the principal landscape designation in Scotland, conferring a degree of protection on areas of outstanding scenic quality. Although NSAs may incorporate National Nature Reserves and Sites of Special Scientific Interest, their purpose is quite distinct: it is to exercise control over developments which might impair the visual integrity of Scotland's finest landscapes. Consultation with SNH (the successor to CCS) is necessary before planning consent can be given to applications for certain types of construction or other development in a NSA. If a local authority wishes to give consent against the Commission's advice, reference has to be made to the Secretary of State. Proposals for the construction of roads and tracks, except those for existing agricultural and forestry purposes, also require planning permission, though prior to 1991 this provision applied only to tracks on high ground, above 300 m. Roads and tracks for existing agricultural and forestry purposes are excluded from the categories of development subject to these procedures.

The Cairngorms NSA includes the core of the mountain area, extending from Glen Feshie in the west to Glen Builg in the east, and from Pityoulish in the north to the Geldie Burn in the south, while towards the south-east it adjoins the Deeside and Lochnagar NSA. Thus, much of the Cairngorm area as understood in this book falls under the umbrella of this designation, but its terms of reference are limited and confer no jurisdiction over land use and management, or use for recreational activities, except where the latter involve buildings or roads. Indeed, the NSA designation was described by the (former) Scottish Office, in a Consultation Paper concerned with the proposed Natural Heritage Area designation, as ineffective and widely misunderstood.

For some time it has also been within the remit of local authorities to identify areas of scenic importance within their Regions or Districts and to adopt policies to guide planning decisions affecting them. They have been given various titles, including 'Areas of Great Landscape Value'. To this extent the

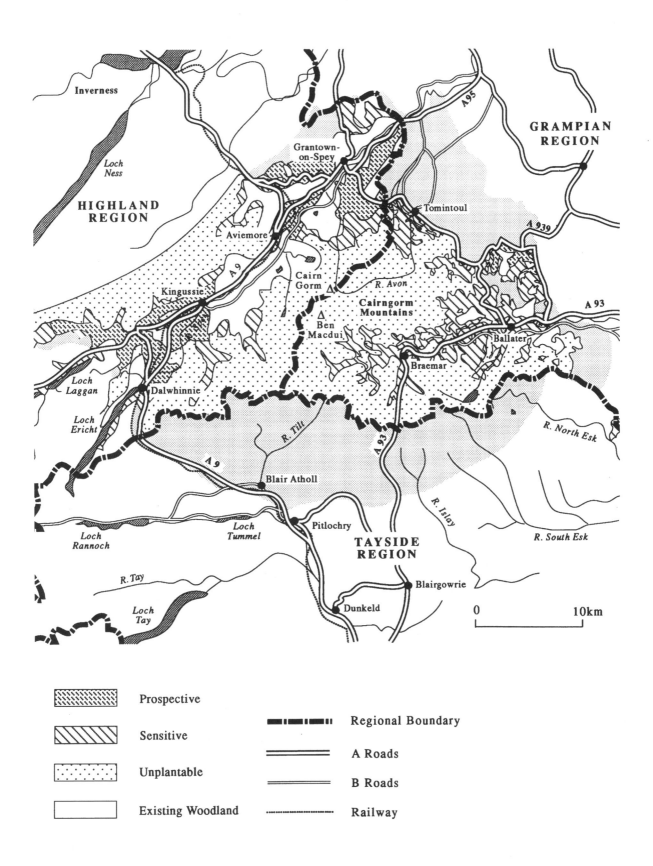

Figure 16.3 Map of indicative forestry strategy zones in the Cairngorms area, extracted from the Highland Region and Grampion Region Indicataive Forest Strategies (1992 and 1991 respectively).

importance of the Cairngorms was recognized before designation as NSA, in the exercise of the statutory functions of local Councils.

Review of management arrangements for popular mountain areas. The publication in 1990 of the Countryside Commission for Scotland's report, *The Mountain Areas of Scotland – Conservation and Management,* was a milestone in the quest for a comprehensive approach to future administration and management. In the light of mounting concern for the welfare of the Cairngorms and recognition of conflicts of interest in this and other mountain areas, the Commission was invited by the Scottish Minister for Home Affairs and the Environment to 'study management arrangements for popular mountain areas such as the Cairngorms, taking into consideration the case for arrangements on national park lines in Scotland'. The review covered much of the Highlands of Scotland, but the specific mention of the Cairngorms in the remit highlighted the importance of this area.

This report was the first to spell out the need for fundamental changes and to identify the prime reasons why a new approach was required, as follows:

- to move away from sectoral policies for rural land management in the mountains,
- to get away from *ad hoc* responses to policy and to promote an anticipatory approach to conservation,
- to influence land management activities that are at present outwith landuse controls and incentives,
- to remedy past landscape and wildlife damage,
- to promote the conservation of mountain areas and community development based on sustainable use of natural resources,
- to command some new resources and to redirect existing funding to policy aims relevant for our time, and
- to put in place a system capable of providing effective management of mountain recreation and access, including regulation if, and where, necessary.

The report recognized that a commitment to quality was among the key issues and that legitimate programmes for use of the countryside must all be judged according to the overriding need to protect areas of 'highest heritage value'. Recreation by the public was seen as now being a key land use in upland Scotland, but requiring a new approach that treated wild land as a sanctuary and a resource for enjoyment. More than in any previous reviews, conservation was regarded as a significant land use in its own right, and integration of multi-purpose land management was advocated. In view of the fact that much of the land is in private ownership, it was seen as essential for government agencies to work more closely with private management interests by means of incentives and agreements. Similarly, local community interests need to be involved, in discussion with national interests, and to benefit from setting new management objectives.

The administrative mechanism advocated by the Commission to achieve these ends will be considered in the next chapter, but in addition a number of valuable and less controversial recommendations were made in respect of the Cairngorms. These included provision for protection from further intrusion of built tracks into the remoter parts, for the control of red deer, for extending the area of native pinewood and improving the quality of forestry elsewhere, for promoting interpretation and the provision of information about the area, and for an improved access network with better footpath maintenance. Of greatest significance, perhaps, was a proposal for indicative zonation of the whole area into: 1) a mountain core, 2) a countryside management zone and 3) a community zone (Fig. 16.4). In the first, the prime objectives of management would be conservation, low intensity recreation and game management; in the second, there would be more traditional land management, together with developed recreation uses, with the aim of enhancing the recreation and conservation value of the area; and in the third, which included the major settlements and trunk routes, a wider range of development would be permitted. The report emphasized the weakness of relying on sectoral interests, often competing and sometimes conflicting, to safeguard the future of the whole.

Drawing the outlines of an integrated management strategy. The Government's response to the submission of the Countryside Commission for Scotland's 'Mountain Areas' report was the establishment in 1991, by the Secretary of State, of a 'Cairngorms Working Party' charged with the task of considering land and land-related uses in the area and advising on what 'changes are necessary to achieve an integrated management strategy . . . , what the aims of such a strategy should be and how they might best be given effect' (Cairngorms Working Party, 1993). This move gave expression to the wide interest and debate which had been generated within and beyond Scotland about the future status of the area. One manifestation of this interest had been the earlier formation of a 'Save the Cairngorms Campaign' which gathered considerable support and published, at the beginning of 1992, a *Manifesto for the Cairngorms* as a contribution both to the public debate and to the work of the Cairngorms Working Party. This document argued the case for a comprehensive management strategy and set out a suggested set of principles and mechanisms. It included nine brief 'Objectives Papers' which presented for discussion fundamental aims on which such a strategy might be based. Although on a few matters the Campaign held a rather more hard-line view than was adopted by the Working Party, most of its ideas were closely in tune with the latter's subseqent recommendations.

The Manifesto noted that in its remit to the Working Party the Government had committed itself to the 'precautionary principle', that precautionary action should be taken even where scientific

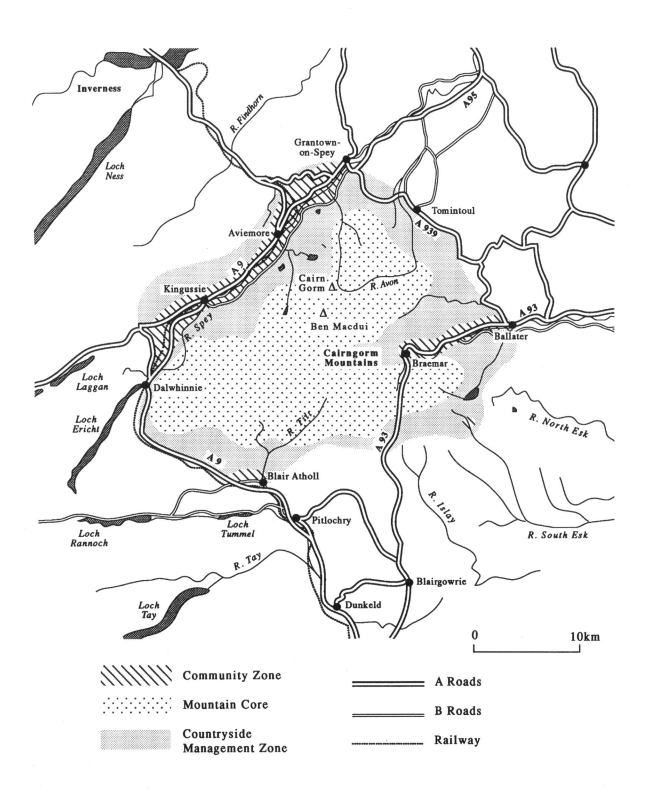

Figure 16.4   Indicative zoning of the Caingorms area as suggested by the Countryside Commission for Scotland (1990).

knowledge is not conclusive, and that it attached great importance to the 'voluntary principle', that future management structures should be built firmly on the basis of co-operation. The Campaign accepted these principles but argued that in an area which is both fragile and of exceptional importance the first must take precedence over the second. Among guiding principles for a management strategy they listed the maintenance and enhancement of the wild land and landscape qualities as prime objectives to be attained through improved development control policies, also the protection and recovery of the richness and diversity of plant and animal communities in the entire Cairngorms area. Contributing to this, they advocated the re-establishment of an extensive forest of natural form, allowing for sustainable forestry based on native species. Implicit in this aim was the need to bring the population of deer and other grazers into long-term sustainable balance with a habitat restored to its full richness and diversity. They supported freedom of access for those recreational activities which are dependent on the natural qualities of the area, but held that the 'long walk in' principle, already advocated by the Countryside Commission for Scotland, should guide the management of the more remote areas. In respect of skiing facilities, the approach was that these should meet 'the principles of sustainability, and be subject to the most rigorous environmental impact assessments'. Tourism and other industries should be of a scale and type appropriate to and sustaining the natural resources on which they depend, and should spread the economic benefits throughout the human communities in and around the Cairngorms area. There were also recommendations regarding land designation, administration, development and planning which will be touched on in the next chapter.

Most of these principles are close to, or indentical with, those which inspired many of the recommendations of the report of the Cairngorms Working Party (1993) *Common Sense and Sustainability: A Partnership for the Cairngorms*. This Report had two main components: first, a detailed treatment of the elements that the Working Party felt a management strategy for the Cairngorms should contain; and second, recommendations for an organizational framework and administrative mechanisms capable of devising and implementing such a strategy. Consideration of the second of these is deferred to the next chapter: here a brief review is given of what was the first serious attempt to outline the requirements of a management strategy applicable to the whole area, most of which have received widespread approval and support.

The proposals are based on the need to achieve balance between measures concerned with protection and enhancement of the 'natural heritage features' of the area, and those concerned with the sustainable use of natural resources, the economic well-being of the residents and the quality of the provision for visitors. The philosophy underlying the recommendations is based on the voluntary principle and dependence on the co-operation and consent of all individuals and agencies involved. The precautionary principle is also accepted where 'there is reasonable doubt about the precise impact of potentially damaging developments'.

In outlining its policies, the Working Party related them to a generalized form of zonation, comprising 1) the mountain and plateau zone, 2) the forest and moorland zone, and 3) the valley zone, but these were used for reference purposes only and were not regarded as a basis for strict zonal management. Attention was drawn to difficulties in setting meaningful boundaries to zones and to the fact that degrees of fragility, sensitivity and conservation importance do not equate neatly with zones. While they provided a useful tool in analysing management requirements, flexibility in response to local circumstances was essential.

The approach of the Working Party to management in the mountain and plateau zone was to advocate caution, and to give priority to repairing damage rather than increasing accessibility. While the economic value of field sports and hill farming were recognized, it was regarded as vitally important that deer and sheep numbers should be reduced and kept at a level which will permit the vegetation to recover – this referred both to natural regeneration of woodland and scrub, and to recovery of damaged or lost heaths and moors. Similarly, the concept of carrying capacity as applied to visitor numbers – the capacity of the ecosystems to withstand pressure without deterioration – and ways of preventing it from being exceeded, were discussed.

The Report indicates that a management strategy should not seek to promote additional means of access to sensitive and remote areas, and that their use for recreation should be constrained by adhering to the idea of the 'long walk in' and discouraging the use of vehicles to penetrate into the mountain area. No new high-level tracks should be permitted and, where possible, the more obtrusive existing tracks in the most remote areas should be closed and restored. There should be a presumption against all new artefacts such as signs, buildings, bridges, etc., in the central montane area. However, reasonable provision should be made for walkers, including footpath repair and maintenance where necessary.

One of the most important elements of the proposed strategy concerns effective protection of the surviving fragments of 'Caledonian' pine forest, and their expansion into two extensive and continuous tracts of native woodland, one in Strathspey and one in Upper Deeside. This was proposed as a long-term project to be achieved as far as possible by natural regeneration and spread from existing centres, the result to be a semi-natural forest including open areas with scattered trees as well as denser woodland, so enhancing habitat and species diversity. Except in protected areas, controlled harvesting of timber would be compatible with the conservation aims. In some localities the forest would lend itself to provision for low-intensity recreational activities and would thus help to reduce pressures on more sensitive types of vegetation. The development of other multi-purpose forests and community woodlands near to towns and villages was also encouraged, as was the Highlands Birchwoods initiative, a partnership aimed at promoting regeneration and active management of birchwoods throughout the Highland Region (with similar initiatives under consideration in Grampian and Tayside).

Heather moorland was regarded as a significant and beautiful feature of the landscape in many parts of the area, as well as providing an important wildlife habitat and a valuable contribution as grouse-moor to the local economy. Recommendations included the maintenance of extensive open heather moors in parts of the area, especially in the east, with emphasis placed on good heather management. On some of the existing moorland areas, however, if not currently managed for grouse, successional change to scrub or woodland should be encouraged, for example in the NNR and the areas earmarked for native woodland expansion.

In the main river valleys, recommendations included reference to promoting regeneration and encouraging expansion of broadleaved woodland, especially birch, and to the need to ensure that the unique aquatic environments of lochs and marshes are not adversely affected by flood control or other works on river channels. The maintenance and safeguarding of the high quality of fresh water was also regarded as a central theme for the management strategy, both in respect of the needs of local residents and visitors and for the protection of river and loch ecosystems, including the salmon fisheries.

The guiding principle adopted by the report as regards agriculture was that, while farming should continue as a central activity in the area, where traditional practices are in sympathy with the maintenance of environmental quality and biodiversity they should be continued rather than give place to intensification. This would require adequate financial encouragement, so the declaration of the Cairngorm Straths as an Environmentally Sensitive Area (p. 204) was welcomed in this connection. Similar provisions for 'environmental management' of stock outside the ESA were also regarded as necessary. In general, there was need for closer co-operation between the farming community and other interests, especially those of tourism, recreation and countryside conservation.

The outline for a strategy also extended to questions of landscape conservation, including not only the openness and 'wildness' of the more natural areas at high altitudes but also the semi-natural or 'cultural' landscapes which have the imprint of human use and management. These are all valued and must figure in plans for the future, so prescriptions for multiple land use and for buildings in the countryside must take them into account. Similarly, conservation must extend to the cultural heritage, including archaeological sites and surviving traditional buildings.

The Working Party made it clear that because of the international significance of the area for its wild life and unique ecological features, conserving the 'natural heritage' must play a major role in any management strategy. In the NNR and SSSIs by definition this should have top priority, so long as management practices are compatible with the overall management strategy for the whole area. It should also be a guiding principle in much of the rest of the land where management practices should be sympathetic to the need to maintain habitat and species diversity. The proposal to nominate the area as a World Heritage Site (p. 206) was supported because, if granted by UNESCO on the advice of IUCN, this designation would be a recognition that adequate long-term protection was in place.

In respect of tourism and outdoor recreation, while acknowledging their economic importance and value in promoting enjoyment of the countryside, the need to keep visitor numbers in balance with the capacity of the different parts of the area to absorb them was stressed. The possibility of introducing a tourism management scheme to control the summer use of various facilities such as the Cairngorm ski-lift was aired. As far as skiing provisions were concerned, the priority should be to renew and improve existing facilities and to prevent adverse impacts on the rest of the mountain zone. The highest standards should be required for all developments and management operations, which must be in keeping with the natural environment. Within these constraints, skiing could be encouraged as an appropriate use of land. No change was felt to be necessary in respect of access to land for informal recreation, but the much valued tradition of freedom of access for this purpose should be maintained. Acknowledging that conflicts may arise over this issue, these should be capable of resolution by appropriate management measures, including better environmental education in the area and interpretation facilities for visitors. There was a very positive proposal for an expanded and co-ordinated ranger service with common standards and objectives for the whole area. The need for this had been recognized as early as 1967 in the Report of the Technical Group (p. 191). In the interim the CCS actively explored the possibility of creating an integrated, independent ranger service for the Cairngorms, concluding however that it was impracticable without some statutory designation for the area.

Finally, the management strategy should seek to promote additional employment opportunities in the area, some of which would be related to countryside and wildlife management. It was recommended that planning for new housing and social and economic development should continue to be carried out within the existing legal framework, with greater attention given to the design and location of buildings.

It was not the intention of the Working Party to present a fully worked-out management strategy, but rather to offer a framework on which such a strategy would eventually be drawn up and submitted for wide consultation (p. 198). The above review has highlighted only a selection of the very comprehensive set of proposals, but it is sufficient to show that the Cairngorms Working Party envisaged a management strategy which treated the area as a whole, as distinct from discrete parcels of land in different ownership. This made it possible for the outline strategy to be based on ecological, environmental, social and recreational needs rather than sectoral interests.

The Cairngorms Partnership management strategy. Following the appointment of the Cairngorms Partnership Board in 1995 (see Chapter 17), the Working Party's proposals outlined above were firmed up and expanded into a Draft Management Strategy (Cairngorms Partnership, 1996). After a period of consultation on that Draft, the Cairngorms Partnership Managaement Strategy was published in 1997. This may be regarded as the culmination of the long process described in this Chapter, leading towards a fully comprehensive and integrated management strategy.

In its Introduction, the Draft Management Strategy set out the major policy objectives for the whole area and placed them in the wider national and international context. Stress was laid on combining provision for the welfare of local communities with the need to maintain and enhance the quality of the natural environment and its wildlife, the two being mutually interdependent. The Cairngorms area was then divided into six 'localities': the Montane Zone (given separate treatment because of the outstanding importance of the high hills), Badenoch and Strathspey, Strathdon and Glenlivet, Upper Deeside, the Angus Glens, and Atholl and Glen Shee. Each area had its own complete and comprehensive chapter, which includes a general description, a 'vision for the future', identification of important issues, and a series of proposals with recommended actions and indications of the mechanisms available for their implementation.

The Management Strategy itself was divided into four sections which, taken together, form 'an integrated framework to guide the future management of the Cairngorms area'. These are: 1) the protection and conservation of the high hills and the sympathetic management of recreational pressures; 2) the protection and regeneration of native pinewoods; the creation of the new Deeside Forest and Forest of Spey; management of the deer population and grazing pressures; and the maintenance and enhancement of extensive tracts of managed heather moorland; 3) the social and economic well-being of local communities; 4) nature conservation and landscape. After detailing strategic objectives for a number of topics in each section, the Board provided a 'vision statement' outlining its aspirations for the condition of the area once the management strategy was fully operative.

In these documents we now have positive proposals and general objectives for the foreseeable future which, if brought to fruition, will for the first time make integrated management a reality, and put a stop to environmental deterioration. This depends upon the enthusiastic co-operation of the Partners, and on the availability of additional funding. The Partnership states its commitment to the 'adoption of the Cairngorms as a model of species and habitat conservation, of land restoration, and of integrated land management for other outstanding areas in the UK and beyond'.

A strategy of this kind is all-embracing, transcending both political and ownership boundaries. Only two ways are open for its implementation: on the one hand, agreement and co-operation between all concerned or, on the other, a measure of compulsion. Differing views on the relative merits of these alternatives and the administrative structures involved are discussed at the close of the next chapter.

REFERENCES

Cairngorms Partnership (1996) *Managing the Cairngorms: a Consultation Paper – The Cairngorms Partnership Draft Management Strategy.* Cairngorms Partnership, Grantown-on-Spey.

Cairngorms Partnership (1997) *Managing the Cairngorms. The Cairngorms Partnership Management Strategy.* Cairngorms Partnership, Grantown-on-Spey.

Cairngorms Working Party (1993) *Common Sense and Sustainability. A Partnership for the Cairngorms.* HMSO, Edinburgh.

Countryside Commission for Scotland (1978) *Scotland's Scenic Heritage.* Countryside Commission for Scotland, Battleby, Perth.

Countryside Commission for Scotland (1990) *The Mountain Areas of Scotland: Conservation and Management.* CCS, Battleby, Perth.

Curry-Lindahl, K. (1974) IUCN Survey of Northern and Western European National Parks and Equivalent Reserves. Report on Great Britain. United Nations Environment Programme, Nairobi. pp.1–20.

Curry-Lindahl, K. (1982) Preface. In: Curry-Lindahl, K., Watson, A. & Watson, R. Drennan. *The Future of the Cairngorms.* North East Mountain Trust, Aberdeen. p.7.

Curry-Lindahl, K. (1990) The Cairngorms National Nature Reserve (NNR), the foremost British Conservation Area of International Significance. In: Conroy, J.W.H., Watson, A. & Gunson, A.R., eds, *Caring for the High Mountains: Conservation of the Cairngorms.* NEAC Institute of Terrestrial Ecology & Aberdeen University Centre for Scottish Studies, Aberdeen. pp.108–119.

Grampian Regional Council (1990) *Managing the Cairngorms. The Issues.* Grampian Regional Council, Aberdeen.

Grampian Regional Council (1991) *Regional Forestry Strategy Consultative Draft.* Grampian Regional Council, Aberdeen.

Grampian Regional Council (1992) *Grampian Structure Plan. Draft Written Statement.* Grampian Regional Council, Aberdeen.

Highland Regional Council (1989) *Highland Region Structure Plan: Consultative Draft Written Statement.* Highland Regional Council, Planning Department, Inverness.

Highland Regional Council (1990) *Highland Region Structure Plan 1990. Written Statement.* Highland Regional Council, Planning Department, Inverness.

Highland Regional Council (1992) *Highland Region Indicative Forestry Strategy and Survey Report.* Highland Regional Council, Planning Department, Inverness.

Highland Regional Council (1993) *Highland Region Structure Plan 1990. Alteration No. 1, October 1993.* Highland Regional Council, Planning Department, Inverness.

McVean, D.N. & Lockie, J.D. (1969) *Ecology and Land Use in Upland Scotland.* Edinburgh University Press, Edinburgh.

Nature Conservancy (1959) *Cairngorms National Nature Reserve. Management Plan.* NC, Edinburgh.

Nature Conservancy (1968) *Management Plan. Cairngorms National Nature Reserve. First Revision, 1967–71.* NCC, Edinburgh.

Nature Conservancy Council (1978) *Cairngorms National Nature Reserve, Management Plan. Second Revision. Statement of Policies.* NCC, Edinburgh.

Nature Conservancy Council (1987) *Cairngorms National Nature Reserve. Interim Management Plan.* NCC, Edinburgh.

Nature Conservancy Council (1991a) *Cairngorms National Nature Reserve. Policy Guidelines.* Internal Report. NCC, Edinburgh.

Nature Conservancy Council (1991b) *Cairngorms National Nature Reserve. Revised Management Policies Proposals.* NCC, Edinburgh.

Save the Cairngorms Campaign (1992) *Manifesto for the Cairngorms.* Save the Cairngorms Campaign, Inverness.

Technical Group on the Cairngorm Area of the Eastern Highlands of Scotland (1967) *Cairngorm Area.* HMSO, Edinburgh.

Watson, A. (1984) A survey of vehicular hill tracks in north-east Scotland for land use planning. *Journal of Environmental Management* **18**, 345–353.

CHAPTER 17
The Cairngorms in the Future

C.H. GIMINGHAM

The various chapters of this book have outlined the past history and present-day environment of the Cairngorms area, its ecosystems and land uses, and some of the key issues affecting current and future land management. Implicit in the treatment has been the conviction that an understanding of the ecology of the area, together with the needs of residents and visitors, should help to establish the principles on which future care and management should be based. The preceding chapter sought lessons from past errors and traced the evolution of attempts to reach a sounder strategy. In this final chapter some of the conclusions arising from the foregoing discussions are examined, leading to an appraisal of the most recent proposals for the future status and administration of the area.

IMPLICATIONS OF ECOLOGICAL ANALYSIS

Perhaps the most general and fundamental contribution of an ecological asessment of the Cairngorms area to any future management strategy is the demonstration that its uniqueness derives from the whole complex of ecosystems, ranging from the high plateau tundra-like systems to those of the surrounding slopes, valleys, lochs, streams, rivers and forests, all set in an oceanic, island climate. 'To an ecologist the importance of the Cairngorms lies not solely in the arctic-alpine ecosystems of the highest altitudes but equally in the complete series extending from low to high ground' (Gimingham,

1989). It follows that it is essential to protect the integrity of the whole, not just certain parts of it. This is the reason why a comprehensive management strategy is so vital, rather than a series of plans dealing with separate parts, and why this must cover a large area, not just the 'mountain core'. It is also the reason why every part of the natural and semi-natural terrain is of importance, because all are interdependent. This is a challenge to the type of argument which holds that because of the relatively small scale and limited distribution of a proposed development in relation to the extensive areas of conservation designations, wildlife and landscape interests will not be significantly affected (e.g. Highland Regional Council, 1990). Similarly, to suggest that if one example of an important habitat were to be adversely affected by development there remain several others in the vicinity, is to misunderstand the value of maintaining the completeness of the whole. In an area in which size and extent are important attributes any losses or intrusions are serious and may have cumulative effects.

Acceptance of this point of view does not imply that there is no place for productive land use or recreation in the Cairngorms area. It does, however, require that decisions concerning them should be made in the light of priorities set in the full knowledge of the ecology of the area, including the dynamics of the ecosystems and the value and fragility of their components, as well as of questions of social and economic benefit. Some examples of the conclusions which may arise from the information assembled in this book are presented here, and may be compared with the outline principles for management strategies reviewed in Chapter 16.

Ecological research in the **mountain core** has established not only that the vegetation and fauna include a number of species which are rare or otherwise of special interest in national and international contexts, but also that they form populations and communities which relate both to arctic tundra and alpine regions. The fact that some of these communities are quite extensive has added significance when viewed against the adverse effects of reductions in area and fragmentation of so many other examples of natural or semi-natural ecosystems. This is a strong argument for firm measures to minimize encroachment of any form of development in this part of the area. Another reason is the fragility of some components of the vegetation, which has been demonstrated by observation and experiment (p. 39). Plant community-types can be ranked according to susceptibility to damaging influences: the most susceptible are readily destroyed when impacts are severe and such damage is often irreversible, leading to spreading erosion. Most of the ecosystems are themselves dynamic, undergoing various forms of cyclical change (pp. 37–8), interruption of which involves the loss not merely of one but of a set of plant communities and their associated fauna. Furthermore, some of these high-altitude ecosystems have recently acquired additional importance because of their potential for the detection of effects of increases in atmospheric CO_2, pollution and global warming (p. 41).

For all these reasons, together with the more subjective landscape and wilderness values, there is clear justification for assigning top priority to conservation objectives in the mountain core, and for reducing interference and human artefacts to a minimum. This does not require a draconian 'keep-out' policy: low-intensity enjoyment of hill-walking, cross-country skiing and similar pursuits by those who understand the terrain causes negligible ecological damage, but in places management of numbers of visitors may become necessary. Further studies on the carrying capacity of different types of vegetation and territory are needed if effective policies are to be devised. More of a problem surrounds the popular ski developments at Cairn Gorm, Glen Shee and The Lecht. From the ecological viewpoint outlined above it is a matter for regret that some of these have encroached into significant and fragile parts of the high-level slopes and plateaux. Realistically, however, it has to be accepted that these locations are among the best in Scotland for skiing and that provision for such a popular sport will continue in them. Unfortunately some of the decisions taken in the early stages of planning and construction are open to the criticism that each locality was developed on its own without reference to the wider considerations outlined above. However, much has been learned about reducing the undesirable impacts of installations and the important thing now is to accept the

principle that there should be a strong presumption against further expansion into the core of the Cairngorms. Viewed in this way, even without invoking landscape or wilderness values, the refusal to permit an extension of skiing facilities into Lurchers Gulley would seem to have been justified, while the approval for extension into the National Nature Reserve on Glas Maol seems regrettable. To resolve future possible conflicts it is now vital to achieve co-operation between ecologists and developers and an accepted management strategy in which the future of the Cairngorms is seen not in isolation but in a national and international context.

The future of the mountain core is bound up with management of its **periphery**, the **'forest and moorland'** or **'countryside management'** zone. Land uses here affect the higher altitudes in several ways. Red deer, for example, range in summer to quite high altitudes and are at least in part responsible for the almost complete loss of the sub-alpine scrub zone and the lack, except in one single locality, of a natural tree-line (p. 31). In the grouse-moor areas failure to observe the rules of good muirburn management has sometimes allowed fires to escape to high altitudes where their effect on vegetation may be extremely damaging. The number of summer visitors at the upper stations of the chair-lift is another type of impact that might be lessened by better provision for recreation at lower levels, using, for example, parts of the native pine forest (Chapter 14).

These instances underline the need for agreed objectives for management. Ecological analysis suggests that efforts should be made to reach a better balance between the more 'natural' vegetation types, especially the woodlands and sub-alpine scrub, and the semi-natural communities such as moorland and grassland. The value of the latter, in ecological, amenity and economic terms, is not disputed but the balance has shifted much too far away from the woodland if reasonable diversity in wildlife and landscape pattern is sought.

Re-creation of a semi-natural sub-alpine scrub zone would add greatly to this diversity and would secure the future of several threatened species. Considerable input of effort and resources might be required to make a start, involving perhaps the fencing of selected areas (Mardon, 1990), but if grazing pressure is reduced in pursuit of a general policy for woodland expansion (p. 134), the sub-alpine scrub would begin to spread from quite small nuclei.

The most far-reaching ecological benefits, however, would result from substantial increases in the areas of semi-natural pine-birch woodland (p. 196). This concept has for some time been part of the conservationist's vision for the future of the Cairngorms (Cairngorms Working Party, 1993; Callander & MacKenzie, 1991; Curry-Lindahl *et al.*, 1982; Peterken, 1992) and the idea has commended itself to a wide range of interested groups, including the Cairngorms Working Party members who have adopted it as an important element in the proposed Management Strategy (Fig. 17.1). Essential to the plan would be a widespread reduction in deer populations, to bring grazing pressure down to levels compatible with natural regeneration of trees. Experiments have shown that this is possible (Chapter 11) and that it is feasible to combine forest regeneration with sustainable populations of red deer, the exact numbers depending on local conditions (though considerably smaller than at present). This would be the only way to bring about forest redevelopment on the scale envisaged, but it might be assisted or hastened locally by the use of fencing or, if necessary, planting. If eventually a plan of this kind is implemented it would serve not only to enhance the vegetation and landscape but also to help sustain viable populations of the characteristic mammals, birds and invertebrate animals which are integral components of the ecosystems (Chapter 4).

This far-sighted approach can be realized only by the agreement of all parties to a management strategy designed for reinstatement of the ecological integrity of the area as a whole, transcending individual or specialist interests. For example, it would envisage a mosaic of vegetation-types and land uses with a balance between woodland, open moors, bogs and other types. This would permit traditional land uses such as deer stalking and grouse shooting to continue in appropriate places, but the mosaic would have to reflect ecological requirements rather than land ownership, and as already indicated there would be an overriding need to reduce deer numbers in areas proposed for forest and scrub expansion or heather recovery. Economic consequences would be inescapable: in some cases the main reward for sacrifices would be the knowledge that they contribute to the general improvements, but financial incentives would also be essential. It should be quite possible to turn these changes to the advantage of local communities because there would be employment opportunities related to countryside management for conservation and recreation, and to environmental education and interpretation.

The above discussion has moved without break from the countryside management zone to the **'valley'** or **'community zone'**, thus emphasizing the interdependence of all parts of the whole. Although land use here is more closely bound up with settlements, communications, agriculture, commercial forestry and tourist accommodation, there is still room for management plans which relate to the rest of the area and are ecologically based. There are localities of high scientific value and importance for diversity of wildlife, such as the Insh Marshes and some of the lochs and rivers, as well as fragments of broadleaved woodland, species-rich heath and unimproved grassland where the priorities as set out above must apply.

Recent studies of the hydrology and ecology of water bodies and water courses (Chapters 6 and 13) show that management must be based not on purely local considerations where, for example, problems of flooding might seem to be capable of solution by localized engineering works, but on the ecology of the water catchment as a whole. The needs and aspirations of local residents must be honoured, but the choice of methods of management should take into account their effects on such factors as water levels in lochs and marshes on which so many components of the ecosystems depend. These range from plankton and higher plants to invertebrate and vertebrate animals, including fish, amphibia, birds and mammals. Some are of considerable economic as well as ecological importance. In the same way, developments in agriculture in the valleys have to be viewed not only in economic terms but in regard to their effects on wildlife habitats and, in the case of fertilizer or pesticide application, to the ecology of drainage systems and watercourses.

In the valley zone some of the priorities will be different from those in other parts, and will permit a wider range of activities. In addition to the current pattern of land uses, there will clearly be scope for farm woodlands and community woodlands as well as commercial forestry (Chapter 10). Again, however, these should submit to generally agreed constraints and objectives, such that as far as possible agriculture should be compatible with maintaining a diversity of habitats and forestry should incorporate diversity of structure and species, with a general preference for native trees where possible.

These examples of the implications of an ecological approach to land use in the Cairngorms have given the objective of nature and countryside conservation high priority. No apology is made for this in view of the exceptional conservation value of the area and the opportunity this gives to make a major contribution to what is now accepted as a national responsibility to conserve the diversity of our wildlife and its habitats. At the same time this approach should serve local as well as national and international interests. It will add to the amenity of the Cairngorms area for residents and visitors, and it need not militate against continued change and evolution of the landscape and its living components, so long as such change is beneficial and not destructive. Changes, both natural and man-induced, have always been taking place and it would not be part of an ecological approach to prevent them. What must be controlled, however, are changes that are too rapid for compensatory adaptation of the living systems, or which cause damage or disruption. All these considerations require a carefully constructed management strategy based on a set of principles and priorities which are understood and agreed. Most of what has been said is incorporated in the recommendations of the Cairngorms Working Party (1993), but the discussion here has drawn special attention to some of the ecological findings and factors that should inform the implementation of policies enshrined in the resulting Management Strategy as finally adopted (Cairngorms Partnership, 1997). If a vision of this kind is to become reality, some mechanism for putting the ideas into practice must be devised. Various possible administrative frameworks have been suggested, and the main options will be reviewed briefly.

PARTIAL SOLUTIONS

A number of provisions are already in force which go some way towards implementing

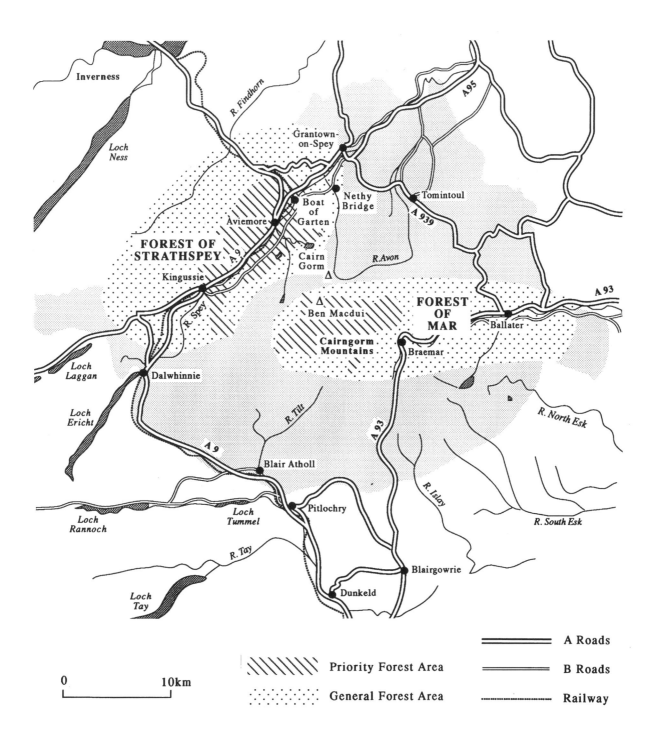

Figure 17.1   Approximate areas proposed by the Cairngorms Working Party for the Forests of Mar and Strathspey (1992) (from Cairngorms Working Party, 1993). Note: These forests are now termed the Deeside Forest and the Forest of Spey respectively.

recommendations contained in the various reports. These include:

a) Management agreements between landowners or landowning agencies and the Scottish Natural Heritage (SNH). Owners of land which has been designated as part of the National Nature Reserves or which contains SSSIs may negotiate agreements which aim to integrate conservation management with the other interests of the estates such as sport, farming, forestry or tourism. Financial support is available, in some cases to compensate for income forgone in the interests of conservation and in others to encourage positive management for the benefit of wildlife or landscape. There are several examples of management agreements in operation in the Cairngorms area and they certainly contribute effectively towards realizing the kind of management which is in tune with conservation aims. Ideally, such agreements should be the precursors of comprehensive estate management plans designed to integrate nature conservation with other activities.

An important example is the agreement between SNH and the National Trust for Scotland, following the acquisition by NTS in 1995 of the Mar Lodge Estate. This is an important area of 31 364 ha lying within the 'core montane zone', on its southern and eastern side. Forty-two per cent of the Estate is designated as SSSI, and part falls within the Cairngorms National Nature Reserve. The Management Agreement sets out an Agreed Management Policy which has the following aims:

(i) The principal and overriding aim is to manage the land in a sustainable manner, for the benefit of the nation, ensuring the continuing conservation and restoration of its internationally important geology, flora, fauna, wild land quality and archaeological value.

(ii) Further, to ensure appropriate public access to the Land, subject to the maintenance of landscape and nature conservation interests.

(iii) To manage the Land as a Highland sporting estate in a manner which is in harmony with the above aims.

(iv) The Owners will favour the continuing use of existing buildings as required including the Lodge itself, providing this does not compromise the wild land quality or conservation of the rest of the Land.

(v) The Owners share with the public an appreciation of the issues involved in managing the Land as a wild land area, through appropriate interpretation and education.

(vi) To aim to manage the Land in a way that enhances the social, economic and cultural well-being of the local community.

(vii) In managing the Land, the Owners will recognise that it forms part of the wider Cairngorm area.

While in this case the agreement is clearly intended to be compatible with any conservation-orientated strategy that may be adopted for the whole of the Cairngorms, management agreements can offer only a partial solution since they normally operate only within NNRs and SSSIs, and do not necessarily relate to any general strategy. Outside the designated areas, management to achieve conservation aims can sometimes be encouraged by the offer of grants from SNH, but these are inevitably limited in scope.

b) Grants for 'New Native Pinewoods'. These can be obtained from the Forestry Authority in areas regarded as within the natural distribution area of the original 'Caledonian' forest. These and other Woodland Grant Scheme grants go some way towards encouraging those aspects of a management strategy concerned with extension of the native pinewood vegetation in the Cairngorms, and with promoting the regeneration of highland birchwoods.

c) The Cairngorms Straths Environmentally Sensitive Area (1992). This ESA designation was welcomed by the Cairngorms Working Party. It was expected to make an important contribution to that part of their management strategy proposals concerned with achieving a sustainable type of agriculture in the area, which would help to maintain habitat diversity and a varied lowland flora and fauna. The designated area (Fig. 17.2) included the Spey Valley, Upper Deeside and an intervening area comprising parts of Strath Avon, Glen Livet and Upper Donside. Here participating farms were to be encouraged with financial help to continue traditional systems of farming where these are in keeping with environmental conservation, and to adopt farm conservation plans which will protect or expand species-rich unimproved pasture or heath, scrub, woodland, etc., and retain or restore ponds, hedges, river banks and dykes as appropriate. In addition to habitat protection or creation, these plans, drawn up in consultation with Farming and Wildlife Advisory Group (FWAG) advisers and Scottish Agriculture College staff, were designed to ensure that the whole farm is managed in ways compatible with nature conservation.

d) International Designations. The 'Wild Birds Directive' and the 'Habitats and Species Directive' of the European Community have required member States to identify areas of special importance for the conservation of species and habitats of significance in a European context. Several sites in the Cairngorms have been designated as Special Protection Areas (SPAs) for birds, while a large part of the area has been recommended to the European Commission by the UK Government as a Special Area of Conservation (SAC) in respect of the presence of 13 of the habitats listed in the 'Manual of European Union Habitats', five of them 'priority habitats'. After acceptance at the European level, this proposed SAC will be incorporated into the 'Natura 2000' network of designated sites, and accorded international recognition of its importance. In addition, a number of high-level lochs together constitute a 'Ramsar Site' under the Ramsar Convention on Wetlands of International Importance.

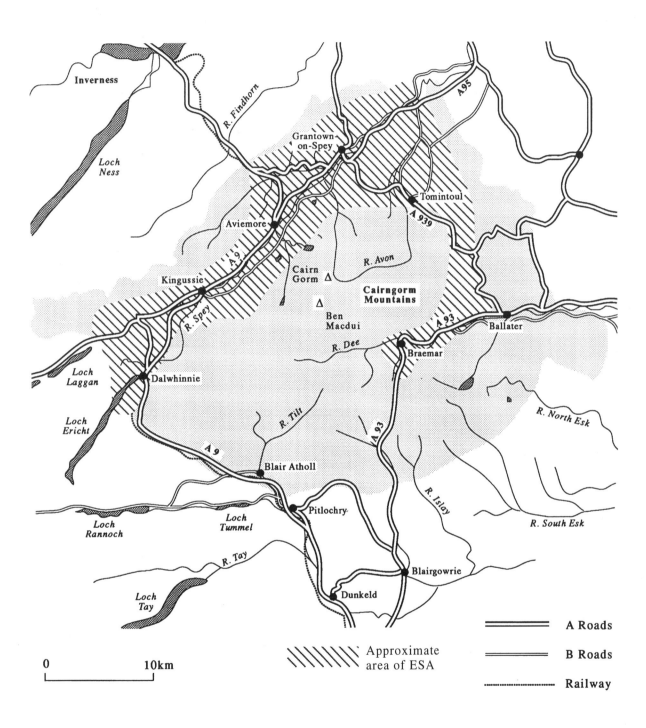

Figure 17.2 Approximate area of the Cairngorm Straths Environmentally Sensitive Area.

205

The Cairngorm Mountains have also been included by the British Government in its second (1999) 'Tentative List' of potential nominations for the status of 'World Heritage Site' in recognition of their natural or cultural significance. The case for the Cairngorms, as one of a small number of top quality 'natural' sites, is to be made primarily on grounds of exceptional geological and geomorphological significance. Submissions are to be made in due course, first for evaluation by the International Union for the Conservation of Nature and subsequently to the World Heritage Committee (UNESCO) for its final decision. If they accept that the site is of 'outstanding universal value' and is effectively protected and managed, the Cairngorms area will be accorded World Heritage Site status, confirming its importance and lending strong support to the measures proposed for conservation and management.

TOWARDS A COMPREHENSIVE ADMINISTRATIVE MECHANISM

While the provisions mentioned above all help towards the achievement of some aspects of a general management strategy, they cover only limited parts of the area and promote only selected aims rather than an integrated policy. For an all-embracing administrative framework two, rather different, options have been proposed. One envisaged the creation of an independent, autonomous Authority, whereas the other favoured a Partnership.

'National Park' proposals for the Cairngorms, 1931–1992.
A national park in the Cairngorms was first recommended to the Government in 1931, and again in the 1940s by the Ramsay Committee. Local authorities have made similar suggestions over the past 40 years, including a proposal for the establishment of national parks, among them the Cairngorms, in the 1989 Highland Regional Council's Consultative Draft, though this disappeared from the eventual Structure Plan. Then in its report on *Mountain Areas* (1990) the Countryside Commission for Scotland took the view that the Cairngorms area, along with Loch Lomond and possibly two other mountain areas, was of particular importance and therefore needed special status and provision for its future management. They argued that the following range of powers and mechanisms was required for its protection and administration:

- the ability to plan for the area in question, both town and country planning and land management planning,
- zoning as a key component of planning for these areas, such as zones for community development, and core sanctuary areas, with appropriate management and buffer zones interposed,
- development control powers,
- powers to enter into and to fund management agreements,
- manpower for land management, including special skills in heritage protection, interpretation and visitor management,

- status to act in co-ordination with other landuse agencies and to operate as their agents within the area,
- powers for recreation land management – including byelaws, orders and powers to secure access and control nuisances,
- the ability to acquire and own land,
- powers of last resort through land management orders to maintain good stewardship,
- status and commitment to be able to deliver national objectives in a local context; and
- linkage to local democratic control and community participation.

One possibility for achieving these objectives through an existing mechanism, that of a Regional Park, was examined, since this would allow for the formation of a management body drawn from the local authorities concerned and including representation of national interests. This solution, however, has already proved inadequate in the case of the Loch Lomond Regional Park. There the several constituent authorities have not all shown an equal degree of commitment, the funding arrangements are inadequate, and it has proved impossible to achieve area-wide integrated management in the face of strong pressures for development. In fact the original intention of the Regional Park designation was focused on provision for recreation management in locations readily accessible from urban areas, rather than for the conservation management of a large tract of country meriting a status which recognizes its national as well as local importance.

After reviewing other possible options for a new approach, the Commission came to the conclusion that existing legislation and structures were not adequate to set up a body having the necessary identity, authority and independence to achieve a balance between conservation, use and enjoyment of the Cairngorms, and between local and national interests, with sufficient funds at its disposal, yet fully accountable to the public. For these reasons, its recommendation was that new legislation should be drawn up to confer national park status on the area and provide for an autonomous Board or Joint Committee to administer and manage it. A body of this kind, the members of which would include representatives of constituent local authorities and national, local and land management interests, would have planning and development control powers and would make its own decisions for the care and management of the area. The Park Board, on which local authority members would be in a majority to ensure local democratic control and accountability, would have its own dedicated staff to administer and run the Park.

The proposed arrangements were in effect based on a European model, though because local government structures in Scotland are similar in many respects to those of England and Wales, the suggested pattern broadly followed that operating in the English and Welsh National Parks, but would be adapted and developed in response to Scottish needs.

In proposing a solution along 'National Park' lines, the Countryside Commission for Scotland took the view that only in this way would a mechanism be created which would be capable of conferring appropriate status and identity on the area, instituting integrated management and control, inspiring commitment and support, and attracting sufficient government and other financial backing. They opted for 'the clearly understood term of National Park', but the substance of their proposal would not be affected if this title did not find favour. It is noteworthy that the proposals of the Countryside Commission for Scotland for national parks in Scotland received strong support from the International Union for the Conservation of Nature (IUCN).

Once these recommendations had been published they caused much debate and aroused a mixed response. They were welcomed in some quarters, particularly by those who enjoy walking and other forms of recreation in the area and by some conservationists, though others were sceptical because of their fear that in the long run a National Park would inevitably promote and increase the popularity of the area to the extent that its remoteness and wilderness qualities would be lost. There was also considerable opposition among local landowners and residents who feared that their interests, independence and livelihood might be adversely affected. On the other hand, the wider public in Scotland showed overwhelming support for the concept of National Parks. In a System Three Public Opinion Poll in March 1991, 84 per cent replied 'yes' to the question 'do you think we should have National Parks in Scotland?', with only four per cent giving a direct negative. In another survey, organized by the Scottish Office, nearly 90 per cent of those questioned expressed themselves in favour.

It quickly became apparent, however, that in Government (Scottish Office) circles opinion had at that time hardened against the concept of National Parks in Scotland. Although the Government's response in 1992 to the Mountain Areas report did not rule it out as a possibility for the future, this aspect of the recommendations was not accepted and instead the Cairngorms Working Party was set up. This was directed to re-examine the question of what administrative arrangements should be made, in the light of the Secretary of State's emphasis on 'the importance the Government attaches to the need to respect the voluntary principle' and on the principle that 'any future management structure should be built firmly on the basis of cooperation' (Cairngorms Working Party, 1993). Thus, between 1989 and 1992 there had been a marked change in attitude on the part of Ministers from one which required the Countryside Commission for Scotland to 'take into consideration the case for arrangements on national park lines' to one which rejected this approach.

The Cairngorms Partnership (1994). With the exception of two of its members who argued for a solution along National Park lines, the Cairngorms Working Party reached the conclusion that the creation of an independent authority was not the right solution for the Cairngorms. Their main reasons were: first, they felt the area taken as a whole did not constitute a convenient administrative unit and that it would be difficult to set the firm boundaries such a unit would require; second, they feared that as a planning authority much of its time might be pre-empted by planning issues in the 'community zone' and in the settlements, rather than being directed towards land management in the area as a whole; and third, they were concerned lest an independent authority might have difficulty in co-exisitng harmoniously with those agencies which have statutory responsibilities for various programmes in the area. They also noted that 'while there is some support nationally for a Cairngorms Authority with full planning powers, there is strong local oppposition'.

In seeking an alternative approach, the Working Party defined a number of principles which guided their thinking:

- Overall, the administrative mechanisms must work to bring about the sustainable use of the natural resources of the Area, while meeting the social and economic requirements and aspirations of the land managers and local communities;
- The Management Strategy must be agreed and implemented by all the public bodies with policy responsibilities relevant to the Management Strategy;
- The planning and development control policies for the Area must be compatible with the agreed aims of the Management Strategy;
- The administrative structure must be capable of ensuring that the Management Strategy is implemented effectively and efficiently;
- Financial resources relating to the public benefits desired, commensurate with the requirements of the Management Strategy, must be made available by the Secretary of State. These financial resources must provide the capacity to deliver effectively the initiative and existing mechanisms identified in the agreed Management Strategy. They should also cover the costs of the necessary staff resources.
- The administrative structure must work with the grain of democratic processes. It should provide effectively for participation in the strategy-forming process by those who will be affected by it, including land managers and local communities.
- Those responsible for the administration must recognise their national and international obligations to the Cairngorms Area as well as their local obligations.

This was the foundation upon which the Working Party's recommendation for the formation of a Cairngorms Partnership was based, its purpose being to bring together all the local authorities and public agencies concerned in the conservation, use and management of the area and the operation of grants, advisory services and regulations. It would be composed of Scottish Natural Heritage, all the relevant local authorities and bodies such as the Forest Authority, Scottish Office Agriculture Environment and Fisheries Department, Deer Commission for Scotland, River Purification Boards (now the Scottish Environment Protection Agency), Scottish Sports Council, Scottish Tourist Board, Scottish Enterprise, and the Local Enterprise Companies. Its task would be to develop, supervise and co-ordinate the implemention of a detailed Management Strategy.

The administrative structure to carry out this remit would consist of a Partnership Board consisting of individual representatives of local authorities, local communities, land managers, and various interests including business, tourism, the environment and recreation. The Board would be advised by a Technical Group consisting of officials of the partner bodies and by several advisory committees or fora reflecting local and sectoral interests. It would have its own operational budget and would appoint a director and a small staff team of professionals 'including an ecologist, a countryside recreational adviser/ranger manager, a planner, a community liaison officer and a land management adviser'.

In carrying out their co-ordinating responsibilities, the staff would aim to bring about implementation of the management strategy on the basis of voluntary agreement and the active and enthusiastic co-operation and compliance of those who will be affected by it. Regulation would be less central and reserved mainly for safeguarding the limits of acceptable change, or as a last resort for protecting environmental features of national and international importance. It was recognized that adequate financial provision is a fundamental prerequisite for the success of the management strategy and that increased availability of incentives would be necessary in certain policy areas. The range of grant schemes currently operating was regarded as capable of meeting the requirements of the strategy. Accordingly it was recommended that, with appropriate augmentation of resources and targeting on the special needs of the Cairngorms area, existing agencies should remain the chief vehicles for funding.

In 1994 the Government then in office followed the recommendation of the Working Party to set up a Cairngorms Partnership and appointed its first Board. Its task was to produce a definitive management strategy, drawing on the support of its many partners and of a number of relevant government agencies and departments, local authorities and local communities. The then Scottish Office recognized, however, that the role of Scottish Natural Heritage (itself one of the Partners) would be vital to the success of the Management Strategy. While its interests relate primarily to the natural heritage of the area and it has statutory obligations in respect of the parts covered by conservation designations, it was clearly in a unique position to provide the Partnership with information and advice on the wider issues of management of the environment, landscape and wildlife of the area. In recognition of this role, the Scottish Office allocated additional resources to SNH, enabling it to set up a 'Cairngorms Project' to provide support to the Partnership and to finance essential research. A three-year Project Plan placed emphasis on building an inventory of key natural heritage areas and establishing a base-line from which to monitor changes. Various programmes of management and conservation were also promoted and initiated.

A new Partnership Board was appointed in 1998, but by that time a new Government was in power and there had been fundamental changes in attitudes to the future provisions for the Cairngorms. The Board's objectives were revised to reflect two priorities: first to co-ordinate the implementation of the Management Strategy and prepare a programme of action to put it into practice, and second to facilitate locally the work of SNH in laying plans for a National Park, which by then had been adopted as government policy. Among its other activities, the Partnership assembled an impressive document on the biodiversity of the Cairngorms (Leaper, 1999), which contains detailed assessments of all the species and habitats listed by the UK Biodiversity Steering Group which are known to occur in the Cairngorms area. This information provides the basis for a Local Biodiversity Action Plan for the Cairngorms.

1997 ONWARDS – A NATIONAL PARK FOR THE CAIRNGORMS

The long saga of discussion and proposals for the future structure and administration of popular mountain areas in Scotland took on a new dimension in 1997, following a General Election in May of that year. The newly elected Government reversed the policy of its predecesor by declaring itself in favour of setting up National Parks in Scotland, beginning with Loch Lomond and the Trossachs, and then (probably) the Cairngorms (with a possibility of others later on). It was decided that the legislation needed to put these plans into operation would appropriately become the responsibilty of the new Scottish Parliament which was due to come into office in 1999.

Scottish Natural Heritage was assigned the task of preparing detailed proposals and carrying out public consultation. Its findings contributed to the drafting of a *National Parks (Scotland) Act* which was passed by the Scottish Parliament in 2000. This contained enabling legislation for the establishment of National Parks, both for Loch Lomond and the Trossachs and for the Cairngorms. It provided for setting up National Park Authorities for each of these areas, and (following further consultation) for the preparation of Designation Orders which would initiate the Parks and detail their constitutions. Consultation on the Proposal for the Cairngorms, with SNH as Reporter, was due to be completed by April 2001. Thereafter the Scottish Executive will prepare a Draft Designation Order, which will be the subject of further discussion and consultation during the remainder of that year, with a view to submission to Parliament in 2002 in the hope that the Park may be up and running in 2003.

The Act enshrines the following four aims and it will be the duty of the Park Authority and its Board to ensure they are effectively pursued:

- to conserve and enhance the natural and cultural heritage of the area;

- to promote sustainable use of the natural resources of the area;
- to promote understanding and enjoyment (including enjoyment in the form of recreation) of the special qualities of the area by the public; and
- to promote sustainable economic and social development of the area's communities.

The Park Board will consist of a maximum of 25 members, at least 20 per cent of whom must be directly elected by those living in the Park area. Of the remaining members, who will be appointed by Scottish Ministers, half will be chosen from nominations submitted by the relevant Local Authorities and half selected to cover national interests and to contribute appropriate expertise. The Park will be core-funded by Scottish Ministers.

Many other details, including the precise boundaries of the Park area, remain to be determined following further consultation. Among these is the important question as to whether the Park Authority will have full planning powers. Scottish Ministers have stated that it is their preferred option for the Cairngorms (unlike Loch Lomond and the Trossachs) that the planning function should remain with the Local Authorities, with the Park Authority as a 'statutory consultee'. However, views are being sought on other options, and many members of the public and other organizations have argued strongly that it is essential for the success of the National Park that it should be secure in its powers, including full planning powers. Only in this way, it is held, will it be able to implement properly an integrated management plan for the entire area. If the Park Authority were merely a statutory consultee there would be no assurance of its ability to maintain a coherent policy of conservation and sustainable development, nor would uniformity of approach among several local authorities be expected. Retention by them of the planning functions would, it is suggested, be a recipe for disagreements and delays.

Whatever the final outcome of this and other issues, the fact that there is now an end to the long history of opposing views on the future management and administration of this magnificent area must be welcomed as a great step forward. It should be possible now to prevent further damage or deterioration of the natural and cultural heritage, and to replace conflict of interests by discussion, co-operation and careful attention to the needs of local

communities as well as visitors. The clear and positive decision on the way forward has met with wide approval, and while some remain unconvinced, many of those who were originally opposed to the idea are now ready to accept it and to help to make it a success. There will certainly be much work to be done to make sure that the arrangements for this National Park in the Cairngorms are well suited to the needs of one of Scotland's finest areas, and that any difficulties encountered elsewhere are avoided.

It is hoped that this book will be of value in providing some of the information essential for this purpose, and for basing future management securely on ecological principles. The protection of the fine landscape and wildlife of the Cairngorms must be accorded the highest priority, recognizing that this will be in the interests of those who live there as well as the great number who also appreciate and value these rare attributes. A unique opportunity is now opening up to make lasting provision for the sympathetic and integrated management of this superb area.

REFERENCES

Cairngorms Partnership (1997) *Managing the Cairngorms. The Cairngorms Partnership Management Strategy.* Cairngorms Partnership, Grantown-on-Spey.
Cairngorms Working Party (1993) *Common Sense and Sustainability. A Partnership for the Cairngorms.* HMSO, Edinburgh.
Callander, R.F. & MacKenzie, N.A. (1991) *The Native pinewoods of Highland Deeside.* Unpublished Report. Nature Conservancy Council, Edinburgh.
Countryside Commission for Scotland (1990) *The Mountain Areas of Scotland: Conservation and Management.* CCS, Battleby, Perth.
Curry-Lindahl, K., Watson, A. & Watson, R. Drennan (1982) *The Future of the Cairngorms.* North East Mountain Trust, Aberdeen.
Gimingham, C.H. (1989) In: *Views on the need for conservation of the Cairngorms.* (Leaflet). Save the Cairngorms Campaign, Inverness.
Highland Regional Council (1990) *Highland Region Structure Plan.* Highland Regional Council, Planning Department, Inverness.
Leaper, G. (1999) *Biodiversity of the Cairngorms.* Cairngorms Partnership, Grantown-on-Spey.
Mardon, D.K. (1990) Conservation of montane willow scrub in Scotland. *Trans Bot. Soc. Edinburgh* 45, 427–436.
Peterken, G.F. (1992) Conservation of old growth: a European perspective. *Natural Areas Journal* 12, 10–19.
Scottish Office (1994) *Cairngorms Partnership.* The Scottish Office Rural Framework, Edinburgh.
Watson, A. & Conroy, J., eds (1994) *The Cairngorms: Planning Ahead.* Kincardine and Deeside District Council, Stonehaven.

List of Figures, Tables and Plates

Figures

Fig. 1.1   The Cairngorms area.   5

Fig. 2.1   Geological map of the Cairngorms area.   11

Fig. 2.2   Reconstruction of the pre-glacial Tertiary relief in part of the Cairngorm massif.   13

Fig. 2.3   Major elements of linear glacial erosion in the Cairngorms.   14

Fig. 2.4   The pattern of glacial meltwater channels on the northern slopes of Cairn Gorm.   16

Fig. 2.5   A continuum of upland soil profiles reflecting the influence of parent material, topography and local climate on pedogenesis.   19

Fig. 3.1   Native Scots pine: boundaries of biochemical similarity.   26

Fig. 3.2   Distribution and relative abundance of silver birch and downy birch on upper Deeside.   27

Fig. 3.3   Maps illustrating the distribution of certain heath communities in the British Isles.   28

Fig. 3.4   Relationship between stand age and composition of major species categories in species-rich heath in north-east Scotland.   29

Fig. 3.5   Graph showing the relationship between average height of heather and altitude on the NNE-facing slope of An t'Aonach, Cairn Gorm.   30

Fig. 3.6   Diagrams illustrating the interaction of altitude, exposure and snow cover on the distribution of the chief plant communities in the Cairngorms.   33

Fig. 3.7   Diagram showing the four main habitats on an idealized small-scale terrace.   34

Fig. 3.8   Diagrams illustrating vegetational zonation on small-scale terraces at various altitudes and degrees of wetness.   35

Fig. 3.9   A vegetational pattern in and around a snowbed at high altitude.   34

Fig. 3.10   Complex of vegetation types around a snowbed in the Cairngorms.   34

Fig. 3.11   Transect data showing the distribution of lichens across a snow patch near the summit of Cairn Gorm.   36

Fig. 3.12   Drawing of prostrate branch systems of heather and bearberry in two successive stripes or waves.   37

Fig. 3.13   Diagram of a transect through a vegetation wave in eroded *Racomitrium* heath at about 1070 m on the northern slopes of Cairn Gorm.   38

Fig. 3.14   Schematic diagram of changes in tussocks of three-leaved rush from immature to degenerate age-states.   38

Fig. 3.15   An example of the effects of experimental disturbance in lichen-rich heather – deer-grass heath on Cairn Gorm.   40

Fig. 7.1   Ownership of the main Estates in the Cairngorms area.   88

210

Fig. 8.1 Map of the Cairngorms area showing Parish boundaries. 99

Fig. 9.1 Main woodland types in the Cairngorms – includes all planted and self-sown woods. 114

Fig. 9.2 Main woodland types in the Cairngorms – proportions of planted and self-sown. 114

Fig. 11.1 Estimated stocking densities of red deer on winter and summer ranges in the Cairngorms. 133

Fig. 11.2 Schematic representation of a culling strategy to counteract any possible movement of deer from high to low density areas. 137

Fig. 12.1 Average grouse bag for managed grouse moors in the Cairngorms. 140

Fig. 12.2 Frequency distribution of mean grouse bags for grouse moors in the Cairngorms during three decades. 141

Fig. 12.3 Relationship between numbers of grouse shot and number of foxes killed on a large estate within the Cairngorms area. 142

Fig. 12.4 Causes of death of red grouse determined from corpses collected on study areas in the Cairngorms. 142

Fig. 13.1 The river systems draining the Cairngorms area. 149

Fig. 13.2 The principal streams and rivers of the Cairngorms area. 149

Fig. 13.3 Main spawning streams for Atlantic salmon in the Cairngorms area. 151

Fig. 16.1 Proliferation of hill tracks in the Cairngorms. 186

Fig. 16.2 Distribution and approximate extent of conservation designations in the Cairngorms area. 190

Fig. 16.3 Map of indicative forestry strategy zones in the Cairngorms area. 193

Fig. 16.4 Indicative zoning of the Cairngorms area as suggested by the Countryside Commission for Scotland (1990). 195

Fig. 17.1 Approximate areas proposed by the Cairngorms Working Party for the Forests of Mar and Strathspey (1992). 203

Fig. 17.2 Approximate area of the Cairngorm Straths Environmentally Sensitive Area. 205

Tables
Table 2a Weather Data for Braemar (1930–1960) 9

Table 3a Classification of vegetation of the Cairngorms into sixteen groups 24

Table 4a Rarer species of birds which breed regularly in the Cairngorms area 44

Table 4b Species which have declined or ceased to breed in the Cairngorms area 44

Table 4c Impacts of various factors on montane birds in the Cairngorms area 46

Table 4d Status of diurnal raptors in the Cairngorms area 47

Table 4e Rare bird species which have colonized, attempted to colonize or re-colonized Scotland and the first time of breeding in the Cairngorms area 52

Table 5a Characteristics of egg batch sites for the Kentish glory moth and survival of larvae at different heights at Muir of Dinnet NNR, Deeside, in 1989 56

Table 5b The number of insect taxa recorded in standardized samples from a series of plots at Forest Lodge NNR, Abernethy, Speyside in 1986 and 1987 57

Table 5c A summary of the numbers of rare insects found in the Cairngorms 58

Provisional list of rare and notable Cairngorm species of insects 59–63

Table 5d The threats to Cairngorm insect communities 64

Table 6a Classification of Spey Valley lochs according to method of formation 68

Table 6b Chemistry of Dee headwater streams and geology 69

Table 6c Chemical charateristics of standing waters 69

Table 6d Major river plant communities of the Cairngorms area 72

Table 6e Aquatic plants locally worthy of special protection 73

Table 6f Classification of Cairngorm streams in relation to pH and alkalinity 76

Table 6g Catchment transfers from the upper Spey 78

Table 7a Goal orientations of estate policy 91

Table 7b Cairngorms population age structure, 1991 94

Table 7c Employment structure in the Cairngorms, 1981 and 1989 94

Table 8a Land use in the United Kingdom, Scotland, the Scottish Highlands and the Cairngorms 100

Table 9a Trees and shrubs native to the Cairngorms 108

Table 9b Areas of wartime fellings 111

Table 9c Native pinewood losses in the Cairngorms 1957–1987 112

Table 10a Area of Forestry Commission land in 1994 – woodland and open areas 124

Table 10b Forestry Commission land 1994 – area by species 124

Table 10c Forestry Commssion land 1994 – area by age classes 124

Table 10d Mid and upper Deeside planted woodland – area by age classes 125

Table 10e Seed origins of planted pine woodland in mid and upper Deeside 125

Table 11a Counts of red deer in the East and West Grampian counting blocks by the Deer Survey and the Red Deer Commission 132

Table 12a List of dependent variables used in the multiple regression for examining factors associated with variations in average grouse bag 143

Table 13a List of fish species found in the
Cairngorms area   150

Table 13b Lochs containing Arctic charr in the
Cairngorms area   153

Table 13c Waters containing pike in the
Cairngorms area   153

Plates
(note these illustrations are distributed throughout the book and do not have page numbers)

Half-title page   The Lairig Ghru, a deep, glacially excavated valley which bisects the Cairngorm massif in a north-south direction.

Frontispiece   The northern slopes of the Cairngorms seen across the Insh Marshes, Strathspey.

Plate 1   The extensive high plateau of the Cairngorms mountain core, dissected by glacial valleys.

Plate 2   A Cairngorms mountain stream descending through heather-dominated moorland with scree slopes and high plateau in the distance. Glen Clova.

Plate 3   Glen Clova viewed from Glen Fee – steep glacial valleys in the southern rim of the mountains.

Plate 4   Snow fields in the Cairngorms.

Plate 5   Icicles on a peat overhang – the Fir Mounth.

Plate 6   Large snow cornices overhang Corrie Bhrochain on the eastern side of Braeriach – approaching the summit from the south.

Plate 7   'Woolsack' jointing and weathering effects on the summit tor of Meikle Pap, Lochnagar.

Plate 8   Gently rolling ancient land surface looking north-west from the south top of Beinn a' Bhuird.

Plate 9   Tors on the summit of Beinn Mheadhoin, showing topographic 'sheeting' structures (dilitation jointing).

Plate 10   The Loch Avon trough viewed from Shelter Stone Crag, looking north-east.

Plate 11   The Lairig an Laoigh breach at the head of Glen Derry.

Plate 12   Classic corries cut into the northern flank of Braeriach.

Plate 13   Boulder moraines of the Loch Lomond stadial interval of glaciation in Coire nan Clach, Beinn a' Bhuird.

Plate 14   Eag a' Chait, a subglacially-cut meltwater channel breaching the spur west of the Coire Cas car park, Cairn Gorm.

Plate 15   Glen Derry and Beinn a' Chaorainn, looking over the site of a former lake.

Plate 16   View north from the summit of Lochnagar, showing the arcuate boulder moraines enclosing the lochan of the great northern corrie.

Plate 17   View up Glen Feshie from Carnachuinn, illustrating the immature braided nature of the post-glacial river channel.

Plate 18   Results of extreme rainfall events on the fragile soils and vegetation of the Cairn Gorm, Allt Mor valley in 1963.

Plate 19   Boulder lobes and terraces – solifluxion terrace system at c. 3500 ft (1070 m) on the north-west slope of Snap Coire na Spreadhe. Cambridge University expeditions 1938/39. (Black & white)

Plate 20   Buried pine stumps exposed by peat erosion and indicating former high-level woodland. Shore of Loch Einich, 1938/39. (Black & white)

Plate 21   Aspects of vegetation of the northern Cairngorms – a view from Rothiemurchus.

Plate 22   Mosaic of heath and species-rich alpine grassland overlying outcrops of limestone – the Cairnwell.

Plate 23   Twin-flower in Abernethy forest.

Plate 24   Invasion of heather-bearberry heath by birch at Dinnet Moor.

Plate 25   Heather-blaeberry heath community. Culblean Hill near Dinnet.

Plate 26   Moss campion on Cairn Gorm.

Plate 27   Heather 'stripes' or waves, on an exposed slope above Coire na Ciste, Cairn Gorm – and close up.

Plate 28   Exposed plateau with three-leaved rush. Beinn Mheadhoin and Beinn a' Bhuird on skyline.

Plate 29   Ptarmigan, a year-round resident at the higher altitudes.

Plate 30   Dotterel. Nests on the high plateaux.

Plate 31   Snow bunting. The Cairngorms support a large proportion of the small Scottish breeding population.

Plate 32   Golden eagle. The mountain core of the Cairngorms sustains an important breeding population.

Plate 33   Osprey. Following its return to breed in Strathspey, the population has steadily increased.

Plate 34   Scottish crossbill. Found only in Scotland, where it inhabits the older pine woods.

Plate 35   Capercaillie. A characteristic species of coniferous forest reintroduced to Scotland in 1837 after it had become extinct.

Plate 36   Mountain hare. White-coated in winter, mountain hares are abundant in parts of the Cairngorms.

Plate 37   Red squirrel. Although its range in Britain has been severely reduced, the red squirrel is still fairly plentiful in the pinewoods of the Cairngorms.

Plates 38 Some Red Data Book insects of the
–41   Cairngorms.

Plate 42   The emperor moth *Saturnia pavonia* (Linn.) (Lepidoptera). Larvae feed on heather, and the moth is common on heaths and moors.

Plate 43   A 'Malaise trap' – one of the methods available for studying insects.

Plate 44   Sap run on a pine tree – one of the microhabitats which are important for rare insects.

Plate 45   River shingle habitat, River Feshie – a type of habitat associated with communities of rare insects, especially Diptera and Coleoptera.

Plate 46   Computer cartography of the aquatic vegetation of Loch Davan.

Plate 47   Wells of Dee.

Plate 48   Lairig Ghru and Pools of Dee.

Plate 49   Loch Morlich and the Cairngorms beyond.

Plate 50   Punch Bowl, Glen Quoich, near Braemar.

Plate 51   Dubh Lochan from Beinn a' Bhuird.

Plate 52   Loch Muick.

Plate 53   River Dee – upper stretches of the Linn.

Plate 54   Loch Einich in snow.

Plate 55   Loch a' Gharbh-Choire, Strathnethy.

Plate 56   River Nethy in Abernethy Forest with semi-natural pinewood vegetation and fallen trees.

Plate 57   Glenlivet – integration of farming and forestry.

Plate 58   Cattle grazing moorland – Tulloch croft, near Nethybridge.

Plate 59   Old croft and sheep, Tulloch.

Plate 60   A site of abandoned crofts, Abernethy.

Plate 61   Deeside from the Forest of Birse.

Plate 62   Scots pine at the natural tree limit, about 650 m above sea level on Creag Fhiaclach.

Plate 63   The dwarf and semi-prostrate Scots pine (krummholz condition) on the slopes of Creag Fhiaclach.

Plate 64   Even-aged stand of Scots pine at Abernethy with blaeberry understorey.

Plate 65   A moribund birchwood in the Cairngorms.

Plate 66   Timber floating at Rothiemurchus, late nineteenth century. (Black & white)

Plate 67   Strathspey – an extract from William Roy's military survey of Scotland (1747–55), showing the natural woodland and areas of settlement and cultivation.

Plate 68   A naturally-grown birch of excellent form amongst lodgepole pine at 610 ASL.

Plate 69   Excellent stem forms in 120-year old naturally regenerated Scots pine at Cur Wood near Dulnain Bridge on the Seafield Estate.

Plate 70   High elevation experimental plots (620 m ASL) on the west side of the Cairngorms, showing plots of lodgepole pine and Sitka spruce.

Plate 71   Natural regeneration of Scots pine following reduction of grazing by red deer. Inshriach.

Plate 72   Red deer stag outside a deer fence showing the dramatic difference in the grazed and protected areas.

Plate 73   Red deer hinds and calves in open birchwood. Creag Meagaidh.

Plate 74   Ponies still provide cost-effective means of extracting deer carcasses.

Plate 75   Stags at winter feed – Luibeg.

Plate 76   Red grouse.

Plate 77   Heather burning – recently burnt patches picked out by snow.

Plate 78   Heather burning.

Plate 79   Fish traps on the Girnock Burn on upper Deeside in winter.

Plate 80   Fish traps on the Baddock Burn, a tributary of the Clunie Water, have also been operated by the Freshwater Laboratory of Fisheries Research Services since 1989.

Plate 81   Adult salmon in the River Avon.

Plate 82   A sea trout in the River Avon.

Plate 83   A small pike in the River Spey.

Plate 84   A pair of adult sea lampreys constructing a nest in the River Spey.

Plate 85   Arctic charr from Loch an t' Seilich in Glen Tromie.

Plate 86   The wild landscape of the northern corries of the Cairngorms.

Plate 87   The summit of Lochnagar, Christmas 1991 – a popular good-weather destination even in winter.

Plate 88   Snow fences and tows at the Glen Shee ski development, as seen from the Cairnwell.

Plate 89   The Day Lodge, car park and chairlift bottom station at Coire Cas.

Plate 90   The Cairn Gorm summit path showing effects of the pressure of many feet, and attempts to channel visitors along a marked footpath.

Plate 91   Members of the Cairngorm Club at the inauguration of the direction indicator on Ben Macdui, 1926. (Black & white)

Plate 92   Members of the Cairngorm Club on a mountain climb, Sgoran Dubh, 1899. (Black & white)

Plate 93   Tackling a snow slope – the Black Spout, Lochnagar, 26 March 1910. (Black & white)

Plate 94   Members of the Cairngorm Club on skis, Loch Avon, 15 March 1908.

Plate 95   Pine-clad lake, forest, moor and hills – the essence of Cairngorm conservation.

Plate 96   A remnant of native Scots pinewood – Derry Wood and Luibeg Wood, Mar Lodge Estate.

Plate 97   The northern slopes of the Cairngorm massif – zonation through forest to moorland and high plateau with Loch Morlich in the foreground.

Plate 98   The bed of the Luibeg Burn draining the high ground – Ben Macdui and Derry Cairngorm.

Plate 99   Open birchwood, heather and bracken – Muir of Dinnet National Nature Reserve.

The Authors

Jim Atterson graduated from Edinburgh University in 1959, joining the Forestry Commission in the same year, as a Research Forest Officer. After further periods as District Officer for Sutherland and Caithness, as Principal Silviculturist (North) responsible for research over upland Britain, and as Conservator successively for West, Mid and North Scotland, he finally became Chief Conservator for the Forest Authority in Scotland before retiring in October, 1994.

Dick Balharry has spent his working life in the Scottish Highlands. He was one of the original team on the Red Deer Commission's field staff in 1959, and then joined the Nature Conservancy as warden at Beinn Eighe National Nature Reserve in Wester Ross. He became Chief Warden in the Nature Conservancy Council for Scotland in 1968, with responsibility for the North West and, later, the North East Regions. He retired from Scottish Natural Heritage as Area Manager for Moray, Nairn and Badenoch and Strathspey in 1997. Dick currently serves on the Executive of the National Trust for Scotland, and is a trustee of the John Muir Trust. He is a well-known contributor to TV and radio on Scotland's countryside and wildlife.

Iain Brown is a Research Fellow in the Environmental Change Institute at Oxford University, investigating the effects of future climate change for the government-sponsored UK Climate Impacts Programme. He was awarded a PhD from Aberdeen University in 1992, based upon research to determine the abrupt climate changes at the end of the last glaciation. This involved an extensive survey of the sediments and geomorphology of the Dee valley. He has also previously worked at the University of Glamorgan and for the Scottish Agricultural Colleges.

Chalmers Clapperton was appointed Assistant Lecturer in Geography at Aberdeen in 1962 and served in the Geography Department until 1999, becoming Professor in 1992. He has studied the evolution of glacial and volcanic landforms in both hemispheres (including the Antarctic), and recently investigated past glacier fluctuations in Patagonia, as part of a wider project to understand whether climatic changes of the last glacial period were synchronous worldwide.

Mike Davidson graduated in biology at Aberdeen University and is Ecology Unit Manager with the Scottish Environment Protection Agency. He has a wide experience of the freshwater ecology of the Cairngorms, his first involvement being a survey of the headwaters of the Dee during 1978/9.

Roy Dennis is an ornithologist, wildlife consultant and crofter living in Strathspey. He has served on various government boards including Scottish Natural Heritage and The Deer Commission for Scotland, and was previously a field ornithologist working for the RSPB and Fair Isle Bird Observatory Trust from 1959 to 1990. He is now Director of the Highland Foundation for Wildlife with a special interest in conservation and reintroduction of large birds of prey in the UK and abroad, and also in the reintroduction of large mammals as part of ecosystem restoration. He is a lecturer and writer and regularly works abroad.

Ross Gardiner is a Senior Scientific Officer at the Fisheries Research Service (FRS) Freshwater Laboratory at Pitlochry on the southern fringe of the Cairngorms area. Much of his work over more than 30 years based at Pitlochry has been on the distribution and population dynamics of salmon, trout and other freshwater fish in Scotland. This work has taken him to many parts of Scotland.

Charles Gimingham is a botanist and plant ecologist, having spent most of his working life on the staff of the

214

Botany Department of the University of Aberdeen (now the Department of Plant and Soil Science). He retired from the post of Professor there in 1988. He was President of the British Ecological Society in 1986-1987, a member of the Countryside Commission for Scotland 1980-1991, and served on the North East Regional Board of Scottish Natural Heritage and on its Scientific Advisory Committee. He is particularly interested in the ecology of the uplands, especially heather moorlands and their management.

Peter Hudson studied for his DPhil in the Edward Grey Institute of Ornithology at Oxford University. After working on seabirds and tropical humming birds, he joined the Game Conservancy Trust to investigate the population dynamics of red grouse. This led him to address problems of parasites in wild animal populations and to a fascination with wildlife diseases both of grouse and other animals. From there he moved to become Professor of Animal Ecology at the University of Stirling where he continues to work on conservation science and population dynamics.

David Mackay retired recently as Director of the North Region of the Scottish Environment Protection Agency. He is now Chairman of the environmental consultancy Envirocentre and is a visiting professor at Stirling and Strathclyde Universities. Last year he was awarded an honorary doctorate by the University of Paisley. Although his career has ranged widely his early dedication to rivers and salmonids continues unabated.

John Mackay is a National Strategy Manager with Scottish Natural Heritage. He is a geologist by original training but has spent most of his career working on research management and policy development with the former Countryside Commission for Scotland and with SNH since its inception.

Neil MacKenzie, a graduate of Aberdeen and Edinburgh Universities, is a freelance consultant based in the Highlands and specializing in native woodland research, surveys and other aspects of land-use management. He is the author of several reports for Scottish Natural Heritage, Forestry Commission and Friends of the Earth (Scotland), co-author of reports on the Deeside Forest Initiative and on the management of red deer in Scotland, and has recently completed a database of montane scrub communities in Scotland. He is currently investigating the progress of native woodland restoration projects in Britain. Previously he worked as a wildlife officer in Nigeria and Borneo.

Mike Matthew's first degree in geography at Cambridge University was followed by an MSc in glacial geomorphology at McGill University in Canada and a Diploma in Conservation from London University (University College, London). He joined the Nature Conservancy in 1964 and has worked for it and its successor bodies (NCC, NCC Scotland, and Scottish Natural Heritage) since then, spending all but six of these years in north-east Scotland. He was Regional Officer for the North East Region from 1975-1991.

Roger Owen is National Ecology Manager for the Scottish Environment Protection Agency and, in current and previous posts, has been responsible for managing the biological aspects of aquatic environmental protection in the Cairngorms area for the past 25 years. He has contributed to a number of national policies on ecological monitoring of water quality, and has had a major influence on the development of methods and networks in this respect. As a mountaineer he knows and loves the Cairngorms and is current Chairman of the North East Mountain Trust.

Irvine Ross graduated in forestry at Aberdeen University in 1973. After working for Tilhill Forestry in the Borders he was appointed Head Forester of Glen Tanar Estate in Deeside in 1977, where he continued the established policies of encouraging natural regeneration in the native pinewood and birchwoods and their expansion, integrating this with provision of informal public recreation facilities. He became an independent forestry consultant in 1992, but still manages the Glen Tanar woodlands. He is Founder Chairman of the Native Pinewoods Managers Group and was a member of the Forestry Commission's Native Woodland Advisory Panel for Scotland, 1992-1999.

Mark Shucksmith has been with the Department of Land Economy at the University of Aberdeen since 1981, after previously working in the Department of Agricultural Economics at the University of Newcastle. He is also Co-Director of the Arkleton Centre for Rural Development Research, and of the Scottish Centre for Social Justice Research. His main areas of interest are social exclusion, agricultural change, and rural development. He was formerly Vice-Chairman of Rural Forum (Scotland) and expert adviser to the Scottish Parliament's Rural Development Committee. He is adviser on rural issues to the Joseph Rowntree Foundation, and programme chair for the 2004 World Rural Sociology Congress.

Brian Staines was head of the Banchory Research Station of the Institute of Terrestrial Ecology from 1986 until he retired in 1997. He has been involved with deer ecology, conservation and management in Scotland since the mid-1960s. His main research areas have been in population dynamics, behaviour, habitat use and impacts. He has published over 100 articles and scientific papers on deer. He was a member of the Deer Commission for Scotland from 1987 to 1998 and, as a Board member for the North East Region of Scottish Natural Heritage, was a key participant in producing SNH's red deer management policy.

Kenneth Thomson is a graduate of the University of Aberdeen and has degrees in mathematics, statistics and economics. After 15 years at the University of Newcastle upon Tyne, he became the senior rural economist and Professor in the Aberdeen School of Agriculture in 1986. His main research interest is agricultural policy, especially in Europe: he has acted as consultant to the European Commission, to UK Government Departments of Agriculture and to the Scottish Parliament, and is President of the UK Agricultural Economics Society for 2001–2002. His main outdoor recreation is mountaineering: he is the current President of the Cairngorm Club, has climbed all the Scottish 'Munros' and knows the Cairngorms intimately.

Kenneth Watt has for many years curated the invertebrates in the Aberdeen University Natural History Museum. A keen and active member of the Scottish Wildlife Trust, he is also a founder member of the Malloch Society for Scottish Dipterists. As the national recorder for the Hoverfly Recording Scheme he has recently produced the first Atlas of the Hoverflies of Scotland.

Mark Young lectures in Zoology at the University of Aberdeen and has a particular interest in the conservation of rare insects and the effect of land-management practices on insect communities. He is a long-time voluntary officer of the Scottish Wildlife Trust and was until recently Editor of the Bulletin of the British Ecological Society.

Index

Note: species are cross-referenced from common to scientific names (exception: red deer). Bold type refers to figures or main discussions, italic to tables not otherwise indexed

Abernethy Forest
  19th C deer forest, 111
  abandoned crofts, *Pl. 60*
  bog habitat, 115
  felling, 110
  NNR, 174
  pinewood losses, *112*
  purchase by RSPB, 114, 174
  River Nethy, *Pl. 56*
  size, 171
  Thomson Scottish Forestry case, 174
Aboyne Estate, 121, 123
  modern sawmills, 125
  Statistical Account, 121
abstraction and catchment transfers, threat to aquatic habitats, 77–8
access problems, leisure pursuits, 136–7
Accipter gentilis (goshawk), 44, 47
Accipter nisus (sparrowhawk), 47, 48
Achnagoichan, 8, 9
Achnanthes scotica, 76
A'Choinneach, 56
acidification
  amelioration, 81
  drainage from peat, 69
  threat to aquatic habitats, 75–7
  threats to fish, 155
Acrocephalus palustris (marsh warbler), 52
Acrocephalus shoeobaenus (sedge warbler), 50
Actitis hypoleucos (common sandpiper), 45
aeolisols, 20
Agabus guttatus (waterbeetle), 80
Agabus wasastjernae (waterbeetle), 57
agriculture *see* farming/agriculture
Agrostis capillaris (common bent-grass), 30
Agrostis stolonifera (creeping bent-grass), 29
Alauda arvensis (skylark), 45, 51
Alchemilla alpina (alpine lady's mantle), 30
alder *also see Alnus glutinosa*
  commercial exploitation, 110
  origins, 108
Alectoria sarmentosa subsp. *vexillifera*, 32
Alliopsis albipennis (fly), 55
Allt an Dubh Lochan, chemistry, 69, 75
Allt Darrarie, chemistry, 69, 75
Alltcailleach, 123
Alnus glutinosa (alder), 27, 118
alpine cinquefoil *see Potentilla cranzii*
alpine lady's mantle *see Alchemilla alpina*
alpine milk-vetch *see Astragalus alpinus*
alpine mouse-ear *see Cerastium alpinum*
alpine saw-wort *see Saussaurea alpina*
alpine saxifrage *see Saxifraga nivalis*
alpine sowthistle *see Cicerbita alpina*
alpine vegetation, 31–2, 170
alpine willow-herb *see Epilobium anagallidifolium*
alternate-flowered water-milfoil *see Myriophyllum alterniflorum*
Alvie, 121
Amara alpinus (beetle), 56
Ameletus inopinatus (mayfly), 74
Anabaena (cyano-bacteria), 77
Anarta cordigera (small dark yellow underwing), 58
Anas acuta (pintail), 44, 50
Anas clypeata (shoveller), 44, 50
Anas crecca (teal), 44, 50

Anas penelope (wigeon), 44, 50
Anas platyrhynchos (mallard), 50
Ancient Woodland Inventory, 116
Anguilla anguilla (eel), 148
Angus glens, 5
Anser anser (greylag goose), 44, 50
Antennaria dioica (cat's foot), 29
Anthelia julacea, 72
Anthus pratensis (meadow pipit), 43, 51
Anthus trivialis (tree pipit), 48
aphids, 55–6
Apium inundatum, *73*
aquatic habitats
  conservation and management, 80–2
    protection measures, 81–2
  ecology, 67–75
    chemical characteristics, 68–9
    fauna, 74–5
    flora, 71–73
    hyporheic zone, 71
    physical interactions, 67–8
    shingle, 70–1
    standing waters, 73
    wetlands, 30, 71–3, 173
    zonation, 70–1
  nutrient enrichment, 81
  threats, 75–80
    abstraction and catchment transfers, 77–8
    acidification, 75–7
    eutrophication, 77
    fish farming, 79
    flood alleviation, 78–9
    forestry, 79
    pollution, 77
    tourism and recreation, 79–80
  vegetation, classification, *72*
Aquila chrysaetos (golden eagle), *Pl. 32*, 44, 46, 47
Arabis petraea (northern rock-cress), 70
Arctic charr *see Salvelimus alpinus*
arctic-alpine species, habitat, 32
Arctostaphylos uva-ursi (bearberry), 29, 37
  Calluna–Arctostaphylos heath, **28**, 29
  Dinnet Moor, *Pl. 24*
  insects, 58
Ardea cinerea (grey heron), 44
Armeria maritima (sea pink), 24, 32
Artemisia (mugwort), 24
Arvicola terrestris (water vole), 52
Asio flammeus (short-eared owl), 46
aspen *see Populus tremula*
Astragalus alpinus (alpine milk-vetch), 32
Athyrium, **34**
Aviemore Centre, 93, 94, 162
  development, 180
awlwort *see Subularia aquatica*
Aythya fuligula (tufted duck), 50
azalea, trailing *see Loiseleuria nigrum*

Badan Mosach wood, 134
Baddoch Burn, chemistry, 69, 76
Badenoch
  employment, 125
  evictions, 87
  flood plain mire, 5, 50
  no regeneration, 117
Badenoch and Strathspey District Council, anti-conservation stance, 181
badger *see Meles meles*
Ballater, 93
  Monaltrie, 122
  tourism, 95
Ballochbuie, 110, 171
  pinewood losses, *112*
Ballogie, tree planting, 123

Balmoral, 8
  Garmaddie woods, 110
  purchase, 110, 123
Barbatula barbatula (stone loach), 148, 154
barn owl, 44
Barns of Bynack, 13
bearberry *see Arctostaphylos uva-ursi*
Beinn a' Bhuird, *Pl. 28*, 9, 17, 31
  Coire nan Clach *Pl. 13*
  Dubh Lochan, *Pl. 51*
Beinn a' Chaorainn, Glen Derry *Pl. 15*
Beinn Bhreac, 11
Beinn Mheadhoin, *Pls. 9, 28*
bell heather *see Erica cinerea*
Ben Avon, 12, 13, 17, 31
Ben Macdui, 8, 9, 12, 18, 32
  Derry burn, *Pl. 98*
bent grasses *see Agrostis* spp.
Betula nana (dwarf birch), 24
Betula pendula (silver birch), 25, **27**
Betula pubescens (downy birch), 26, **27**, 115
Betula woodland, 26–7
  commercial exploitation, 110
  grazing pressure, *Pl. 65*
  Highland Birchwoods, 126–7
  invasion, Dinnet Moor, *Pl. 24*, 26
  losses, 112
  origins, 107
  regeneration, recent, 112
  species distribution, **27**
  timber properties, 126
bibliography, 6
Biodiversity Action Plans, 118
birds, 43–52
  diurnal raptors, 46–7
  lochs, rivers, marshes, 49–50
  moorland species, 46
  native woodlands, 48–9
  rarities, 52
    Annex One species, 171
    and recreation/tourism, impact, 166
Birse, Forest of, Deeside, *Pl. 61*, 112, 116, 117
  history, 122
bitter vetch *see Lathyrus montanus*
black grouse *see Tetrao tetrix*
black mountain moth *see Psodos coracina*
black-headed gull *see Larus ridibundus*
blaeberry *see Vaccinium myrtillus*
Blair Atholl, 5
Blechnum spicant (hard fern), 27
Blindia acuta, 72
bluethroat *see Luscinia svecica*
blunt-leaved pondweed *see Potamogeton obtusifolius*
Boat of Garten, modern sawmills, 125
bog whortleberry *see Vaccinium uliginosum*
bogbean *see Menyanthes trifoliata*
bogs
  blanket, 20
  wooded, 115, 171, 174
Bombycilla garrulus (waxwing), 52
Botrychium lunaria (moonwort), 24
bottle sedge *see Carex rostrata*
boulder lobes, 17, *172*, *Pl. 19*
boulder moraines, arcuate, *Pl. 16*
Brachionycha nubeculosa (Rannoch sprawler moth), 56
bracken *see Pteridium aquilinium*
Braemar, 8, 9, 93, 95
  forests, 122
  Morrone, *Betula–Juniperus* woodland, 27, 31
  weather data, *9*
Braeriach, 9, 17

Coire Beanaidh, 17
cornices, *Pl. 6*
and Lairig Ghru, *Pl. 12*
Braeriach–Cairn Toul plateau, 12, 32
braided river, *Pl. 17*
brambling *see Fringilla montifringilla*
Briza media (quaking grass), 30
broad-leaved pondweed *see Potamogeton natans*
broadleaf forest, Forestry Commission land area (1994), 124
brook lamprey (*Lampetra planeri*), 148, 150
brown long-eared bat *see Plecotus auritus*
brown trout *see Salmo trutta*
bryophytes *see*
  Anthelia; Blindia; Cephalozia;
    Cratoneuron; Dicranum; Hygrobiella;
    Hygrohypnum; Hylocomium;
    Hypnum; Nardia; Oligotrichum;
    Philonotis; Plagiothecium;
    Polytrichum; Ptilium; Racomitrium;
    Rynchostegium; Scapania; Sphagnum;
    Thuidium
Bucephala clangula (goldeneye), 44, **49–50**, 52
bulbous rush *see Juncus bulbosa*
burning *see* muirburning
Buteo buteo (buzzard), 47
Buteo lagopus (rough-legged buzzard), 47
buzzard *see Buteo; Pernis*

caddis-fly *see Cyrnus flavidus; Neureclepsis bimaculatum*
Caenlochan, 18
Caenlochan Glen, Coire Sharroch, 31
Cairn Gorm, 9, 12, 15
  Allt Mor valley, *Pl. 18*
  Eag a' Chait meltwater channel, *Pl. 14*
  Ptarmigan building, 178
  ski development, *Pl. 88, 89*, 163–5, 173, 175, 178
  summit path, *Pl. 90*, 180
Cairn Gorm–Ben Macdui plateau, 12, 32
Cairn Toul, 166
Cairngorm Club
  (1899), *Pl. 92*
  (1908), *Pl. 94*
  (1926), *Pl. 91*
  formation (1887), 160
Cairngorm parishes, **99**
Cairngorm Winter Sports Development Association, 163
Cairngorms
  conservation designations, **190**
  forest
    extent, 114–16
    status and management, 116–17
  future prospects, *Pl. 95*, 182–3, 200–9
  industries, 180
  integrated management, 4, 185–200
  land use, 100
  Management Plan and revision, 172–3
  maps, 5, *88*, 99, *186*, 190, 193, *195*, 203
  mountain core and periphery, management, 201–6
  Northern Corries, *Pl. 86*, 114
  northern slopes, *Pl. 97*
  ownership, **88**, 89–91
  plateau, *Pl. 1*
  snowfields, *Pl. 4*
  from Strathspey, *frontispiece*
  streams, pH and alkalinity, 76
  transport, **190**
  wider area, 171–2
  zonation, 4, 5
  see also history
Cairngorms Consultative Panel (1953), 172

Cairngorms National Nature Reserve, 189–91
  size, 92
Cairngorms Partnership
  Board, new, 208
  Board (1995), 105, 198, 208
  Common Sense and Sustainability (1993), 196–8
  composition, 207
  foundation, 207–8
  Management Strategy (1997), 177, 198
  objectives, 91, 127
  origin (1994), 91, 177
  proposals on forests, 114, 128
  ski development, 175
  Technical Group on the Cairngorm Area (1967), 191, 208
Cairngorms Working Party, 91, 92–3, 99, 105, 113, 167, 194–8
  origin (1991), 113, 176, 194, 207
  principle, statement of, 191, 207
  recommendations
    criticisms, 177
    farming, 105
    forests, 113–14
    management, 92–3, 176–7
    red deer, 132, **133**, 177
  report (1993), 196
  successor, Cairngorms Partnership, 113–14, 167
  sustainability, 127
Cairnwell
  vegetation, *Pl. 22*, 32
  see also Glen Shee
Calcarius lapponicus (lapland bunting), 45, 52
calcicole species, 23, 32, 170
Caledon, ancient wood, 1, 48, 108
Calidris alba (sanderling), 45
Calidris alpina (dunlin), 44, 45
Calidris maritima (purple sandpiper), 44, 45, 52
Calidris temminckii (Temminck's stint), 52
Callicera rufa (fly), *Pl. 40*
Callitriche hamulata (intermediate water-starwort), 72
Callitriche stagnalis (common water-starwort), 72
Calluna vulgaris (heather), 24, 25, 29, 40
  branch systems, **37**
  patterns
    linear and radial, 34–8
    stripes, *Pl. 27*
Calluna – Arctostaphylos heath, *Pl. 24*, **28**, 29, **35**, 58
Calluna – Erica cinerea heath, 27, **28**, 29
Calluna – Trichophorum heath, **40**
Calluna – Vaccinium heath, *Pl. 25*, 27, **28**, 29, **35**
Caloplaca nivalis (lichen), **36**
Caltha palustris (marsh-marigold), 73
Canadian pondweed *see Elodea canadensis*
Canadian Timber Corps (1939–45), 123
capercaillie *see Tetrao urogallus*
Capnia atra (stonefly), 75
Capnia vidua, 74
Capreolus capreolus (roe deer), 52, 131
Caprimulgus europus (nightjar), 44
Carduelis flavirostris (twite), 44, 46
Carex aquatilis (water sedge), 73
Carex binervis (ribbed sedge), 27
Carex caryophyllea (spring sedge), 30
Carex lasiocarpa (slender-sedge), 73
Carex limosa, 73
Carex paniculata, 73
Carex bigelowii (stiff sedge), 31, 32
Carex rostrata (bottle sedge), 73
Carex rupestris (rock sedge), 32
Carex vesicaria, 73

Carex – Racomitrium heath, 38
Carn Ban Mor, 11
Carnachuin, Glen Feshie, *Pl. 17*
Carpodacus erythrinus (scarlet rosefinch), 52
Carrbridge, 93
  Landmark Centre, 124, 180
cat's foot *see Antennaria dioica*
Cephalozia bicuspidata, 72
Cerastium alpinum (alpine mouse-ear), 24
Cervus elaphus see red deer
Cetraria islandica (lichen), 25
Cetraria nivalis, 25
chaffinch *see Fringilla coelebs*
Charadrius apricaria (golden plover), 44, 45
Charadrius hiaticula subsp. *tundrae* (ringed plover), 44, 45
Charadrius morinellus (dotterel), *Pl. 34*, 44, **45–6**
chickweed wintergreen *see Trientalis europaea*
Cicerbita alpina (alpine sowthistle), 135
Cicuta virosa (cowbane), 73
Circus aeruginosus (marsh harrier), 47
Circus cyaneus (hen harrier), 44, 46, **47**, 50
  predation of red grouse, 145
Ciste Mhearaid, Cairn Gorm, 9
Clach Bhan, 13
Clach Bun Rudhtair, 13
Cladonia (lichen spp.), 24–5
  C. arbuscula, 25, 32
  C. ciliata, 25
  C. furcata, 25
  C. gracilis, 25
  C. maxima, 34
  C. portentosa, 25, 31
  C. rangiferina, 25
  C. stricta, 34
  C. uncialis, 25
Clais Fhearnaig, 16
clearances, 86–7
climate, 8–10, 68
  evapo-transpiration, 10
  history, 24–5, 108–9
  precipitation, 9, 68
    acid, 81
    extreme, *Pl. 18*
    wet grass moors, 29
climate indicators, global warming, 41
cloudberry *see Rubus chamaemorus*
Clova Hills, 30
club-moss *see Huperzia; Lycopodium*
club-rush *see Schoenoplectus*
Clunie Water, Baddoch Burn, fish traps, *Pl. 80*
coal tit *see Parus ater*
Coccinella quinquepunctata (5-spot ladybird), *Pl. 38*
Coelocaulon aculeatum (lichen), 25
Coilacreach, pine regeneration, 112, 115, 116–17
Coire an Lochain, 9, 12, 15, 68, 77
Coire Beanaidh, 17
Coire Cas, 3, 8, 9, 10, 12
  Cairn Gorm, visitors, 164
Coire Garbhlach, 10–11, 18
Coire nan Clach, Beinn a' Bhuird, *Pl. 13*
Coire Odhar, 10–11
Coire Raibeirt, 13
Coire Sharroch, Caenlochan Glen, 31
Coire Uaine, 15
Coleophora spp. (case-bearing moths), 58, 65
Coleoptera, 59–60, 75, 79
common gull *see Larus canus*
common sandpiper *see Actitis hypoleucos*
Common Sense and Sustainability (1993), 196–8

conflicts of interest, 2–3
conservation, 172–8
    aquatic habitats, protection measures,
        81–2
    see also history
conservation designations, **190**
conservation value, 2
Corduelis spinus (siskin), 48
corn bunting *see Miliaria calandra*
corncrake *see Crex crex*
cornices, Braeriach, *Pl. 6*
Corrie Bhrochain, Braeriach, *Pl. 6*
corrie lochs, 170
    see also Coire -
corries, 15
Corrour Bothy, 74
Corvus corax (raven), 44, 46
Corvus monedula (jackdaw), 51
cotton grass *see Eriophorum*
Countryside Commission for Scotland
    (CCS)
    indicative zoning, **195**
    management arrangements, review, 194
    merger with NCC to form SNH, 176
    Mountain Areas of Scotland –
        Conservation and Management
        (1990), 194
    origin (1968), 173
cowbane *see Cicuta virosa*
cowberry *see Vaccinium vitis-idaea*
Coyles of Muick, 171
Craig a' Chleirich, 122
Craig Leek, 15
Craig Nordie, *Betula* woodland, 115
Craigellachie, *Betula* woodland, 115
Craigendarroch, 15
    oak woodland, 115
Crambus furcatellus (grass moth), 55
crane *see Grus grus*
crane-fly *see Tipula montana*
Crannach, 116
Crathie, 18
Cratoneuron commutatum, 71
Creag an Dail beg, 32
Creag Fhiaclach
    krummholz zone, 31
    pine forest limit, *Pl. 62, 63*, 114, 126,
        170
Creag Meagaidh
    deer culling and forest regeneration,
        136, 174
    deer grazing pressure, 134
    NNR, 174
creeping bentgrass *see Agrostis stolonifera*
creeping ladies tresses *see Goodyera repens*
Crenobia alpina (flatworm), 80
crested tit *see Parus cristatus*
Crex crex (corncrake), 44
crofts, abandoned, *Pl. 60*
Cromdale, 93
cross-leaved heath *see Erica tetralix*
crossbill *see Loxia curvirostris; Loxia scotica*
crowberry *see Empetrum nigrum*
Crown, and ownership of land, 89–90
cryosols, 19
Culblean Hill, heather–blaeberry heath,
    Pl. 25
curled pondweed *see Potamogeton crispus*
curlew *see Numenius arquata*
cyanobacteria *see Anabaena; Microcystus*
Cygnus olors (mute swan), 50
Cyrnus flavidus (caddis-fly), 75
Dactylorhiza maculata subsp. *ericetorum*
    (heath spotted orchid), 27
Dalradian rocks, 18
Dalwhinnie, 5
Daubenton's bat *see Myotis daubentoni*
Dee valley, 9, 14, 15, 17
deer, *see* red deer

Deer Commission *see* Red Deer
    Commission
deer fencing *see* fencing
deer forests, origins, 111
Deer (Scotland) Act (1996), 177, 179
deer-grass *see Trichophorum cespitosum*
Deeside, 3, 5
    birch woodland, 112
    estates and Forestry Commission
        replanting, 124
        Working Group (1991), 178
    exotic species, 123
    extent of woodland, 171
    forest destruction, 122
    Highland Deeside, defined, 113, 124–5
    National Scenic Area, 3
    pinewoods, origins, 125
    survey (1900), 124–5
    timber exploitation, second world war,
        111, 123
    see also River Dee
Deeside Forest, 110, *112*, 114, 117, 118,
    203
    promotion
        extent, **203**
        objectives, 127–8
    replanting, area (1800s–1990), 124
defoliation
    insects, 58
    ling and blaeberry, *Operophtera brumata*
        (winter moth), 58
deforestation, and aquatic habitats, 80–1
Delia pilifemur (fly), 55
Derry burn, Ben Macdui, *Pl. 98*
Derry Wood *Pl. 96*
Deschampsia flexuosa (wavy hair-grass), 25,
    32, 187
diatoms, 71, 73, 76
Dicranum spurium, 24, 29
Dinnet Moor, *Pl. 99*, 16, 171
    birch invasion, *Pl. 24*, 26, 112
    birch regeneration, 65
    meltwater features, 16, 172
    new timber production, 116
    oak replanting, 123
Diptera, 55
    list, 60–2
disturbance and restoration, 39
    experimental, **40**
Diura bicaudata (stonefly), 74
dog's mercury *see Mercurialis perennis*
Donside, 5
dotterel *see Charadrius morinellus*
downy birch *see Betula pubescens*
downy willow *see Salix lapponum*
Drumochter Hills, 5, 171
Dryas octopetala (mountain avens), 32
Dubh Lochan, 68, 76
Dulnain, 110
dunlin *see Calidris alpina*
dwarf birch *see Betula nana*
dwarf cudweed *see Gnaphalium supinum*
Dytiscus lapponicus (water-beetle), 79

Eag Mhor of Dorback, 15
ecological assessment for management,
    200–2
Ectaetia christii (fly), 57
eel (*Anguilla anguilla*), 148
Elatine hexandra (waterwort), 73
Elodea canadensis (Canadian pondweed),
    73
Ematurgia atomaria (common heath
    moth), 57
Emberiza citrinella (yellowhammer), 44, 51
Emberiza shoeniclus (reed bunting), 50
emperor moth (*Saturnia pavonia*), *Pl. 42*,
    57
Empetreto – Vaccinietum, **34**

Empetrum nigrum (crowberry), 24, 27
    subsp. *hermaphroditum*, 31, 32, 37, 38
Empetrum – Racomitrium heath, 39
employment, rural economy, 94–5
enchytraeids, 70
Endromis versicolor (Kentish glory moth),
    55, **56**, 65
environment, and farming/agriculture,
    102–3
Environmental Change Network, 180
Environmentally Sensitive Area
    (Cairngorm Straths), 93, 103, 105,
    178, 197
    area, **205**
Ephemeroptera, 75
Epilobium anagallidifolium (alpine willow-
    herb), 32
Erica cinerea (bell heather), 24, 25, 29, 30
Erica tetralix (cross-leaved heath), 29, 30
Erica–Callunetum, 27–9, **28**
Eriophorum angustifolium (cotton grass),
    30, 187
Eriophorum vaginatum, 24, 29
Eromophila alpestris (shore lark), 45, 52
erratics, 14
Esox lucius (pike), *Pl. 83*, 148, 153
EU (European Union)/EC (European
    Community)
    Common Agricultural Policy, 101–3
    LFAs, 101
    European Wild Birds Directive (1979),
        Special Protection Areas (SPAs),
        173–4, 177, 204
    Special Areas of Conservation (SACs),
        81, 177, 204
    Water Framework Directive, 77
eutrophication, 77
    threat to aquatic habitats, 77
exotic species
    Deeside, 123
    Forestry Commission land area (1994),
        124
exploitation *see* commercial exploitation;
    forest destruction

Falco columbarius (merlin), 44, 46, **47**
Falco peregrinus (peregrine), 46, **47**
Falco rusticolus (gyr falcon), 47
Falco subbuteo (hobby), 47
Falco tinnuculus (kestrel), 46, 47
Falco vespertinus (red-footed falcon), 47
Farm Woodlands Grant Scheme, 93, 102
farming/agriculture, 51, 97–106
    birds, 51
    Common Agricultural Policy, LFAs,
        101
    and environment, 102–3
    Farm Accounts Scheme, 101
    and forestry, 102
    future, 104–6
    hill farming, 100–2
    history, 97–100
    impact on landscape, 179–80
    and leisure sector, 104
    livestock numbers, 100
    no. of holdings, 100
    physical features, 100
    subsidies, 92, 100–2
    support agencies, 104
    see also land use
Felis sylvestris (wild cat), 52
fencing of woodlands, *Pl. 72*, 116, 134,
    179
    removal by RSPB, 116
Festuca ovina (sheep's fescue), 30
Festuca vivipara (viviparous fescue), 30,
    32
feudal title, 89–90
field gentian *see Gentianella campestris*

Filipendula almeria (meadowsweet), 31
Finzean Estate, 122
fir club-moss *see Huperzia selago*
fish, 148–59
  list, 150
  threats to populations, 155–7
   acidification, 155–6
   forestry, 156
   hydro-electric developments, 156–7
   land use, 156
   new introductions, 157
   obstruction of migration routes, 157
   overfishing, 157
   pollution, 156
   predator species, 157
fish farming, threat to aquatic habitats, 79
fish traps
  Baddoch Burn, Clunie Water, *Pl. 80*
  River Dee, *Pl. 79*
fisheries, 154–7
  sporting estates, 154–5
Fisheries Research Services Freshwater
  Laboratory, 151, 152
flatworms (*Crenobia alpina*; *Polycelis felina*), 80
flood alleviation
  proposal, 176
  threat to aquatic habitats, 78–9
floods, Muckle Spate, 18
footpaths, Cairn Gorm, *Pl. 90*
forest, *see also* native woodlands
Forest Enterprise, Glenmore, 113, 116
Forest Habitat Network, 114
Forest of Spey, 25, 114–18
  estates and Forestry Commission, replanting, 124
  extent, 171, **203**
  promotion, objectives, 127–8
Forest of Strathspey *see* Forest of Spey
forestry
  commercial, impacts, 179
  commercial exploitation, 109–11, 122–5
  and farming/agriculture, 102
  forest destruction, 109, 120–9
  future, 127–8
  threat to aquatic habitats, 79
  threats to fish, 156
  tree cover removal, 113
  see also timber
Forestry Commission
  Advisory Panel, 113
  Broadleaves Policy, 113
  Guidelines, 127
  land area (1994), 124
  management plan for Glenmore Forest, 178
  Native Pinewood Guidelines, 117
  new policies, 181
  origin, 123
  register of pinewoods, 116, 117
  replanting, 124
  Woodland Grant Scheme, 113
Forestry Strategies, Regional Indicative, 192, **193**
fox, predation of red grouse, **142**, 144–5
Fragaria vesca (wild strawberry), 26
fragrant orchid *see Gymnadenia conopsea*
Fringilla coelebs (chaffinch), 48
Fringilla montifringilla (brambling), 52
fungi, 38–9, 39
future prospects, Cairngorms, *Pl. 95*, 182–3, 200–9

Gaick Forest, 13, 15
Galium boreale (northern bedstraw), 70
Galium saxatile (heath bedstraw), 30
Gallinago gallinago (snipe), 46, 50
Gallinula chloropus (moorhen), 44
Garbh Choire, 15

Garbh Choire Mor, 9, 17
Garmaddie, 110
Garmouth, 110
Gasterosteus aculeatus (stickleback), 148, 154
Gavia stellata (red throated diver), 44, **50**
Genista anglica (petty whin), 29
Gentianella campestris (field gentian), 30
geology, 10–12
  maps, **11, 14, 16**
geomorphology, 14–17
  glacial breaches, *Pl. 11, 12*
  meltwater features, subglacial channel, *Pl. 14, 172*
  periglacial and contemporary processes, **14**, 17–18, 169–70
  pre-glacial, 12–13, 169–70
Geranium sylvaticum (wood cranesbill), 31
glacial lochs, 170
Glas Maol NNR, 18, 201
Glen Avon, 11, 12, 15
  purchase by RSPB, 175
Glen Builg, 15
Glen Callater, 15
Glen Clova, *Pl. 2, 3*, 12, 15, 31
Glen Cluny, 29
Glen Dee, 15
Glen Derry, 15, 16, 29, 174
  Beinn a' Chaorainn, *Pl. 15*
  Lairig an Laoigh, *Pl. 11*
Glen Einich, 10–11, 15, 17, 18, 29
Glen Feshie, 10, 17, 18, 20, 29, 118, 173
  Carnachuin, *Pl. 17*
  Coire Garbhlach, 31
  pinewood losses, *112*
Glen Feshie Estate, purchase/sale by Will Woodlands, 177
Glen Gairn, 11, 12
Glen Geusachan, 15, 18
Glen Muick, 15
Glen Quoich, 16, 174
  Punch Bowl, *Pl. 50*
Glen Shee, ski development, *Pl. 88*, 163, 173, 175
Glen Tanar, 171
  Aboyne, new timber production, 116, 121–2
  beetles, 57
  pinewood losses, *112*
  seed harvest, 123
Glen Tilt, 12, 15
Glenlivet, 5, 8, 9, *Pl. 57*
Glenmore Forest, 117, 166–7
  19th C, deer forest, 111
  Forest Enterprise, 113
  lodgepole pine, 125
  management plan, 178
  pine destruction, 110, 122
  pine regeneration, 122
  pinewood losses, *112*
  Ryvoan Pass, 115, 117, 175
  tree planting, 123
Glenmore Lodge, 8, 9, 162
  winter sports training, 164
Glenmore (ship), 122
Glenshee, 3, 5
global warming, climate indicators, 10, 41
Gnaphalium supinum (dwarf cudweed), 32
golden eagle *see Aquila chrysaetos*
golden plover *see Charadrius apricaria*
goldeneye *see Bucephala clangula*
Gomphonema (stalked diatom), 71
Goodyera repens (creeping ladies tresses), 25
goosander *see Mergus merganser*
goshawk *see Accipter gentilis*
Grampian Orogeny, 10
Grampian Regional Council, pro-conservation stance, 181

Grampians, 10
Grantown-on-Spey, 9, 93
grass moth *see Crambus*
grasshopper warbler *see Locustella naevia*
grayling (*Thymallus thymallus*), 154
grazing pressure
  Betula woodland *Pl. 65*
  loss of heathlands, 29, 134–5
  Pinus forest, 25
  post deforestation, 187
  red deer, 134
great grey shrike *see Lanius excubitor*
green sandpiper *see Tringa ochropus*
greenshank *see Tringa nebularia*
grey heron *see Ardea cinerea*
grey partridge *see Perdix perdix*
greylag goose *see Anser anser*
grouse, 139–47
  shooting, 111
  wild, deaths, deer fencing, *Pl. 72*, 134
grouse moor management, 179
growth rates, trees, 126
Grus grus (crane), 44, 52
Gymnadenia conopsea (fragrant orchid), 30
gyr falcon *see Falco rusticolus*
Gyrinus opacus (water-beetle), 79

Habitat Action Plans, 118
Haematopus ostralegus (oystercatcher), 44, 50
hairy woodrush *see Luzula pilosa*
Haliaetus albicila (white-tailed eagle), 47
Hammerschmidtia ferruginea (fly), 57
hard-fern *see Blechnum spicant*
hare *see Lepus timidus*
hazel, origin, 107
heath bedstraw *see Galium saxatile*
heath spotted orchid *see Dactylorhiza maculata* subsp. *ericetorum*
heather *see Calluna vulgaris*
heather – bearberry heath *see Calluna – Arctostaphylos* heath
heather – blaeberry heath *see Calluna – Vaccinium* heath
heathlands, 27–30
  altitudinal zonation, 30–2
  burning, *Pl. 77, 78*, 126, 135, *Pl. 77, 78*, 111, 126, 187
  composition, **29**
  insects, 57–8
  loss, grazing pressure, 134–5
Helianthemum nummularium (rock rose), 24, 30
Hemiptera, list, 62
hen harrier *see Circus cyaneus*
high altitude
  insects, 55–6
  interaction with snow cover, **33**
  pattern and process, 32–8
  tree line, 114, 126
  zonation of vegetation, 30–2
  heathlands, 30–2
Highland Birchwoods
  birch timber, 126–7
  establishment, 113
Highland Deeside *see* Deeside Forest
Highland Regional Council, Structure Plan, 175
Highlands and Islands Development Board (HIDB)
  policies, 94, 182
  ski development, 175
hill tracks, access by recreationists, 136–7, **186**, 187
Hippolais icterina (icterine warbler), 52
Hippuris vulgaris (mares-tail), 73
history of Cairngorms
  agriculture, 51, 97–100
  clearances, 86–7

climate, 24–5
commercial exploitation, 109–11, 122–5
conservation, 172–8
early proposals, 172
Nature Conservancy, 172–3
Nature Reserves established, 173
decline of forest, 111
early forest clearance, 109
forest destruction, 120–1
land use, 86–9
Napoleonic Wars, 110
post-glacial native woodlands, 107–9
vegetation, 24–5
hobby *see Falco subbuteo*
Holocentropus picicornis, 75
Homogyne alpina (purple coltsfoot), 135
honey buzzard *see Pernis apivorus*
house sparrow *see Passer domesticus*
housing *see* settlements
Huperzia selago (fir club-moss), 24
hydro-electric developments, threats to
fish, 157
hydrology studies (IoH), Insh, 78, 176
Hygrobiella laxifolia, 72
Hygrohypnum ochraceum, 71
Hygrotus novemlineatus, 75
Hylocomium splendens, 25, 26
Hymenoptera, list, 62
Hypericum pulchrum (St John's Wort), 29
Hypogymnia physodes (lichen), 31
Hypnum, 24, 31

icterine warbler *see Hippolais icterina*
Inchriach 118
red deer, 131
tree planting, 123
Inchrory, 15, 18
Indicative Forestry Strategies, 192, **193**
insects, 54–65
defoliation, 58
heathlands, 57–8
high tops, 55–6
Malaise trap, *Pl. 43*
rarities, 58–64
Red Data Book, 171
threats, 64–5
see also named species and orders
Insh Marshes, **50**, 78, 172
flood plain mire, 50
hydrology studies (IoH), 78, 176
Kincraig flood alleviation proposal, 176
nature reserve, 50
Inshriach
natural regeneration, 174
pinewood losses, *112*
Institute of Terrestrial Ecology (ITE,
1973), 173
intermediate bladderwort *see Utricularia
intermedia*
intermediate water-starwort *see Callitriche
hamulata*
intermediate wintergreen *see Pyrola media*
International Association for
Conservation of Nature (IUCN)
General Assembly, 176
national park proposals, 207
interrupted club-moss *see Lycopodium
annotinum*
Invercauld, 122, 123
Inverdruie, 79
Invereshie, natural regeneration, 174
invertebrates, 74–5
benthic, 75
Red Data Book, 171
Isoetes lacustris (quillwort), 72, 73

jackdaw *see Corvus monedula*
John Muir Trust, 177
Juncus bulbosus (bulbous rush), 73

Juncus trifidus (three-leaved rush), *Pl. 28,
32*, **38**
Juniperus communis (juniper), 25, 31, 115
Betula woodland, 27
origins, 107
Jynx torquilla (wryneck), 52

Kentish glory moth *see Endromis*
kestrel *see Falco tinnuculus*
kettleholes, 16
Kiaeria starkei, 34
Kincraig, 94
flood alleviation proposal, 176
oak woodland, 115
Kingussie, 93, 121
Kinrara, evictions, 87
Kinveachy Forest
19th C deer forest, 111, 171
pinewood losses, *112*
krummholz zone, pine scrub, *Pl. 63*, 31,
114

Ladder Hills, 5, 171
Lagopus l. scoticus (red grouse), *Pl. 76*, 29,
43, 44, 46
caecal nematodes, 144
chick food, 145
chick production, 143–5
louping ill (flavivirus infection), 144
numbers, 140
bag records, 140–3
causes of death, **142**
spatial variation, 142–3
temporal change, 143
predation, 144–5
research, 140–2
Lagopus mutus (ptarmigan), *Pl. 29*, **45**, 46,
146
Lairig an Laoigh, Glen Derry *Pl. 11*
Lairig Ghru, 15, 17, 18
and Braeriach, *Pl. 12*
Pools of Dee, *Pl. 47*
see photo half-title page
Lampetra spp. (lampreys), 148, 150
Land Reform - Identifying the Problems, 91
Land Reform Policy Group, 91
land use/management, 86–96, 185–98
deforestation, 185–8
ecological assessment, 200–2
history, 86–9
inadequacies in administrative
framework, 188–9
integrated strategy, 4, 194–8
legislature and fiscal interests, 91–3
restrictions, 92
models, 127
objectives, 90–1
ownership interests, **88**, 89–93
partial solutions, 202–6
present-day, 89–93
present-day settlements and local
economy, 93–5
review of arrangements, 194
threats to fish, 156
UK vs Scotland vs Cairngorms, 100
see also farming/agriculture
landforms *see* geomorphology
Landmark Centre, 180
sawmills, 124
landscape conservation, 169–83
Lanius collurio (red-backed shrike), 52
Lanius excubitor (great grey shrike), 52
lapland bunting *see Calcarius lapponicus*
lapwing *see Vanellus vanellus*
Larus canus (common gull), 45
Larus ridibundus (black-headed gull), 44,
50
Lathyrus montanus (bitter vetch), 29
least water-lily *see Nuphar pumila*

least willow *see Salix herbacea*
Lecanora leptacina, 34, **36**
Lecht, ski development, 163
Lecidea caesioatra, **36**
Lecidea griseoatra, **36**
Lecidella bullata, **36**
legislature, and fiscal interests, land
use/management, 91–3
leisure pursuits *see* recreation/tourism
Lepidoptera
list, 62–3
as prey, 145
Lepraria neglecta, **36**
Leptophlebia spp. (mayflies), 75
Lepus timidus (mountain hare), *Pl. 36*, 52
Less Favoured Areas (LFAs), 92, 101
lesser spearwort *see Ranunculus flamula*
lesser twayblade *see Listera cordata*
Leucoptera orobi (moth), 58
lichen-rich heath, 32
lichen-rich *Pinus* forest, 25
lichens
ground cover disturbance, 40
snow cover, 34, **36**
see also Caloplaca; Cetraria; Cladonia;
Coelocaulon; Hypnogymnia; Lecanora;
Micarea; Miriquidica
Linnaea borealis (twin-flower), *Pl. 23*, 25
Listera cordata (lesser twayblade), 27
Littorella uniflora (shoreweed), 72, 73
liverworts *see* bryophytes
livestock numbers, 100
Lobelia dortmanna (water lobelia), 73
Loch a' Bhanain, 73, 153
Loch a' Gharbh-Choire, Strathnethy, 153,
Pl. 55
Loch Alvie, 79
Loch an Eilein, chemistry, 69
Loch Avon, *Pl. 10*, 15, 170
Loch Callater, 73, 153
Loch Coire an Lochan, 76
Loch Davan, 68, 69, 73, 77
chemistry, 69
vegetation map, *Pl. 46*
Loch Einich, *Pl. 54*, 68, 73, 170
exposed buried pine stumps, *Pl. 20*
Loch Garten, 16, 77
beetles, 57
chemistry, 69, 77
goosanders, 50
ospreys, 44, **47–8**, 50, 52
Loch Insh, 68, 77
chemistry, 69, 70
flooding, 50, 78–9
hydrology studies (IoH), 50, 78, 176
Kincraig flood alleviation proposal, 176
Loch Kinord, 73
chemistry, 69
Loch Lomond
National Park, 208
Regional Park designation, 206
Loch Lomond Readvance, 16
Loch Lomond Stadial, 17
Loch Morlich, *Pl. 49, 97*, 16, 68, 73, 77,
78
chemistry, 69
Loch Muick, *Pl. 52*, 68, 75
chemistry, 69
Loch nan Eun, 76
Lochan Uaine, 76
Lochnagar, 3, 5, 12, 13
Black Spout (1910), *Pl. 93*
corrie moraines, 172
lochan, 68, 69, 76
Meikle Pap, woolsack jointing, *Pl. 7*
summit, *Pl. 16*, 87
Lochnagar Ring Complex, **11**, 12
lochs, 68
birds, 49–50

eutrophication, 77
nutrient enrichment, 81
see also aquatic habitats
Locustella fluviatilus (river warbler), 52
Locustella naevia (grasshopper warbler), 50
Loiseleuria nigrum (trailing azalea), 31, 32
long-tailed skua *see Stercorarius longicaudis*
louping ill (flavivirus infection in grouse/sheep), 144
Loxia curvirostris (common crossbill), 48, 49
Loxia pytyopsittacus (parrot crossbill), 48, 52
Loxia scotica (Scottish crossbill), *Pl. 34*, 44, **48–9**
Luibeg Wood, *Pl. 96*
Lupinus nootkatensis (Nootka lupin), 70
Lurcher's Gully, 175, 201
see also ski development
Luscinia luscinia (thrush nightingale), 52
Luscinia svecica (bluethroat), 52
Lutra lutra (otter), 52
Luzula pilosa (hairy woodrush), 25
Luzula sylvatica (greater woodrush), 31
Lycopodium annotinum (interrupted club-moss), 24

MacSharry reforms, farming/agriculture, 101
mallard *see Anas platyrhynchos*
mammals, 52–3
management of Cairngorms, integration, 4, 185–200
Manifesto for the Cairngorms (1992), 194–5
maps
Cairngorms, **5**, **88**, **99**, **186**, **190**, **193**, **195**, **203**
geology, **11**, **14**, **16**
Mar, Forest of Mar *see Deeside Forest*
Mar Lodge Estate
deer numbers, 174
Derry and Luibeg Woods, *Pl. 96*
management policy aims, 204
pinewood losses, *112*
purchase by NTS, 114, 177, 204
mares-tail *see Hippuris vulgaris*
Margaratifera margaratifera (freshwater mussel), 81
marsh harrier *see Circus aeruginosus*
marsh marigold *see Caltha palustris*
marsh warbler *see Acrocephalus palustris*
marshes *see* aquatic habitats; wetlands
Martes martes (pine marten), 53
mayfly *see Ameletus; Leptophlebia; Rhithrogena; Siphlonurus*
meadow pipit *see Anthus pratensis*
meadow rue *see Thalictrum alpinum*
meadowsweet *see Filipendula almeria*
Meikle Pap, 13
Meles meles (badger), 52
meltwater features, subglacial channel, *Pl. 14*, 15, **16**, 172
Menyanthes trifoliata (bogbean), 73
Mercurialis perennis (dog's mercury), 31
Mergus albellus (smew), 52
Mergus merganser (goosander), **50**
Mergus serrator (red breasted merganser), 50
merlin *see Falco columbarius*
Micarea viridiatra, 34
Microcystus (cyanobacteria), 77
Miliaria calandra (corn bunting), 44
Milvus milvus (red kite), 44, 47
minnow (*Phoxinus phoxinus*), 148, 154
Miriquidica griseoatra, 34
Moine Bhealaidh, 12, 18, 20
Moine Mhor, 12, 20
Moine rocks, 12, 13, 18

Monadh Liath hills, 30
monadnocks, 13
Monaltrie, Ballater, 122
Moneses uniflora (one-flowered wintergreen), 25
montane communities, calcicole species, 170
moonwort *see Botrychium lunaria*
moor mat-grass *see Nardus stricta*
moorhen *see Gallinula chloropus*
moorlands
bird species, 46
burning, *Pl. 77*, 78, 111, 126, 187
management, 139–47
wet grass moors, 29
Moray, 9
Morrone, 8, 18
Betula–Juniperus woodland, 27, 31, 115, 116
Morven, 13, 14, 18
moss campion *see Silene acaulis*
mosses *see* bryophytes
mossy saxifrage *see Saxifraga hypnoides*
Mount Keen, 13
Mountain Areas of Scotland – Conservation and Management (CCS, 1990), 194, 206
mountain avens *see Dryas octopetala*
mountain hare *see Lepus timidus*
mountain sorrel *see Oxyria digyna*
mugwort *see Artemisia sp*
muirburning, *Pl. 77*, 78, 111, 114, 126, 187
Mullach Dubh, 171
Munros (peaks over 3000 feet), 165
mussel, freshwater *see Margaratifera*
mute swan *see Cygnus olors*
Myotis daubentoni (Daubenton's bat), 52
Myotis nattereri (Natterer's bat), 52
Myriophyllum alterniflorum (alternate-flowered water-milfoil), 72, 73
myrtle-leaved willow *see Salix myrsinites*

Nardia compressa, 72
Nardus stricta (moor mat-grass), 20, 24, 30, 32
National Nature Reserves (NNRs), 116, 172
Cairngorms NNR, 3, 172, **190**
declaration, 180–1
Dinnet Moor, Morrone, Glen Tanar (1970s), 174
distribution and extent, **190**
Abernethy (1982), 174
National Park Development Areas (1951), 162, 172
National Park Reserve, defined, 172
'National Park' status for Cairngorms, 177, 206–9
case (1931–1992), 177, 206–7
case (1997 onwards), 208–9
popularity, 207
see also Cairngorms Partnership
National Parks and Access to the Countryside Act (1949), 92, 172, 180
National Parks (Scotland) Act (2000), 208–9
National Scenic Area, 3, 187, **190**, 192–3
National Trust for Scotland (NTS), purchase of Mar Lodge estate, 114
Native Woodland Discussion Group, 113
native woodlands, 107–19
birds, 48–9
commercial exploitation, 109–11, 122–5
destruction, 48, 111, 120–9
discussion, 126–7
early forest clearance, 109
future, 127–8
insects, 56–7

management initiatives, 113–15
post-glacial origins, 107–9
present extent/composition, 114–16
present status/management, 116–17
recent time, 111–14
research, 125–6
species list, 108
SSSIs, 113, 116
Natterer's bat *see Myotis nattereri*
Natura-2000 sites, 177, 181, 204
Natural Heritage (Scotland) Act (1991), 78, 176
Nature Conservancy
conservation history, 172–3
Institute of Terrestrial Ecology (ITE, 1973), 173
Management Plan, Cairngorms, 172–3
Nature Conservancy Council for Scotland (NCCS), 173–4
break-up and merger (1989), 176
compulsory purchase powers, 181
criticism of, 181
Institute of Hydrology studies, 78
policies, 189
selection of SSSIs, 180
see also Scottish Natural Heritage (SNH)
Nature Conservation Areas (four), 172
Nature Conservation Review, 81
site assessment, 2
Nature Reserve Agreements (NRAs), 172, 181
nematodes, red grouse, 144
Neomys fodiens (water shrew), 52
Nethybridge, 93
Tulloch, *Pl. 58*
Neureclepsis bimaculatum (caddis-fly), 75
nightjar *see Caprimulgus europus*
Nitella, 73
Nootka lupin *see Lupinus nootkatensis*
northern bedstraw *see Galium boreale*
Northern Corries SSSI, *Pl. 86*, 114, 175
northern rock-cress *see Arabis petraea*
Norway
climate, 80
landscape model, 182–3
Numenius arquata (curlew), 44, 50
Nuphar lutea (yellow water-lily), 73
Nuphar pumila (least water-lily), 72
nutrient enrichment, effects, aquatic habitats, 81
Nyctea scandiaca (snowy owl), 45
Nymphaea alba (white water-lily), 73

Odonata, 63
Oenanthe oenanthe (wheatear), 45
Oligotrichum hercynicum, 72
ombrotrophic (rainfed) bogs, 114–15
one-flowered wintergreen *see Moneses uniflora*
Operophtera brumata (winter moth), 58
orchids *see Gymnadenia; Pseudorchis*
Ord Ban, 18
Oscillatoria, 77
osprey *see Pandion aliaetus*
otter *see Lutra lutra*
ownership of land, **88**, 89–93
Oxalis acetosella (wood sorrel), 26
Oxyria digyna (mountain sorrel), 24, 70
oystercatcher *see Haematopus ostralegus*

Pandion aliaetus (osprey), *Pl. 33*, 44, **47–8**, 50, 52
parrot crossbill *see Loxia pytyopsittacus*
Parus ater (coal tit), 48
Parus cristatus subsp. *scoticus* (crested tit), 44, **48**, 49
Parus montanus (willow tit), 44
Passer domesticus (house sparrow), 43, 44

paths, impact of heavy use, 166
peat, 20
  erosion, 30
  icicles, *Pl. 5*
perch (*Perca fluviatilis*, 148, 154
Perdix perdix (grey partridge), 44, 51
peregrine *see Falco peregrinus*
perfoliate pondweed *see Potamogeton perfoliatus*
Pernis apivorus (honey buzzard), 47
Petromyzon marinus (sea lamprey), *Pl. 84*, 148, 150
petty whin *see Genista anglica*
Phaloropus lobatus (red necked phalaropes), 52
Philonotis fontana, 71
Phoenicurus phoenicurus (redstart), 48
phosphorus, 126
Phoxinus phoxinus (minnow), 148, 153
Phragmites (rush), 73
Phylloscopus sibilatrix (wood warbler), 48
physical geography, 8–22
  climate, 8–10
  geology, 10–12
  glacial geomorphology, 14–17
  periglacial geomorphology and contemporary geomorphic processes, 17–18
  pre-glacial geomorphology, 12–13
  soils, 18–20
Picea sitchensis (Sitka spruce), experimental (620m), *Pl. 69*
pike (*Esox lucius*), *Pl. 83*, 148, 153
Pilularia gobulifera (pillwort), 72
pine forest
  Deeside group, 25, 114–18
  even-aged stand, selective felling, *Pl. 64*
  exposed buried pine stumps, *Pl. 20*
  Forestry Commission land area (1994), 124
  grants for new native pinewoods, 204
  krummholtz zone, *Pl. 63*, 31
  lichen-rich, 25
  losses, 112
  origins, 108
  replanting, 121–2
    timber produced, 127
  scope for merging, 117
  Speyside group, 25, 114–18
  timber, properties, 126
  tree limit, *Pl. 62*
pine marten *see Martes martes*
pintail *see Anas acuta*
Pinus radiata (lodgepole pine)
  Pl. 68, 69
  Glenmore, 125
Pinus sylvestris (Scots pine), 25, 26
  genetic conservation, 117
  genetics
    map, **26**
    terpenes, 26, **26**
  longevity, 112
  origins, 108
  regeneration, *Pl. 70, 71*, 25–6, 112, 114–17, 121–2, 134, 136, 174
  sap run *Pl. 44*
  seed harvest, 123
Pipistrellus pipistrellus (pipistrelle), 52
Pitlochry, 5
Plagiothecium undulatum (moss), 27
planning process, 191–2
plant cover *see* vegetation
Plecoptera, 63
Plecotus auritus (brown long-eared bat), 52
Plectrophenax nivalis (snow bunting), *Pl. 31*, 44, 45, **46**
Podiceps auritus (Slavonian grebe), 44, **50**
podsols, 18–20
Pohlia (moss), 34, 72

pollution, 75–7, 180
  threat to aquatic habitats, 77
  threats to fish, 156–7
Polycelis felina (flatworm), 80
polygons, 18
Polygonum viviparum (viviparous bistort), 31, 32
Polytrichum alpinum (moss), 34
Polytrichum sexangulare, 34
pondweeds *see Potamogeton* spp.
pony transport, deer carcass, *Pl. 74*
population trends, 93–4
Populus tremula (aspen), 25
  ancient, indicator, 57
  indicator *Hammerschmidtia ferruginea* (fly), 57
Porzana porzana (spotted crake), 44, 50
Potamogeton (pondweeds), 72, 73, 77
  P. alpinus (red), 72
  P. crispus (curled), 73
  P. filiformis (slender-leaved), 72
  P. natans (broad-leaved), 72
  P. obtusifolius (blunt-leaved), 73
  P. perfoliatus (perfoliate), 73
  x *zizii*, 73
Potentilla cranzii (alpine cinquefoil), 32
pre-glacial geomorphology, 12–13, 169–70
Primula vulgaris (primrose), 26
Procloeon bifidum, 75
protalus ramparts, 17
protection measures, conservation of aquatic habitats, 81–2
Protonemura montana (stonefly), 74
Pseudorchis albida (small white orchid), 30
Psodos coracina (black mountain moth), 55
Ptarmigan building, Cairn Gorm, 178
ptarmigan *see Lagopus mutus*
Pteridium aquilinum (bracken), 27
Ptilium crista-castrensis , 25
purple sandpiper *see Calidris maritima*
Pyrola media (intermediate wintergreen), 29

quaking grass *see Briza media*
Quercus petraea (sessile oak), 26
  replanting, Dinnet, 123
  woodland, Craigendarroch and Kincraig, 115
quillwort *see Isoetes lacustris*

Racomitrium aciculare, 72
Racomitrium aquaticum, 72
Racomitrium heterostichum, 34
Racomitrium lanuginosum (woolly hair-moss), 24, 32, 37, 38, 39
Racomitrium–stiff sedge heath, 32, 38
rafting *see* timber floating
Rallus aquaticus (water rail), 50
Ramsar sites, 50, 78, 173, 204
Ramsay Report, 162, 206
Rannoch sprawler moth *see Brachionycha nubeculosa*
Ranunculus flamula (lesser spearwort), 73
raven *see Corvus corax*
recreation/tourism, 94–5, 104, 160–8
  access problems, 136–7
  changing patterns, 162–7
  disturbance and restoration, 39
  farming diversification, 104
  and farming/agriculture, 104
  future prospects, 167
  impact on terrain and landscape, 165–6, 187–8
  management and planning, 166–7
  threat to aquatic habitats, 79–80
  value of landscape, 161–2
  visitor numbers, 79, 164–5, 180
  visitor surveys, 165
  see also ski development

red backed shrike *see Lanius collurio*
red breasted merganser *see Mergus serrator*
Red Data Book
  birds, 51–2, 170
  insects, *Pl. 38–42*, 58–64, 171
red deer (*Cervus elaphus*), *Pl 75*, 29, 130–8
  biology
    hefting, 132
    sexual segregation, 131–2
  ecological issues, 134–7
    forest regeneration, *Pls. 70, 71*, 25–6, 112, 114–17, 121–2, 134, 136, 174
  economics, net annual cost, 135
  feeding and land fertilizing, 135
  fencing, *Pl. 72*, 116, 117, 134
  habitats, 131
  hinds and calves, *Pl. 73*
  history, 130–1
  management
    culling strategy, 137, 174
    deer forests, 111
    present numbers, 178–9
    reduction of numbers, 116
  population, 132–4
    stocking densities, 132, **133**, 179
  research
    Rum, 136
    stalking and culling, 136
  see also sporting estates
Red Deer Commission, 112, 174, 176, 177–8
red footed falcon *see Falco vespertinus*
red grouse *see Lagopus l. scoticus*
red kite *see Milvus milvus*
red necked phalaropes *see Phaloropus lobatus*
red squirrel *see Sciurus vulgaris*
red throated diver *see Gavia stellata*
redshank *see Tringa totanus*
redstart *see Phoenicurus phoenicurus*
reed bunting *see Emberiza schoeniclus*
regeneration *see Betula* woodland; *Pinus sylvestris* (Scots pine)
Regional Indicative Forestry Strategies, 192, **193**
Regional Park designation, Loch Lomond experience, 206
research
  forestry, 125–6
  native woodlands, 125–6
  plants, 39–41
  red deer, 136
  red grouse, 140–2
Rhadiurgus variabilis (fly) *Pl. 39*
Rhithrogena semicolorata (mayfly), 75
Rhizocarpon geographicum, 36
ribbed sedge *see Carex binervis*
ring ouzel *see Turdus torquatus*
ringed plover *see Charadrius hiaticula*
River Avon, headwaters, 170
river corridors, 81–2
River Dee
  characteristics, 70, 72, 74
  chemistry, 69
  fish traps, *Pl. 79*
  Forest of Birse, *Pl. 61*
  geology, 67–8
  headwaters, 156, 170
  Pools of Dee, Lairig Ghru, *Pl 47*
  Special Area of Conservation 152
  upper Linn, *Pl. 53*
  Wells of Dee, *Pl. 47*
River Don, 121
  characteristics, 70, 72
  geology, 67–8
River Druie, 79
River Feshie

flood, 74, 78–9
Institute of Hydrology studies, 78
shingle fan, *Pl. 45*, 70
SSSI, 78
River Garry, characteristics, 70
River Luineag, 110
River Nethy, Abernethy Forest *Pl. 56*
River Spey
  catchment transfers, 78
  characteristics, 70, 72
  Special Area of Conservation, 152
River Tay – Special Area of Conservation, 152
River Tromie, 77, *78*
River Truim, 77, *78*
river warbler *see Locustella fluviatilus*
rivers
  birds, 49–50
  Cairngorms, **149**
  fish, 148–54
  fisheries, 154–7
  nutrient enrichment, 77, 81
  SERCON, 82
  see also aquatic habitats
Rivers Prediction and Classification
  Scheme (RIVPACS), 75
roches moutonnées, 15
rock rose *see Helianthemum*
rock sedge *see Carex rupestris*
roe deer *see Capreolus capreolus*
Rothiemurchus Estate, 20, 118
  19th C
    deer forest, 87, 111
    timber floating, *Pl. 66*
  NCC agreements, 174
  pine regeneration, recent, 112
  pinewood losses, *112*
rough-legged buzzard *see Buteo lagopus*
rowan *see Sorbus aucuparia*
Roy, William, military survey of
  Strathspey, *Pl. 67*
RSPB, 181
  purchase of Abernethy Forest, 114, 174
Rubus chamaemorus (cloudberry), 30
run-rig, 86, 98
rural economy, 94–5
rush *see Juncus*; *Phragmites*
Rynchostegium riparioides (moss), 74
Ryvoan Pass, Glenmore Forest, 115, 118, 175

Saddle, The, 15
St John's Wort *see Hypericum pulcrum*
Salix spp. (willows), 27, 115
  S. herbacea (least w.), 24, 32, 34
  S. lanata (woolly w.), 31
  S. lapponum (downy w.), 31
  S. myrsinites (myrtle-leaved w.), 31
Salix woodland, origins, 107
Salmo salar (Atlantic salmon), *Pl. 81*, 148, 150–2, 154, 155
Salmo trutta (brown/sea trout), *Pl. 82*, 148, 152–3
salmon fisheries, 154–7
Salvelinus alpinus (Arctic charr), *Pl. 85*, 148, 153
sanderling *see Calidris alba*
Saturnia pavonia (emperor moth), *Pl. 42*, 57
Saussaurea alpina (alpine saw-wort), 32
Save the Cairngorms Campaign, 93, 194
  Manifesto for the Cairngorms (1992), 194–5
sawmills
  Bridge of Potarch, 124
  modern, 125
Saxifraga azoides (yellow mountain s.), 32, 70
Saxifraga cespitosa (tufted s.), 31

Saxifraga hypnoides (mossy s.), 32
Saxifraga nivalis (alpine s.), 24
Saxifraga stellaris (starry s.), 32
Scapania marsupella, 72
Scapania undulata, 71
scarlet rosefinch *see Carpodacus erythrinus*
Schoenoplectus (common club-rush), 73
Scirpus lacustris, 73
Sciurus vulgaris (red squirrel), *Pl. 37*, 52
Scolopax rusticola (woodcock), 48
Scots pine *see Pinus sylvestris*
Scottish crossbill (*Loxia scotica*), 44, 48, 49
Scottish Development Department, report
  (1967) on ski development, 173
Scottish Environment Protection Agency, 74, 75, 81
Scottish Executive Rural Affairs
  Department (SERAD), 92
Scottish National Park Committee, 172
Scottish Native Woods, 113
Scottish Natural Heritage (SNH)
  Cairngorms Partnership Board, 208
  on funicular project, 178
  origin, 79, 176
  ownership of land, 189
  policies, 114
    management agreements with
      landowners, 204
    selection of SSSIs, 180
Scottish Wildlife Trust (SWT), Ryvoan
  pass management, 175
sea lamprey (*Petromyzon marinus*), *Pl. 84*, 148, 150
sea pink *see Armeria maritima*
sea trout, *Pl. 82*, 152, 154, 155
Seafield Estate, 123, 174
second world war
  commercial exploitation of timber, 111, 123
  and farming, 98
sedge *see Carex*
sedge warbler *see Acrocephalus shoeobaenus*
Semiothisa carbonaria (netted mountain
  moth), 57
sessile oak *see Quercus petraea*
settlements, 93–5
  affordable housing, 95
  population trends, 93–4
  rural economy, 94–5
sewage disposal, 77
Sgoran Dubh, 14
sheep, louping ill (flavivirus infection), 144
sheep's fescue *see Festuca ovina*
Shelter Stone, 160, 164
shingle, aquatic habitat, 70–1
shore lark *see Eromophila alpestris*
shoreweed *see Littorella uniflora*
short-eared owl *see Asio flammeus*
shoveller *see Anas clypeata*
Sibbaldia procumbens, 32
Silene acaulis (moss campion), *Pl. 26*, 24, 32
silver birch *see Betula pendula*
Siphlonurus lacustris (mayfly), 75
siskin *see Corduelis spinus*
ski development, 163–4, 188
  Cairn Gorm, *Pl. 89*, 163–5, 173, 175, 178
  funicular railway plan, 163–4, 177, 178
  Glen Shee, *Pl. 88*, 163, 173, 175
  impact on terrain and landscape, 165–6, 187–8
  Nordic/langlauf, 164
  Scottish Development Department
    report (1967), 173
  visitor surveys, 165
  see also recreation/tourism

skylark *see Alauda arvensis*
Slavonian grebe *see Podiceps auritus*
slender sedge *see Carex lasiocarpa*
slender-leaved pondweed *see Potamogeton
  filiformis*
Slochd Mor, 15
small white orchid *see Pseudorchis albida*
smew *see Mergus albellus*
Snap Coire na Spreadhe, *Pl. 19*
snipe *see Gallinago gallinago*
snow bunting *see Plectrophenax nivalis*
snow cover, 9, 34, **36**
  interaction with high altitude, **33**
  snowbed vegetation, 34
  see also climate
snowy owl *see Nyctea scandiaca*
soils, 18–20, **19**, 126
  base-rich, 30
solifluction lobes, 33
solifluction terrace system, *Pl. 19*, 17
sorrel *see Oxyria digyna*
Sparganium angustifolium, 73
sparrowhawk *see Accipter nisus*
Special Areas of Conservation (SACs), 81, 150, 152, 177
Special Protection Areas (SPAs), 177
  European Wild Birds Directive (1979), 173–4, 177
Spey valley *see Strathspey*
Speyside, 10, 13
Speyside *see Forest of Strathspey; River
  Spey; Strathspey*
Sphagnaceae, 29, 30, **40**, 74
sporting estates, 87–9, **88**
  deer stalking, 111, 136–7
    tracks, access by recreationists, 136–7, **186**, 187
  fishing, 154–5
  goal orientations, *91*
  grouse shooting, 111, 139–40
  management
    legislature and fiscal interests, 91–3
    objectives, 90–1
  ownership, **88**, 89–91
spotted crake *see Porzana porzana*
spotted redshank *see Tringa erythropus*
spring sedge *see Carex caryophyllea*
SSSIs (Sites of Special Scientific Interest)
  distribution and extent, **190**, 191
  management agreements with
    landowners, 204
  origins, 113, 172
  renotification, 174–5
  selection, 180
  woodlands, 113, 116
starling *see Sturnus vulgaris*
starry saxifrage *see Saxifraga stellaris*
Stercorarius longicaudis (long-tailed skua), 45
stickleback (*Gasterosteus aculeatus*, 148, 154
stiff sedge *see Carex bigelowii*
stoat, predation of red grouse, 145
stone loach (*Barbatula barbatula*), 148, 154
stone polygons, 18
stoneflies, 75
  *see also Capnia; Diura; Protonemura;
    Taeniopteryx*
Strath Nethy, 15
Strathnethy
  Loch a' Gharbh-Choire, *Pl. 55*
  Nethybridge, *Pl. 58*
Strathspey, 5, 9, 14, 15, 17
  employment, 125
  estates and Forestry Commission,
    replanting, 124
  extent of woodland, 171
  Forest of Spey, 25, 114–18

William Roy, military survey, *Pl. 67*
see also Forest of Spey
strawberry *see Fragaria vesca*
Structure Plans, 191–2
Sturnus vulgaris (starling), 51
sub-alpine scrub, 31, 114, 115, 118
subsidies, farming/agriculture, 92, 100–2
Subularia aquatica (awlwort), 72

Taeniopteryx nebulosa (stonefly), 74
teal *see Anas crecca*
Technical Group on the Cairngorm Area (1967), 191, 208
Temminck's stint *see Calidris temminckii*
terrace systems, 33–4, **35**
solifluction, *Pl. 19*
Tetrao tetrix (black grouse), 44, 46, 146
Tetrao urogallus (capercaillie), *Pl. 35*, 44, 48, **49**, 145–6
Thalictrum alpinum (meadow rue), 24
Thamnolia vermicularis, 32
Thereva sp. (fly) *Pl. 41*
Thomson Scottish Forestry case, 174
three-leaved rush *see Juncus trifidus*
thrush nightingale *see Luscinia luscinia*
Thuidium cf *tamariscinum*, 72
Thymallus thymallus (grayling), 154
Thymus praecox (wild thyme), 30
ticks, louping ill (flavivirus infection), 144
Tilt Complex, **11**, 12, 13
timber
  birch, properties, 126
  commercial exploitation, 109–11, 122–5
    second world war, 111, 123
  commercial needs, UK, 128
  iron ore production, 109–10
  new production, 116
  Scots pine, properties, 126
  for shipping, 109–10
  see also forestry
timber floating, 19th C, 110
  Rothiemurchus, *Pl. 66*, 121
  Speymouth, 122
Tipula montana (crane-fly), 55
Tomintoul, 15, 93, 163
tors
  sheeting structures, *Pl. 9*, 12
  woolsack jointing, *Pl. 7*, 12–13
tourism *see* recreation/tourism
towns *see* settlements
tree limit, line, 31, 108, 114, 115, 126, 170
tree pipit *see Anthus trivialis*
trees, growth rates, 126
Trichophorum cespitosum (deer-grass), 24, 29, 30, 40, 187
Trichoptera, 63, 75
Trichostrongylus tenuis (nematode), red grouse, 144
Trientalis europaea (chickweed wintergreen), 27
Trifolium repens (white clover), 30

Tringa erythropus (spotted redshank), 52
Tringa glareola (wood sandpiper), 44, 50, 52
Tringa nebularia (greenshank), 44, 46
Tringa ochropus (green sandpiper), 52
Tringa totanus (redshank), 44, 50
trout, (brown/sea *Salmo trutta*), 148, 152–3
tufted duck *see Aythya fuligula*
tufted saxifrage *see Saxifraga cespitosa*
Tulchan
  fisheries, 79
  new timber production, 116
Tullich Burn, 115
Tulloch Moor, nr Nethybridge, *Pl. 58, 59*, 65
Turdus torquatus (ring ouzel), 45
twin-flower *see Linnaea borealis*
twite *see Carduelis flavirostris*

Umbilicaria cylindrica, **36**
unemployment, 95
Utricularia intermedia (intermediate bladderwort), 72, *73*
Utricularia minor, *73*

Vaccinium – Calluna heath, 27, **28**, 29, 35
  Culblean Hill, *Pl. 25*
Vaccinium myrtillus (blaeberry), 25, 27, 37, 38
Vaccinium uliginosum (bog whortleberry), 32
Vaccinium vitis-idaea (cowberry), 25
Vanellus vanellus (lapwing), 43, 50
Vat Burn, 73
vegetation, 23–42, 170
  altitudinal zonation, 30–2
    alpine, 31–2
    tree limit, 31
  Cairngorms, *Pl. 21*
  classical studies, 23–4
  classification (16 groups), 24, *72*
  disturbance and restoration, 39
  fungi, 38–9
  high altitude pattern and process, 32–8
  history, 24–5
  National Vegetation Classification system, 115
  new plant research, 39–41
  patterns, linear and radial, 34–8
  potential forest zone, 25–7
  replacement of tundra, 25
  snow cover, 34, **36**
  standing waters, 73
  terrace systems, 33–4, **35**
  see also aquatic habitats; bogs; heathlands; moors; native woodlands; wetlands
Viola riviniana (common violet), 26
visitor numbers, Cairn Gorm, 164–5, 180
viviparous bistort *see Polygonum viviparum*
viviparous fescue *see Festuca vivipara*

Voluntary Conservation Bodies (VCBs), 175, 177
  influence, 181
voluntary principle, 182

water beetles *see Dytiscus; Gyrinus*
Water Framework Directive, EC, 77–8
water lobelia *see Lobelia dortmanna*
Water Orders, 78
water rail *see Rallus aquaticus*
water sedge *see Carex aquatilis*
water shrew *see Neomys fodiens*
water starwort *see Callitriche*
water vole *see Arvicola terrestris*
waterwort *see Elatine hexandra*
wavy hair-grass *see Deschampsia flexuosa*
waxwing *see Bombycilla garrulus*
weather *see* climate
wet flush montane habitat, 32
wetlands, 30, 71
  birds, 49–50
  Ramsar sites, 50, 78, 173, 204
  vegetation, 30, 71, 73, 173
wheatear *see Oenanthe oenanthe*
whisky industry, 94
white clover *see Trifolium repens*
white water-lily *see Nymphaea alba*
white-tailed eagle *see Haliaetus albicila*
Wiedemannia impudica (fly), 55
wigeon *see Anas penelope*
wild cat *see Felis sylvestris*
wild thyme *see Thymus praecox*
Wildlife & Countryside Act (1981), 50, 92, 174–5, 180
  Amendment (1985), 113
Will Woodlands, purchase of Glen Feshie Estate, 177
willow tit *see Parus montanus*
willows *see Salix* spp.
windthrow, 120
wood cranesbill *see Geranium sylvaticum*
wood sandpiper *see Tringa glareola*
wood sorrel *see Oxalis acetosella*
wood warbler *see Phylloscopus sibilatrix*
woodcock *see Scolopax rusticola*
Woodland Grant Scheme, 93, 102, 113
woodlands *see* native woodlands
woolly hair-moss *see Racomitrium*
woolly willow *see Salix*
woolsack jointing, Meikle Pap, Lochnagar, *Pl. 7*, 12
World Conservation Strategy (WCS), 175, 181
World Heritage Area designation, proposal, 176, 183, 197, 205
World Wilderness Conference, 176
wryneck *see Jynx torquilla*

yellow mountain saxifrage *see Saxifraga azoides*
yellow water-lily *see Nuphar lutea*
yellowhammer *see Emberiza citrinella*